D1062567

SOIL
CONSERVATION

Prentice-Hall Field Crop Production Series
Henry L. Ahlgren, editor

J. H. Stallings

*Research Specialist in the United States
Department of Agriculture*

SOIL

CONSERVATION

Foreword by R. B. Alderfer

Prentice-Hall, Inc.   *Englewood Cliffs, N. J.*

This book is dedicated to the memory of my son,
Second Lieutenant George Drummand Stallings,
killed over England August 6, 1944

*Library of Con-
gress Catalog Card
Number: 57-5096*

Current printing (last digit):

14   13   12   11   10   9   8   7

*Printed in the
United States
of America*

8 2 1 8 1-C

FOREWORD

Agriculture in the United States during the last twenty years has benefited from more revolutionary developments than at any time or place in history. These changes have been the result of an unprecedented use of the findings of this age of chemistry and mechanization in just about everything that is done on the modern farm or ranch.

This period of modernization of agriculture has been distinguished by a history-making effort to find a practical solution to the age-old problem of achieving a permanently productive agriculture. All agricultural production starts with the soil. It follows, therefore, that in considering what could or should be done to ensure the continued productivity of the soil, the first essential is to keep it in place. Many of our past and present farm, forest, and grazing land management practices have not met this requirement. Loss of soil by wind and water erosion has been severe enough to have lowered the productivity and thus increased the cost of production on over 50 per cent of the agricultural land in the United States. Results from experiments in many important farming regions of this country show that under many existing land management systems the average annual loss of soil by erosion exceeds the most liberal estimates of the amount of soil formed each year by as much as a hundredfold. This can have only one effect on much of our agricultural land. Although there are certain places where the removal of poor, unproductive topsoil might be desirable, loss of surface soil from most areas results in a decrease in productivity.

The objectives of modern soil and water conservation are: (*1*) To reduce to a minimum accelerated loss of soil that attends the use of land for a great many of our agricultural crops, and (*2*) to attempt to find ways of reclaiming eroded land. The outstanding feature of modern soil and water conservation, which makes it different from most previous efforts, is that it combines, integrates, and uses all those applicable conservation practices in accordance with the needs and capabilities of the land. The task of doing this on every acre of agricultural land is tremendous. That conservation farming is being practiced as never before is to be seen by anyone traveling across the United States.

Runoff and erosion have been going on throughout geological time and have been studied by geologists, hydrologists, physicists, and engineers for many years. Accordingly, a considerable amount of basic information has been available to soil and water conservationists regarding these two processes. By 1930 the influence of climate, topography, soil, and vegetation on runoff and erosion had been well established. Since then a great deal of effort has been spent in measuring the influence of rainfall intensity, wind velocity, length and steepness of slope, permeability and erodibility of the soil, different kinds of crops and cultural practices, contouring, strip-cropping, and terracing on runoff and erosion. Knowledge from all this research is combined with the experience of professional conservationists in developing a conservation plan for a farm, ranch or watershed.

Today the emphasis in conservation is not so much on runoff and erosion control as on the whole soil and crop management program for a farm or watershed. This is a much more realistic approach, since accelerated runoff and erosion on agricultural land are the results of the way the soil is managed. In no situation does the adage which states that an ounce of prevention is worth a pound of cure apply better than in the field of soil and water conservation.

It is the purpose of this book to document the efforts and the accomplishments of the soil and water conservation movement during the past two decades. They are well worth telling.

R. B. ALDERFER
Rutgers University

PREFACE

This book is based on twenty years' experience in different capacities in the Soil Conservation Service of the U.S. Department of Agriculture. This experience started with the establishment of the soil conservation program in North Carolina and its direction for four years. The next 16 years were spent in the Washington office. About four years were spent in flood control planning and another four in over-all farm planning. This was followed by eight years as Research Specialist in the Research Division of the Service.

It was in the last-named capacity that the various segments of a sound soil and water conservation program took shape and fell into place, and it was then that the manuscript was written. One of my major duties was to assemble, analyze, and interpret all available data bearing on soil and water conservation. When assembled, the data automatically fell into broad subject-matter divisions. Analysis and interpretation showed the part each group played and the proper relation of the data in one group to those in each of the other divisions. The organization of the book is based on these divisions.

Part I deals with historical phases of soil erosion. Part II deals with the fundamental problems of soil conservation. Part III lists and describes soil conservation practices. Part IV deals with the planning phase of the program.

J. H. S.

CONTENTS

Part I: Introductory and Geographical Aspects

1 | Man's Ancient Struggle with Soil Erosion | 1

2 | Soil Erosion and Related Problems | 28

Part II: Fundamental Considerations of Soil Conservation

3 | How Water Erodes Soil | 51

4 | How Wind Erodes Soil | 71

5 | Soil Aggregates and How They Are Formed | 84

6 | Maintaining Soil Structure | 103

7	Soil Surveys	117
8	Soil Testing	140
9	Plant Cover and Conservation	158

Part III: Conservation Practices

10	Interrelationship of Land, Plants, and Animals	177
11	Erosion and Productivity	195
12	Water-Erosion Control on Cultivated Land	221
13	Wind-Erosion Control	238
14	Mulch Farming for Row Crops	270
15	Wheat Production with Stubble-Mulch Tillage	293
16	Grassland Farming	313
17	Protect the Soil and Improve the Range	333
18	Woodland Farming	359
19	Surface Water Disposal System	381

Part IV: Farm and Watershed Planning

20	Land Use Capability and Land Judging	424
21	Planning the Farm Program	456
22	Irrigation	476
23	Farm Drainage	510
24	Watershed Management	526
25	The Conservation Movement	548
	Author Index	565
	Topical Index	571

SOIL
CONSERVATION

Man's Ancient Struggle
with Soil Erosion

Man's struggle with soil erosion is as old as agriculture itself. It started when the earliest nomadic tribes, perhaps in the Zagros Mountains separating Persia and Mesopotamia, first upset Nature's delicate balance between plant cover and the erosive forces of wind and water. As man became civilized, his demands upon the land for additional food and clothing grew. He changed from nomadic herding to a fixed mode of agriculture and began cultivating the soil. This intensified use of the land led to further destruction of plant cover, and exposed more of the soil to the erosive forces.

Records of man's efforts through the ages to find a lasting adjustment to the land are written on the landscapes around the globe. The ruins of works along this amazing trail tell us that failures were far more numerous than successes. It behooves us to try to understand the causes of these failures and successes, lest we unknowingly contribute to the downfall of our own civilization.

An examination of the records of man's struggle with the forces causing soil erosion reveals that the efforts were mainly attempts to prevent the scouring effects of surface runoff. There is little evidence that he attempted to control wind erosion. Nowhere in the record of the ages is there anything to indicate that man knew the exact nature of the forces with which he was contending. In some cases, he was aware of the fact that erosion was practically nonexistent when the land surface was adequately protected by plant cover. Man learned, however, that as soon as this cover was removed by cultivation of the land, or destroyed by overgrazing, erosion became active. It seemed uncontrollable when the land was deprived of the protection of plants. The protective influence of plant cover, even when it was employed, was thought to be that it retarded the flow of surface runoff and kept it spread uniformly over the surface as it moved downhill. Some attribute this protective effect to plant roots binding the soil and stabilizing it against the erosive action of wind and water.

Less than a decade ago, it was discovered that the impact of raindrops on bare soil and the resulting splash was a major cause of soil erosion by water. Scouring by surface flow turned out to be only a partner. At the same time, it was shown that plant cover—so abundantly supplied by Nature nearly everywhere—is the counter measure provided to shield the soil from the beating raindrops. Discovery of the effects of raindrops' part in the erosion process also explained the failure of previous attempts to save the soil. Nowhere in the almost uninterrupted chain of land tragedies is there anything to indicate that anyone suspected that the presumably innocent raindrop had anything more to do with soil erosion than to supply water to create the runoff.

With this in mind let's review the record of these failures, which began with the origin of civilization in the Near East some 7,000 years ago, as reported by Lowdermilk.

SOIL EROSION IN THE OLD WORLD

So far as known, western civilization arose in the Near East. The cultures that developed through the ages moved eastward to China and westward through Europe, and across the Atlantic Ocean to the Americas. We are constantly reminded of our debt to the Sumerian peoples of Mesopotamia whenever we use a wheel, which they invented more than 6,000 years ago. We do homage to their mathematics each time we look at a clock or our wrist watches to tell the time. Our calendar is a revision of the ancient Egyptians' method of figuring the year.

Tillage of the soil had its beginning at least 7,000 years ago and developed in two great centers in Mesopotamia, along the valleys of the Tigris and Euphrates rivers, and in the Nile River Valley. On these alluvial plains, in an arid climate, tillers of the soil began to grow crops, with irrigation, in quantities greater than their own needs. For the first time, it was possible for some of the people to do other things than produce food. They had time to develop arts, science, statecraft, and means of expressing the aspirations of the human spirit. This gave rise to what we call civilization.

The history of Mesopotamia is one of a nation that grew up and lived constantly under the threat of raids and invasions by the peoples of the grasslands and the desert. Part of the story is of a precarious agriculture and of the failure of the irrigation canals due to silt deposition. It is the supposed place of the Garden of Eden and the "Tower of Babel" and the confusion of tongues. Its glories and tragedies are known to the historians and archaeologists. It was a land of dense populations, and of great cities. All that now remains are scattered villages—and the ruins of the great cities, which had been hidden by deep blankets of erosional debris for centuries. At least eleven empires have risen and fallen in this land.

In Mesopotamia, the irrigation waters were made muddy by erosional debris washed down from the cutover forest lands and overgrazed hill lands that drained into the Tigris and Euphrates rivers and from the mountain gorges through which these rivers flowed. The sediment these waters carried was the ultimate reason for the empire's fall. As the velocity of the water slowed down upon entering the irrigation canals, the silt was deposited and choked the canals. Much time and labor were required to keep the canals open, so that they could supply the life-giving waters to the farm lands and the cities of the plains. As populations grew, canals were extended further from the rivers until they formed a great system. As the canals grew, so did the task of keeping them clear of debris.

Repeated conflicts—both revolts within and onslaughts by invaders—interrupted the great task of maintaining the canals. Finally, the combined task of restoring the canals and repelling invaders became too great. Without irrigation water, the Babylonian agriculture failed. Without water, and without an agriculture to provide food and fiber, the villages and cities failed, too. A great empire disappeared. It is known now that failure of the agriculture had more to do with its disappearance than the slaughter by invading armies. Without irrigation, there could be only a small agricultural production, and without food, fiber, and water there could be no great cities.

Erosion on the hill lands, which resulted from depletion of the plant cover, had aggravated the sediment problem in waters of the Twin Rivers, as they were drawn off into the ancient canal system. Little did Nebuchadnezzar realize how defenseless he was leaving mighty Babylon against the forces of the raindrops when he removed the timber from the mountain sides above the city, for he boasted (25)*:

> That which no king before had done, I did . . . A wall like a mountain that cannot be moved, I builded . . . great canals I dug and lined them with burnt brick laid in bitumen and brought abundant water to all the people . . . I paved the streets of Babylon with stones from the mountains . . . magnificent palaces and temples I have built . . . Huge cedars from Mount Lebanon I cut down . . . with radiant gold I overlaid them and with jewels I adorned them.

The site of Kish, the first capital after the Great Flood that swept over Mesopotamia in pre-historic times, was above the alluvial deposits laid down by that flood. This thick deposit of brown alluvium marked a break between the earliest recorded civilization here and a succeeding culture as recorded in artifacts.

The other great cradle of modern civilization is in the valley of the Nile, where the mysterious Sphinx seems to ponder the problems of the ages as

---

* Numbers in parentheses refer to literature cited at the ends of the chapters.

FIGURE 1. Excavated ruins of Kish, the first capital of Mesopotamia following the Great Flood. These ruins had been completely covered with shifting sands and silt deposits from times past until recent excavation.
(Soil Conservation Service)

she looks out over the narrow green valley of the Nile cutting across a brown and sun-baked desert. Here, as in Mesopotamia, tillers of the soil early learned to sow food plants of wheat and barley and to grow the surplus food that released their fellows for other works. From this beginning arose the civilization in the Nile Valley.

A muddy flow watered the lands along the Nile, as well as in Mesopotamia, but it was flood water from the river. The silt-laden river waters, spreading over the plain, deposited thin layers of silt over the land, raising it higher and higher. The silt made the soil more fertile. Water from Mesopotamia came from eroding upland, where the plant cover had been depleted, and was taken to the land in canals. When the canals failed, because of erosional debris, so did the nation's agriculture. But the waters of the Nile fell on primitive lands, where only geologic erosion was occurring.

The flood waters of the Nile originated in the highlands of Ethiopia some 2,000 miles from the flood plain. Ethiopia consists of a series of tablelands, varying in elevation, and of numerous high and rugged mountain ranges. Many of the mountain peaks have elevations of from 7,000 to 8,000 feet. The highest peaks exceed 15,000 feet.

From these mountains flow vast quantities of water. At certain seasons of the year the water flows in torrents, flooding the Nile Valley. This contributes large amounts of fertile silt to the plains below, for it is only the silt that reaches the plains. The flood water spreads thinly over large areas. The flat, flood-watered lands along the Nile never had serious erosion problems. Today, after thousands of years of continued cultivation, the Nile River Valley is still an area where intensive cultivation is practiced.

Moses' route from the fertile, flood-irrigated Nile River Valley led into mountainous lands, where forests and fields were watered by rain. Here, where sloping land was cleared for cultivation, falling raindrops and flowing water eroded the soil and carved gullies. Today, most of those slopes are sorry to behold.

Sinai, where the Israelites wandered with their herds for 40 years, is a picture of desolation. The brown soil mantle is eroded into enormous gullies. Between Sinai and Aqaba is a plateau that has been eroded through the years almost to a peneplain. This broad flat surface is covered with small stones that have been fitted together through the ages to form a classic example of desert pavement. The peneplain surface dates back to Miocene times. There is evidence of accelerated cutting of the plain by torrential streams. But there is no indication that climate has changed since the Miocene era. Here, then, is a cultural record dating from the Ice Age which proclaims that the climate has been remarkably stable.

Ezion Geber, which has been partly uncovered by archaeologists, was Solomon's seaport on the Gulf of Aqaba and the ancient Pittsburgh of the Red Sea—where copper was smelted—2,800 years ago.

Petra, the capital of the Nabatean civilization which flourished at the same time as the Golden Age of China—from 200 B.C. to 200 A.D.—is a desolate ruin. There are those who maintain that the climate is drier now than it was 2,000 years ago and, therefore, this land cannot support as great a population as it did once. On the other hand, slopes of the surrounding valley are covered with the remains of terrace walls that have fallen into ruin, allowing the soils from large areas to be washed off to bare rock. Food is grown locally, but soil erosion has damaged the land beyond use for extensive cropping. Before we can ascribe decadence of the region to change of climate, we must know how much the breakdown of intensive agriculture contributed to the fall and disappearance of this Nabatean civilization.

The Jordan River is now a muddy stream, and the soils from more than half the upland area of the Promised Land have been washed off the slopes to bedrock and lodged in the valleys. There, they are still being cultivated and still being eroded by heavy rains that enlarge the great gullies in this alluvium. At Hebron, likewise, the soils have been washed off to bedrock and only dregs of the land left behind in narrow valley floors to be cultivated for meager crops.

Soil erosion also has taken a heavy toll in the denuded highlands of Judea, as is illustrated in the drainage of Wadi Musrara. The records of abandonment of village sites in Wadi Musrara during the past 1,500 years bear mute evidence of the decline of the land. The rate of abandonment is related to the progress of erosion. Students of the area have divided the drainage into three altitudinal zones: the plain, 0-325 feet; foothills, 325-975 feet; and mountains, 975 feet and over. In the plain, 34 village sites are occupied and 4 abandoned; in the foothills, 31 occupied and 65 abandoned; and in the mountains, 37 occupied and 124 abandoned.

FIGURE 2. The soil on the slopes on the left has been washed off to bed
rock. The slopes on the right still retain enough soil to produce
light-yielding barley crops.
(Soil Conservation Service)

Where soils have been held in place by stone terrace walls which have
been maintained through the centuries to the present, they are still cultivated after several thousand years. They still are producing—not heavily,
to be sure, because of poor soil management. The glaring hills of Judea, not
far from Jerusalem, are dotted with only a few of its former villages—places
where terraces have been kept in repair for more than 2,000 years.

Present conditions are in sad, shocking contrast to those reported to prevail in the Holy Land 3,000 years ago. Moses, after having led the Israelites
through 40 years of wandering in the wilderness and bringing them to Mt.
Nebo, across the Jordan Valley from the Promised Land, described it to
his followers in these words:

> For the Lord thy God bringeth thee into a good land, a land of brooks of
> water, of fountains and depths that spring out of valleys and hills; a land of
> wheat, and barley, and vines, and fig trees, and pomegranates; a land of olive
> oil, and honey; a land wherein thou shalt eat bread without scarceness; thou
> shalt not lack any thing in it; a land whose stones are iron and out of whose
> hills thou mayest dig brass.*

Jerash, a settlement of 3,000, was once a center for some 250,000 people.
The country about it is now sparsely settled with semi-nomads. When dis-

* *Deuteronomy* 8:7-9.

covered, the ruins of this once-powerful city of Greek and Roman culture were buried to a depth of 13 feet by erosional debris washed from the nearby slopes. In Biblical times, this region was famous for its oaks, wheat fields, and well-nourished herds. This area supplied grain to Rome and supported thriving communities. The reason for its decline is found in the loss of the soil—washed off to bedrock, in spite of rock-walled terraces.

In north Syria—in the limestone country between Hama, Aleppo and

FIGURE 3. View of bench terraces and eroded land around a partially deserted village in Syria. Many of the stone terraces and houses have been ruined. A few of the terraced strips are still being farmed after thousands of years of use. (*Soil Conservation Service*)

Antioch—an area of over a million acres lost from 3 to 6 feet of soil by erosion. One hundred cities and villages were abandoned as a result.

The Phoenicians, however, were the first tillers of soil to encounter the severe soil erosion caused by rain on sloping cultivated land. Some 5,000 years ago, Phoenician tribes swept out of the desert, occupied the eastern shore of the Mediterranean, and established the harbor towns of Tyre and Sidon. In time, they began to clear the timber from the hillsides. As forests were cleared, either for domestic use or for commerce, the slopes were cultivated. Soils of the slopes eroded under heavy rains. The Phoenicians apparently recognized the problem of establishing a permanent agriculture on sloping lands, for they tried to control erosion by constructing walls across the slopes. Ruins of these walls may be found today. The measures failed, however, and the soil mantle slipped downhill under the action of progressive erosion.

When the Romans were at the height of their power, the Lebanon forest was protected to grow timber for their fleet. Emperor Hadrian, determined to have it properly protected, had the boundaries designated by permanent markers. But only four small groves of this famous forest are left today. The most important is the Tripoli grove, in the cup of a valley. Of some 400 trees in the grove, 43 are old veterans or "wolf" trees. About 300 years ago, it is reported, the grove had nearly disappeared, with no less than 43 scattered veterans standing. These trees with wide-spreading branches grew up in an open stand. About that time, the trees were declared sacred and a little church was built in their midst. A stone wall was built to protect the grove from the goats that grazed on the mountain. Seeds from the old trees fell to the ground and germinated. The seedlings grew up into a fine close-growing stand of tall straight trees. Such natural restocking is evidence that this famous forest had not disappeared because of an adverse change of climate. Instead, it shows that it would probably extend itself even under the present climate if it were safeguarded against the rapacious goats that graze on every accessible living plant.

The story of North China is much the same as that of the Lebanon forest. The line of cultivation in the Province of Shansi was pushed up the slopes as the forests were cleared away. Soils that formerly were protected by forest litter were thus exposed to the beating rains, and soil erosion began a headlong process of land destruction and filling streams with soil waste and detritus. Runoff and erosion from cultivated land were many times as great as when the forest covered the land. Still visible are the remnants of terraces that were in use before Shansi Province was riddled by huge gullies.

Temple forests in China, like the forest of Lebanon, demonstrate beyond a doubt that the present climate would support a generous growth of vegetation that is capable of preventing erosion on such a scale. Human occupation of the land has set in motion processes of soil wastage that are, in themselves, sufficient to account for the decadence and decline of this portion of China.

The land-use problems of the Mediterranean are epitomized in a comparatively small area in eastern Cyprus, the plain of Mesaoria, where there is a Byzantine church on the outskirts of the village of Asha. This church is surrounded by a graveyard and its wall. The alluvial plain stands 8 feet above

FIGURE 4. The ruins of the ancient Roman city of Guicul in Algeria may be seen in the middle distance. The eroded land seen around the site indicates why this city has not been rebuilt—there is no productive land to support it.
(Soil Conservation Service)

the level of the churchyard. Measurements showed that sediment deposits on the plain were at least 13 feet deep. This was soil washed off the surrounding slopes.

Over a large portion of this ancient granary of Rome, the soil has washed off to bedrock and the hills have been seriously gullied because heavy grazing removed the vegetative cover. The valley floors are still cultivated, but the runoff from the eroded slopes has cut great gullies there. At Djemila was found the ghost of Guicul, a city that once was great, populous, and rich. Except for about three feet of a single column, the city was completely covered by erosion debris washed from the surrounding hills. In 20 years, French archaeologists unearthed great temples, two great forums, splendid churches, and great warehouses for wheat and olive oil. The surrounding slopes once had been covered with olive groves.

South of Guicul is Thamugadi, now called Timgad, another great Roman city founded by Trajan in the first century A.D. It was laid out in a symmetrical pattern and adorned with magnificent buildings, with a forum embellished by statuary and carved porticos, a public library, a theater to seat some 2,500 persons, and 17 great Roman baths with marble flush toilets for the public. After the invasion of the nomads in the seventh century had completed the destruction of the city and the dispersal of its population, this great center of

Roman culture was lost to knowledge for 1,200 years. It was buried by the dust of wind erosion from surrounding farm lands until only a portion of Hadrian's arch and 3 columns remained, like tombstones above the undulating mounds, to indicate that once a great city was there. Water erosion cut a gully down into the land and exposed an ancient aqueduct that supplied water to the city from a spring some three miles away. Within and around Timgad are ruins of great olive presses, where now there is not a single olive tree within the circle of the horizon.

At El Jem, on the plain of Tunisia, are the ruins of a great coliseum, second in size only to Rome's. It had a seating capacity for 65,000 people. The ancient city now lies buried under a modern village.

There is no evidence that a change in climate brought about the abandonment of these great cities. The claim that the climate is more arid is not substantiated. Lowdermilk cited evidence indicating there has been no appreciable decline in rainfall during the last 2,000 years. The most logical explanation is that the soil reservoir has been reduced by erosion and that far less rain water enters the ground because of the compacting action of falling raindrops. Because of this there is less available soil moisture for plants to draw on, and it may seem that there is less rainfall.

On the plains about Sfax, ruins of olive presses but no olive trees were found by early travelers. To test the climatic theory, olive trees were planted 40 years ago on an unexcavated portion of the city, in the manner prescribed

FIGURE 5.   Once magnificent and a glory of Rome, the city of Timgad, North Africa is now in deserted ruins, surrounded by a desolate countryside.
(Soil Conservation Service)

FIGURE 6. View of portion of the ruins of the city of Timgad, where compress stones of great diameter were found in place. One is in the middle ground to the right, above a collector basin in stone. The presence of these and ruins of oil presses about 1 kilometer apart between Timgad and Lambese 20 miles away is considered evidence that olive culture was general in that region. Until recent plantings, however, no olive trees were to be found in the region.
(Soil Conservation Service)

in Roman literature, and they are thriving now. Now, more than 150,000 acres are so planted and their products support thriving industries in the modern city of Sfax. These plantings indicate that the climate of today, as far as production of olives is concerned, is not unlike that of Roman times. At Sousse is an olive grove whose trees are reported to be at least 1,500 years old.

Indications of what happened to the soils of the granary of ancient Rome are on hillsides between Constantine and Timgad. Some of these hills, according to botanists, were covered with savannah vegetation of scattered trees and grass. Vegetation had conserved a layer of soil on these hills for unknown ages. With the coming of a grazing culture, brought in by invading nomads of Arabia, erosion was unleashed by overgrazing. Accelerated run-off cut gullies into the upper edge of the soil mantle, working it downhill as if a great rug were being pulled off the hills, and depositing the material at lower levels.

Plato must have had some of the beneficial effects of plant cover in mind when, according to Toynbee, he wrote of Attica (*41*):

> Contemporary Attica may accurately be described as a mere relic of the original country, as I shall proceed to explain . . . All of the rich, soft soil has moulted away, leaving a country of skin and bones . . . There were also many lofty cultivated trees, while the country produced boundless pastures for cattle. The annual supply of rainfall was not lost, as it is at present, through being allowed to flow over the denuded surface into the sea, but was received by the country, in all its abundance, into her bosom, where she stored it in her impervious potters earth and so was able to discharge the drainage of the heights into the bottoms in the form of springs and rivers with an abundant volume and a wide territorial distribution.

EARLY AMERICAN EXPERIENCES

No sooner had the early settlers of America begun to clear away the native plant cover and put the land in cultivation than they found themselves confronted with accelerated soil erosion. As long as land was plentiful, a farmer could clear new land as fast as the old was "worn out." Eventually, however, American farmers came to the time when they had to live with the land they had in cultivation, for there remained no new land to be cleared.

Jared Eliot and Samuel Deane were two of the earliest American colonists to become interested in soil erosion. Jared Eliot, a minister and doctor of Killingsworth, Connecticut, practiced farming in his spare time. When he called upon his parishioners and the sick in his community, he noticed their methods and their problems.

He noticed that water running from a vegetated hillside was clear, but that water running from a bare hillside was muddy. He believed that the mud in the water was fertile soil from above. Most of New England was hilly, and every time muddy water ran off one of the fields, that field got poorer. Eliot became so much interested in farming that he carried on many experiments.

Because land was so plentiful and capital was so scarce, colonial agriculture was wasteful and inefficient. Eliot resolved to do what he could to improve the crops and to conserve the soil. After many years of experimentation and observation he incorporated his ideas into the first American book on agriculture, a series of essays, the first of which was published in 1748.

Eliot's ideas on agriculture were influenced greatly by the work of Jethro Tull and "Turnip" Townsend, but perhaps even more by John Bartram, the first native American naturalist (1699-1777). For many years Eliot and Bartram corresponded and their letters showed a recognition of the erosion problem which was unusual for the period.

Eliot believed that the richness of the valleys was caused by deposition of fine material washed from the hills, and that most water contained fine particles of soil. Although sedimentation might enrich a valley, the removal of the soil from hills left them sterile. He also believed in the use of manure, calcareous manures, and soil-building crops. He realized that grasses and legumes were valuable crops for building up poor land.

Samuel Deane, who lived a generation later than Eliot, was the first to attempt to control wind erosion. The lives of the two men were somewhat similar. Both were ministers, both were farmers, and both accepted little on faith alone.

Like Eliot, Deane recognized the ill effects of erosion by water in New England and developed ways to overcome it. He observed in his book, *The New England Farmer; or Georgical Dictionary* (1790), that with heavier rainfall in the hills "more of the fine mould would have been washed down into the hollows; and deeper channels would have been made in the soil by the running of water which are considerable inconveniencies" Deane also observed that ". . . certain crops do not impoverish the soil, but rather improve it. Such crops, for instance, as peas, and other things which form a close shade over the ground, which kill weeds, and increase the putrefaction in the soil . . ."

To prevent the blowing and drifting of sand, Deane recommended hedge fences as well as plantations of locust trees. Speaking of the black locust he stated:

> This tree grows best in a sandy soil, and will propagate itself in the most barren places, where the soil is so light as to be blown away by winds. By sheltering such places and dropping its leaves on them, it causes a sward to grow over them, and grass to grow upon them. . . . those who possess hills of barren sand . . . should not delay to make forests of these trees on such spots.

Early in the existence of this nation, many of the farsighted agricultural leaders and some of the farmers became frightened about the future. They advocated measures to prevent erosion from taking the bread out of their mouths. Since they were groping in the dark, however, they merely repeated the errors of the past by adopting practices which appeared to be different but which in reality were based on the same fundamental principles.

Deep plowing, contour tillage, hillside ditches and terracing were advocated more than 100 years ago. They were practiced by some farmers. Broadbase terraces with a slope for drainage and grassed outlets were described on a Virginia farm in 1838.

Sorsby of Hinds County, Miss., wrote a prize essay on "Horizontal Plowing and Hillside Ditching" in 1857. He cited work of this type done on the plantation of his father-in-law. In 1858, Garland D. Harmon, an enterprising overseer in western Georgia, was employed by Dr. M. W. Philips of Hinds County and claimed to have run the first terraces in that county. Harmon had learned of terracing from the earlier work of Richard S. Hardwick of Hancock County, Ga. During the 1880's, P. H. Mangum of Wake Forest, N.C., developed a broadbase terrace that became widely accepted in that state. Soils were plowed 12 inches or more in the Connecticut Valley 80 years ago.

Many other farmers in the South made contributions to the development of terracing. A field study of terracing in the South was made by C. E. Ramser of the U.S. Department of Agriculture in 1915 and reported on in Farmers' Bulletin 997. An improvement in terrace channel design resulted in the Nichols terrace. Refinements have since been made in terrace placement and use of natural drainageways as outlets.

Sorsby, in presenting his essay before the North Carolina Agricultural Society in October 1857, stated:

> I was induced to write it from the interest I feel for the progress of the Society, and the advancement of the Agriculture of the State, and as the only and best way I am able to assist them. . . .
>
> It may be considered as a new branch of agricultural science, founded upon correct and well established principles of the sciences of engineering and hydraulics; and essential to the welfare of the farmer, to the preservation of the soil, and to good husbandry.
>
> Forced, almost by necessity, and the strong sense of self interest and foresight, a few intelligent minds have been brought to discover the urgent need of reforming the old destructive system of plowing in straight rows up and down hills, and substituting the better mode of horizontal culture.

Sorsby realized that the up- and downhill method of culture then in general use was leading to the destruction of the land. In discussing this, he said:

> The absurdity of the old method is really a subject of astonishment and mortification to those who practice the new methods. The arable lands of the South have been nearly exhausted by it and a careless and wasteful culture.

Horizontal culture was defined as "cultivating land in parallel lines run by a leveling instrument to direct and control rain water with the plow."

Bonner, in making a study of the agricultural reform movements of the Cotton Belt, came across the following:

> . . . the abundance of land and the relative scarcity of labor had encouraged soil exhaustion and emigration. The effects of this brought citizens to a sober contemplation of a disintegrating social and economic system. It was out of the welter of abandoned homesteads, decaying communities, and low cotton prices of the early 1840's that a movement for agricultural reform was crystallized in middle Georgia. This reform movement gathered up the loose ends of the older movement in Maryland, Virginia and the Carolinas and spread into the southwest. In Hancock County, the first successful planters' club in the Georgia Cotton Belt was organized and it early furnished information and guidance to communities in surrounding areas (*Southern Cultivator*, Vol. 18, p. 341. 1860). Later the achievement of its members attracted attention throughout the south. . . . They came to be known far and wide for their agricultural progressiveness and their optimistic enthusiasm for the agrarian way of life. In the course of 20 years, they rose out of the depths of economic despair to active prosperity and public acclaim through their improved methods of agricultural practice.

Concerning the work of Richard S. Hardwick (a prime mover in this agricultural movement) the *Milledgeville Recorder* said in 1856: "The county owes a debt of gratitude to Mr. Hardwick for the improvement of its lands, which has been induced and so much aided by his practical and successful method" (*Southern Cultivator,* Vol. 14, p. 304. 1856). In 1850 Daniel Lee, a Northerner, said ". . . in South Carolina and Georgia nothing has left so enduring an impression as the skillful manner in which hillside ditches are constructed. . . . In this matter, the planters of these states have excelled all we have witnessed elsewhere in the Union, and we have seen most of it" (*Southern Cultivator,* Vol. 13, p. 49. 1850).

Despite the exhortations of Hardwick, Sorsby, and their followers, there were some who realized that terracing, contour cultivation, deep plowing, and other such practices were not enough. Some were even fearful of these operations. This view was clearly stated by Massey in 1907. Crop rotation, deep plowing, and use of cowpeas in corn were advocated more than a century ago. The dependence on terracing as the main erosion-control measure persisted in the South until recent years. Moorehouse discussed control measures without terracing for Oklahoma in 1901. Massey found terraces and row ridges worse than no treatment when floods overtopped and broke them. Several farmers reported similar views. Some were bitterly disappointed with deep plowing on slopes on 10 to 15 per cent.

Edmund Ruffin realized that the type of farming employed in that area was destroying the land. In 1853 he wrote:

> The great error of Southern agriculture is the general practice of exhausting culture—the almost universal destruction of the productive power of the soil, which power is the main and essential production of all agricultural wealth.
>
> . . . the great error of exhausting the fertility of the soil is not peculiar to cotton culture or to the Southern States. It belongs, for necessity, to agriculture of every newly settled country, and especially where the land, before being brought under tillage, was in the forest state. . . . Even in a new country, while land is yet fertile, it is cheaper to preserve that fertility from any exhaustion than it is to reduce it considerably. And in an older agricultural country, like South Carolina, having abundant resources in marl and lime for improving fertility, it would be much cheaper and more profitable to improve an acre of land before exhausted than it is to clear and bring under cultivation an acre of ordinary land from the forest state, allowing that both pieces are to be brought to the same power and rate of production.
>
> The average life of a man is long enough to reduce the fertility of his cultivated land to one half, or less. Thus, one generation of exhausting cultivation, if working together, would reduce this country to one-half of its former production.
>
> . . . when tillage so ceases, and any space is thus left at rest, nature immediately goes to work to recruit and replace as much as possible of the wasted fertility, until another destroyer, after many years, shall return again to waste, and in much shorter time than before, the smaller stock of fertility so renewed.
>
> There is another and stronger reason for the greater exhausting effects of Southern agriculture. . . . the great crops . . . and especially of the more southern . . . corn, tobacco, and cotton . . . are all tilled crops. The frequent turning and loosening of the earth, by the plow and hoe . . . and far more when continued, without intermission, year after year . . . advance the decomposition and waste all organic matter, and expose the soil of all but the most level surfaces to destructive washing by rains. . . .

These early fears are set forth in the leading agricultural literature of the day. The agricultural volume, *Report of U.S. Commissioner of Patents, 1852,* reflects their anxiety. The following is from this publication:

> Twice the quantity of rain falls in the Southern States in the course of a year than falls in England, and it falls in one-third the time. It is not so much the atoms removed in crops as those washed out in solution, or suspended in water as fine mud, that impoverishes the arable fields of the planting States.
>
> . . . *it is painful to contemplate the fact that we so misapply our physical and intellectual energies as needlessly to improverish the land in every State and Territory of the Republic. We have a continent for the basis of agricultural operations, embracing climates and physiological and material resources, equal to the want of a thousand million of prosperous and happy people.*
>
> . . . Cotton has destroyed more land than earthquakes, eruptions of burning volcanic mountains or anything else. Witness the red hills of Georgia and South Carolina that have produced cotton till the last dying gasp of the soil forbids any further attempt at cultivation and the land turned out to nature reminding the traveler, as he views the dilapidated country, of the ruins of Greece.
>
> . . . I was raised in a hilly country of the Old World, but I never saw these hillside fields . . . so badly washed as they are here . . . in one single year. Some of our hill places are already ruined beyond redemption . . . and this is a new country. Farming in the old style will do no longer; . . . we are bound . . . to put more of our land in clover and grass. . . .
>
> There is not one of the industrial classes of mankind more estimable for private worth and social virtue than the landlords and cultivators of the Southern States. . . . Honorable, highminded, kindly in feeling and action, both to neighbors and to strangers, ready to sacrifice self interest for the public weal . . . such are the ordinary qualities and characteristics of southern planters. Most of the intelligent men of this generally intelligent class are ready enough to accept and to apply to themselves and their fellow-planters the name of "land killers." They have regarded their "land killing" policy and practice merely as affecting their own personal individual interests. . . . But with the impoverishment of its soil, a country, a people, must necessarily and equally be impoverished.
>
> . . . And these evils to the community and to posterity, greater than could be effected by the most powerful and malignant foreign enemies of any country, are the regular and deliberate work of benevolent and intelligent men, of worthy citizens and true lovers of the country.

SEARCH FOR NEW METHODS

Some of those who lost faith in the prevailing methods of managing cultivated land began a search for new and better methods. Some had observed that the rate of erosion was reduced by the use of crop rotations or decreasing the length of time soil was exposed to rains.

Pendleton found that one of the greatest difficulties in the cultivation of rolling lands was the washing off of the surface soil and the formation of gullies, especially where corn and cotton are the principal crops. According to him, the best remedies were deep plowing, hillside ditching, and horizontal culture. Pendleton realized that soils stood up against the forces of erosion

better when crop rotation was used than when the fields were cropped continuously. He observed that land deteriorated when planted to cultivated crops and improved when abandoned and allowed to grow up to weeds. The organic matter was preserved when the land was devoted to weeds and grass.

Even prior to this discovery by Pendleton, Agricole had noticed that where a straw mulch was used, much better stands of clover were obtained in newly-seeded wheat and clover. In many instances when the straw mulch was not used, the clover catch was a failure.

Kefauver found that good stands of clover could be secured on clay galls and other bare spots if they were mulched at seeding time. He also observed that the best way to utilize such areas was to put them back to grass. Abandoned areas that were fertilized, seeded, and mulched produced good crops while adjacent plots, fertilized, seeded, but not mulched produced none.

Moorehouse suggested that the cotton grower must reject the methods that were followed in the early days, in favor of deeper plowing. He reasoned that deep plowing facilitated the flow of water through the soil and broke up hardpan layers. According to him, such treatment enabled the upper layers of soil to absorb and retain larger quantities of water.

Spillman recommended the use of terraces as a substitute for shallow plowing. He observed that land in Georgia, which eroded badly when planted to cotton, did not wash when planted to grass or when kept in clover or other cover crops. U.S. Department of Agriculture Farmers' Bulletin 20 stated:

> Erosion of a soil is caused by the wearing of the rain and snow waters which cannot penetrate into the soil fast enough to be carried away under drainage, and which, by reason of the slope and contour of the land, run off over the surface, carrying along particles of sand and clay. Washing of the land may be prevented by methods of cultivation and underdrainage. Side hill ditches were considered a part of cultivation.

Massey found that land gullied badly as a result of being planted continuously to cotton and shallow plowed. The use of horizontal banks with narrow ditches above them checked the downward rush for a time, but the ultimate result was that these ditches eroded into gullies. Instead of this practice, he recommended the construction of broad banks around the contour of the hills with a broad leveled space on the upper side to spread the water out and allow it to move slowly downhill. He admitted, however, that these often broke during hard rains. According to him, the real cure for the trouble was the abandonment of the methods of culture responsible for the washing—the shallow plowing and the constant working of the land in clean-hoed crops. Terracing was only a partial remedy; the soil continued to wash even after the field was terraced.

Massey thought that the only real cure of erosion was to return the land to the condition that existed when it was freshly cleared, and to plow the land so deeply that it would retain more water without running. He suggested that the use of crop rotations in which the legumes came frequently enough for the restoration of the humus, accompanied by deep plowing and subsoiling, would do more to check washing than would terracing.

U.S. DEPARTMENT OF AGRICULTURE DEVELOPS PROGRAM

By the turn of the current century, the U.S. Department of Agriculture had begun to formulate a soil erosion program for the nation. Like all such programs previous to this, the basic elements centered around the problem of scour by surface runoff. Farmers' Bulletin 20, 1894, discussed eroded soils and how to reclaim them. The Department of Agriculture Yearbook of 1903 discussed the relation of soil porosity and granulation to the washing of soils, and the use of deeper plowing and terraces to prevent washing. Two years later, in the Yearbook of 1905, limiting the cultivation of soils subject to washing during fall and winter was held to be desirable. Department of Agriculture Farmers' Bulletin 245, *Soil Conservation,* was published the next year and re-issued four years later. Apparently, a clearly defined desirable national policy had been outlined in the Department by 1907. The Secretary of Agriculture gave the following in his Report of 1907:

> Another line of work in the Bureau (of Soils) relates to soil erosion. According to the latest determinations (beginning with the classic measurements of the Mississippi by Humphreys and Abbott), the rivers of the mainland United States are annually pouring into the seas 1,000,000,000 tons of sediment. . . . The volume of material thus lost to the land is increasing with settlement and cultivation; it is almost wholly washed from the surface and is the very richest soil material, the cream of the soil. The value of the material is not easily fixed, but at a moderate appraisal the annual loss would exceed all the land taxes of the country. . . .
>
> Erosion is due directly to the runoff of water of which the ratio is dependent partly on slope, but chiefly on the nature of the soil and its produce; indeed, with any reasonable slope, a full cover of forest or grass with an abundant mulch, or close crop on deeply broken soil, or a friable furrow slice kept loose by suitable cultivation, will so fully absorb precipitation as to curtail the runoff or even to reduce it to slow seepage through the surface soil . . . the ideal condition, and the one toward which modern agriculture should be bent. . . .
>
> The immediate source of our prosperity is the soil of the American farm and it is a national duty to see that the soil is conserved and the farm improved for the immediate benefit of the farmer and ultimate welfare of the country. One of the richest assets of the nation is the water that falls on the farms, permeates the soil, permits organic growth and, after enriching the land, flows seaward through the commonwealth to furnish substance and power and afford means of commerce; and it is coming to be recognized as one important duty of the nation to see that this water shall be so controlled and conserved as to yield the greatest benefits to the holders of the land on which it gathers and eventually to all the people. At the same time, the evils of soil erosion begin on the farm and, while they extend thence to the pollution of the streams of the states and the obstructions of interstate rivers, it is becoming clear that the remedy must begin with the farm and it is a national duty to see that the remedy is prescribed and applied.

RESEARCH ON SOIL EROSION

In studying the effect of a vegetative canopy on the structure relationship of soils, Wollny, a noted German scientist, working at Munich, found that vegetation protected the soil from the impact of raindrops to such an extent that the noncapillary porosity was from 34 to 53 per cent higher than in unprotected soils. His results (Table 1) showing these differences were attributed to the protective effect of the leaves against the dispersive action of raindrops on the soil. Not only was the loose, granular structure of the unprotected soils broken down to cause their compaction, but the noncapillary porosity was also decreased as a result of the percolation of turbid water into the large pores and a subsequent clogging up of these pores with fine particles.

TABLE 1. The influence of plant cover and shading on soil structure (25)

Soil type	Type of protection	Soil porosity — Volume percentage					
		Protected			Unprotected		
		Soil	Water	Air	Soil	Water	Air
Humus calcareous	Wood laths*	34.2	41.7	24.1	42.7	40.6	16.7
Humus calc. sand	Rye	37.8	28.7	33.5	41.7	36.2	22.1
Humus calc. sand	Peas	36.4	31.3	32.3	40.8	38.2	21.0
Humus calc. sand	Vetch	30.8	30.2	39.0	34.5	36.5	29.0
Quartz sand	Sw. clover	54.0	2.1	43.9	54.6	10.5	34.9
Loam	Sw. clover	44.6	10.1	45.3	49.1	19.0	31.9

*Wood laths were placed above plot to protect soil from direct impact of raindrops.

In 1879, Wollny found that the volume decrease of a cultivated soil was related to the density of the vegetation and the rapidity with which a plant cover was established (Table 2). He concluded that the major effect of vegetation upon the properties of the soil was due to the protective influence of the cover against the impact of the raindrops.

TABLE 2. The effect of density of plant cover on changes in soil structure during the growing season

Number of plants per 1,000 sq. cm.	Per cent decrease in volume of soil under oats from May 1 to September 12, 1879
0	12.8
3	9.2
6	6.9
12	6.1
12 (fertilized)	5.3
24	4.9

Wollny's results were confirmed by Lowdermilk and Hendrickson, who reported data showing that the pore space in the immediate surface becomes clogged by the clay entering those pores in muddy water. Neal and Free showed that the impact of raindrops destroyed the open structure of the top inch or more of soil and formed a dense, nearly impervious surface which hindered infiltration of water. In 1880, Wollny investigated the effect of plant cover upon the interception of rainfall. He found that, depending upon the type of crop and the number of plants per unit area, only 45 to 88 per cent of the total rainfall reached the land surface directly. The results with ordinary farm crops are given in Table 3. Corn, when planted thick, was found to be the most effective intertilled crop for intercepting rainfall. Red clover and lupines were the most effective forage crops. These results are of the same order of magnitude as those reported by Haynes.

TABLE 3. The effect of plant cover on the interception of rainfall

Crop	Per cent of total rainfall penetrating vegetative canopy					
	Number of plants per 4 sq. meters					
	0	36	64	100	144	196
Corn	100	62.9	60.7	57.0	44.5	—
Soybeans	100	88.4	78.2	65.9	64.3	—
Oats	100	—	78.5	78.4	78.9	74.6
Vetch	100	—	—	78.1	—	—
Beans	100	—	—	75.4	—	—
Lupines	100	—	—	57.9	—	—
Peas	100	—	—	87.8	—	—
Red clover	100	—	—	61.3	—	—

In 1882, Wollny studied the effect of various factors on runoff and erosion from small plots. These plots were 80 cm. square and 5 cm. deep. They were placed under natural rainfall and the runoff and erosion determined. In one set of plots, exposure, slope, and vegetation were kept constant, and runoff and erosion were studied as a function of the type of soil. The results in Table 4 point out that the finer the texture of the soil, the greater the percentage of runoff. On a 20 per cent slope, however, quartz sand eroded the most because of a lack of coherence or binding material. This was confirmed with the use of artificial rain by Duley and Hays.

In another set of plots, Wollny kept exposure and soil type constant, so as to study the effect of degree of slope on runoff and erosion from bare and

TABLE 4. The effect of the type of soil on runoff and erosion

Type of soil	Runoff Per cent of Rainfall	Erosion Tons per Acre*
Loam	12.64	11.5
Humus calcareous sand	11.84	11.0
Quartz sand	5.97	15.4

Rainfall from April 1 to Oct. 1, 1882 = 23.8 inches
Degree of slope with south exposure = 20°
Soil kept bare

* The amount of erosion has been converted from grams per square meter to tons per acre.

grass-covered soils. The results shown in Table 5 are exceedingly interesting in light of more recent investigations. In the first place, erosion increases more rapidly with the degree of slope than with runoff. It may also be observed that a grass cover reduces runoff and erosion, especially the latter.

TABLE 5. The effect of degree of slope and vegetation on runoff and erosion

Description	Degree of slope		
	10°	20°	30°
1882— Runoff—% of rainfall (23.8")			
Bare plot	1.89	3.27	4.70
Grass plot	2.02	3.29	3.96
Erosion—tons per acre*			
Bare plot	4.6	7.8	13.2
Grass plot	0.45	0.35	1.4
1883— Runoff—% of rainfall (24.5")			
Bare plot	3.11	4.65	6.55
Grass plot	1.17	2.11	4.71
Erosion—tons per acre*			
Bare plot	3.7	6.1	14.0
Grass plot	0.06	0.19	0.23

Soil = humus with south exposure

* The amount of erosion has been converted from grams per square meter to tons per acre.

Wollny attributed the conserving action of grass to a decreased rate of run-off and to the effect of the roots in binding the soil together. The grass was more effective the second year than the first because of the better cover that was produced. In spite of the slight increase in rainfall during the second year, there was less erosion on the 10 to 20 per cent slopes.

In still another set of plots, Wollny kept soil type, slope, and vegetation constant, and studied the effect of the direction of exposure on runoff and erosion. These results are given in Table 6. It will be noted that runoff increased according to the following series: north, west, east, south. Erosion, on the other hand, was greatest according to this series: east, south, north, west. These effects of exposure are attributed to differences in moisture content and degree of packing of the surface soil. Experimental data show that the north and west exposures were more moist than the east and south plots. The order was: north, west, east, south. Consequently, the south and east exposures were less compact. A compact surface permitted less soil movement per unit runoff than a loose soil. Since most of the rains at Munich came from the west, this plot was more compact than the north plot. The effects of compaction can be seen by comparing the runoff and erosion results for two years. There was much less erosion in 1883, in spite of increased rainfall and runoff. Neal showed that surface compaction during a given storm increased runoff but decreased the rate of soil movement.

TABLE 6. The effect of direction of exposure on runoff and erosion

Description	Exposure			
	North	South	East	West
1882 — Runoff — % of rainfall (23.8")				
15° slope	4.42	2.16	3.08	3.25
30° slope	6.77	4.45	4.59	7.76
Erosion — tons per acre*				
15° slope	4.5	6.3	8.2	2.8
30° slope	8.8	10.5	13.1	8.5
1883 — Runoff — % of rainfall (24.5")				
15° slope	5.38	3.92	4.08	4.79
30° slope	9.85	5.71	6.77	8.68
Erosion — tons per acre*				
15° slope	2.1	2.6	3.2	1.4
30° slope	4.6	4.9	5.6	4.0

Soil = humus calcareous sand with no vegetation

* The amount of erosion has been converted from grams per square meter to tons per acre.

Miller, like Wollny, found that erosion was directly related to the amount of plant cover on the land. Erosion from cultivated, uncropped land totaled approximately twice that from land in continuous corn. Erosion from continuous wheat was only about half and that from a good rotation was less than 20 per cent as much as the erosion from continuous corn. Erosion from continuous sod was negligible. Miller also found that the use of fertilizer markedly decreased erosion losses. On this point he stated: "The reasons are obvious, since both manures and fertilizer stimulate crop growth, usually both tops and roots, thus giving a better surface cover and more roots to hold the soil." Even though he made this statement, there is nothing to indicate he really understood the processes involved.

Miller and Krusekopf found plowing 8 inches deep to be but little more effective in controlling erosion than plowing 4 inches deep. Following a checkup on an experimental field that had been terraced the modern way, Cox found that over an 8-year period it had lost by erosion from 6 to 8 inches of soil. These investigations showed that plowing or terracing per se did not control erosion. They could easily have concluded from Miller and Wollny's results that plant cover was necessary.

IMPORTANCE OF PLANT COVER EMERGES

Conard thought that mosses prevented erosion by catching the runoff water and suspended soil, and by matting the soil and covering it so that it did not move. Lowdermilk discovered that the accumulation of a layer of ground litter under forest vegetation exercised influence of far-reaching significance in controlling storm runoff and soil erosion. Borst and Woodburn found that straw used as mulch almost completely controlled erosion, both when placed directly on the ground and when suspended slightly above the ground. The runoff was not materially different from these two plots. This showed that something besides surface flow was responsible for erosion.

Larsen observed that natural vegetation in southeastern Ohio changed with the degree of erosion. As erosion increased, the type of vegetation declined in the ecological scale. When eroded land was allowed to grow back to grass, this process was reversed. He also noted that land covered with dense bluegrass sod absorbed more rain water than land covered with poverty grass or weeds. He was of the belief that where less of the rain water was absorbed by the soil more of it ran over the surface and became instrumental in causing erosion.

Lowdermilk and Rowe concluded that a mantle of undisturbed vegetation serves in heavy rainstorms to maintain the soil's ability to absorb rainfall rapidly, and that stripping the soil of its natural cover of vegetation increases surface runoff. This increased surface runoff increases erosion far above that which takes place while the soil is under a mantle of natural vegetation.

Sreenivas and his associates found that soil detachment and erosion were closely correlated and that plant cover was effective in reducing splash erosion. They developed a method—termed "soil cover rating"—for measuring the effectiveness of different plant covers in reducing splash. Hubam sweet clover had a "soil cover rating" of 95.8, whereas that of buffalo grass was 98.5.

Detachment of soil increased with the increase in the height of vegetative cover and decreased with an increase in the percentage of cover. Oat straw at the rate of two tons per acre was effective in checking soil detachment. Oat straw mulch was more effective per unit weight than sweet clover mulch.

Free, working with samples of Honeoye soil in elevated pans exposed to natural rainfall, found that a straw mulch reduced splash loss 98 per cent and wash-off losses to 66.6 per cent compared with losses from bare soil. A marked decrease in infiltration occurred, despite the fact that most of the splashed soil left the pan. Crusts were formed on the surface. This crust had a volume weight of about 1.4 compared with a weight of 1.1 or less for the soil beneath the crust.

Laws found a direct relation between the amount of energy expended by falling raindrops and the resulting soil loss. The rate of soil loss was affected by variation in either the size, drop velocity, intensity, or amount of rainfall. By using rain applicators to apply spray to trays of soil, Laws found that as the drop size increased from one to five mm. in diameter the infiltration rate decreased as much as 70 per cent, and the erosion losses—measured in terms of the concentration of soil in the runoff water—increased up to 1200 per cent.

Forsling observed that only 4.6 per cent of the average annual surface runoff was caused by summer rainstorms, when there was a 16 per cent cover of vegetation, but this runoff caused 84.5 per cent of the erosion. The other 95.4 per cent of runoff, which was from melting snow, caused far less erosion. After the vegetation had increased to 40 per cent of a complete cover, only 1.3 per cent of the annual runoff was from summer rains.

Runoff and soil loss by erosion from rainfall were reduced 64 per cent and 54 per cent, respectively, by increasing the density of plant cover from 16 per cent to 40 per cent. The runoff from melting snow was not affected by this increase in density of cover.

Forsling's results indicated that factors other than scour by surface flow were involved.

CHANGING CONCEPTS

The soil erosion movement is now passing into a new stage. There is no better way to illustrate the advance in the knowledge gained during the years than to present the explanations of earlier and later scientists concerning the nature of the forces responsible for the erosion of our farm lands.

Ayres believed that water erosion manifested itself in two forms, sheet washing and gullying. The first tendency of intense rains, he believed, is to pack the soil; but while the rain packs the soil, it pounds loose grains of soil that float away. The flow of excess water, carrying soil and humus with it, begins soon after the start of a rain. With water falling in all parts of the field at the same time, the thin sheet of water and soil increases in thickness as it moves from the top to the bottom of the slope. The removal of a rather uniform amount of soil from the surface with every hard rain is the process known as *sheet erosion*.

Since surface runoff may occur without erosion but erosion never without runoff, Ayres felt that the effect of the various factors on runoff was an indirect measure of their effect on erosion. He apparently was thinking principally of the scouring action of surface runoff.

Lowdermilk was of the opinion that "physical measures for safeguarding sloping lands may be combined into three groups, i.e., contour farming, bench terracing, and stream base level control for long-range control of the land."

Bennett thought of water erosion as being the transportation of soil by rain water, including melted snow, running rapidly over exposed land surfaces. He discussed water erosion under three major types: sheet erosion, rill erosion, and gully erosion.

To Bennett, sheet erosion was considered as sheet washing which was the more or less even removal of soil in thin layers over an entire segment on sloping land by flowing water. He did recognize that the impact of the falling raindrop had a place in the erosion process, but he associated it principally with the sealing of the surface soil which in turn meant increased runoff and more scouring.

The discovery that raindrop splash is a major factor in the water erosion process marks the end of one era in man's struggle with soil erosion and ushers in another which, for the first time, holds out hope for a successful solution to the problem. The exact nature of the effects of raindrop splash is the phase of the water-erosion process that escaped detection during the first 7,000 years of civilization. It explains why the efforts at protecting the land against scour erosion these 7,000 years have failed. It explains why there is little or no erosion on land with ample plant cover. It explains many things that have puzzled agricultural leaders and practitioners throughout this long and troublesome period.

Knowing these things, man knows that vegetative cover, which has long been known as a means for controlling wind erosion, also is the best measure for control of water erosion.

Had the Babylonians, Phoenicians, and other ancient peoples understood the importance of protecting their cultivated and grazing lands from the impact of falling raindrops, their history might have been far different. Likewise, there would not be the extensive areas of eroded and abandoned land there are in the world today.

Egyptian civilization started in the Nile Valley, where there was no erosion, about the same time Babylonian civilization started in the valleys of the Tigris and Euphrates, where there were erosion problems. The Egyptians are with us today, but the Babylonians disappeared, as did at least ten other civilizations which followed them in the same area.

It remained for Ellison to recognize the true role of the falling raindrop in the water-erosion process. He was the first to realize that the falling raindrop was a complete erosive agent within itself and that little or no erosion occurred when the ground surface was protected by ample cover. He showed that the protective effect of plant cover was due to the fact that it robbed the falling raindrop of its kinetic energy.

Ellison's discovery opened a new field of soil erosion science. For the first time, it was known why bare cultivated fields eroded severely during hard rains while, at the same time, portions of the same or adjoining fields which had a good plant cover experienced little or no damage. Foliage and litter of the plants intercepted the falling raindrops, absorbed their kinetic energy, and eased the broken drops to the ground as clear water.

Since the falling raindrop was prevented from making direct contact with the ground surface before being de-energized, the physical properties of the soil were not disturbed. The clear water could enter the soil freely. These findings were verified by Mihara who worked independently of Ellison. The findings of these two men show that without raindrop splash there would be little erosion outside of rills and gullies. These findings have been verified by Ekern, Free, and others.

REFERENCES

1. Agricole. 1838. *On the benefit of using straw as top dressing for young clover.* Farmers' Register, 6(2): 112.
2. Anonymous. 1894. *Washed soils: how to prevent and reclaim them.* USDA Farmers' Bull. 20.
3. Ayres, C. Q. 1936. *Soil erosion and its control.* McGraw-Hill Book Co., Inc., New York.
4. Bennett, H. H. 1939. *Conservation.* McGraw-Hill Book Co., Inc., New York.
5. ———, Bell, F. G., and Robinson, B. 1951. *Raindrops and erosion.* USDA Cir. 895.
6. Bonner, J. C. 1943. *Genesis of agricultural reform in the Cotton Belt.* Jour. Southern History, 9(4): 475-500.
7. Borst, H. L., and Woodburn, 1942. *The effect of mulching and methods of cultivation on runoff and erosion from Muskingum silt loam.* Agr. Engin., 23(1): 19-22.
8. Conard, H. C. 1935. *Mosses and soil erosion.* Iowa State Coll. Jour. Sci., 9(3): 347-351.
9. Cox, M. B. 1947. *Quart. Sum. Repts.* USDA, SCS, 2(4). Mimeo.
10. Deane, S. 1822. *The New England Farmer; or Georgical Dictionary,* 3rd ed. Wells and Lilly, Boston.
11. Duley, F. L., and Hays, O. E. 1932. *The effect of the degree of slope on runoff and soil erosion.* Jour. Agr. Res., 45: 349-360.
12. Ekern, P. C. 1953. *Problems of raindrop impact and erosion.* Agr. Engin., 34(1): 23-25, 28.
13. ———. 1950. *Raindrop impact as the force initiating soil erosion.* Soil Sci. Soc. Amer. Proc., 15: 7-10.
14. Eliot, J. 1934. *Essay upon field husbandry in New England, and other papers, 1748-1762.* Edited by H. J. Carmand and R. G. Tugwell. Columbia Univ. Press, New York.
15. Ellison, W. D. 1944. *Studies of raindrop erosion.* Agr. Engin., 25(4): 131-136.
16. Forsling, C. L. 1931. *A study of the influence of herbaceous plant cover on surface runoff and soil erosion in relation to grazing on the Wasatch Plateau in Utah.* USDA Tech. Bull. 220.
17. Free, G. R. 1952. *Soil movement by rainstorms.* Agr. Engin., 33(8): 491-494.
18. Gold, T. S. 1872. *Fifth Annual Report of the Secretary of the Connecticut Board of Agriculture.* 183.
19. Haynes, J. L. 1938. *Interception of rainfall by vegetative canopy.* USDA, SCS Mimeo Rept. 2668.
20. Hendrickson, B. H. 1934. *The choking of pore space in the soil and its relation to runoff and erosion.* Trans. Amer. Geophys. Union, 15(11): 500-505.
21. Kefauver, P. F. 1890. *Practical experiments in reclaiming "galled" or washed lands, with notes on mulch and mulch materials.* Tenn. Agr. Expt. Sta. Bull., 3(4): 60-72.

22. Larsen, J. A. 1935. *Natural revegetation on eroded soils in southeastern Ohio.* Iowa State Coll. Jour. Sci., 9(3): 365-376.

23. Laws, J. O. 1940. *Recent studies in raindrops and erosion.* Agr. Engin., 21(11): 431-433.

24. Lowdermilk, W. C. 1935. *Certain aspects of the role of vegetation in erosion control.* Iowa State Coll. Jour. Sci., 9(3): 337-346.

25. ———. 1953. *Conquest of the land through 7,000 years.* USDA, SCS. Information Bull. 99.

26. ———. 1930. *Influence of forest litter on runoff, percolation and erosion.* Jour. Forestry. 28(4): 474-491.

27. ———. 1941. *Physiographic engineering: Land-erosion control.* Trans. Amer. Geophys. Union, 316-320.

28. ———, and Rowe, P. B. 1934. *Still further studies on absorption of rainfall in its relation to surficial runoff and erosion.* Trans. Amer. Geophys. Union, 509-515.

29. Massey, W. F. 1907. *Practical farming.* The Outgoing Pub. Co. New York. 143-147.

30. Mihara, Y. 1951. *Raindrops and soil erosion.* Natl. Inst. Agr. Sci., A:1-59.

31. Miller, M. F. 1936. *Cropping systems in relation to erosion control.* Mo. Agr. Expt. Sta. Bull. 366.

32. ———, and Krusekopf, H. H. 1932. *The influence of systems of cropping and methods of culture on surface runoff and soil erosion.* Mo. Agr. Expt. Sta. Res. Bull. 177.

33. Moorehouse, L. A. 1910. *Some soil problems in Oklahoma.* Jour. Amer. Soc. Agronomy, 1: 234-238.

34. Neal, H. J. 1938. *The effect of the degree of slope and rainfall characteristics on runoff and soil erosion.* Mo. Agr. Expt. Sta. Res. Bull. 280.

35. Nichols, M. L. 1937. *The Nichols Terrace—An improved channel-type terrace for the southeast.* USDA Farmers' Bull. 1790.

36. Pendleton, E. M. 1876. *A textbook of scientific agriculture.* 2nd ed. A. S. Barnes & Co., New York.

37. Ruffin, E. 1853. *Southern agricultural exhaustion, and its remedy.* U.S. Pat. Off. Rept. 1852, Agriculture. 373-389.

38. Sorsby, N. T. 1857. *Horizontal plowing and hillside ditches.* N. C. Agr. Soc. Prize Essay.

39. Spillman, W. J. 1906. *Renovation of worn-out land.* USDA Farmers' Bull. 245.

40. Sreenivas, S. L., Johnston, J. R., and Hill, H. O. 1947. *Some relationships of vegetation and soil deterioration in the erosion process.* Soil Sci. Soc. Amer. Proc., 12: 471-474.

41. Toynbee, A. J. 1948. *A study of history,* 2nd ed. Oxford Univ. Press, London. 2:39.

42. Veneable, A. W. 1838. *On hillside ditches.* Farmers' Register, 6: 752-753.

43. Wollny, E. 1877. *Der einfluss der pflanzendeke und beschattung auf die physikalischen eigenschaften und die frushtbarkeit des bodens.* Berlin.

44. ———. 1887. *Untersuchungen uber den einfluss der pflanzendecke und der beschattung auf die physikalischen eigenschaften des bodens.* Forsch. Geb. Agri.-phys., 10: 261-344.

45. ———. 1889. *Untersuchungen uber den einfluss der pflanzendecke und der beschattung auf die physikalischen eigenschaften des bodens.* Forsch. Geb. Agri.-phys., 12: 1-75.

46. ———. 1890. *Untersuchungen uber das verhalten der atmospharischen niederschlage zur pflanze zum boden.* Forsch. Geb. Agri.-phys., 13: 316-356.

47. ———. 1895. *Untersuchungen uber das verhalten der atmospharischen niederschlage zur pflanze und zum boden.* Forsch. Geb. Agri.-phys., 18: 180-204.

2

Soil Erosion
and Related Problems

A reconnaissance survey was made by the Soil Erosion Service (now Soil Conservation Service) in 1934
to determine the nature and extent of soil erosion
throughout the country. The seriousness of the erosion problem as indicated by this survey was reveal-
ing even to those already acquainted with the subject.
The survey indicated that out of a total land area of
1,903,176,620 acres in the United States, 282, 218,-
000 acres of formerly productive farm land had been
so severely damaged by soil erosion that their use for
crops or grazing was economically unfeasible; that
775,678,000 acres had become so seriously eroded
as to urgently require erosion-control measures to in-
sure continued productivity; and that 144,768,000
acres were wastelands, roads, and other land of no
crop-producing value. A portion of the data obtained
in this survey is presented in Table 7.

A more detailed survey of the erosion conditions in
Arkansas, Louisiana, Oklahoma, and Texas was completed in 1948 by the Soil Conservation Service. This
survey recognized five erosion-condition classes: medium to slight, medium, medium severe, severe, and
very severe. It also divided the land into three major
divisions on the basis of use: cultivated, pasture, and
woodland. The acreage appearing in each of the five

28

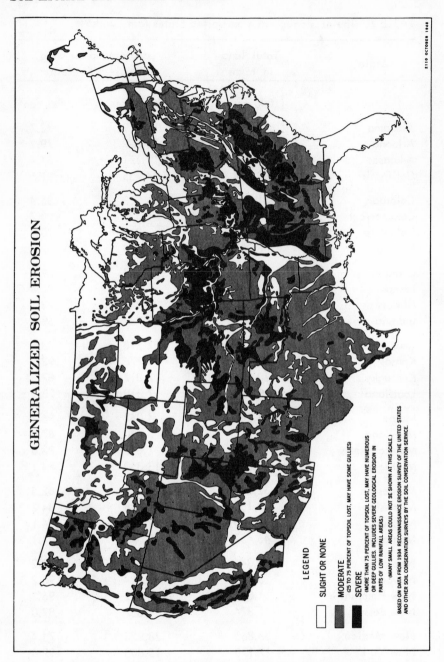

FIGURE 7. Map showing the extent of erosion damage in the United States. Based on a reconnaissance survey made in 1934 by the Soil Conservation Service.
(Soil Conservation Service)

TABLE 7. The erosion menace on United States farm lands*

State	Total land in farms	Land eroded, eroding, or subject to erosion	
	(1000 acres)	(1000 acres)	Per cent
Alabama	19,143	13,919	72.7
Arizona	25,651	20,329	79.2
Arkansas	18,045	12,171	67.4
California	30,524	27,935	91.5
Colorado	31,527	26,923	85.4
Connecticut	1,512	1,371	90.7
Delaware	896	810	90.4
Florida	8,338	4,340	52.1
Georgia	23,684	16,554	69.9
Idaho	10,298	9,521	92.4
Illinois	31,033	21,941	73.1
Indiana	19,801	13,784	69.6
Iowa	34,149	27,593	80.8
Kansas	48,174	44,776	92.9
Kentucky	20,294	17,817	87.8
Louisiana	9,996	7,310	73.1
Maine	4,223	4,062	96.2
Maryland	4,198	3,690	87.9
Massachusetts	1,938	1,802	93.0
Michigan	18,038	13,360	74.1
Minnesota	32,607	26,910	82.5
Mississippi	19,156	16,138	84.2
Missouri	34,740	29,220	84.1
Montana	46,452	39,076	84.1
Nebraska	47,344	37,080	78.2
Nevada	3,785	3,414	90.2
New Hampshire	1,809	1,739	96.1
New Jersey	1,874	1,667	89.0
New Mexico	38,860	28,923	74.4
New York	17,170	15,803	92.0
North Carolina	18,845	14,573	77.3
North Dakota	37,936	34,286	90.4

* From Soil Conservation Service

TABLE 7. (Continued)

State	Total land in farms	Land eroded, eroding, or subject to erosion	
	(1000 acres)	(1000 acres)	Per cent
Ohio	21,908	16,510	75.4
Oklahoma	34,803	26,554	76.3
Oregon	17,988	16,228	90.2
Pennsylvania	14,594	13,466	92.3
Rhode Island	222	203	91.4
South Carolina	11,239	7,702	68.5
South Dakota	39,474	32,405	82.1
Tennessee	18,493	16,160	87.4
Texas	137,683	121,063	87.9
Utah	7,302	5,710	78.2
Vermont	3,667	3,280	89.4
Virginia	16,445	14,135	85.9
Washington	15,182	13,757	90.6
West Virginia	8,909	8,010	90.0
Wisconsin	22,876	19,906	87.0
Wyoming	28,026	26,011	92.8
TOTAL U.S.	1,060,842	897,937	82.9

erosion-condition classes was determined for each of the three major land-use divisions for each state. These data are presented in Table 8.

The figures in Table 8 show that soil erosion is a major problem in each of the three land-use divisions. As is to be expected, it is more severe in the cultivated and pasture-use divisions than in the woodland division. About 49 per cent of the cultivated land was in the last four erosion condition classes. The pasture and woodland divisions had about 38 and 20 per cent, respectively, in the same four erosion condition classes.

As serious as the erosion condition is, as depicted by this survey, it represents only the problems inherent in the land. It does not touch upon the many associated problems directly traceable to this condition. The soil removed by erosion from cultivated fields, overgrazed pastures, and mismanaged woodlands sets up a chain of damaging reactions which is far-reaching in its effect.

The soil erosion problem is not the same in all parts of the country. For example, the soils of New England are naturally low in fertility, are high in acidity, generally contain illite-type clays, are sandy-textured, and respond to fertilization. Generally they are not inclined to erode except in areas that

TABLE 8. Erosion conditions in Arkansas, Louisiana, Oklahoma, and Texas divided into five erosion classes

	Erosion Class				
	Medium to slight [1]	Medium [2]	Medium severe [3]	Severe [4]	Very severe [5]
	Cultivated Land				
Arkansas	6,548,894	3,642,026	1,789,743	964,743	133,813
Louisiana	7,365,357	2,135,423	553,985	72,898	17,567
Oklahoma	7,624,063	5,771,475	5,991,438	1,459,174	417,160
Texas	29,564,651	17,368,004	8,629,615	621,738	206,031
Total	51,102,965	28,916,928	16,964,781	3,118,553	774,571
	Pasture				
Arkansas	1,672,163	1,484,560	1,085,548	230,009	76,976
Louisiana	2,850,082	856,753	305,165	57,061	22,977
Oklahoma	8,600,955	1,720,541	1,449,915	646,210	357,035
Texas	61,837,101	22,675,106	10,840,377	2,232,494	1,846,450
Total	74,960,301	26,736,960	13,681,005	3,165,774	2,303,438
	Woodland				
Arkansas	14,290,861	1,256,385	377,007	117,494	73,778
Louisiana	8,499,147	1,460,055	530,630	85,901	130,342
Oklahoma	8,400,330	486,125	287,475	59,403	54,579
Texas	9,797,044	1,816,908	970,224	217,411	109,006
Total	40,987,382	5,019,473	2,165,336	480,209	367,705
	Total				
Arkansas	22,511,918	6,382,971	3,252,298	1,312,246	284,567
Louisiana	18,714,586	4,452,231	1,389,780	215,860	170,886
Oklahoma	25,625,348	7,978,141	7,728,828	2,164,787	888,774
Texas	101,198,796	41,860,018	20,440,216	3,071,643	2,161,487
Total	168,050,648	60,673,361	32,811,122	6,764,536	7,490,893

[1] Removal of less than 25% of topsoil or soil accumulations 0-6" high caused by wind.

[2] Removal of less than 25% with occasional crossable gullies (more than 100' apart), or removal of 25% to 75% of topsoil with no gully erosion, or removal of 25-50% by wind, or soil accumulations 6-12" high caused by wind.

[3] Removal of less than 25% of topsoil with occassional uncrossable gullies, or removal of 25-75% of topsoil with occasional crossable gullies, or removal of 25-75% of topsoil with occasional uncrossable gullies and frequent crossable gullies, or removal of 50-75% of the topsoil by wind, or soil accumulations 12-36" high, caused by wind.

[4] Removal of 75% of topsoil to 25% of subsoil with or without occasional crossable or uncrossable gullies, or soil accumulations 36-60" high caused by wind.

[5] Removal of 25-75% of topsoil with frequent uncrossable gullies; 75% of topsoil to 25% of subsoil with frequent crossable and uncrossable gullies and all areas with very frequent or large gullies that can be delineated, or all of topsoil and removal of over 25% of subsoil, or accumulations over 60" high caused by wind.

are intensively farmed. In contrast, Prairie soils are naturally fertile. They are low in acidity, have montmorillonite-type clays, are generally fine-textured, show medium response to fertilization, and generally are moderately eroded.

MAN RESPONSIBLE FOR ACCELERATED EROSION

Based upon extensive study in the Great Plains, a physiographic province covering about 67 per cent of the Missouri River Basin and practically all of the Basin where annual rainfall is less than 20 inches, the Great Plains Committee concluded its 1936 report as follows:

> There is no evidence that in historic times there was ever a severe drought to destroy the grass roots and cause erosion comparable to that which took place in 1934 and 1936; that phenomenon is chargeable to the plowing and overcropping of comparatively recent years.

Many measurements made throughout the United States show the relationship of rates of erosion to the use and condition of the land. Although the results vary from one location to another, and from time to time, they constantly show that rates of erosion and soil loss have been accelerated by man's use of the land.

The evidence shows that man's use of the land not only has materially accelerated rates of land surface erosion, but is also responsible for much of the gullying, valley trenching, and arroyo cutting in this country. Thorn-

FIGURE 8.   Sand deposited on valuable cropland by the Ohio River Flood of January, 1937. This field produced 100 bushels of corn per acre in 1936. Its present condition is a result of accelerated erosion of farm lands of the watershed. (Ohio)
(Soil Conservation Service)

FIGURE 9. Soybeans were planted in this Posey County, Indiana farm field in 1938. The silt in the foreground was brought down from higher up the slope by one heavy rain. (Posey County, Indiana)
(Soil Conservation Service)

FIGURE 10. This power supply reservoir in South Carolina is completely filled with erosional debris. The tragedy here is not only that this reservoir has been destroyed, but that other suitable sites for reservoirs are also being destroyed by the products of erosion. (Spartanburg, South Carolina)
(Soil Conservation Service)

FIGURE 11. A Mississippi farmer attempted to open up this drainage ditch—the sand spoil on the left—in June, 1951, but the following month one heavy rain refilled it with sand washed down from surrounding slopes. (New Albany, Mississippi) *(Soil Conservation Service)*

thwaite, Bailey, and others reported many instances on range lands where accelerated erosion in the form of valley trenching and gully development followed shortly after the introduction of heavy grazing on the contributing watersheds. Land clearing and cultivation opened the way for gullying of the uplands in other agricultural areas of the United States.

Accelerated erosion produces abnormal quantities of sand, silt, and gravel that are carried from fields and stream systems and deposited at lower levels. The resulting accumulations of sediment impair the drainage and fertility of the soil on the lower slopes of fields and on bottomlands. They also cause abnormally rapid filling of stream channels and reservoirs, with consequent damage to water- and power-supply, irrigation, drainage, navigation, and flood-control developments. Deposition of sediment on roads and highways necessitates expensive maintenance. Accumulation of erosional debris in irrigation supply canals adds to the cost of agricultural production.

Bennett expressed the opinion that this erosion debris is by far the most important stream pollutant in terms of its widespread effect, the monetary damage it causes, and its influence on the health and well-being of our people. It causes tremendous damage to 10 major classes of public and private enterprise and the general welfare. These are: (a) public health, (b) public and industrial water supply, (c) fisheries, (d) valley agriculture, (e) drainage, (f) irrigation, (g) flood control, (h) river commerce, (i) recreation, and (j) electricity production.

Some erosion is natural. That is, it occurs without our aid. Natural erosion developed our main river systems. It was responsible for sedimentation of river flood plains prior to cultivation of the adjacent hill-lands. The Mississippi and Nile River valleys are examples. Natural sedimentation resulted in the development of fertile soils.

LOSSES ON CROPLAND

Agricultural losses due to soil deterioration are of considerable local importance in many forest and range areas but they reach significant national proportions primarily on land used for cultivated crop production. For the base period 1942-51 this cropland area, including rotation pasture, averaged about 450 million acres.

Consideration is given here primarily to those losses which arise from physical soil deterioration, not including the unrelated losses of replaceable organic matter and plant nutrients which are the normal result of crop production. These types of soil deterioration include soil erosion and deterioration of soil structure (Table 9). It should be recognized that the tremendous increase in production that would be physically attainable if all farmers made the fullest use of all available land, labor, and capital greatly outweighs the production losses arising from these causes, as serious as they are.

TABLE 9. Losses of soil from deterioration, including erosion, and watershed damage

Nature of losses	Annual losses in value
Soil deterioration on crop land	$750,000
Soil erosion on grazing and forest lands	205,000
Watershed damage including flood-water and sediment	557,000
	1,512,000

* USDA unpublished data.

The different sources of soil deterioration discussed below generally occur in combination, not singly. Soil erosion, for example, nearly always involves loss of organic matter. In evaluating broadly the effects of soil deterioration, it is not possible therefore to make any sharp distinction as to the specific individual effects of the various types. While these types are recognized and have been measured in many local situations, highly reliable data are lacking as to the magnitude and distribution of the aggregate losses on a national basis. Even if such data were available in physical terms, no satisfactory method has yet been devised for the precise evaluation of the economic effects of such losses to the farmer and to the consuming public. Under the conditions of inelastic demand which so frequently characterize the agricultural "economy of scarcity," the full social value of agricultural production, or of any decrease of such production, cannot adequately be expressed by the dollar-and-cents price tag of the market value.

With full regards for the above limitations as to accuracy, attempts are made to aggregate loss estimates in terms of (a) physical losses and (b) their economic evaluation.

PHYSICAL LOSSES

In terms of the actual physical soil loss from cropland for the base period, estimates run as high as 4 billion tons per year. Of this amount, an estimated one-third to one-fourth ultimately enters the major stream system with resultant damages from flooding, sedimentation, and the like. It is estimated that 35 million acres of land originally suited for cultivation have been rendered unfit even for temporary cultivation by the effects of the various types of soil deterioration, principally soil erosion. For the base period, the annual rate of such cropland loss is estimated at 500,000 acres per year. In addition, 50 to 100 million acres of land once cultivated, but orginally not entirely suitable for long-time cultivation, have been so severely affected by soil deterioration that they are no longer in cultivation.

While the above losses apply to land which is no longer in cultivation, soil deterioration has given rise to losses of a much more serious nature in terms of decreased yield and/or increased costs on land that has remained in cultivation. A survey made by the Soil Conservation Service in 1948 indicated the following conditions of soil deterioration on the 451 million acres of cropland and rotation pasture covered in the survey:

Degree of deterioration	Number of years, at current rate (1948), in which the land would be degraded one capability class if no remedial measures taken*	Millions of acres
Critical	10 to 15	114
Serious	15 to 30	120
Slight to none	30 and over	217

It should not be inferred from these estimates that, during the base period, soil deterioration was occurring on the entire acreage of cropland. Actually, millions of acres in the "slight to none" category were being maintained and even improved through the application of sound soil management, including soil conservation.

* See Chapter 7.

ECONOMIC LOSSES

While there is no completely satisfactory method for the economic interpretation of physical soil deterioration on cropland on a national scale, various estimates have been made.

The annual losses from erosion alone, expressed in terms of the cost of replacing, through commercial fertilizers, the major nutrient elements removed through soil erosion, have been estimated at several billions. The cost (at 1947 prices) of replacing only the nitrogen and phosphorus removed annually through soil erosion is estimated at $4.3 billion. For replacement of the nitrogen, phosphorus, and one-fourth of the potassium removed, the estimate is $7.75 billion. In addition, the effects of soil erosion on the physical properties of the soils are often more important than are the chemical effects.

Another estimate in 1947, based upon the estimated annual decrease in value of cropland resulting from soil deterioration, placed the annual loss for the base period in the order of $1.0 to $1.5 billion.

Assume that figures given for "critical," "serious," and "slight to none" erosion conditions applied throughout the base period, that soil deterioration losses are capitalized into decreased cropland value, and apply the results to an estimated average cropland value for the period of $75 per acre. The estimated annual loss figure is then about $750 million.

It may be estimated that the average annual loss from soil deterioration on cropland for the base period 1942-1951 was of the magnitude of three-quarters of a billion dollars, with full recognition that the loss was perhaps not less than 60 per cent of the estimate nor more than 200 per cent.

If the equally rough estimates of $180 million for such losses on grazing land and $25 million on forest land be considered as well, the losses are of the magnitude of $1 billion.

NATURE AND EXTENT OF LOSSES
DUE TO SOIL DETERIORATION ON CROPLAND

Soil erosion. The destructive action of soil erosion has forced the abandonment for cultivation of an estimated 25,000,000 acres of land which was originally suitable for crop production. For the base period, the annual rate of such loss was an estimated 400,000 acres per year. In addition erosion has rendered perhaps 75,000,000 acres of land once cultivated but not originally well suited to cultivation unfit even for very occasional cultivation. On the remaining cropland, erosion continues to take its toll of productivity.

The specific effects of physical soil loss upon crop yield vary widely with soil type, the kind of crop grown, and the nature and amount of other inputs applied. Clearly, a loss of several inches of topsoil from a shallow stony soil, with the resultant exposure of bare rock, would be agriculturally disastrous. A similar loss from a deep, fertile, granulated soil or alluvial soil, on the other hand, might result in decreased yield and land value but, most likely, not in abandonment.

Of the 450 million acres used for crops and rotation pasture in the base period, about 80 per cent was subject to erosion of varying degree. Of these 450 million acres, an estimated 41 per cent included deep, fairly uniform soils which could withstand considerable erosion while, with increasing in-

Soil Erosion and Related Problems

puts, continuing in cultivation. About 48 per cent were deep soils with heavy subsoils which, if eroded, would require shifts to much longer rotations; or to permanent pasture or woodland use. The remaining 11 per cent were areas, such as shallow soils over rock, hardpan, and claypan, upon which any considerable erosion would mean the virtual end of use for cultivated crops.

Among many examples of empirical evidence of erosion effects on crop yields, Table 10 is suggestive of the relationship as it exists on some Corn Belt soils.

TABLE 10. Relation of corn yields to depth of surface soil, Iowa

Depth of surface soil in inches	Corn yield in bushels per acre		
	Marshall silt loam	Tama silt loam	Shelby silt loam
11–12	119.9	63.9	—
9–10	109.0	58.1	—
7–8	92.7	45.8	49.8
5–6	79.6	42.8	45.2
3–4	65.4	38.4	38.9
1–2	52.3	31.8	35.1
0	—	—	24.7

The yield figures represent various outputs from comparable inputs. Yield effects of soil erosion are more commonly masked, or even reversed, where more and more inputs are applied to eroding soils. There are cases where surprisingly high yields have been obtained from badly eroded soils, but only where other inputs have been increased far above what would have been required for equivalent production from the uneroded soil. Thus, the true effects of erosion might be reflected more in costs of production, or in input-output ratios, than in physical yield values.

In terms of total soil lost, the southeastern section of the nation has suffered from soil erosion more than any other area. The wide adaptation of needed land-use adjustments, however, has reduced the rate of loss in the Southeast. For the base period, the area suffering the greatest annual soil loss was the Corn Belt, particularly in problem areas such as western Iowa, where in many fields almost continuous corn was grown on long, unbroken slopes. For the country at large, recent Soil Conservation Service estimates indicate that about 80 per cent of soil erosion losses have occurred in the area east of the 100th meridian.

Deterioration of soil structure. While loss of favorable structure frequently results from soil erosion through the exposure of harsh, cloudy subsoils, it is also a widely prevalent consequence of cultivation even where no soil loss has occurred. Yield reductions from this cause may be permanent. They can be brought back only by good soil management and the use of large quantities of fertilizer.

Wind erosion. While few reliable figures are available on the extent of areas affected by wind erosion, it may be assumed that over 100,000,000 acres are subject to this type of loss, of which perhaps 10,000,000 acres are seriously affected.

The effects upon crop yields of loss through soil blowing are similar to those due to erosion by water. The most fertile parts of the soil are removed, conveyed in the air for considerable distances, and then deposited on the land, in cities and towns, or in the sea. A considerable part of the soil removed is redeposited on farm land where it remains available for use. Much of it, however, is deposited where no use can be made of it or where it creates major problems of removal. The dust storms which characterize the more serious cases of wind erosion cause additional damage through abrasive action on crops, and on machinery and farm equipment.

Generally limited to arid and semiarid regions, losses from soil blowing are widely distributed but have reached the greatest magnitude in the so-called "Dust Bowl" area of northwestern Texas, northeastern New Mexico, western Kansas and Oklahoma, and eastern Colorado. Although less serious than in the drier areas, soil blowing does create acute local problems in the humid regions, particularly on areas of drained and cultivated organic soils (peat and muck) and on areas of very sandy soils.

LOSSES ON GRAZING LAND AND FOREST LAND

The estimates in the following discussion apply to the 631,000,000 acres of range and pasture, the 320,000,000 acres of forest range, and the 257,-000,000 acres of ungrazed forest and woodland in the United States.

Kinds of losses on grazing land. Agricultural losses on grazing lands are due to a variety of causes, some of the most important of which are discussed below.

The removal of topsoil over vast areas by wind and water has caused a decline in both the quality and quantity of vegetation. Furthermore, the runoff and erosion debris from grazing lands has increased the destructiveness of floods and added to the silting problems of reservoirs and irrigation works.

Generally, overuse has been the cause of soil erosion. This factor has also been widespread and has seriously reduced the productivity of grazing lands.

The invasion of trees and shrubs into areas previously unoccupied by such plants and the thickening of existing stands has also operated to reduce the production of usable forage on range lands particularly, and to some extent on pasture lands. Estimates of the area seriously affected by such invasions range from 80 to 168 million acres in the West, and as high as 240 million acres for the entire United States.

Drought, which normally occurs 3 years out of every 10 over great areas of range land, contributes to range depletion and causes other "losses" through increased production costs. Although commonly assumed to be nonpreventable, the effects of droughts on grazing lands actually can be greatly reduced by the continued practice of good management.

All the above causes of "agricultural losses" on grazing lands frequently operate on the same lands simultaneously. For example, overuse may deplete the stand of herbaceous forage cover enough to stimulate the thickening of brush species. This process may be accentuated by drought, and, in turn, may accelerate wind and water erosion. The combined effects are a loss in productivity of the land, a reduction in taxable wealth, and lowered possibilities for current income.

WATERSHED DAMAGE, FLOOD WATER, AND SEDIMENT

Flood water and sediment take a heavy toll from agriculture each year in the United States. In terms of 1942-51 price levels, the average annual loss to agriculture alone is estimated to be about $557,000,000. These agricultural losses are of several kinds: damage to crops and pasture, land damage in the form of flood plain scour, streambank erosion, gullying and valley trenching, infertile overwash or deposition of sediment and swamping; damage to farm buildings, fences, roads, stored crops, livestock and drainage facilities; and indirect losses, such as delays in field work, disruption or delays in marketing of farm products, and others.

These damage estimates are presented and discussed in two parts, (a) those occurring along tributary or headwaters of major rivers and (b) those occurring downstream, or in major river valleys. In general, the term "tributary or headwaters" as used here refers to areas *above* existing, authorized, or proposed major flood-control structures, and the term "downstream" refers to those areas *below* such structures. For the nation as a whole, these estimates indicate that the average annual upstream agricultural flood water and sediment damage amounts to about $391,774,000 (Table 11). This constitutes the largest share of the total annual agricultural losses from flood water and sediment—perhaps as much as 50 per cent. This is primarily because flooding is much more frequent on small tributary streams. It should also be recognized that a large amount of protection has already been provided to major river valleys by levees and floodwalls, channel improvements and major reservoirs. Were it not for the protection already afforded, downstream or major river valley damage would be about 60 per cent greater than it is at present. The average annual agricultural damage downstream is estimated to be about $165,000,000.

In the upstream areas, damage to crops and pasture constitutes over 50 per cent of the total, and other agricultural damage, about 20 per cent. Flood-plain damage by scour, streambank erosion, gullying and valley trenching, infertile overwash and swamping, though not so important monetary-wise as the foregoing, is quite important from the standpoint of our agricultural resources. Some 5 per cent or more of our total agricultural land lies in the alluvial flood plains of tributary valleys. This land, on the average, is the most productive that we have. If given reasonable degree of flood protection it will remain productive for a long time to come. Some land damage is temporary in nature, in that full productivity can be restored within a relatively few years. In other cases the damage is more or less permanent and productivity is impaired for future generations. In some cases deposition of sediment may actually be beneficial to bottomlands. This beneficial effect, however, is slight in upstream areas.

TABLE 11. Estimated average annual upstream agricultural damage from floodwater and sediment, United States

Type of damage	Average annual damage	Totals
Floodwater		
Crops and pasture	$205,694,000	
Floodplain scour,		
gully and valley trenching	31,468,000	
Other agricultural		
(farm buildings, stored crops,		
etc.)	73,059,000	
		310,221,000
Sediment		
Infertile overwash	20,320,000	
Swamping	13,977,000	
Drainage and irrigation facilities	12,634,000	
		46,931,000
Indirect		
Interruption of essential farm		
work, etc.		34,622,000
Total		$391,774,000

Sediment damage occurs more often in the cultivated farm land areas of the country. Areas under cultivation are usually more subject than others to washing and to other forces of erosion. Erosion contributes large amounts of sediment to the headwater tributaries and consequently to downstream and mainstream areas. Such sediment fills channels, is deposited on the highly productive flood plains, and is carried into major reservoirs. Damages from sedimentation tend to be cumulative. Sediment that is brought down from the top of the hills into tributary and major valleys will tend to produce damage in future years through decreasing the channel capacities, gradual destruction of the productive bottomland, and swamping of the bottomland and consequent raising of ground-water levels.

In most upstream tributary valleys, a large share of the total losses from floods are caused by comparatively small storms—those that occur on an average more frequently than once in 10 years. These floods on creeks and small tributary streams are usually caused by short intensive storms which cover relatively small areas. Such floods occur far more often than do the storms of longer duration over the large areas which are required to produce a main stem flood. Because of the thousands of headwater streams that drain our vast agricultural regions, it is evident that the damage caused each year by many frequent floods will build up to a staggering total. At 1951 prices, it is estimated that the average annual agricultural and non-agricultural flood-water damages in the major river valleys is about $500 million. In terms of 1942-51 prices the figure would be about $410 million and of this amount it is estimated that $165 million is agricultural damage. In addition, it is estimated that average annual downstream sediment damage will approximate about 28 to 30 million dollars. These sediment damages, unlike those occurring in the headwaters of streams, are predominantly non-agricultural.

EFFECT OF SOIL EROSION ON VALLEY AGRICULTURE

The ill effects of flooding and the deposition of infertile sediments on valley croplands are widely distributed throughout the United States. The total annual loss to valley crops and croplands from floods and sediment is measured in terms of hundreds of millions of dollars. The Little Tallahatchie Watershed in northern Mississippi is an example. A survey of this area showed that erosion had advanced to a critical stage. This watershed, containing 887,476 acres, was opened for settlement about a century ago. Approximately 8.25 per cent of the area consisted of alluvial flood plains. In three generations, 294,-000 acres of the total area had been forced out of cultivation as a result of erosion, and another 75,000 acres had been virtually ruined by gullying. As a result, runoff is so rapid and stream channels so clogged with sediment that a half-inch rain sometimes causes damaging floods. Extensive damages now affect 65 per cent of all the 71,800 acres of bottomland. In a normal year, about 15 floods occur somewhere in the watershed. Of these, four usually occur during the growing season. The average annual flood-water damage to crops alone in this valley amounts to $301,483. Over and above this cost, present agricultural damage resulting from sedimentation of flood plains and stream channels is estimated at $591,023 annually. This figure represents the cumulative loss in productivity of all flood-plain areas affected by sedimentation.

EFFECT OF EROSION ON DRAINAGE

Up to 1940, more than $690,000,000 had been invested in drainage enterprises in the United States. Over half of this was spent in the construction of open ditches. Annual expenditures for maintenance of these ditches amount to approximately $1,800,000. A large share of this cost is for removal of sediment washed down from eroding farm lands. The actual cost of this sedimentation to drainage enterprises is probably much greater than this figure would indicate, for a great many ditches are not properly maintained, and for that reason the entire capital investment is gradually being lost.

EFFECT OF EROSION ON IRRIGATION

More than a billion dollars had been invested in irrigation enterprises in the western states as of 1940. The area that could be irrigated by these installations comprised around 28,000,000 acres. Annual cost of maintenance and operation was something over $43,000,000. A considerable share of this cost was for cleaning silt from irrigation canals.

In addition to the large annual ditch-cleaning cost, irrigation enterprises in many localities are faced with the serious problem of silt accumulation in their water-storage reservoirs. More than 1,800 such reservoirs have been

built in the western states at an estimated cost of $395,000,000, not includ-
ing the approximate cost of multiple-purpose reservoirs such as Boulder
Dam. Silting damage to these reservoirs amounts to several million dollars
annually, according to recent surveys.

Golze estimated the cost of removing sediment from the 120,000 miles of
irrigation supply canals and laterals in the western United States to exceed
$4,500,000 annually. This estimate was based on actual average costs of $40
per mile in 1948 on 2,590 miles of canals and laterals in representative federal reclamation projects.

EFFECT OF EROSION ON FISHERIES

Ellis conducted a number of surveys to determine the effect of erosion silt on
fisheries. He concluded:

> Among the substances which must be excluded (from streams) erosion
> silt stands out conspicuously. . . . Although erosion silt is clearly the major
> problem in inland waters, locally various industrial silts continue to be
> serious stream pollutants.

According to investigations of specialists on aquatic life, erosion silt in
streams and lakes affects fisheries in a number of ways. Silt blankets the bottoms of streams and destroys the many organisms that normally live there in
abundance and provide food for fish. Such sediments also eliminate the nesting
and spawning areas of a great many kinds of fish.

Studies made by Ellis at more than 700 stations on streams in the Mississippi, Ohio, and Missouri river systems and other interior waters revealed
that silt screens out light in stream waters and thus develops an environment
unfavorable to the better fish. In 5,000 determinations of light penetration, it
was found that a clear mountain stream permitted light of certain intensity to
penetrate the water to depths of 50,000 millimeters, but water taken from
the Missouri River contained so much silt that light of the same intensity
penetrated only 84 millimeters.

The turbidity of the Mississippi River illustrates what silt is doing to our
streams. In the relatively clear unpolluted headwaters of the Mississippi,
above Grand Rapids, Minn., light penetrated to depths of 6,000 to 34,000
millimeters. Below the mouth of Chippewa River, which brings in large
quantities of erosion debris, readings of light penetrations as small as 1,500
millimeters were not unusual even during low-water periods. At Davenport,
Iowa, the readings averaged 466 millimeters. Below the mouth of the Missouri, the average depth of light penetration was less than 200 millimeters.
Between Cairo, Ill., and New Orleans, La., the average was consistently less
than 175 millimeters.

With reference to the cause of this condition, Ellis said:

> The most outstanding factor producing changes in river conditions at
> present throughout the Mississippi system was found to be erosion silt. As a
> result of deforestation, current methods of tilling the land, and various im-
> provements incident to commercial progress, as road building, the amount
> of erosion silt which is being received by the various streams of the Mississippi

system has been progressively greater during the past 10 years until it now presents perhaps the most acute fisheries problem in our inland rivers. . . . The erosion silt now carried by the streams of the Mississippi system is so great that any obstruction to stream flow results in rapid deposition of quantities of silt on the upstream side of this obstruction. This is particularly true in times of high water, but most of the tributaries of the Mississippi system, even in low water, are now quickly clouded by the large quantities of erosion silt which are poured down into them from the surface runoff following even local storms. This condition did not obtain years ago when swamps, forested lands, and other natural features impeded the surface runoff.

SOIL EROSION AND PUBLIC HEALTH

The pollution of streams by erosion-produced silt is one of the principal obstacles to effective control of malaria. The endemic malarial area of the United States is roughly bounded on the north by a line from northern Virginia to St. Louis, Mo., and on the west from this point to San Antonio, Tex. There are three other smaller regions—the Rio Grande Valley in New Mexico, portions of the Sacramento and San Joaquin Valleys of California, and a small area in the Willamette Valley of Oregon. These are also areas of some of the most serious erosion and sedimentation problems in the United States.

Swamp and pond areas have developed extensively in the valleys of the southern states during the past 25 to 50 years as a result of the clogging of natural drainage channels by sediment.

Engineers of the Tennessee State Planning Commission made an investigation of the drainage impairment in the south fork of Forked Deer River, in western Tennessee, in 1935. Drainage on this stream was good until about 1929, when the channel became clogged by fallen trees and silt washed down from the heavily cultivated uplands. By 1935, backwater from the clogged channels had covered more than 14,000 acres of rich bottomlands and had ruined thousands of board feet of standing timber. But the most significant finding of the survey concerned malaria. Deaths from malaria in the area adjacent to the newly formed swamps had increased more than 50 per cent from 1929 to 1935.

In Georgia, in 1938, some counties had as high as 35 deaths from malaria per 100,000 population and as many as 1,500 new cases per 100,000 population were reported. In the same year, the Georgia State Department of Public Health found malaria control to be a troublesome and expensive problem in nine counties in the northern part of the state. The disease was epidemic but localized among people living in and near the creek bottoms. These areas were not naturally subject to malaria, but had become so as a result of expanded agricultural and lumbering operations, which had resulted in clogging the stream channels and ponding water on many of the bottomlands. State health officials concluded that "malaria will continue to smoulder and occasionally burst into flame as long as these practices are continued."

Even in the arid country of the middle Rio Grande Valley in New Mexico, malaria has become a serious problem as a result of rapid silting of the channel of the Rio Grande. Investigations by the Soil Conservation Service showed that as a result of a rise of the river bed at a rate of one foot in 12 years, due to silting, numerous areas of ponded water occur over the adjacent alluvial plain. These ponds cannot easily be drained into the river because most of them are lower than the present river bed. This poor drainage, which has greatly aggravated the malaria problem, is solely the indirect result of filling the stream with erosion debris.

SOIL EROSION AND PUBLIC WATER SUPPLY

The costly effect of silt pollution of streams on the public water supply of the nation is not generally understood. The Soil Conservation Service made a study of water-filtration operations by 22 cities in the Piedmont area of North Carolina. Over and above the cost of water treatment was the damage from silting to the water-supply reservoirs.

The Soil Conservation Service also made detailed and reconnaissance sur-

FIGURE 12.   Some 30 inches of silt were deposited in the O'Shaughnessy Reservoir near Columbus, Ohio, during a 10-year period under water depth of 20 feet. In addition to adding to the cost of filtering the water and depleting the reservoir's storage capacity, the loss of this silt from farm fields in the drainage basin resulted in lower crop yields. (Columbus, Ohio) *(Soil Conservation Service)*

veys on approximately 375 reservoirs, which, together with data on about 75 reservoirs surveyed by other agencies, gave information on silting in approximately 450 lakes, of which 151 were used primarily for water supply. These were sufficiently well distributed to give a fairly reliable picture of the regional aspects of silting in water-supply reservoirs throughout the country.

It was assumed that the useful life of the average reservoir was ended when 80 per cent of its capacity was gone. A uniform silting rate based on past performance was projected into the future. On this basis, the data on 151 water-supply reservoirs—which were believed to be fairly representative, though a small sample of the 2,700 in the United States—showed that 21 per cent would have a useful life of less than 50 years as a result of silting. Another 25 per cent would last 50 to 100 years. Only 54 per cent would retain enough storage to satisfy present requirements 100 years hence.

SOIL EROSION AND SILTING OF RESERVOIRS

In November, 1941, the national reservoir inventory of the Soil Conservation Service contained records of about 8,900 dams and reservoirs, exclusive of more than 3,800 listed farm ponds, conservation ponds, and dams that generate a small amount of power. It was estimated that more than $4,450,-000,000 had been invested in these water-utilization developments, including those under construction during 1941. That vast sum represented for the most part only the cost of the dams and the reservoirs. Except for power plants built into dams, it did not include dependent developments, such as water-filtration plants, irrigation canals, and power transmission lines.

Among the more important problems in the development and maintenance of impounding reservoirs is the loss of storage capacity caused by silting which results from the deposition of stream-borne soil waste or sediment. The primary cause of this condition is accelerated erosion.

In the study of 30 reservoirs and their watersheds in the loess hills region of the Missouri River Basin, Glymph found that sheet erosion was by far the largest single source of sediment. Sheet erosion was the only source of sediment in nine of the reservoir watersheds. It accounted for from 95 to 98 per cent of the total sediment in nine other watersheds. In only five of the watersheds did sediment derived from gully and channel erosion exceed 10 per cent of the total.

Sediment is an inevitable consequence of erosion. To understand the sediment problem, it is first necessary to understand its relation to erosion. Though sediment production is dependent upon erosion, the terms "rates of erosion" and "rates of sediment production," as commonly used, are seldom synonymous.

The rate of erosion is a measure of the total amount of soil or soil material moved from a fixed position within or on any area per unit of time. The rate of sediment production, on the other hand, is the net amount of solids moved out of a natural watershed area of unspecified size per unit of time. As commonly used, sediment production excludes removal of dissolved matter and removal by wind action.

Glymph estimated that the loss of storage capacity by sedimentation in existing and partially completed reservoirs in the Missouri Basin would amount to at least 175,000 acre-feet per year. The estimated average sediment accumulation in the 38 primary reservoirs in the Missouri Basin would amount to 152,138 acre-feet annually. This volume of sediment was equivalent to the volume of water required to irrigate 50,000 acres of land. It represented the storage required to hold 6 inches of runoff from 304,000 acres, or 475 square miles. In addition to the 38 primary reservoirs, records indicate that there are 1,130 more reservoirs having capacities larger than 25 acre-feet, which store water for power, irrigation, flood control, recreation, domestic water supply, and other purposes in the Basin. These additional reservoirs are accumulating an estimated 22,000 acre-feet of sediment annually.

Analysis of the sediment surveys made in Ohio showed that the ratio (c/w ratio = capacity/watershed) of the storage capacity of a reservoir to the area of watershed draining water to it had a close relation to the annual rate of sedimentation in the reservoir. A reservoir with a large capacity and a small watershed area filled with sediment very slowly. The rate of sedimentation increased when the reservoir capacity was small and the watershed area large. Reservoirs that had storage capacities of 120 acre-feet (39 million gallons) or greater for each square mile of watershed area accumulated sediment at an annual rate of 0.75 per cent, or less, of the original reservoir capacity, whereas reservoirs with a c/w ratio of less than 120 acre-feet per square mile showed an annual rate of loss of capacity greater than 0.75 per cent, the rate increasing as the c/w ratio became smaller.

EROSION AND SEDIMENTATION OF HARBORS

The effect of sedimentation on the abandonment of many early American ports is illustrated by Hartford-on-the-Bush and Joppa Town in Maryland. At the site of these two early colonial ports, stone mooring posts that once held the hawsers of seagoing vessels are now two or more miles from navigable water. Rapid sedimentation in the embayments and navigable rivers of the eastern seaboard is an abnormal condition developed after the white man settled in this region. Both historical and geological evidence indicates that the pre-agricultural rate of silting of eastern tidal estuaries was slow.

The history of sedimentation of ports in the Chesapeake Bay area is an epic of the effects of uncontrolled erosion since the beginning of wholesale land clearing and cultivation more than three centuries ago. The colonists in this area found a deep, rich, virgin-forest soil, which produced abundantly. Hundreds of thousands of acres of forest land were cleared for agriculture by ax and fire. Most of this was planted to tobacco, though a few acres on each plantation were usually set aside for the growing of corn, wheat, and other necessary food crops. The first plantations were scattered. Each settler had his own landing on tidewater, where tobacco could be loaded directly on ships or lightered to larger vessels by barge.

Tobacco of good quality requires rich land, of which the colonists seemingly had plenty. But tobacco is hard on the land. It is clean tilled and permits high rates of erosion. Consequently, the planters found that only two or three good crops of tobacco could be produced from a field before the decrease in yield and quality made further production less profitable. A new field was then cleared, for it was easier to acquire new holdings than

to maintain or restore productivity of "worn out" land. Old fields were sometimes planted to corn or wheat, but oftener they were abandoned. This exploitive system of agriculture set the stage for vicious soil erosion and land destruction.

The most significant effect of sedimentation in colonial times was the filling of navigation channels. Most of the early port towns were purposely located on water bodies as far inland on tidewater as possible, in order to lessen the laborious task of hauling hogsheads of tobacco overland. Unfortunately, the head of navigation is usually the point of heaviest sedimentation. It was only a short time, often 50 years or less, before early open-water ports were converted into mud flats by the erosion debris. Thus, towns that otherwise might have grown into great cities and seaports were destined to die in infancy, choked by the very industry that had promoted their founding.

One of the early towns to acquire importance in colonial times was Joppa Town, Md., founded on the Gunpowder arm of Chesapeake Bay about 1700. Once the county seat of Baltimore County, Joppa Town was the most prosperous and important seaport of Maryland during the early part of its brief history. Sixteen miles north of Baltimore, it lay near the head of a wide, deep bay that afforded an excellent harbor for the largest merchantmen, which loaded at its wharf and sailed thence to all parts of the world. The drainage area of the Gunpowder Falls and Little Gunpowder Falls rivers above Joppa Town comprised about 430 square miles, mostly in the Piedmont Plateau, where soils are generally highly erodible when cultivated. The clearing of the land in the watershed started the destruction by erosional debris of the drainage basin that filled the upper part of the estuary. Decline began about 1750, and in 1768 the county seat was moved to Baltimore.

A hydrographic chart of the Gunpowder estuary issued by the United States Coast and Geodetic Survey in 1846, a hundred years after the town had reached its peak of development, shows the above-tidewater delta surface to be a mile and a half long. By this date, it had encroached within a quarter of a mile of the wharf. By 1897, when a second hydrographic chart was issued, the above-tidewater deposits had filled the entire estuary opposite the wharf and extended along a front three-fourths of a mile below the town. According to computations from data on these two charts, 7,900,-000 cubic yards of sediment were deposited in the upper part of the Gunpowder estuary in the 51-year period between 1846 and 1897. This is equal to an average annual rate of about 15 cubic feet per acre, exclusive of the sediment carried through to the lower reaches and into the Chesapeake.

The rate of sedimentation in this watershed today is well above the average of the southern Piedmont, a region noted for soil erosion. Recent surveys of the Baltimore water-supply lakes above Loch Raven and Prettyboy Dams, which control the runoff from a large part of the watershed, indicate that the rate of soil loss in this watershed for the 29 years, 1914-1943, averaged 46 cubic feet per acre per year.

Today, the above-tidewater deposits extend nearly a mile and a half below the town site. The scene of Joppa Town is one of desolation. Old foundations are still visible through the tangled growth of weeds and underbrush. At a distance of 20 to 30 feet out from the original shore line is a heap of stones, the remnants of the old wharf. A hundred feet beyond is tree-covered land where ships once rode at anchor.

REFERENCES

1. Bailey, R. W., and Craddock, G. W. 1948. *Watershed management for sediment control.* Proc. Fed. Inter-Agency Sedimentation Conf., Denver, Colo., May 6-8, 1947. U.S. Dept. Int., Spec. Pub.
2. Bennett, H. H. 1945. *Stream pollution by erosion silt.* Hearings before the Committee on Rivers and Harbors, House of Representatives, 79th Cong., 1st sess., on Bills for the control of water pollution. 318-327.
3. Brown, C. B. 1941. *Silt takes heavy storage toll.* Water Works Engin., 94(15): 874-877.
4. ———. 1944. *Downstream interests.* Soil Cons., 109(6).
5. ———. 1944. *Sediment in reservoirs.* Soc. Civil Engin. Trans., 109: 1080-1086.
6. ———. 1944. *The control of reservoir silting.* USDA Misc. Pub. 521.
7. Brown, R. H. 1943. *Mirror for Americans: On conditions in the Chesapeake Bay region.* Amer. Geogr. Soc. Spec. Pub. 27, Chap. 12.
8. Ellis, M. M. 1931. *U.S. Dept. Commerce, Bureau of Fisheries Cir. 7.*
9. ———. 1936. *Erosion silt as a factor in aquatic environment.* Ecology, 17.
10. ———. 1937. *Pollution and aquatic life.* Amer. Wildlife, 28(3).
11. Ford, E. C. 1952. *Upstream floodwater damages.* Jour. Soil and Water Cons., 8(5).
12. Gahn, B. W. 1940. *George Washington's Headquarters in Georgetown.* Westland. Silver Spring, Md., 94-95.
13. Georgia Department of Public Health. 1938. The Malaria Bull. (9-10):54-57.
14. Glymph, L. M., Jr. 1951. *Relation of sedimentation to accelerated erosion in the Missouri River Basin.* SCS-TP-102.
15. Golze, A. R. 1950. *Problems of irrigation canals.* Applied Sedimentation, Edited by P. D. Trask. John Wiley and Sons, Inc., New York. Chap. 21.
16. Gottschalk, L. C. 1943. *Report on the reconnaissance sedimentation surveys of Loch Raven and Prettyboy Reservoirs, Maryland.* SCS Spec. Rept. 5.
17. ———. 1945. *Effects of soil erosion on navigation in upper Chesapeake Bay.* Geog. Rev., 35: 219-238.
18. Great Plains Committee. 1936. *The future of the Great Plains.* U.S. Govt. Printing Office, Washington, D.C.
19. House Doc. 892, 77th Cong., 2nd sess. 1942. *Survey of the Little Tallahatchie Watershed in Mississippi.*
20. Ireland, H. A., Sharpe, C. F. S., and Eargle, D. H. 1939. *Principles of gully erosion in the Piedmont of South Carolina.* USDA Tech. Bull. 633.
21. Stallings, J. H. 1950. *Erosion of topsoil reduces productivity.* USDA, SCS-TP-98.
22. Swanson, C. L. W., Kardos, L. T., Mehring, A. L., and Terman, G. L. 1954. *The changing fertility of New England soils.* USDA Agr. Inf. Bull. 133.
23. Tennessee State Planning Commission. 1936. *Plan Topics.* 1(3): 7.
24. Thornthwaite, C. W., Sharpe, C. F. S., and Dosch, E. F. 1942. *Climate and accelerated erosion in the arid and semiarid Southwest, with special reference to the Polacca Wash Drainage Basin, Arizona.* USDA Tech. Bull. 808.
25. Youngquist, C. V. 1948. *Sedimentation of reservoirs in Ohio.* Ohio Dept. Pub. Works, Water Resources Board, Bull. 17.

How Water Erodes Soil

Water causes erosion by detaching soil particles from the surface soil mass and transporting them, usually downhill. It may do this on any area where there is natural precipitation or where water is applied artificially to land surfaces. Water's erosive action is greatest and most destructive where the protective cover of vegetation has been removed, exposing bare land surfaces to the direct action of rainstorms.

The movement of soil by water is a complex process. It is influenced by the amount, intensity, and duration of rainfall, amount and velocity of surface flow, nature of the soil, ground cover, slope of the land surface, and many other factors. In each case, the erosive power of water is determined by the interaction or balance of several factors, some favoring soil movement and others opposing it. Soil material must first be dislodged (detached) from its position on the surface of the land before it can be transported. It may then be splashed, rolled, slid, or carried in suspension along the surface. These processes are largely the result of raindrop splash, turbulence of moving water caused by raindrop splash, and flowing water.

Differences in soil erodibility suggest that both inherent soil properties and those brought about by land use, especially by cultivation and other disturbances, play a major part in the water-erosion process.

51

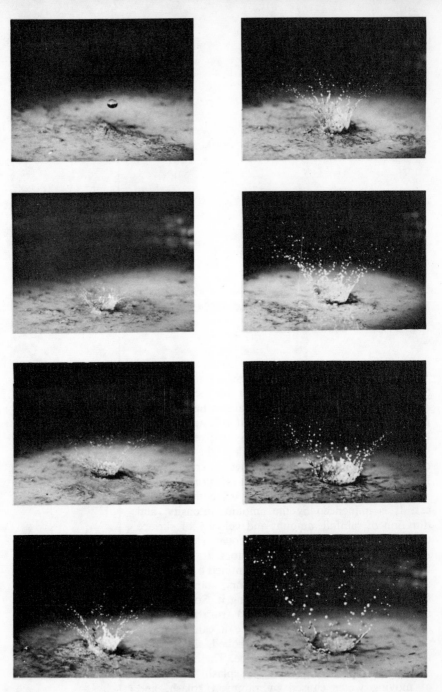

FIGURE 13. These photographs show the splash resulting from a falling drop of water striking bare soil surface. The drop of water fell from a height of about 7.5 feet. The set of photographs shows a succession of stages in the splash action. The final product is the crater shown in the photograph at the lower right.
(Naval Research Laboratory)

Erosion, in its physical aspects, is simply the accomplishment of a certain amount of work in tearing apart and transporting soil material. The water-erosion process begins when raindrops strike the surface of the soil and break down the clods and aggregates or when snow melts. It consists of three steps. In the first step, the soil particles are torn loose from their moorings in the soil mass; in the second step, detached soil material is transported; and in the third step, soil material is deposited. The products of the first two processes cannot be expressed in a single quantitative result, because they cannot be expressed in like units. Detachment is expressed in terms of weight or volume per unit area, such as tons per acre. Transportation, on the other hand, is expressed in terms of weight or volume moved through distance, such as ton-miles per acre.

The two principal erosive agents that become active on land during rainstorms are falling raindrops and flowing water. The energy of falling

FIGURE 14. Erosion damage caused by snowmelt occurs in two distinct forms: (1) rills and gullies, as shown across the center of the photograph, and (2) landslides, as shown in the left background. Water from melting snow usually concentrates into channelized flow to form rills and gullies. In some cases, where the surface soil is underlain with an impervious layer, water seeping into the ground collects on top of this impervious layer to act as a lubricant and the soil above it sloughs off. (Idaho)
(Soil Conservation Service)

raindrops is applied from above, and their principal function is to detach soil particles from the soil mass. The energy of flowing water is usually applied parallel with the surface and, outside of rills and gullies, its principal function is to transport soil material. Both raindrops and flowing water are complete erosive agents in themselves, but in one phase of the erosion process they work together. That is when there is a shallow surface flow, in prechannel stages, which lacks rotational energy to keep soil in suspension. Then the falling raindrops, by keeping the water turbid, increase the ability of surface flow to transport soil particles.

Falling raindrops and surface flow produce widely different effects on the soil. The force of falling raindrops is applied uniformly over the whole surface on which the rain falls. Erosion caused by raindrops is more of a smoothing, or leveling, agent. This is demonstrated on a small scale by the way the beating raindrops flatten small sandpiles by bringing soil material from the crest and depositing it lower on the slope. Flowing water tends to collect in channels—first, in small rills and then, as these small channels converge, in streams. The result of erosion caused by the flowing streams is to roughen the surface by cutting channels, or gullies.

FIGURE 15.   About 2 inches of soil were removed from this plowed field, mainly as a result of raindrop splash. The stone-capped pedestals show that the force causing the erosion was applied from above, as by falling raindrops, and not from the side, as by flowing surface water. The dead plant roots in the foreground protected the soil immediately beneath them while the soil between and around them was splashed away. (South Carolina)
(Soil Conservation Service)

FIGURE 16. Falling raindrops beating on the insufficiently protected ground surface of this corn field splashed particles of soil into the air. These particles fell into the film of water that was on the surface and were floated downhill, to be deposited when the gradient of the slope was decreased and the velocity of the flowing water was consequently reduced. (Tuscarawas County, Ohio)
(Soil Conservation Service)

FIGURE 17. The effects of raindrop splash in the erosion process are frequently most pronounced on the short, steep slopes near the crest of hills. On such slopes falling raindrops are effective in moving soil downhill without much assistance from flowing surface water. (Izent County, Michigan)
(Soil Conservation Service)

SPLASH-EROSION PROCESS

The erosive capacity of a falling mass of water depends on the energy per unit area of the individual drop. The kinetic energy of the falling drop determines the force of the blow that must be absorbed at each point of impact, while the horizontal area of the drop determines the amount of soil that must sustain that blow. It is the application of this energy in the form of raindrop impact that accounts for the greatest part of the dispersion of soil particles. We know now that, on some terrain, the washoff soil losses alone actually account for only a small part of the erosional damage from a heavy rain. The rest of the damage is attributable to soil splash. The secret of preventing most erosion, therefore, is to remove this energy from the raindrop before it is brought to bear on the surface of the soil.

The kinetic energy of raindrops amounts to 10^4 ergs for drops of 2 mm. radius. The kinetic energy contained in a drop of 2.5 mm. radius is sufficient to raise by 1 cm. a body weighing 46 grams. As the intensity of rainfall increases, the kinetic energy increases at the rate of 1.2 powers of the intensity. All the kinetic energy of the raindrops, except a small part which is transformed to sound and heat energy, is expended instantly against the soil surface. The movement of soil caused by the impact of falling raindrops is downward, to the sides, and upward. The downward movement consumes the greater part of the kinetic energy of raindrops at the beginning

FIGURE 18. Splash erosion acts as a leveling agent. It moves sloping topsoil in sheets. Much of the erosional debris is deposited at the base of slopes, often filling the valleys and depressions. *(Soil Conservation Service)*

of a rain. The movement to the sides and upward is related to the spreading and splashing action of raindrops.

The compacting action by the falling raindrops causes soil to suddenly lose its capacity to infiltrate water. It is thus responsible for the high run-off during heavy rains. This is illustrated by the fact that rain falling on sand decreases its infiltration rate without producing turbid water. It can be illustrated also by letting raindrops fall on wire gauze suspended a short distance above the ground surface. The energy of the falling raindrops will be reduced and the rate of water intake will be high.

When the surface soil is pounded by raindrops, the infiltration rate de-creases rapidly as the proportion of large drops and their velocity in-creases. In the same rainfall, the decrease in the infiltration rate is greatest on the flat land. The decrease is progressively less as the degree of slope increases. The hammer-like action of the raindrops brings more direct and stronger pressure to bear on the flat land than on slopes. A test rain totaling 4.4 inches in 2½ hours penetrated a bare granitic soil to a depth of only 7 cm. About 80 per cent of the rain was lost as runoff.

The splash-erosion process is affected by variation in either the size of raindrops, drop velocity, or rainfall intensity. Using rain applicators to apply spray to trays of soil, it was found that as the drop size increased from 1 to 5 mm. in diameter the infiltration rate decreased as much as 70 per cent, and the erosion losses—measured in terms of the concentration of soil in the runoff water—increased up to 1200 per cent. As the size or velocity of raindrops increase, the concentration of soil in the runoff water increases and the infiltration rate decreases. This shows a direct relation between the energy expended by the falling raindrops and the resulting soil loss. The concentration of soil in the runoff water varies with the time at which comparisons are made. This indicates that the erodibility of the soil surface changes during the run.

The amount of damage done by falling raindrops is proportional to their kinetic energy, which ranges from 1,000 to 100,000 times the work capac-ity of surface flow. When raindrops strike bare soil, or thin films of water covering it, they blast it with a multitude of explosions. These blasts bounce water back into the air carrying with it, in muddy splash, fine particles of earth. These splashed particles reach varying heights, ranging up to more than two feet, and they move horizontally more than five feet on level surfaces. Their trajectories are shown in Figure 13. This photograph shows a series of stages of the splash resulting from a drop of water falling from a height of about 7.5 feet onto soil contained in a pan which cannot be seen in the picture. On bare soil which is highly detachable, more than 100 tons per acre may be splashed by the most beating types of rain.

On level surfaces, the splashed material tends to scatter uniformly over the surface in all directions when the raindrops have a vertical drop. In such cases, the outgoing splash normally balances the incoming splash in a given area. But when raindrops strike sloping land surfaces, the major por-tion of the splash moves downhill. Since most of this splash moves in a downhill direction, relatively large quantities of soil may be transported by raindrop splash acting alone. The per cent of soil splashed downhill has been found to be 50 + the degree of slope of all the soil splashed.

The amount of raindrop energy dissipated on the soil during a storm may be measured indirectly by measuring the soil carried in raindrop splash. A favorable place to observe transportation by splash is on a large sandpile that is free of surface flow. The top of the pile will be lowered by splashing the sand particles downhill, while sand at the lower edge will be piled deeper and the pile made wider. The results of this same process are apparent on many small knolls and hummocks, and along the crests of many hills. Figure 17 illustrates these conditions, where the crests of hummocks, knolls, and steep hills in cultivated fields and on overgrazed pastures are often devoid of topsoil while a deep bank of topsoil may be found along the base of the slope. Examination of these soil banks often shows that they do not have the characteristics of alluvial deposits.

Some hilltops may never have had deep topsoil. But what little topsoil was present was splashed downhill when the natural vegetation was removed.

The splash process produces at least three different types of erosional damage: (a) puddle erosion, (b) fertility erosion, and (c) sheet erosion.

PUDDLE EROSION

As previously stated, falling raindrops have great capacity to damage soils. The sharp impact, as the drops beat on the naked earth during violent storms, shatters the clods and soil crumbs and breaks down the soil structure into a puddled condition. The beating and churning action of these drops compacts the soil's finely broken parts into an impervious layer of surface mud.

This compacted surface layer is made denser and more impervious as it collects colloids and other particles from the turbid rain water that filters down from the surface. Eventually, the porosity of this surface layer is materially reduced by the infiltration of muddy surface materials. Then the important entrance channels to deep soils are closed. The soil-profile material can no longer absorb air freely, nor can it receive and store abundant supplies of rainfall.

A single storm leaves visible effects of this puddling only on the surface of the soil. These show as crusts on plowed fields. The surface is glazed like the icing on a cake. The puddling process may be demonstrated by playing a heavy spray from a garden hose on bare ground. Puddling can actually be seen taking place on the surface. Where the ground surface is protected by low-growing plants or by a cover of mulch, it is shielded against the impact of falling raindrops. Under these conditions the soil retains its natural structure, and any water that accumulates on the surface remains clear.

FERTILITY EROSION

When raindrops loosen the soil and splash it into the air, nearly all of the particles that are dislodged seem to be 2 mm. or less in diameter. They also splash some particles larger than this. As these splashes fall back into the

FIGURE 19. The impact of falling raindrops beating on the naked earth during violent storms shatters the clods and soil crumbs and breaks down the soil structure into a puddled condition. The beating, churning action of these drops compact the soil's finely broken parts into an impervious surface mud. (New York)
(Soil Conservation Service)

FIGURE 20. The view in the middle foreground shows the puddling effect of a single rain on a corn field. The surface is glazed like the icing on a cake. (Anderson County, South Carolina)
(Soil Conservation Service)

surface water, many of the finer particles are carried away and the coarser material settles out after being moved a short distance downhill. This produces what is known as fertility erosion. It results in the accumulation of excessive coarse material on the surface within a short time after the beginning of rainfall.

Storms of small drop size, which fall at relatively low velocities and of light intensity, intense rains of very short duration, or intense rains which terminate abruptly all tend to leave an excess of coarse particles on the surface of the field.

Even though the land is practically level, much of the organic matter and fertility-bearing elements of the soil may be floated away.

The action which produces fertility erosion can be demonstrated by washing a bucket of sandy soil in a washing machine. Just dump the soil in the tub while the agitator is working, and keep a small stream of water entering the tub in order to maintain a constant overflow. The overflow will carry out the fine and light materials as the agitator stirs them into suspension. Soon, nothing is left in the bottom of the tub but coarse sand.

SHEET EROSION

Practically all so-called sheet erosion is actually splash erosion. Because of the very nature of the splash-erosion process, it tends to remove the sloping topsoil in thin sheets. The effects are demonstrated in miniature every time beating raindrops flatten and level small sandpiles. It works about the same

FIGURE 21.   Organic matter, silt, and clay "picked" loose by falling raindrops and floated downhill by flowing surface water to be deposited in depressions or floated off the field. The deposit on this corn field is several inches thick.
(Soil Conservation Service)

way on a hill, bringing material down from the crest and depositing it lower on the slope. The energy of the splashing raindrops is applied uniformly throughout the area on which the rain falls. This favors production of the greatest amount of soil movement at the crest of the hill, where the least amount of energy is required to transport soil and more of it can be devoted to dislodging the soil particles. At some point downhill, all the energy of the raindrops may be consumed in resplashing soil that has been splashed down from above. Below this point, the land will not experience a net loss of soil through the splash process acting alone. Figure 20 shows a typical pattern of erosion that is largely caused by raindrop splash where the greatest soil loss per unit area is near the crest of the hill and on the steepest and shortest slope.

While splash erosion alone can move quantities of soil downhill, it does not transport it away from the base of the slope to any appreciable extent. But there is a shallow prechannel surface flow of water during the time that splash erosion is active. Some of the soil splashed is kept in suspension in the surface flow, which moves into rills and then to larger channels. The combined action of raindrop splash and the flow of water accounts for nearly all of the sediment removal from individual fields.

SURFACE-FLOW EROSION PROCESS

Flowing surface water is usually the major transporting agent when erosion is caused by rainstorms. This flow moves across the land in two principal forms. It may move as a shallow sheet of water across broad surfaces that have no perceptible channels, in which case it is referred to as sheet, or prechannel, flow. Or, it may move in rills, gullies, or valley channels, in which case it is referred to as rill or gully flow, or merely as channelized flow.

In contrast with the energy from falling raindrops, applied to the surface of the land vertically from above at velocities that may exceed 30 feet per second, surface flow of water ordinarily has velocities of not more than a few feet per second. On smooth surfaces, outside the rills and gullies, these velocities are usually less than one-fourth foot per second. Surface water tends to concentrate and take on the characteristics of stream or channel flow as it moves downhill. Whereas the results of raindrop erosion are most apparent at the tops of hummocks and hills, erosion by surface flow is usually most apparent near the base of the slope, where the greatest amounts of surface flow concentrate.

The amount of force generated by surface flow of water is definitely related to the concentration and velocity with which it moves downhill. Running water gains the energy to perform work by gaining mass in its movement downhill, or by gaining velocity as it falls over a rapid change in slope. Maximum erosion occurs when the detaching and transporting capacities of surface flow are balanced. That is, when the surface flow contains just enough abrasive material to detach as much soil as the flow will carry. This condition of balance changes with each change in the erodibility characteristics of the soil. Beginning at the top of a hill, where the slope is usually steep, the transportation process usually tends to make the soil loss per unit area decrease with each increase in the length of slope over which the water flows.

FIGURE 22. Once surface water becomes sufficiently concentrated, it cuts rills and gullies and is known as channelized flow. (Goldendale, Washington)
(Soil Conservation Service)

FIGURE 23. Surface water tends to concentrate and take on the characteristics of channelized flow as it moves downhill. (California)
(Soil Conservation Service)

FIGURE 24. Flowing surface water gains energy to perform work by
gaining mass as it concentrates at the foot of the slope, or
by gaining velocity as it falls over a rapid change in slope.
(Herrington, Washington)
(Soil Conservation Service)

Because the source of its energy is so related to the concentration and
velocity with which it moves downhill, flowing water does not operate evenly
over the surface of a field. Therefore, it could not cause so-called sheet
erosion. Instead, it usually acts as a carving or grooving agent and roughens
the surface by scouring.

Prechannel surface flow of water may be expected to be laminar
(smooth) in the absence of falling raindrops. Laminar sheet flow is without turbulence and its energy is all energy of translation (transporting). As
the surface flow concentrates into stream or channel flow, it develops turbulence. The scouring and transporting capacities usually increase because the
flow of turbulent fluids contains both energy of translation and rotational
(scouring) energy.

The energy of surface flow is a function of mass and velocity of the flowing water. The mass is determined by the quantity and quality of the flow.
The velocity for any given mass is affected principally by the length of the

path of flow for each unit of vertical fall, and the resistance to flow in each unit of slope length. A reduction in either the mass or the velocity will reduce kinetic energy.

The detaching and transporting capacity of surface flow may vary, each independently of the other. If, for example, clear water is permitted to flow over well-compacted clay soil, it may not have sufficient detaching capacity to cause much erosion and the runoff will be clear. But if soil containing highly abrasive fractions is injected into this flow at the point where the clear water flows over the clay soil, the detaching capacity of the water will be increased and the rate of erosion will be accelerated. Increasing the amount of soil injected into the flow will increase its detaching capacity. At the same time, it will decrease the transporting capacity. Increase the amount of soil in the flowing water to the point where it is all that the flow can transport, and there will be very little erosion of the clay soil.

An increase in the energy of surface flow will increase its carrying capacity, and generally will cause an increase in rates of erosion. Increases in soil erosion that result from increases in velocity may vary greatly in different soils, and even within the same soil. No fixed relationship exists between the velocity head and rates of erosion during the course of a single rainfall, because conditions within the soil which affect its erodibility may undergo a change while the soil is being wet. During storms, these changes occur within a matter of minutes. They usually come about more slowly during the drying period between storms. Just as an emery wheel traveling at a fixed speed will abrade different metals at different rates, so will a given amount of flow energy erode soils of different erodibility at different rates. However, high energy of surface flow may cause more or less damage to all soils, regardless of type or of its condition. It may be assumed that any increase in velocity head increases soil erosion.

When broad sheets of water move across open fields in prechannel stages during rainstorms, velocities which have sufficient soil-suspending capacity will seldom develop. It is the energy of turbulence imparted to flow by splashing raindrops that gives it much of its suspending capacity. The same is true of many shallow channelized flows. Raindrops bombarding these water surfaces may often increase their transporting capacity by several hundred per cent.

The kinetic energy imparted to shallow surface water by impact of raindrops not only increases the transporting capacity of flowing water, but it may give soil-suspending capacity to standing water. Standing water that is churned by splashing raindrops has been found to contain as much as 20 per cent of soil.* This soil content is affected but little, if any, by velocity when the standing water starts to flow, so long as it moves across smooth surfaces as sheet flow.

The soil-transporting capacity imparted to shallow surface water by falling raindrops varies widely with sizes of drops and velocities of their impacts. The turbulence imparted by splashing raindrops may cause much coarse sand and some gravel to be moved by surface water that is barely flowing.

* W. D. Ellison, unpublished data.

FIGURE 25. Soil transportation in these gullies is by channelized flow. Between the gullies the soil is transported in prechannel stages, and splashing raindrops impart to this shallow water a high soil–suspending capacity. (Moscow, Idaho) *(Soil Conservation Service)*

Under certain conditions, raindrop impact can at times move stones as large as 10 mm. in diameter when they are partially or wholly submerged in water. Raindrops striking these submerged stones cause them to rise and frequently move some distance downhill. Surface flow assists the downhill motion even though, if acting alone, it would not move them. With the removal of the raindrop impact from the flowing water, both the detaching and transporting capacities rapidly decrease. This explains why muddy water passing in a thin sheet under an automobile parked on a street may drop most of its load. The car intercepts the raindrops and the flowing water quickly loses its transporting capacities.

If the surface of a field is fully protected against the impact of raindrops, very little soil will be transported except that which is detached and moved by channelized flow. In such cases, the topsoil between rills and gullies may remain practically unimpaired throughout the storm.

Free water acquires both rotational and translational energy as it concentrates to form channelized flow. The rotational energy detaches soil by scouring. The energy of translation enables the flowing water to transport the detached material downhill. Since these energies are concentrated and applied to restricted areas of the ground surface, the flowing water carves grooves into the surface soil. In their initial stages, and near the crest of slopes, these grooves are known as rills. Rills are preceded by small undulations formed on the surface of the ground by the impact of raindrops during hard rains. As the water continues to concentrate and acquires additional energy for scouring, these grooves become deeper and broader and eventually some of them develop into gullies. Scour erosion made the Grand Canyon and carved out our river systems.

The energy of surface flow tends to concentrate and be greatest on the longest slopes. Each additional unit of slope length at the lower end of a watercourse tends to increase the quantity of water that flows off the lower end of the slope. It also adds a unit of head through which the water must be lowered in the runoff process. As a result, surface flow tends to produce the largest gullies and cause the greatest soil losses near the lower ends of the longest slopes. Figure 23 shows a typical pattern of soil erosion that is caused mainly by flowing surface water. Note how the sizes of the gullies increase from top to bottom of the hill.

Usually, shallow surface flow acting alone cannot detach soil in thin sheets or layers from broad surfaces of a field. Irregularities in surface smoothness and in the soil's structural properties cause the flowing water to form rills just as soon as the scour process becomes active. Once these rills are formed, the only significant erosion caused by the surface water will be within these channels.

If the soil is both highly detachable and highly transportable, so that only small amounts of flow can detach and transport it, rills may be formed very close together. Rills occur every few feet. These channels drain their water and soil loads into several larger rills, which extend down the full length of the hillside. The field's soil is highly detachable, and it is higher than average in transportability. It is considered to be a highly erodible soil.

Gullies crossing such fields are fairly uniform in cross-section. This indicates that the gully flow took on no increased amounts of soil as it moved downhill. Since the soil is highly detachable, it would be reasonable to expect the flow to take up more soil and make the gullies larger near the base of the hill if there had been capacity to transport more soil. Apparently, however, the surface water was almost fully charged from the time the raindrop impact produced a muddy slush on the surface until the time of runoff at the base of the slope. The shallow flow moving into these gullies is capable of transporting as high percentage of soil as is the gully flow itself. Actually, the splashing raindrops may keep the shallow layer of surface water even more highly charged than the gully flow, if the soil is bare and highly detachable.

This condition, in which the water flowing into the gully contains as much soil as the gully flow can transport, usually will continue for only a short period at the beginning of a storm. As the storm progresses, the surface soil tends to become compacted and its detachability decreases. Then the water flowing into the gully may be low in soil content, and the gully flow may continue to take up soil en route until it reaches the very bottom of the slope. Thus, it may be assumed that gullies of the type described above may have been caused by a storm of short duration or by failure of the soil to consolidate and undergo a decrease in its detachability.

A soil that is of low detachability will withstand considerable concentrations of surface flow before large amounts of its materials become dislodged. A soil that is of low transportability will withstand considerable concentrations of flow before the detached particles are transported. Because of this, the rills will tend to be considerable distances apart in soils that are of either low detachability or low transportability. Figures 26 and 27 show the typical erosion pattern developing on these erosion-resistant soils. Only one rill of appreciable size was formed during a heavy rainstorm on the field shown in Figure 26. Differences in soils at various elevations on a hillside, changes in slope between the top to bottom of a hill, and a lack of uniformity in other factors may prevent development of gullies of the type described above. If soils are of either low detachability or of low transportability, or both, however, these factors will tend to make any gullies that are formed have cross-sections that increase in size from top to bottom of a hillside.

There are at least three different soil-detaching processes in scour erosion. They may be termed rolling, lifting, and abrading.

When surface flow moves across a smooth soil surface, it tends to roll or drag soil particles along with it. Surface velocities may even reach such magnitude that they will dislodge particles from their moorings in the soil mass. This process of soil detachment is known as *rolling*. The extent of soil particle dislodgements by this process will depend primarily on how well the particles are moored and on the energy of the surface flow.

FIGURE 26.   This soil is less detachable than sandier soils and the single gully shown does not reach to the upper edge of the watershed. When the water moves downhill, its detaching capacity increases, and when soil detachment limits the erosion process this increased detaching capacity will accelerate the erosion. (Torrance County, New Mexico)
(Soil Conservation Service)

FIGURE 27. On this soil the gullies increase in size as they approach the bottom of the slope. This could be caused by the flow's not being fully charged, in which case its detaching capacity may continue to increase as the gully flow moves downhill. (Jo Davies County, Illinois)
(*Soil Conservation Service*)

The soil detachment process described as *lifting* occurs when water moves upward past soil particles on the surface. A surface that contains many small depressions between clods and crumbs of soil will retain considerable amounts of free water which have no horizontal velocity, while the water just above it will be flowing. This difference in velocities sets up pressure differences between the layers, which undergo change with each pulsation in the upper layer. The changing pressure differences cause vertical currents and eddies to be set up, and the upward flowing water may lift soil particles from their moorings and set them in motion. Here again the amounts of soil materials detached by this process depend upon the detachability of the soil and the energy of flow.

The soil detachment process known as *abrading* occurs when soil fractions in motion in the flow are pounded against, or dragged along in contact with, the surface soils. The amounts that will be abraded will depend upon the factors of (a) energy of the surface flow, (b) soil detachability, (c) amounts of abrasive materials in transport, and (d) abrasive properties of the materials in transport.

SOIL DEPOSITION

Soil materials deposited by moving water are usually separated by particle sizes. The first materials to be deposited will be those of lowest transportability, whereas the materials of highest transportability will be deposited last—the farthest downstream.

The amounts of fine and highly transportable materials that are removed from a watershed tend to be proportional to the amount of splash erosion. Soil aggregates eroded by the splash process are broken up more finely than when the soil is eroded by the action of flowing water. This results in a greater release of silt and clay fractions and organic matter, which are highly transportable. These fine and light materials are often floated miles downstream to be deposited in large reservoirs. The less easily transportable parts of the eroded soil are usually deposited upstream. Thus, farm ponds and small upstream reservoirs located near the bases of sloping fields are likely to be filled with the products of rill and gully erosion which are composed of coarser materials. On the other hand, large downstream reservoirs are most likely to be filled with products of the splash-erosion process—the light organic matter and silt and clay fractions which are much more highly transportable.

One may gain a general idea of the effects of splash erosion on streams and reservoirs by comparing streams in the wooded and grassed mountainous areas with streams of much lesser gradients in more nearly level cropped areas. The water in the mountain streams is often crystal clear but the water in streams draining cultivated areas is heavily charged with erosional debris. This condition exists despite the fact that the flow usually moves to mountain streams over much greater energy gradients than the gradients of cropped fields. The surface of the mountainous areas usually has enough tree and grass cover to check splash erosion effectively, or it is practically devoid of soil.

Other things being equal, the steeper the slope gradient the faster will be the rate at which erosional debris is moved downhill from the crests of hills by raindrop splash. It moves faster at higher levels than it does further downhill where gentler slopes are usually encountered. The organic matter and the light silt and clay particles, which are the fertility-bearing elements of the topsoil, are moved out first. They usually are not deposited until the flowing water comes to rest in depressions at the bases of slopes or in ponds or reservoirs. The coarser materials in the topsoil follow, and eventually the materials comprising the subsoil are moved by erosion. This erosional debris may be found deposited on many soils all along the slope course, from the point of origin to the sea.

Deposition is particularly noticeable where breaks in the slope slow the flow of water abruptly, or in the lower portion of slopes where raindrops expend most of their energy in resplashing soil material that has been splashed down from uphill. The movement of topsoil that is splashed from the crest of a slope becomes slower on the gentler slopes near the bottom of the hill. This causes "telescoping" of the soil. That is, soil from high on the slope overtakes the material that is in motion lower down. The result is that topsoil piles up in a bank near the bottom of the hill. Often this is later covered with subsoil brought down from uphill.

This process may be illustrated by what happens when a sandpile is leveled by rainstorms. The material at the base of a sandpile tends to be more transportable than the material near the top. This is because of the process of selective erosion, which causes fine sands to be moved downhill more rapidly than the coarser materials. The phenomenon will be most apparent in early stages of erosion. After many years of unchecked erosion, the coarse sands may be carried downhill also. On the very crest of those hills, where the slopes are less steep, however, very little of the fine sands may be washed out.

The situation is usually different on clay soils. Soil materials at the base of a clay slope are usually less transportable than those higher on the hillside, largely because of selective transportation. When deposits occur near the base of the hill, they include a high percentage of the materials that are of low transportability. The clay fractions and other very light materials may float far beyond the base of the slope.

Evidences of erosion by channelized flow of water are most readily apparent. It is easy to watch a few large streams as they carry soil down the hillsides, often transporting tons of erosional debris as fast as a fleet of large trucks might move dirt away from a power shovel. But it is impossible for us to see the billions of raindrops doing the "pick and shovel work" which loads these water streams with the fertile topsoil from the many acres of smooth field surfaces.

Most of the soil-laden streams, and the gullies they carve in the hillsides, are outward manifestations of deeper and more basic troubles. As the raindrops "pick" the soil loose, they also separate the particles, break down the granules. They also mix, puddle, and compact a shallow layer of the surface soil until a highly impervious surface seal is formed. In some soils, this seal will almost "waterproof" the land. It increases and determines to a large extent the nature and character of the deposition that results.

REFERENCES

1. Borst, H. L. 1942. *The effect of mulching and methods of cultivation on runoff and erosion from Muskingum silt loam.* Agr. Engin., 23: 19-22.
2. ————, and Woodburn, R. 1940. *Rain simulator studies of the effect of slope on erosion and runoff.* USDA, SCS-TP-36.
3. Cook, H. L. 1936. *The nature and controlling variables of the water erosion process.* Soil Sci. Soc. Amer. Proc., 1: 487-94.
4. Ekern, P. C. 1950. *Raindrop impact as the force initiating soil erosion.* Soil Sci. Soc. Amer. Proc., 15: 7-10.
5. ————. 1953. *Problems of impact erosion.* Agr. Engin., 34: 23-25, 28.
6. Ellison, W. D. 1944. *Raindrops, surface flow and erosion.* Soil Cons., 10: 128-129.
7. ————. 1945. *Some effects of raindrops and surface-flow on soil erosion and infiltration.* Trans. Amer. Geophys. Union, 26(3): 415-29.
8. ————, and Ellison, O. T. 1947. *Soil erosion studies—Part VII: Soil transportation by surface flow.* Agr. Engin., 28:442-444, 450.
9. Horton, R. E., Leach, H. R., and Van Vleit, R. 1934. *Laminar sheet flow.* Trans. Amer. Geophys. Union, (2): 393-404.
10. Laws, J. O. 1940. *Recent studies in raindrops and erosion.* Agr. Engin., 21:431-33.
11. Mihara, Y. 1951. *Raindrops and soil erosion.* Natl. Inst. Agr. Sci., Ser. A, pp. 1-59. Tokyo, Japan.
12. Osborn, B. 1950. *Range cover tames the raindrop—a summary of range cover evaluations, 1949.* USDA, SCS. Fort Worth, Texas. Multi.
13. Stallings, J. H. 1951. *Soil fertility losses by erosion.* Better Crops with Plant Food, 35: 21-26, 45-47.
14. ————. 1952. *Raindrops puddle surface soil.* Jour. Soil and Water Cons., 7: 70-74, 88.

4

How Wind Erodes Soil

The wind has been active as an erosive agent throughout geologic times. It takes up soil from one place and deposits it in another. Outstanding examples are the extensive loess deposits in China and along the Missouri and Mississippi rivers in this country.

Although wind erosion has been active in some degree since prehistoric times, it has become much more active and more destructive because of the activity of man. This "accelerated" erosion has been due to wrong methods of handling the land or to use of the land for purposes to which it is not adapted.

Wind erosion is perhaps most active in arid and semiarid regions where the land surface is often dry and vegetation is sparse or absent. The wind also may move large quantities of soil material in humid regions; and, agriculturally considered, wind activity in such regions may be more important because of the greater value of much of the land affected.

The movement of soil by wind is a complex process influenced by conditions of wind and soil (including the nature of the eroding surface and amount of water in the soil) and many other factors. The cutting and transporting power of wind is determined by the interaction of several factors—some favoring soil movement, others opposing it. The activity in each individual case depends upon the net effect of these factors acting together. Soil material, in order to be

71

transported by wind, must first be loosened from its position on the surface of the land. It may then be lifted, slid, or bounced along on the surface of the ground. These processes are largely the result of wind turbulence, mainly eddies and irregularities of wind movement.

Differences in soil erodibility suggest that properties inherent in the soil and those brought about by land use—especially cultivation and other man-made disturbances—play an important part in the wind erosion process. Only dry soils are moved. Wet or damp soils are not appreciably affected. The structure of the soil in an air-dry state is, therefore, a much more reliable index of erodibility than the structure in a wet state.

The amount of soil which is erodible by wind at a given velocity depends upon the critical height* of and distance between the nonerodible fractions that are exposed at the surface. The ratio of height of projections to distance between projections which will barely prevent the movement of erodible fractions is designated as the critical surface-roughness coefficient. Under a given wind velocity the critical roughness constant remains the same for the whole range of size and proportion of the nonerodible clods. The critical surface-roughness constant required to assure soil stability, however, varies with other factors, such as the wind velocity and the size and apparent specific gravity of the erodible fractions. These factors, in the aggregate, add considerably to the complexity of the wind-erosion process.

TYPES OF SOIL MOVEMENT

There are three types of soil movement in the process of wind erosion: (a) saltation, (b) suspension, and (c) surface creep. These usually operate simultaneously.

The movement of soil by wind is dependent not so much on forces at the surface as on the velocity of the various strata of air through which the grains rise in saltation (moves in series of short bounces). This height is definitely limited. Wind erosion is mainly a surface phenomenon and it is directly dependent on the condition of the wind depth through which it rises.

Movement of soil by saltation. Most of the soil carried by wind is moved in saltation. Saltation is caused by the direct pressure of the wind on the soil particles and their collision with other particles.

After being pushed along the ground surface by the wind, the particles suddenly leap almost vertically in the first stage of the saltation movement. Some grains rise only a short distance; others leap one foot or higher, depending directly on the velocity of rise from the ground. They also gain considerable forward movement from the pressure of the wind upon them, and acceleration of the horizontal velocity continues from the time the grains begin to rise until they strike the ground again. In spite of this acceleration, the grains descend in almost a straight line with an average angle of descent of between 6 to 12 degrees from the horizontal. On striking the ground, they either rebound and continue their movement by saltation or lose most of their energy by striking other grains—causing these to rise —and sink into the ground to form part of the movement in surface creep.

---

* Critical height is the height that slows wind velocity to 9 miles per hour or lower.

Whether the movement is initiated by impact of descending particles or by impact of rolling grains, the initial rise of a grain in saltation is generally in a vertical direction.

The vertical rise appears to be due to two causes—the spinning of the grain and the steep velocity gradient near the ground. Grains carried in saltation may rotate at a speed of 200 to 1,000 revolutions per second; perhaps more than 75 per cent of the grains carried by saltation spin.

The variation in air velocity near the ground causes a substantially higher rate of air flow at the upper than at the lower surface of a grain at rest on the ground surface. Consequently, if the total difference in pressure between the upper and lower surfaces is greater than the force of gravity, the grain will rise in a vertical direction. This difference in pressure may be expected to intensify the spinning of the grain in a current of air.

After being shot into the air, the grains rise to varying heights and fall at accelerated speed as a result of gravity. On the whole, the vertical distance through which a grain continues to rise in saltation is about one-fifth to one-fourth the horizontal length of a single leap. The soil moved by saltation consists chiefly of fine grains ranging in diameter from 0.1 to 0.5 mm. The grains most easily moved by erosive winds range from 0.1 to 0.15 mm. in diameter. The removal in saltation appears to be the same for all soil types but some variation is found in the proportion of grains carried at different heights. Coarse granulated soils drift closer to the ground than more finely pulverized soils.

The relative concentration of soil particles at a given height remains the same under a wide range of wind velocities. The ratio of saltation to suspension decreases rapidly with height above ground. Grains in saltation do not generally rise higher than a few feet above the ground. Soil carried above this height is in true suspension and capable of being carried much higher and landing far from its original location. Virtually a straight-line relationship exists between height and the logarithm of the rate of flow in saltation and suspension over all soils.

Soil loss by wind erosion was found to vary directly as the 2.5 power of the surface drag of the wind and the 3.5 power of the per cent of soil fractions less than 0.42 mm. in diameter. It varied inversely as the 0.8 power of the weight of surface residue. Other elements of soil structure and surface residues influence the phenomenon of soil erosion by wind. Soil conditions at the immediate surface, such as crusting, stability of structure, puddling, and grading of the materials on the immediate surface by the impact of raindrops, as well as the effects of freezing, thawing, wetting, and drying, all play a part.

Movement of dust in suspension. In the mechanism of soil transportation by wind, very fine dust particles less than 0.1 mm. in diameter are carried in true suspension. Such particles make up a substantial proportion of the total soil carried. They have a lower falling velocity than the upper velocity of the turbulent wind and are carried more or less parallel with the general wind direction. Their transportation has been termed "suspension movement." Small particles transported by suspension enter the air-stream when the soil is bombarded by the saltation movement. Once entrained in the

FIGURE 28. Suspension movement: Very fine dust particles, less than 0.1 mm. in diameter, are carried in true suspension. They enter the air-stream when the soil is bombarded by the saltation movement. Once entrained in the air-stream they are suspended by the turbulence of the wind. (Lamar, Colorado) (*Soil Conservation Service*)

air-stream they are suspended by the turbulence of the wind.

The presence of fine dust in suspension, even in large quantities, does not affect the general character of the movement in saltation or surface creep, but its presence in the soil greatly influences both threshold wind velocity and the intensity of erosion for a given wind.

The mechanism by which the fine dust is lifted from the ground may be entirely different from that of saltation. Soils composed of fine dust particles are extremely resistant to erosion by wind. The movement of fine dust in an air current is mainly the result of saltation. Thus, without saltation movement, dust clouds would not arise except on a relatively limited scale as a result of disturbances by objects moving over the surface of the ground, or at the windward edge of an eroding area.

In contrast to the movement of grains in saltation, the movement of fine dust in suspension (after being lifted from the soil surface) is completely governed by the character of the wind movement. This fine dust is carried to great heights and long distances from its original location and thus may be considered a loss to the eroding area. On the other hand, the soil moved in saltation and surface creep usually remains within the eroding area or its immediate vicinity—especially when winds blow from varying directions.

The proportion of soil moved by the three types of movement varies widely for different soils. Coarsely granulated soils erode by saltation and surface creep; finely pulverized soils, by saltation and suspension.

MOVEMENT OF SOIL IN SURFACE CREEP

Quartz grains of about 0.5 to 1.0 mm. in diameter are too heavy to be moved by saltation but are pushed along the surface by the impact of particles in saltation to form "surface creep." Unlike grains in saltation, which receive most of their impact energy from the direct pressure of the wind, the grains moving in surface creep derive their kinetic energy from the impact of grains moving in saltation.

FORMS OF WIND EROSION

The wind-erosion phenomenon may be more easily understood by recognizing the close interdependence of the five main ways in which soil particles are loosened and transported. These five ways may be considered as different phases of the same phenomenon.

Detrusion. Detrusion is the dislodgement of coarse soil grains from peaks or surface projections by wind pressure or by the bombarding action of highly erosive grains coming from the windward side.

Effluxion. Effluxion is the removal of soil grains ranging from 0.05 to 0.5 mm. in diameter, and is initiated and maintained by the direct pressure of the wind. The removal is almost entirely by saltation, but a minor portion of the soil may be removed in surface creep, and some fine particles may be picked up directly by the wind and carried away in true suspension.

FIGURE 29. Surface creep movement. Quartz grains of about 0.5 to 1.0 mm. in diameter are too heavy to be moved by saltation but are pushed along the surface by the impact of particles in saltation. (Texas)
(Soil Conservation Service)

Extrusion. Extrusion is the forward thrust of soil particles which are too coarse to be removed by direct wind pressure. If a field composed of these particles has on its windward side an area containing particles removable by effluxion, many of these coarse fractions may be removed as a result of bombardment by the smaller grains. Extrusion is carried out chiefly by surface creep.

Efflation. Efflation is the removal of soil in suspension, resulting mainly from movement of coarser grains in saltation. It is serious because it constitues a removal of fine soil constituents, leaving the less mobile and inert sand and gravel behind.

Abrasion. Abrasion is the chipping off of particles of dust and coarse fractions from soil clods and other hard materials as a result of impacts from grains moving in saltation.

Some or all of these forms of erosion may be operating at the same time. However, none of these can exist without effluxion. In other words, effluxion is a prerequisite to and cause of the other forms of wind erosion. Therefore, a program of wind-erosion prevention and control should be based on either reducing the amount of particles ranging from 0.05 to 0.5 mm. in diameter in a soil to an allowable minimum, or slowing down the movement of wind at the ground surface.

WIND-EROSION PROCESS

The wind-erosion process consists, in general, of three distinct phases: (a) initiation of the movement of soil particles, (b) their transport, and (c) their deposition.

The wind acts as a fanning mill on the soil—removing organic matter, fine silt and clay fractions, and leaving sand and gravel behind. This sorting action, when continued year after year, tends to make a soil coarser in texture and consequently more erodible and less productive than it was originally.

In addition to the sorting action of wind, the intensity of the movement increases progressively with distance across eroding areas. The intensity of the movement at the windward edge of an eroding area, whether it be the edge of a field or the beginning of a highly erodible spot in the field, is approximately zero. From this point the amount of soil being moved may increase progressively up to certain limits, if no obstruction or trap intervenes. The gradual increase in the amount of soil movement toward the leeward side of eroding areas may be identified by certain easily recognized earmarks: (a) the progressive accumulation of erodible soil grains toward the leeward side of the eroding areas, (b) the gradual decrease in surface roughness resulting from the leveling-down process or detrusion, and (c) the cumulative degree of abrasion of the surface crust or clods by impacts from saltation.

The increasing intensity of soil movement downwind across eroding areas has an important bearing on plans and measures for controlling wind erosion. It points to the importance of trapping the soil where it first starts to move; the value of trap strips, such as those employed in "wind stripping" in reducing the amount of erosion by wind; and the need for community action in preventing the spread of wind erosion to unaffected areas. Wind erosion

FIGURE 30. Wind erosion is in some respects like an epidemic disease. It must be controlled at its source before it gets out of hand entirely. This photo shows a portion of a sand dune area covering approximately 175,000 acres of rangeland in Crane and Ector Counties, Texas. (Crane County, Texas) *(Soil Conservation Service)*

in some respects is like an epidemic disease. It must be controlled at its source before it gets out of hand entirely.

INITIATION OF SOIL MOVEMENT

Surface winds are turbulent for all velocities over approximately 2 miles per hour. Turbulence of the wind in the open is indicated by irregular velocity fluctuations known as "gusts." This turbulence, together with velocity, is responsible for starting the movement of soil in the wind-erosion process.

The minimum velocity of wind required to initiate soil movement is known as threshold velocity. The greatest single factor influencing the threshold velocity is the size of the soil grains. The threshold velocity is the lowest for grains 0.1 to 0.15 mm. in diameter. These require a velocity of 8 to 9 miles per hour at 6 inches above the ground. The threshold velocity increases with either an increase or decrease in the size of grains from these diameters.

The high resistance of fine dust particles to erosion by wind appears to be due partially to cohesion but mainly to the fact that the particles are too small to protrude above a laminar and viscous layer of air close to the surface of the ground. Fine dust is lifted from the ground mainly by impacts of larger grains, which are more erodible because they protrude farther into the fast-moving, turbulent currents of higher air. Due to cohesion, the threshold velocity is raised considerably by dust and coarser grains.

The threshold velocity for undecomposed crop residues and weeds, even when these are merely scattered on the surface of the ground, is higher than for most of the erodible soil grains. Thus, if the wind is not too strong, some or all of the drag is absorbed by this material and erosion of the soil is reduced considerably; but if the wind is strong enough to remove crop residues, the threshold velocity at the affected surface is reduced and movement of the soil will continue under lower wind velocity than previously.

In like manner, the minimal threshold velocity for bare fields and for fields that are unprotected by crop residues from the start is usually much higher for the first windstorm than for succeeding ones. This may be due to several reasons. A thin surface crust which is not eroded may become completely disintegrated under continued abrasion by loose grains and thus lose its protective value. On cultivated soils, the sorting action of the wind may result in accumulations of dunes which have a much lower threshold velocity than the uneroded soils. The threshold velocity for dune materials is lowest and varies little with soil type.

There is, therefore, a range of threshold velocities for any soil, depending on the previous history of the field. This range varies from 13 to at least 30 miles per hour at a height of one foot above smooth ground surfaces.

Erosion, once under way in a field, is maintained by impacts of particles moving in saltation and not by the direct pressure of wind against the ground, except on the extreme windward edge of the eroding area. Knolls, ridges, sand pockets, and areas with very limey soils start to erode at a lower wind velocity than other parts of a field. But when erosion starts, it spreads fanwise to leeward and the bombarding action of the particles in salation causes movement of soil in areas that would otherwise remain in place under an equal wind velocity. The minimum threshold velocity for the less exposed parts of a field is therefore determined by the minimum threshold velocity for the most erodible spots and is consequently equal to the minimum impact required to dislodge particles rather than the minimum fluid threshold velocity.

For the initiation by wind of particle movement on desert sand, a "static-threshold wind" depends on (a) the former history of the surface, (b) the extent to which the sand removed has collected to form a protective layer with the largest grains on the surface, (c) the surface turbulence of the wind, and (d) the length of the exposed surface.

Once particles begin to move, a "dynamic threshold velocity" lower than the static threshold velocity maintains continued movement downwind. This behavior may be likened to the action of the particles as projectiles which rebound upon striking the surface and continue their movement downwind or cause the movement of one or more other particles upon striking the surface.

TRANSPORTATION OF SOIL

The lifting of loose material lying exposed on the surface is largely the work of eddies and irregularities of movement in the wind. The air currents are exceedingly variable and made up of many cross currents and eddies.

The movement is, in fact, very complex, and there is much mixing of air molecules except in the exceedingly thin layer of air at the surface. The numerous momentary currents of the wind blow up and down as well as horizontally. Wind direction is the result of this great variability. It characterizes the general movement of the whole air mass rather than its motion at any particular point and instant. These eddies and cross currents are of great importance in promoting the thorough mixing of the atmosphere and enabling it to lift fine material from the surface of the ground. The threshold velocity depends on the maximum momentary velocity of turbulent flow, not on the average forward velocity. Eddies are thus of greater importance in lifting and transporting soil than is the average velocity of the wind.

It has been found that the rate of sand movement varies directly with the range of size of the erosive grains and the square root of their average diameter. The rate of soil movement depends little on the density of the air, but varies greatly with the drag velocity, and with the degree of gustiness of the wind. The rate of soil movement in saltation, suspension, and surface creep varies as the cube of the drag velocity of the wind.

The ability of the wind to transport soil is enormous. The carrying capacity of the winds blowing over the basin of the Mississippi River, for example, has been estimated to be 1,000 times the transport capacity of the river itself. It has been calculated that the combined force of wind storms strong enough to create dust storms during a 12-month period in the western states would be equal to at least two strongly active dust storms (each lasting 24 hours) of high soil-carrying capacity annually. Assuming an average wind velocity in the lowest mile in the atmosphere to be 30 miles per hour, the carrying capacity of these storms would be equivalent to about 853,700,000 tons of dust carried about 1,440 miles. During such a period the wind would accomplish about 1,229,342,400,000 ton-miles.

The estimated load of sand and dust that may be carried by the atmosphere ranges from 150 to 126,000 tons per cubic mile of air, depending on the velocity of the wind. A dust storm on March 25, 1895, was estimated to have loaded the atmosphere with 1,600 tons of dust per cubic mile of air at Rock Island, Illinois.

The capacity of the atmosphere for transporting particles of soil smaller than 0.1 mm. in diameter is very great. It has been estimated that one cubic foot of air, agitated to an average velocity of 5 miles per hour, is capable of sustaining the following amounts of soil:

Average diameter of particles Millimeters	Weight of soil per cubic foot of air Grams
0.08	0.020
.04	.057
.007	.118
.001–	.530

Measurements of the concentration of wind-borne particles indicated that most of the soil movement in saltation was carried below the height of 2 to 3 feet. In fact, over 90 per cent of the soil was transported below the height of 12 inches. Over 50 per cent of it remained below the 2-inch level.

The rate of flow at the 0- to 38-inch height amounted to about 490 pounds per hour per 1-foot width for an 18-mile-per-hour wind and 990 pounds for a 25-mile-per-hour wind.

Wind erosion of a soil that ranges in composition from fine clay and organic particles to larger soil grains gives rise to all modes of transport. Fine particles in suspension are lifted to great heights.

As much as 200 pounds of dust per acre, which originated in the Texas-Oklahoma Panhandle region after a dust storm on February 7, 1937, was deposited on snow in Iowa 500 miles away. Analysis of samples of the "black" snow showed that the deposits contained three times as much humus as the best soil remaining in the source region of the storm.

Soil particles, after being lifted from the surface (except the very fine dust that becomes part of the atmosphere), eventually come to rest again when the wind subsides or when surface obstructions alter the velocity distribution and turbulence structure.

Soil material moved by wind and deposited in dunes has an average diameter range of approximately 0.16 to 0.35 mm. and constitutes only a part—though a major part—of the total movement. Fine dust, once lifted into the air, may be carried great distances from the eroding area. On sandy soils, the fine particles usually make up a minimum part of the total volume of soil moved in comparison with the amount moved along the surface of the ground. In some cases, however, the removal of the finer particles constitutes a much more serious aspect of the wind erosion problem on these soils. In contrast, the "hardlands" seem to break down to their primary particles and go into suspension. This often results in the removal of the whole soil mass.

Smaller soil particles, within specific limits, are more easily moved by the wind. Consequently, in attacking a heterogeneous deposit, the wind tends to remove the finer particles and leave the coarser ones.

The gradual increase in the rate of soil movement with distance away from the windward edge of eroding fields is due mainly to the steadily increasing amounts of erosive particles, and the cumulative degree of abrasion along the direction of the wind.

The steadily increasing accumulation of erodible soil fractions on the ground surface toward the leeward side of eroding fields produces a condition that is increasingly more susceptible to erosion by wind. Eventually, for material composed only of erodible fractions, the rate of soil flow is the highest possible for the particular soil and wind velocity.

The second factor accounting for increased soil movement is the cumulative degree of abrasion resulting from impacts of grains in saltation. As the concentration of erodible grains increases gradually to leeward, so likewise the rate of break-down of soil clods and surface crust increases. These break down into fractions that are fine enough to abrade and erode more soil clods and surface crust in their journey with the wind.

DEPOSITION OF ATMOSPHERIC LOAD

Material carried either in suspension or saltation is deposited primarily when the wind velocity decreases. Due to the variable character of the wind,

FIGURE 31. Soil material carried either in suspension or saltation is deposited primarily when the wind velocity decreases. Whatever helps to decrease wind velocity will favor retention as well as deposition. By reducing the velocity of the wind, this fence caused it to deposit its soil load. Likewise, it prevents the wind from picking the soil up again. (Childress, Texas) *(Soil Conservation Service)*

however, and indeed to the very nature of the process of saltation, the process of picking up and depositing material is virtually continuous. Since both the removal and transportation of material depend upon the violence of the wind, the problems of retention in the final analysis are closely related to wind velocity. Whatever helps to decrease wind velocity will favor retention as well as deposition. Thus, by decreasing the wind velocity, vegetation and other surface obstructions not only cause the wind to deposit its suspended matter but also prevent the wind from picking it up again.

Because of their retentive ability, plants are particularly efficient in collecting drifting sand and other material moving along the surface in a series of short leaps. A clump of plants in an area of moderate sand drift will thus collect blown material around it, forming a small mound. As the sand heap grows, the plants, if adapted to sandy soil, also grow and continue to accumulate soil until a heap several feet high may be formed.

It is obvious that mounds may also be produced by the removal of soil from the spaces between plants instead of by the accumulation of soil brought in from more distant places and deposited around the plants. In the case of desert mounds, both forces may be at work at the same time. Because of the great mobility of the surface material, mounds in plant-protected spots tend to grow rapidly at the expense of the interspaces which lack this advantage. The wind is only one cause of this growth, plants being the other.

Decrease of the wind velocity and the consequent deposition of soil may be due to conditions not connected with vegetation or other surface obstacles, but which are much more general and affect much larger areas. The more or less constant winds caused by climatic and other general meteorological conditions or by large topographical features are known to lose their velocity habitually in certain areas. If these winds are dust-laden, such areas will become areas of aeolian deposition. Of course, there must be somewhere complementary areas of aeolian removal from which the winds have obtained their load. The accumulation of aeolian material over wide areas depends in the most complex way upon climatic factors—not only as they influence the path and velocity of the wind, but also as they control the presence or absence of vegetation and its nature and permanence.

FIGURE 32. Because of their retentive ability, plants are particularly efficient in collecting drifting sand and other material moving along the surface in a series of short leaps. By reducing its velocity the plants in the background caused the wind to deposit its sand load. Likewise they prevent the wind from picking the sand up again. A ton or more per acre of growing plants or crop residue has prevented wind erosion during severe wind storms. (Beadle County, South Dakota) *(Soil Conservation Service)*

REFERENCES

1. Bagnold, R. A. 1941. *The physics of blow sands and desert dunes.* Methuen & Co., Ltd., London.
2. Chepil, W. S. 1945. *Dynamics of wind erosion: I. Nature and movement of soil by wind.* Soil Sci., 60(4): 305-320.
3. ———. 1945. *Dynamics of wind erosion: II. Initiation of soil movement.* Soil Sci., 60(5): 397-411.
4. ———. 1945. *Dynamics of wind erosion: III. The transport capacity of the wind.* Soil Sci., 60(6): 475-480.
5. ———. 1946. *Dynamics of wind erosion: V. Cumulative intensity of soil drifting across eroded fields.* Soil Sci., 61(3): 257-262.
6. ———. 1950. *Properties of soil which influence wind erosion: I. The governing principle of surface roughness.* Soil Sci., 69(2): 149-162.
7. Free, E. E. 1911. *The movement of soil material by the wind.* USDA, Bur. Soils Bull. 68.
8. Maline, F. J. 1941. *Recent developments in the dynamics of wind erosion.* Trans. Amer. Geophys. Union, 2: 262-284.
9. Udden, J. A. 1894. *Erosion, transportation, and sedimentation performed by the atmosphere.* Jour. Geol., 2(3): 318-331.
10. ———. 1896. *Dust and sand storms in the west.* Pop. Sci. Mon., 49: 658-663.
11. Zingg, A. W., and Chepil, W. S. 1950. *Aerodynamics of wind erosion.* Agr. Engin., 31(6): 379-382.

5

Soil Aggregates and
How They Are Formed

Aggregates or crumbs are building blocks for good soil tilth. They are masses or clusters of soil particles held together by "cement" in the form of granules. They consist of a close arrangement of a number of soil grains, such as silt and clay, into crumbs. The process by which these aggregates are formed is of fundamental importance in developing and maintaining soil structure. Stability of aggregates is one of the major factors in developing and preserving good soil tilth.

Soil aggregates have been studied for more than a century. Many investigators have endeavored to determine how they are formed. A number of theories have been advanced to explain the mechanism of their formation. It is only within the last decade that substantial progress has been made in clarifying this point.

It has been generally conceded that some type or types of cementing materials are responsible for binding soil grains together and holding them in clusters. Lime has been credited by some as being responsible for this phenomenon. Others have suggested clay, iron hydroxide, organic matter, humus, and soil micoorganisms as being the binding agents.

More recent studies indicate the binding material

consists of substances such as polysaccharides* and polyuronides** produced or synthesized by microorganisms.

Contrary to general belief, clay crystals have both negative and positive charges. They are negatively charged on their flat surfaces and positively charged on their edges.

The co-existence of these positive and negative charges has been shown to be responsible for flocculation of soil—the first step in aggregate forma-

---

* A carbohydrate when decomposed by hydrolysis forms two or more molecules of simple sugar or monosaccharides.

** A complex aldehyde acid derived from sugars; negatively charged nonmetallic or negative element or radical (of a binding compound).

FIGURE 33. Soil from a virgin Flanagan silt loam in Illinois. It is well aggregated.
(Soil Conservation Service)

tion. The flocs may have either edge-to-face or face-to-face arrangement of crystals depending on the electrolytic concentration.

The flocs are expanded by organic complexes* forming between the flat surfaces of the clay crystals as well as along their edges. These organic compounds (polymers**) consist of polysaccharides and polyuronides which stabilize or "freeze" the flocs into crumbs or aggregates. They are held to the surface of the silicate layers both by forces of ionic binding and attraction of the molecules to the surface.

The interlayer expansion of clay crystals is brought about through base exchange. The extent of expansion is determined by the size, charge and total amount of cations present. Organic molecules attached to clay crystals through base-exchange reaction are attracted in their entirety onto the surface of the mineral plates, the non-cation portions being held by adsorptive forces.

Material for the production of polysaccharides and polyuronides is supplied in the form of water-soluble organic matter which serves as food for soil microorganisms. Rain water washing over the foliage of growing plants, or rain water and snow melt passing through plant litter on the ground, dissolves out certain substances which are carried into the ground in solution in the soil water. The dissolved substance is held in the capillary film surrounding individual soil particles. It is in this uniform layer in the capillary film around the individual soil grains where soil microorganisms use it as food. And, it is here where soil microorganisms produce the polysaccharides and polyuronides which bind soil grains into stable crumbs or aggregates.

These soil-binding materials serve as food for other types of soil microorganisms, and therefore are only temporary in nature. No batch of binding material is effective for more than about three to four weeks, depending on climatic conditions. If new raw material for producing polysaccharides is not fed into the ground at frequent intervals the old material is destroyed and the soil crumbs lose their stability.

Nature has a unique way of ensuring a continuing supply of binding material in the soil. She does this by keeping the ground covered with plant material—both growing plants and plant litter. Every time water passes over or through this plant material it dissolves out soluble matter and carries it into the ground. In this way new bonding products are created as fast or faster than the old is destroyed and the crumbs remain stable.

The humate fraction of the organic colloids produced in the course of decomposition of organic matter by soil microorganisms appears to be one of the main factors—if not the chief factor—contributing to the formation of soil aggregates. Polysaccharides and polyuronides have been shown to be responsible for much of the aggregation in soils.

Some of these humate (decomposed organic matter) fractions are presumed to be negatively-charged hydrophylic colloids (water-soluble poly-

---

* Complex ion formed by linkage of an ion to atoms or molecules of equal rank, i.e., copper ammonium complex, $Cu(HN_3)4$.

** Long chain molecule.

anions) distributed uniformly throughout the soil aggregates. As previously stated, these substances when attached to clay crystals through base-exchange reaction are attached in their entirety onto the surface of the mineral plates, the non-cation portion being held by adsorptive forces.

Locked to the soil particles, the humate fraction or hydrophylic colloids act like bridges between them, keeping them from separating yet at the same time holding them at "arm's length" to prevent tight packing.

FLOCCULATION AND AGGREGATION

Inadequate knowledge of the mechanics of aggregate formation resulted in its being confused with that of flocculation. Flocculation is but one step in the process by which stable aggregates are formed. It is primarily electro-chemical in nature. Flocculation is not a result of cementation. In the flocculation process primary particles, such as silt and clay, which are negatively charged, repel each other in suspension. Lime or calcium is positively charged. When it is added to a clay suspension it attracts the negatively charged clay particles. This results in the formation of floccules. Consequently the floccule is stable only as long as the flocculating agent is present. The loose grouping of soil particles into clusters, as in flocculation, is only the first step in the aggregation process.

In water-stable aggregates the grains are so firmly held together by cements that they do not readily break down in water. Accordingly, flocculation only aids in the aggregation process.

CALCIUM AND SOIL AGGREGATION

It has been recognized for many years that, under certain conditions, the use of lime improves the physical properties of the soil, and that clay suspensions can be flocculated by calcium salts. It has been shown that the improved structure resulting from the addition of lime to alkali soils is due to the replacement of sodium with calcium. These facts led to the erroneous conclusion that the beneficial effects of lime are due to its ability to flocculate the soil colloids.

It is generally conceded that the favorable effect of calcium in the reclamation of alkali soils is due to the difference in the way in which the calcium and sodium ions react on the properties of the soil colloids. The calcium ion has a more favorable reaction on the soil colloids than does the sodium ion. Baver showed that sodium-saturated soils are more highly hydrated and dispersed than calcium-saturated soils.

Contrary to general belief, calcium does not appear to be a major contributing factor in the formation of stable aggregates in acid soils. Recent experimental observations indicate that the direct effect of the calcium ion on aggregation of acid soils is of minor importance. Alderfer found that liming under field conditions produced little or no structural improvement unless used in connection with a management system that maintained a good supply of biologically-active organic matter.

These observations call attention to the fact that flocculation is not the same as granulation. In order to have stable granulation there must be a cementation of the flocculated particles. A possible "linking" action of calcium in the binding of clay and polyuronides to form good water-stable cements was advanced by Peterson. Some investigators believe, however, that the chief effect of calcium upon aggregate formation may be indirect— that is, it affects the nature and amount of organic matter produced.

TYPES OF CEMENTATION IN SOILS

Most of the cementing agents in soils were thought at one time to be ir- reversible or slowly reversible organic and inorganic colloids. Accordingly it was assumed that sands and silts could not form crumbs or aggregates. More recent investigations have shown this latter assumption incorrect. Four distinct agents have been suggested as functioning in crumb formation through cementation of soil particles. They are clay, iron hydroxide, organic matter, and substances produced by soil microorganisms. An organic-inor- ganic linkage of calcium and polyuronides with clay fractions has also been suggested.

CLAY AND SOIL AGGREGATION

Under some conditions clay functions directly as a binding agent in the formation of soil aggregates. Baver and Boller and Stephenson and others found that the smaller clay particles are usually more effective in the forma- tion of aggregates than the larger ones.

Forsyth found clay and dispersible organic matter in mixture was better than clay alone for cementing fine sand. However, the aggregation produced by the mixture was less than the total amount of aggregation produced in the sand when clay and organic matter were used separately.

While clay and organic matter can interact to form a new complex if they are both free from exchangeable bases, there is no evidence that this new complex plays any special role in aggregate formation.

Russell expressed the view that interaction between exchangeable cations on the clay particles and the dispersion liquid is essential for soil aggregate formation. He suggested that three conditions were essential for aggregate formation, i.e., the clay particles must be small—less than 1 micron in diameter, they must have a relatively high base-exchange capacity, and the molecules of the liquids in which they take place must have an appreciable dipole moment. Russell thought that a dipole liquid was essential and that solvation of the exchangeable ions of the clay complex is necessary for max- imum formation of water-stable aggregates.

This theory can be extended to explain qualitatively certain experimental results obtained by Henin. By using a single soil he found an inverse rela- tion between the hardness of the crumb and its water-stability as the ex- changeable ion and some other conditions were varied, provided that me- chanical mixing of the paste before drying was done in the same way. If, as already suggested, water instability is caused by a high proportion of the exchangeable ions dissociating from the clay surface, this inverse relation would follow as a natural consequence, for the greater the dissociation of the exchangeable ions the greater the number of links that can be formed. Thus the harder the crumbs on the one hand, the greater their water-instability on the other.

This hypothesis also explains why crumbs, such as those of a sodium soil, may be unstable in water but stable in a salt solution of suitable concentration. For if water-instability of crumbs is caused by the larger resultant negative charges built up on adjoining clay particles by a proportion of the exchangeable ions dissociating and moving away from the immediate vicinity of the surface, this action will be decreased by the presence of an electrolyte.* The electrolyte in this case lowers the electrokinetic potential of the clay surface. This reduces the resultant positive charge on adjoining clay particles, and thus increases the force of repulsion between them.

Geltzer showed that the structure-producing capacity of decomposing organic matter was due to a sticky substance produced during the decomposition.

The drawing together of the colloidal particles, which occurs during the formation of the phases of the aggregate state, leads to a deformation of the ion envelope around these particles. This deformation is expressed in a compression of the ion layer or in a decrease of the distance of the electric double layer, and must affect all the properties depending on the dimension of the electric double layer.

The former conception that the particles forming the soil aggregate are held together by the tension of the water film is supplemented by the finding that surface film creates a definite orientation of the particles in relation to one another. The tenacity of the bond between the separate parts of the soil structural aggregate lies in the stability of the group arrangement of the particles. The most stable arrangement of particles is the homogeneous one.

IRON HYDROXIDE AND SOIL AGGREGATION

Iron hydroxide, or probably iron hydroxide combined with some form of organic matter, can cement soil particles together. In extreme cases, often seen in B horizons of some soil profiles, the bonding has progressed so far that the particles form hard concretions devoid of pore space and requiring drastic treatment to be redispersed into their component particles. But in the initial stages of cementation, aggregates are produced which have a more normal pore space and can be readily redispersed. The iron oxide is then simply acting as a weak cement which becomes stabilized upon drying.

Free iron was once thought to be an important factor influencing the granulation of lateritic and semilateritic soils. It was thought to serve a dual purpose, the part in solution functioning as a flocculating agent and the other as a cement.

Sideri found that admixtures of iron and aluminum oxides to clay hindered the aggregation of clay particles. He thought that the presence of oxides in large amounts destroyed the orienting properties of clay in respect to humus. In this case, he found that a mere coagulation occurred with a confused distribution of particles. The elimination of iron and aluminum oxides

---

* A substance which when decomposed conducts electricity.

from the surface of clay particles increased the ability of these particles to aggregate. A particular "rod" structure arose, the "rods" being officially homogeneous and possessed positive double refraction.

ORGANIC MATTER ESSENTIAL TO AGGREGATION

It is generally recognized that organic matter in some way has a favorable effect on the formation of aggregates in the soil. It also has been observed that the beneficial influence of organic matter is more or less directly proportional to the amount and character of the organic matter applied to the soil. This led to the erroneous conclusion by some that the binding of the soil particles into aggregates was due to the physical effect of organic matter.

It has been noted during recent years, however, that applications of large quantities of fresh or unleached organic matter in the form of barnyard manure, crop residues, mulches, or other substances usually produced a rapid increase in the number of aggregates in soils immediately following application. It has also been noted that the quality of the organic matter involved, as well as its quantity, is important. However, unless the initial application of organic matter was sufficiently large to produce a continuous supply of dissolved substances to the soil or was supplemented by additional applications at later dates, this initial increase in aggregate formation soon reached a climax. Subsequently the number of aggregates in the soil underwent a steady decline.

Organic materials which decompose rapidly increase aggregation within a few days after they are incorporated with the soil, have their maximum effect in about 20 to 30 days, and then gradually lose their effectiveness. Materials that are slower in decomposing require a longer period of time to exert their binding effect but continue to be effective over a longer period. Materials that are relatively inert have little, if any, effect upon aggregation. The more rapid the rate of decomposition of the organic matter, the more rapid is the rate of aggregation.

Decomposing organic matter imparts a good structure to the soil, and the more rapid the decomposition the better is the structure. This indicates that some substance, which has only temporary existence in the soil, is formed during decomposition.

A single application of organic matter, when added to soils containing only a small amount of cementing materials necessary for the formation of stable aggregates, increases the number of large aggregates. On the other hand, the addition of organic matter to soils containing considerable quantities of either active inorganic or organic colloidal material does not change aggregation appreciably.

Havis produced a high state of aggregation under straw mulch on Wooster silt loam. Unleached wheat straw and alfalfa were more effective than leached materials. Bluegrass sod increases and maintains a high percentage of aggregates of the larger sizes but is not as effective as mulch. The value of mulch in the formation of aggregates is out of proportion to the amount of organic matter added. Mulch and sod are more effective in aggregate formation in the topsoil than in the subsoil or B horizon. Mulch favors the formation of large aggregates.

MICROORGANISMS AND SOIL AGGREGATION

It has been generally assumed that the presence of inorganic colloidal materials is essential to the formation of soil crumbs and that aggregates can not be formed from pure sands and silts. During recent years the latter part of this assumption has been disproved. Many investigators have shown that mucus and other substances produced by soil microorganisms are effective binding agents in the formation of water-stable soil granules. Substances synthesized by bacteria are the most active aggregating agents.

The organic binding forces may, for convenience, be divided into three groups. The first group is made up of colloids consisting of the decomposition products of plant residues, probably of the lyophobic* and similar types, most of which are removed from well-decomposed organic matter by treating it with dilute alkali solutions.

The second group consists of cells of microorganisms and their secretory products, such as mucus, slime, or gum, produced during growth and resembling colloids and gels in their physical state. The third group consists of materials, such as polysaccharides, synthesized by certain soil microorganisms.

The addition to the soil of rapidly decomposable substances, such as sucrose and finely ground crimson clover, results in a large increase in the number of bacteria and a rapid increase in water-stable aggregates. The improved aggregation persists long after the bacterial population declines. All size-classes of organic matter decompose. This indicates that some factor other than the quantity of decomposition products accounts for the greater effectiveness of the finely ground organic matter in promoting aggregation. The more rapid the decomposition of cellulosic organic matter, the greater is the production of mucus; hence the better is the resulting structure. The stability of the aggregates varies with the mucus produced by the various organisms. The most viscous produces the most stable aggregates. It does not necessarily follow that all viscous substances will improve soil structure.

Aggregation in Cecil sandy loam is greatly improved through the activity of certain fungi and bacteria. Inoculation of nonsterile Cecil sandy loam in pots with certain cultures of bacteria and fungi, following addition to the soil of sucrose or ground oat straw, results in marked increases in aggregation over soil receiving similar organic-matter treatments without inoculation.

The addition of microbial decomposition products of plant material into loessal subsoil results in marked increase in the water stability of the soil structure. This increase in stability is proportional to the amount of decomposition products added.

Increased structure stability resulting from biological activity is temporary, apparently remaining only as long as the stabilizing decomposition products exist. Quantity of organic matter does not seem so important as quality in producing stability. Knox topsoil, with an accumulation of decomposition products, was found by McCalla to have higher stability than Peorian loess devoid of these products.

Soil organisms and their metabolic products are active in the formation

---

* Lacking strong affinity between a colloid and the liquid in which it is dispersed.

and stabilization of soil structure, although they play a greater role in the stabilization than in formation. The presence of living microbes is essential to the formation of aggregates in calcareous soils. Beneficial organisms break down plant and animal residues, liberate plant nutrients, and produce soil structure-stabilizing substances. Re-aggregation of soil is aided by the biological effects of added organic matter.

A species of the fungus *Cladosporium,* and a soil bacillus thought to belong to the *Bacillus subtilis-mesentericus* group, when given suitable energy source by Martin and allowed to develop in sterilized soil, brought about a very marked aggregation of the silt and clay particles of Pontneuf sandy loam. When these organisms were grown in liquid media and the microbial cell substance was removed, the remaining material produced marked aggregation in the case of the bacillus, but only moderate aggregation in the case of the fungus. Up to 50 per cent of the aggregating effect of the fungus was brought about by substances produced by the cell material, and the remainder was due to the binding influence of the fungus mycelium. The soil-bacillus cells, on the other hand, produced 20 per cent of the aggregating effect, and substances produced by the cells accounted for 80 per cent.

A hemicellulose-like polysaccharide synthesized by the soil bacillus was found to be primarily responsible for the marked aggregating effect. The organism synthesized a polysaccharide and brought about marked soil aggregation when supplied with organic nitrogen or when a number of sugars were utilized as energy material. The greatest aggregation and greatest production of polysaccharide occurred with sucrose.

Warren and Gray showed that a viscous constituent, composed of some type of polysaccharide, surrounding normal cells of *Pseudomonas aeruginosa* acted as an intercellular cementing substance resulting in the formation of cell aggregates.

A variety of polysaccharides synthesized by soil bacteria brought about very marked aggregation of Delco loam soil. The polysaccharides consisted of three fructosans and three dextrans containing varying amounts of uronic acid. The effectiveness of the preparations did not depend on the structural units (sugars) involved.

In general, the bacterial polysaccharides were better aggregating substances than was casein or lignin. When combined with casein and lignin, the polysaccharides, with minor exceptions, were as effective as when used alone. After the polysaccharides were incubated for 30 days, their aggregating influence had changed but slightly or had decreased. In combination with casein and lignin, they either induced little change or caused an increase in aggregation. After incubation of the sucrose-treated soil, the aggregation was considerable but was less than that resulting from any of the polysaccharides, casein, or lignin treatments. Since sucrose, as such, has little influence on soil structure, the effect after incubation resulted from the production of soil-binding substances by the microorganisms decomposing it.

High aggregation is brought about largely by microbial cells, decomposition products or organic residues; and synthesized substances, although synthesized by some microorganisms, may be slowly destroyed by others, and as a result, aggregation may decrease. It would be expected that the polysaccharides composed entirely of straight sugar-groups would undergo more or less complete decomposition, and thus their aggregating effect would be completely passive in nature. On the other hand, those containing the active uronic acid groups or those linked with nitrogenous complexes would be expected to undergo physiochemical reactions with other active substances in the soil and in some instances become resistant to further decomposition. Should such occur it is probable that only a small percentage of the total polysaccharides produced would be stabilized in this manner. However, with a continuous supply of organic material, such as occurs under sod or with heavy mulch, the cumulative total of stabilized polysaccharides would be considerable. The bulk of soil humus consists of lignin-derived substances, nitrogenous complexes, and polysaccharides.

Polysaccharides are normal metabolic products of microorganisms. Numerous species of bacteria, fungi, and actinomycetes are capable of producing a wide variety of complex polysaccharides as cell constituents or as extracellular products. Hence, it is reasonable to expect that under natural conditions the diverse flora of the soil may synthesize many polysaccharides from the constituents of vegetable material, and that these substances may be of considerable importance in the formation of crumb structure in soil.

Bacterial polysaccharides of the levan and dextran types exert a pronounced binding effect on soil particles. Soil crumbs containing small amounts of levan are extraordinarily stable to the dispersing actions of water, heat, and shaking, but are eventually broken down by the activities of other microorganisms. Preliminary investigations indicate that levans are fixed on soil particles.

Rennie and his associates found that the bacterial polysaccharide synthesized by *Agrobacterium radiobacter* in pure culture had a marked aggregating effect when added to Spencer and Miami silt loams. Addition of as little as 0.02 gm. of this gum to 100 gm. of soil caused a 50 per cent increase in aggregates over 0.1 mm. diameter.

HUMUS AND SOIL AGGREGATION

The first investigators of the problem of soil structure attached great importance to clay and humus. Schloesing thought that these substances were able to cement the mineral element in soil. The ideas of Schloesing were later developed further by Dumont, who suggested that the important properties of soil depend on colloid envelopes. He thought the active colloidal material was a jelly-like amorphous mass, enveloping solid mineral grains. This idea was afterward supported by Hall, who held the opinion that since the colloidal envelope has no defined external surface it can be considered as surrounding the soil particles in a series of cells with a gradually increasing hydration, so that there is a gradual transition from the solid grain to the solution. The colloidal envelopes alter essentially the properties of mineral particles and render the soil structure cellular and reticular.*

* Net-like in operation.

Similar conclusions are suggested by Comber and by Haines, who demonstrated by their experiments how greatly the colloidal envelope affects the properties of mineral grains and how far it aids aggregation.

There exists, however, another point of view, according to which the ability to aggregate depends on the surface water film. Manegold determined the force of cohesion on the basis of the properties of a liquid ring lying between two spheres of equal size, if all excess liquid is eliminated. According to Nutting, the thin absorption film binds the particles into aggregates. In his words, ". . . the cohesive pressure may mount to a respectable figure, depending largely upon the size and shape of the grains." According to Norton, the thin water film plays a decisive part in the formation of the structure of clay. Clay particles attract strongly to their surface their water films, which they have in common with the adjoining particles. This phenomenon determines cohesion and lubrication simultaneously. Norton thought it possible to determine the nature of surface films by studying the mechanism of shrinkage during drying and the curves of shrinkage.

Wetting with water loosens the bonds between the particles. In this case swelling is understood as a sufficient increase in the thickness of the layer of adhesion that it reaches the value of the radius of the sphere (grain). The liquid rings between the sphere disappear during swelling and, because of this, are lost. According to Derjaguin water lowers the friction between the crystalline lamellas. A fine-structural breaking-up of the tridimensional periodic structure of the crystal into a one-dimensional and a two-dimensional structure of the mesomorphous type takes place under the influence of water. For bromphenanthrene sulfonic acid this has been established by Rinne; for clays, by Sideri.

The aggregates in soil, however, do not always break up after being wet. There exist tenaceous structures which are not affected by distilled water; and it has been found by Sideri that such structures are resistant to alkalis as well.

The conception that the particles forming the soil structural aggregate are held together by the tension of the water film was supplemented by Sideri.

Tyulin supported the theory of Schloesing as to that part of the organic matter which is loosely attached to the entire mass of organo-mineral gels. Besides loosely-attached humus, however, these gels contained considerable quantities of organic substances that are more firmly held.

Humus, as defined by Geltzer, appears to play an important role in the formation of soil aggregates. According to this definition, humus is that fraction of the organic colloids which possesses the capacity of combining with the mineral part of the soil to form organo-mineral aggregates.

More specifically, the humate fraction of the organic colloids produced in the course of the decomposition of organic matter by soil microorganisms appears to be an important factor—perhaps the most important factor—in the formation of soil aggregates. These organic colloids, or binding agents, are distributed uniformly throughout the soil aggregates and are adsorbed on soil particles. They are able effectively to produce stable aggregates, perhaps by chemical union, such as calcium or hydrogen bonding with inorganic colloids. This chemical reaction is believed to take place mainly by polar adsorption, resulting from the decomposition of fresh organic matter.

These humic substances form a protective layer at the surface of soil colloids and are held at the surface of mineral gels. Cation exchange reactions take place in the entire protective action layer in the vicinity of those carboxyl groups whose cations are capable of exchange.

Organic colloids, when saturated with either calcium or hydrogen ions, are several times more effective in cementing sand particles into stable aggregates than are corresponding inorganic colloid systems. Phenolic and alcoholic OH groups, and possibly NH_2 groups of lignin-derived material in the organic matter, appear to be important aggregating agents. Surface active clay is necessary where polar organic substances are the aggregating agents.

Humic acids extracted from a number of soil groups are similar in physical and chemical properties. They are negatively charged hydrophilic colloids. Their acetyl and methoxyl contents are almost identical with those of lignin extracted from a prairie soil. Their base exchange is high. They possess hydroxyl groups as well as a carboxyl group. The non-nitrogenous fraction of the humic acid consists of a slightly modified lignin complex.

Soil colloids contain humate fractions which appear as two distinct fractions. One fraction appears as loosely-bound organic matter and the other as organic matter more firmly attached to the mineral colloids.

A glycosidic fraction was present in the uronic acid group derived from a pure polysaccharide isolated from four soils in Iowa. The fluvic nitrogen was in part contained in nitrogenous acidic complexes and in part as simple decomposition products.

The carbon dioxide-yielding constituents in soil which are dissolved when boiled in 12 per cent hydrochloric acid are uronic in nature and are of microbial origin. Soil uronic constituents are distinctly different from those of plants and are not likely to originate directly from plants. Uronic constituents of plants and soil organic matter differ not only in the rate at which their uronic units decarboxylate* but also in their reaction to alkali and acetyl bromide treatment. The uronic units that are extractible from soils decarboxylate at a rate similar to that of units retained in the soil and units of the original soil, rather than like the units of plant materials and extracted plant constituents such as pectin and polyuronide** hemicelluloses.***

The changes in the proportion of uronic to total carbon in soil appear to be closely related to the total carbon content. The lower the carbon content of a given soil, the higher is the percentage of uronic carbon in the organic matter. The hypothesis that the structure-forming fraction of humus was composed of the autolytic† products of bacteria was advanced by Geltzer but many other workers failed to verify it.

The form of the typical granular structure of soil is a sign of the accumulation of amorphous (shapeless) humus at the periphery of the aggregate. The

* Take away carboxyl (CO_2H).
** Contain complex aldehyde acids derived from sugar.
*** Polysaccharides which resemble cellulose in certain respects.
† Capable of self designation.

appearance of amorphous humus at the periphery of the aggregate is closely related to the exchange capacity. Water-stable aggregates contain more humus, especially loosely bound humus, which is the main structure-forming agent, than ungranulated soil. If organic matter is firmly bound with clay as an anistrophic* formation, no marked increase in the adsorption capacity occurs.

A supply of amorphous, or loosely bound, humus forms in the soil under the influence of manure. Soil organic matter content is a good indication of soil-aggregate stability.

To form active humus under sod, the slow fungal process by which aerobic (in presence of oxygen) decomposition usually starts must be quickly replaced by the more active bacterial process. The bacterial microflora of the surface layer of soil is the most significant factor in the formation of active humus under permanent grasses. Surface soil bacteria of the *Pseudomonas* type are active in the formation of exceptionally stable soil structure under these conditions.

POLYELECTROLYTES AND AGGREGATION OF CLAY

Ruehrwein and Ward used clays to determine the mechanism by which synthetic polyelectrolytes were able to aggregate soil. The experimental methods employed were: (a) x-ray diffraction by montmorillonite clay treated with polyelectrolytes; (b) measurement of adsorption of polymers by kaolinite clay; and (c) flocculation of clay suspensions by polymers. From the results of these experiments it was possible to obtain an insight into the mechanism of the stabilizing action of polyelectrolytes on clays.

They found that the cation adsorbed between the layers in a particle of montmorillonite could be replaced or exchanged with other cations, including organic cations as demonstrated by Gieseking and Hendricks. They demonstrate that the polycation is adsorbed on the faces of the montmorillonite layers, probably by means of cation exchange. Since the faces of the

TABLE 12. C-axis spacing of montmorillonite treated with polyelectrolytes

Polymer	Polymer per clay	Distance
	Gram	Angstrom
Sodium polymethacrylate	0	9.7–10.1
Sodium polymethacrylate	0.01	9.8
Sodium polymethacrylate	0.54	9.9
DMAEM	0.035	11.8
DMAEM	0.075	11.4
DMAEM	0.202	12.8
DMAEM	0.665	14.4

* When tested along axis in different directions it exhibits different properties.

montmorillonite layers have no sites for anion adsorption, polyanions will not adsorb thereon. It is not unlikely, however, that polyanions do adsorb by means of anion exchange on the edges of the montmorillonite layers where anion-exchange sites do occur.

Schofield and Samson showed that kaolinite crystals, in addition to their permanent negative isomorphous replacement charge, can become positively charged at their edge faces. They and Emerson suggested the positive charge arises from the uptake of hydrogen ions by the oxygens and hydroxyls of the octahedral layers, exposed along the edge faces.

Schofield and Samson also showed that the co-existence of these positive and negative charges on clay crystals was responsible for flocculation in kaolinite and montmorillonite. Flocs may have either edge-to-face or face-to-face arrangement of the crystals, depending on the electrolytic concentration.

Barshad suggested the negative charge on the interlayer oxygens originates from the isomorphous substitution of Al^{+++} for Si^{++++} in the tetrahedra positions, as in micas and vermiculites, or Mg^{++} for Al^{+++} in octahedra positions, as in montmorillonite. This charge is evenly distributed among the interlayer oxygens. On the other hand, the positive charge which neutralizes this negative charge is limited to a relatively small number of cations. They are, therefore, sparsely distributed in the interlayer boundary.

Barshad and Hendricks and Jordan showed that interlayer expansion in montmorillonite and vermiculite may be brought about with various organic substances through base exchange. Barshad demonstrated that the extent of this expansion was determined by the size, charge and total amount of cations present. Hendricks showed that organic cations are held to the surface of the silicate layers by forces of ionic binding and attraction of the molecules to the surface.

Gieseking and Hendricks pointed out that organic molecules attached to montmorillonite through base-exchange reaction tend to be attracted more or less in their entirety onto the surface of the mineral plates, the non-cation portions being held by adsorptive forces.

Jordan suggested the swelling that took place in organophilic bentonite, prepared by the reaction of bentonite with various alaphatic ammonium salts, was due to adsorption of polar molecules between the bentonite plates. Adsorption of non-polar molecules did not cause swelling or separate the plates. The rate of expansion or swelling was in direct proportion to the degree of polarity of the molecules adsorbed.

Emerson believes carboxylated polymers link the edge faces of two clay crystals by a series of hydrogen bonds to the edge atoms of the octahedral layers. This is suggested also by infrared measurements made by French and others. The bonding is believed to be lateral rather than vertical—not parallel with the c-axis. In this case polymers should be effective on all the common lateritic minerals, since these have almost identical spacings along the a- and b-axis.

Emerson suggested that polymers stabilize soil crumbs both by increasing the c-axis spacing and by linking the edge of the crystals. Polymers such

TABLE 13.   Flocculation of 4 gm./l. kaolinite suspension by cations

Cation	Flocculation concentration
	eq./l. $\times$ 10^6
Na+	1300–2700
Ca++	430–500
Al+++	400–600
DMAEM	5–20
Polyvinylbutylpyridonium bromide	5–10

as polyvinyl alcohol and dextran increase the c-axis spacing by entering between the crystal faces to form interlamellar complexes. Polymers containing carboxyl groups as the only charged groups link themselves in some way to the edges of the crystals. The presence of divalent cations is not essential for this linkage, so the existence of calcium bridges as suggested by Peterson is unnecessary. They do not increase the c-axis spacing; consequently, it is assumed they do not enter between the crystal faces.

This agrees with Ruehrwein and Ward and Hagin and Bodman. Furthermore, Emerson produced no swelling of montmorillonite flakes in water by the addition of polyvinyl alcohol, but produced large swollen gels by adding carboxylated polymers.

Emerson expressed the opinion and Jordan verified it that under some conditions polymer-polymer bonds may be formed instead of clay-polymer bonds. This suggests that several types of bonds may be formed such as clay-polymer-clay, clay-polymer-polymer-clay, and clay-polymer-polymer-polymer-clay.

Emerson's findings imply that if the clay fraction in a soil crumb is stabilized, the crumb will be stabilized, and that sand and silt grains are bound to the clay, probably by hydrogen bonds. In this case, a crumb would consist of parallel ribbons of clay separated by sand and silt grains. Sideri, working with a synthetic mixture and a microscope, observed this kind of linkage between fine quartz and parallel clay laminas.

Hagin and Bodman suggested that the interaction of the organic polymer CRD-186 with the mineral particles of sand and clay-mineral mixtures is a surface reaction and that definite amounts of the polymer react with definite surface areas—no ion exchange mechanism being involved.

Bradley and MacEwan showed that organo-clay complexes may be formed by certain organic compounds entering between montmorillonite sheets. They also showed a C—H . . . O bond between methylene groups and oxygen surface of the clay. Emerson established the fact that a grass sod materially increases the cohesion of soil crumbs and that the organic matter produced by the sod is responsible for the improvement. He concluded that the grassland crumbs are established by the formation of interlamellar complexes within the clay in the crumb.

REFERENCES

1. Alderfer, R. B. 1946. *Seasonal variability in the aggregation of Hagerstown silt loam.* Soil Sci., 62(2): 151-168.

2. ———, Gribbins, M. F., and Haley, D. E. 1944. *Effect of sulfite liquor on aggregation of soil particles.* Ind. and Engin. Chem., 36(3): 272-274.

3. Atkinson, J. H., and Turner, R. C. 1944. *Soil Colloids: I. Separation by peptization.* Soil Sci., 57(3): 233-240.

4. Barshad, I. 1952. *Factors affecting the interlayer expansion of vermiculite and montmorillonite with organic substances.* Soil Sci. Soc. Amer. Proc. 16: 176-182.

5. Bradley, W. F. 1945. *Molecular association between montmorillonite and some polyfunctional organic liquids.* Amer. Chem. Soc. 67: 975-981.

6. Baver, L. D. 1935. *Factors contributing to the genesis of soil microstructure.* Amer. Soil Survey Assoc., 16: 55-56.

7. Boller, G. A., and Stephenson, R. E. 1946. *Some effects of mulches on soil properties.* Amer. Soc. Hort. Sci. Proc., 48: 37-39.

8. Bolt, G. H., and Peech, M. 1953. *The application of the Gouy theory to soil-water systems.* Soil Sci. Soc. Amer. Proc., 17: 210-213.

9. ———, and Miller, R. D. 1955. *Compression studies of illite suspensions.* Soil Sci. Soc. Amer. Proc., 19: 285-288.

10. Chapek, M. V., and Sakum, N. 1944. *Uber die wechselwirkung des humats mit den mineralischen bestandteilen des bodens.* Kolloid-Ztschr., 107: 41-55.

11. Comber, N. 1920, 1921. *The flocculation of soils.* Jour. Agr. Sci., 10: 425-436, 11: 450-471.

12. Dean, L. A., and Rubins, E. J. 1947. *Anion exchange in soils: I.* Soil Sci., 63(5): 377-386.

13. Demolin, A., and Henin, S. 1932. *The structure of loams and the synthesis of aggregates.* Soil Res., 3: 1-9.

14. Derjaguin, B., and Lasarew, W. 1934. *Die Untersuchung der aussern reibung und gilmmerflachen.* Kolloid Ztschr., 69: 11-16.

15. Dumont, I. 1909. *Les enduits de revetement des particules terreuses.* Compt. Rend. Acad. Sci., 140: 1087-1089.

16. Elson, J., and Lutz, J. F. 1940. *Factors affecting aggregation of Cecil soils and effect of aggregation on runoff and erosion.* Soil Sci., 50: 265-275.

17. Emerson, W. W. 1955. *Complex formation between montmorillonite and high polymers.* Nature 176: 461.

18. ———. 1956a. *Synthetic soil conditioners.* Jour. Agri. Sci. 47: 117-121.

19. ———. 1956b. *A comparison between the mode of action of organic matter and synthetic polymers in stabilizing soil crumbs.* Jour. Agri. Sci. 47(3): 350-353.

20. Forsyth, W. G. C. 1947. *Studies on the more soluble complexes of soil organic matter: I. Method of fractionation.* Biochem. Jour., 41(2): 176-181.

21. ———. 1947. *The characterization of the humic complexes of soil organic matter.* Jour. Agr. Sci., 37(2): 123-138.

22. French, R. O., Wardsworth, M. E., Cook, M. A., and Cutler, I. B. 1954. *The quantitative application of infrared spectroscopy to studies in surface chemistry.* Jour. Phys. Chem. 58: 805-811.

23. Fuller, W. H. 1945. *Evidence of the microbiological origin of uronoides in the soil.* Soil Sci. Soc. Amer. Proc., 11: 280-283.

24. ———. 1947. *Investigations on the separation of uronoides from soils.* Soil Sci., 64(5): 403-411.

25. ———. 1947. *Influence of some cropping and fertilizing practices on the uronoides of soil.* Soil Sci., 64(6): 435-444.

26. Geltzer, F. Y. 1936. *Influence of the type of organic matter on soil structure.* Trans. Sov. Sect. Int. and C., Soil Sci., 5: 115-120.

27. ———. 1937. *The role of organic substances in the formation of soil structure.* Chim. Sotsial. Zemled., 8: 53-63.

28. ———. 1943. *The process of formation of active humus of the sod type.* Pedology, 9-10: 62-74.

29. ———. 1944. *A Russian view of humus.* Soil and Fertilizer, 7(3): 119-121.
30. Geoghegan, M. J. 1947. *Influence of microorganisms on aggregate formation in soils.* Soc. Appl. Bact. Proc., 2: 77-82.
31. ———. 1950. *Aggregate formation in soil: Influence of some microbial products and other substances on aggregation of soil particles.* Trans. Internat. Cong. Soil Sci., 1: 198-201.
32. ———, and Brian, R. C. 1946. *Influence of bacterial polysaccharides on aggregate formation in soils.* Nature, 158(4023): 837.
33. ———. 1948. *Aggregate formation in soils: I. Influence of some bacterial polysaccharides on the binding of soil particles.* Biochem. Jour., 43(1): 5-13.
34. ———. 1948. *Aggregate formation in soil: II. Influence of various carbohydrates and proteins on aggregation of soil particles.* Biochem. Jour., 43(1): 14.
35. Gieseking, J. E. 1939. *Mechanism of cation exchange in the montmorillonite-beidellite-nontronite type of clay minerals.* Soil Sci., 47: 113.
36. Gilman, W. S. 1940. *A study on the chemical nature of humic acid.* Soil Sci., 49: 433-453.
37. Gilmour, C. M., Allen, O. N., and Truog, E. 1948. *Soil aggregation as influenced by the growth of mold species, kind of soil, and organic matter.* Soil Sci. Soc. Amer. Proc., 13: 292-296.
38. Gouy, G. 1910. *Sur la constitution de la change electrique a la surface d'un electrolyte.* Jour. Physique, 4: 457.
39. Hagin, J., and Bodman, G. B. 1954. *Influence of the polyelectrolyte CRD-186 on aggregation and other physical properties of some California and Israeli soils and some clay minerals.* Soil Sci., 78: 367-378.
40. Haines, W. B. 1925. *Studies in the physical properties of soils.* Jour. Agr. Sci., 15: 178-200.
41. Hall, D. A. 1912. *The soil.* E. P. Dutton and Co., Inc., New York.
42. Hardy, F. 1928. *Studies in tropical soils.* Agr. Sci., 24: 59.
43. Havis, L. 1943. *Aggregation of an orchard and vegetable soil under different cultural treatments.* Ohio Agr. Expt. Sta. Bull. 640.
44. Hendricks, S. B. 1941. *Base exchange of the clay mineral montmorillonite for organic cations and its dependence upon adsorption due to van der Wall's forces.* Jour. Phys. Chem., 45: 65-81.
45. ———, Nelson, R. A., and Alexander, L. T. 1940. *Hydration mechanism of the clay montmorillonite saturated with various cations.* Am. Chem. Soc. 62: 1457-1464.
46. Henin, S. 1935. *Soil structure.* Ann. Agron., N. S., 5: 44-50.
47. ———. 1936. *Regeneration of structure of loams.* Ann. Agron., N. S., 6: 455-472.
48. Jordan, J. W. 1949. *Organic bentonite: I. Swelling in organic liquids.* Jour. Phys. & Col. Chem. 53: 294-306.
49. Jung, V. E. 1943. *Zur Kenntnis der Ton-Humusbindung.* Boden. Pfleranhr. 32(6): 325-336.
50. Kanivetz, I. I., and Koreneva, N. P. 1937. *Importance of biochemical forms.* Pedology, 32: 1492-1541.
51. Kojima, R. T. 1947. *Soil organic nitrogen: I. Nature of the organic nitrogen in a muck soil from Geneva, New York.* Soil Sci., 64(2): 157-165.
52. ———. 1947. *Soil organic matter: II. Some studies on the amino acids of protein material in a muck soil from Geneva, New York.* Soil Sci., 64(3): 245-252.
53. Kolodny, L., and Neal, O. R. 1941. *The use of micro-aggregation or dispersion measurement for following changes in soil structure.* Soil Sci. Soc. Amer. Proc., 6: 91-95.
54. Kroth, E. M. 1946. *Aggregate formation in soils with special reference to cementing substances.* Ohio State Univ. Abst. Doctoral Diss., 52: 185-200.
55. ———, and Page, J. B. 1945. *Aggregate formation in soils with special reference to cementing substances.* Soil Sci. Soc. Amer. Proc., 11: 27-34.
56. Lutz, J. F. 1937. *Relation of free iron in the soil to aggregation.* Soil Sci. Soc. Amer. Proc., 1: 43-45.
57. MacEwan, D. M. C. 1948. *Complexes of clays with organic compounds: I. Complex formation between montmorillonite and halloysite and certain organic liquids.* Trans. Farad. Soc. 44: 349-367.

58. Manegold, E., and Stuber, C. 1933. *Ueber Kapillar-System.* Kolloid Ztschr., 64: 12.

59. Marshall, C. E. 1949. *The colloidal chemistry of the silicate minerals.* Academic Press, Inc., New York.

60. Martin, J. P. 1942. *The effect of compost and compost materials upon the aggregation of the silt and clay particles of Collington sandy loam.* Soil Sci. Soc. Amer. Proc., 7: 218-222.

61. ————. 1945. *Microorganisms and soil aggregation: I. Origin and nature of some of the aggregating substances.* Soil Sci., 59(2): 163-174.

62. ————. 1946. *Microorganisms and soil aggregation: II. Influence of bacterial polysaccharides on soil structure.* Soil Sci., 61(2): 157-166.

63. ————, and Waksman, S. A. 1950. *Influence of microorganisms on soil aggregation and erosion.* Soil Sci., 50(1): 29-47.

64. Mazurak, A. P. 1949. *Aggregation of inorganic particles in Hesperia sandy loam.* Soil Sci. Soc. Amer. Proc., 14: 28-34.

65. McCalla, T. M. 1942. *Influence of biological products on soil structure and infiltration.* Soil Sci. Soc. Amer. Proc., 7: 209-214.

66. ————. 1945. *Influence of microorganisms and some organic substances on soil structure.* Soil Sci., 59(4): 287-297.

67. ————. 1945. *Influence of some microbial groups on stabilizing soil structure against falling water drops.* Soil Sci. Soc. Amer. Proc., 11: 260-263.

68. ————. 1946. *The biology of soil structure.* Jour. Soil and Water Cons., 1(2): 71-75.

69. McHenry, J. R. 1945. *Mechanics in the formation of water-stable soil aggregates.* Iowa State Coll. Jour. Sci., 20(1): 25-27.

70. ————, and Russell, M. B. 1943. *Elementary mechanics of aggregation of puddled materials.* Soil Sci. Soc. Amer. Proc., 8: 71-78.

71. Meyer, L., and Rennenkamp, V. von. 1936. *A new automatic apparatus for crumb analysis by Tinlin's method.* Ztschr. Pflanz. Dung., 43: 268-280.

72. Molina, J. S., and Spaini, L. S. 1949. *Colloides producidos en la decomposicion aerobia de la celulosa y su influencia sorbe la estructura del suelo.* Rev. Agr. Agron., 16: 33-49.

73. Myers, H. E. 1937. *Physical reactions between organic and inorganic colloids as related to aggregate formation.* Soil Sci., 44(4): 331-357.

74. ————, and McCalla, T. M. 1941. *Changes in soil aggregation in relation to bacterial numbers, hydrogen-ion concentration, and length of time soil was kept moist.* Soil Sci., 51(3): 189-200.

75. Norman, A. G. 1943. *The chemistry of soil organic matter: II. Hypoiodite oxidation of the organic matter in some soil profiles.* Soil Sci., 56(3): 223-233.

76. Norton, F. H. 1933. *Some notes on the nature of clay: II.* Jour. Amer. Ceramic Soc., 16: 86-92.

77. ————, and Hodgdon, F. B. 1932. *Some notes on the nature of clay.* Jour. Amer. Ceramic Soc., 15: 195.

78. Nutting, P. G. 1927. *Some mechanical properties of moist granular solids.* Jour. Wash. Acad. Sci., 17: 185.

79. Peele, T. C. 1940. *Microbial activity in relation to soil aggregation.* Jour. Amer. Soc. Agron., 32(3): 204-212.

80. ————, and Beale, O. W. 1940. *Influence of microbial activity upon aggregation and erodibility of lateritic soils.* Soil Sci. Soc. Amer. Proc., 5: 33-35.

81. ————. 1941. *Effect on runoff and erosion of improved aggregation resulting from the stimulation of microbial activity.* Soil Sci. Soc. Amer. Proc., 6: 176-182.

82. ————. 1943. *Microbial activity and soil aggregate formation during the decomposition of organic matter.* Soil Sci. Soc. Amer. Proc., 8: 254-257.

83. Peterson, J. B. 1947. *Calcium linkage, a mechanism in soil aggregation.* Soil Sci. Soc. Amer. Proc., 12: 29-34.

84. Rennie, D. A., Truog, E., and Allen, O. N. 1954. *Soil aggregation as influenced by microbial gums, level of fertility and kind of crops.* Soil Sci. Soc. Amer. Proc., 18(4): 399-403.

85. Retzer, J. L., and Russell, M. B. 1941. *Difference in the aggregation of a prairie and gray-brown podzolic soil.* Soil Sci., 52(1): 47-48.

86. Rinne, F. 1932. *Uber parakristallines und kristallines anisol-, benzo-, lazo-, naphtylamine.* Ztschr. Krist., 83: 227-242.
87. Robinson, D. O., and Page, J. B. 1950. *Soil aggregate stability.* Soil Sci. Soc. Amer. Proc., 15: 25-29.
88. Rubishov, A. B. 1949. *The genesis of water-stable structure and its role in soil fertility.* Pedology, 129-139.
89. Rudakov, K. I., and Birkel, M. R. 1951. *The formation of a stable soil structure by microorganisms.* Doklady Vesesoyuz. Akad. Sel'sko-Khoz. Nauk. im. V. I. 16: 22-27.
90. Ruehrwein, R. A., and Ward, D. W. 1952. *Mechanism of clay aggregation by polyelectrolytes.* Soil Sci., 73(6): 485-492.
91. Russell, E. W. 1934. *Interaction of clay with water and organic liquids as measured by specific volume changes, and its relation to the phenomenon of crumb formation in soils.* Phil. Trans. A, 233: 361-389.
92. ———. 1938. *Soil structure.* Imp. Bur. of Soil Sci. Tech. Commun., 37.
93. Schloesing, T. 1874. *Etudes sur la terre vegetale.* Ann. Chim. et Phys., Ser. 15, 11: 514-546.
94. ———. 1874. *Ueber die bestimmung des Thons in der ackererde.* Compt. Rend. Acad. Sci., 78: 1276-1279.
95. ———. 1902. *Etudes sur la terre vegetale.* Compt. Rend. Acad. Sci., 134: 631-605.
96. Schofield, R. K., and Samson, H. 1954. *Flocculation of kaolinite due to the attraction of oppositely charged crystal faces.* Disc. Farad. Soc. 18: 135-145.
97. Shrinkhande, J. G. 1933. *The production of mucus during the decomposition of plant materials.* Biochem. Jour., 27: 1551-1562.
98. Sideri, D. I. 1936. *On the formation of the structure of soil: II. Synthesis of aggregates on the bonds uniting clay with sand and clay with humus.* Soil Sci., 42: 461-480.
99. ———. 1938. *On the formation of the structure of soil: IV. The structure of mixed clay-sand and clay-humus formations.* Soil Sci., 46(2): 129-136.
100. ———. 1938. *On the formation of structure in soil: V. Granular structure.* Soil Sci., 46(3): 267-271.
101. ———. 1938. *On the formation of structure in soil: VI. Method of microscopic investigation of soil structure in reflected light.* Soil Sci., 46(4): 337-345.
102. Stallings, J. H. 1952. *Soil aggregate formation.* USDA, SCS-TP-110.
103. Stauffer, R. S. 1946. *Effect of corn, soybeans, their residues and straw mulch on soil aggregation.* Jour. Amer. Soc. Agron., 38(11): 1010-1017.
104. Stockli, A. 1946. *Die Biologische Kimponate der Verdung, der Gare und der Nahrstoffpufferung.* Schweiz Landw. Monatsh., 24: 286-295.
105. Strickland, E. 1950. *The effect of soybeans on volume weight and water stability of soil aggregates, soil organic matter content, and crop yield.* Soil Sci. Soc. Amer. Proc., 15: 30-34.
106. Swaby, R. J. 1949. *The influence of humus on soil aggregation.* Jour. Soil Sci., 1(2): 182-194.
107. Tyulin, A. T. 1938. *The composition and structure of soil organo-mineral gels and soil fertility.* Soil Sci., 45(6): 343-357.
108. ———. 1938. *On the forms of the bond between substances and the mineral part of the soil colloids and their significance for the understanding of the different properties of soil colloids.* Pedology, 6(10): 977-999.
109. Vilensky, D. G. 1940. *Studies on the process of soil aggregation.* Pedology, 8: .28-37.
110. ———, and Germanova, V. N. 1934. *Experimental study of the problem of structure formation.* Pedology, 29(1): 34-60.
111. Waksman, S. A., and Martin, J. P. 1939. *The role of microorganisms in the conservation of soil.* Science, 90: 304-305.
112. Warren, G. H., and Gray, J. 1955. *Studies on the properties of a polysaccharide constituent of* Pseudomonas aeruginosa. Jour. of Bact., 70(2): 152-157.
113. Woodburn, R. 1944. *Aggregate studies of Houston clay in Mississippi.* Soil Sci. Soc. Amer. Proc., 9: 30-36.

6

Maintaining Soil Structure

It was pointed out in the preceding chapter that organic matter serves as food and energy for soil microorganisms and is the source of the cementing substances that bind soil grains into aggregates. Soil microorganisms acting on fresh matter produce or synthesize these cementing substances. Since these substances are subject to destruction by other soil microorganisms, a continuous supply of fresh organic matter must be available to provide replacement as these substances are destroyed—otherwise aggregation of the soil deteriorates. Organic matter is more effective as an aggregating agent when fresh and when utilized on the surface of the ground. Cropping systems and other soil and crop management practices that disrupt the surface supply of organic materials affect soil aggregation adversely.

The plant residue on forest floors, meadows, pastures, and other relatively undisturbed areas is a most efficient device of Nature for maintaining healthy, productive soils. The surface organic materials, through leaching by rain and snow melt, supply substances essential to the formation of soil aggregates. They also provide food for the myriad of soil microorganisms. These aggregates give soil the tilth favorable to the growth of cultivated plants and high crop production.

RENEW HUMATES FREQUENTLY

The portion of the organic matter that forms the humates is soluble in water, and easily leached out of the fresh organic matter by rain and snow melt and carried into the ground. When the material enters the soil, it serves as food and a source of energy for the microorganisms that produce the humates. The aggregating effect of these materials is only temporary. It rises rapidly from the time they enter the soil and reaches a peak within 20 to 30 days. After this its effectiveness declines steadily, causing the aggregate structure of the soil to deteriorate unless additional supplies of fresh organic materials are applied.

Other microorganisms destroy these cementing or aggregating substances. Thus, in order to maintain a high aggregate soil structure, a continuous supply of organic matter must be present to keep feeding this material into the soil by way of leachings. This can be done only where the surface of the ground is kept covered with litter, which is replenished frequently to provide a fresh supply to the soil each time it rains.

It is the soluble portion of the organic matter and not its mere physical presence that is responsible for the formation of soil aggregates. The practice of incorporating organic matter into the soil makes large amounts available for shorter periods but does not provide continuous supplies. It follows, then, that incorporating organic matter into the soil is not as effective as

FIGURE 34. The bluegrass sod on the strip between the pavement and fence provides a continuous cover of grass and litter. The corn in the field to the right provides plant cover only during the period that the corn occupies the land. During most of this period the corn is growing and does not provide dead plant material for aggregation. (Illinois)
(Soil Conservation Service)

FIGURE 35. The sample of soil on the right was taken from the bluegrass sod area shown in Figure 34. The one to the left was taken from the corn field just 25 feet away. These two samples clearly show the effects of cultivation on soil tilth. The virgin soil has a permeability rate of 5 inches of water per hour. The cultivated soil has a permeability rate of only 0.26 inch per hour. The soil is a Flanagan silt loam. (Illinois)
(Soil Conservation Service)

leaving it on the surface of the ground where it can be replenished in maintaining a high level of aggregation.

Those organic substances that are most easily decomposed and that support a maximum of biological activity are the most effective in producing and maintaining a high state of aggregation in the soil.

The effect of this process on soil aggregation may be observed by comparing virgin soil with similar soil that has been in cultivation for a number of years. The virgin soil, or that found under continuous sod, or on a forest floor, will be mellow and easily stirred. If a handful of it is spilled through the fingers, it will have a grainy, crumb-like texture. Those tiny particles—the aggregates or "little clods"—play an important part in crop production. By way of contrast, the soil in a bare, cultivated field will be firm and hard. It will not have the crumb-like structure, and when it is plowed, the "clods" will be large and lumpy.

The difference in these two soils is due mainly to soil aggregation. The "little clods," the particles that run easily through the fingers, are soils that have had a continuous supply of organic matter, such as meadows or forest land. They have good structure, with many aggregates, whereas cultivated soils or soils inadequately supplied with organic matter may have very few or none at all.

The organic matter responsible for this structure also serves as food for the vast hordes of microorganisms in the soil. These organisms, in addition to playing an active part in the production of soil aggregates, are instrumental in maintaining a healthy condition in the soil. The complex microflora of a given soil is Nature's means of maintaining a sanitary condition in the soil. Certain soil microorganisms, in addition to reducing organic matter to humates, also produce antibiotics capable of destroying germs that cause specific plant diseases and viruses as well as controlling some insect pests.

ORGANIC MATTER AND SOIL AGGREGATION

The aggregate condition of a soil is determined by both the amount and quality of the supply of decomposition products or organic matter present. If the supply of organic matter is ample, as in continuous sod, the soil will be in a high state of aggregation. On the other hand, if the supply of organic matter is inadequate, as in fields of clean-tilled crops, there may be little or no aggregation in the soil. This is illustrated in part by Table 14, which

FIGURE 36. *Left.* This sample of virgin soil was put in a bottle of water and shaken 50 times, then dumped on paper and dried. The aggregates remained intact. It has a well developed granular structure. *Right.* This sample of soil came from a corn field that had been row-cropped for a number of years. It was treated exactly as the sample on the left. It is compacted and the aggregate structure has been destroyed. (Illinois)
(Soil Conservation Service)

shows the effect of the rate of application of different organic materials on the percentage of aggregates exceeding 0.25 mm. in diameter.

TABLE 14. The effect of the rate of application of different organic materials on the percentage of soil aggregates exceeding 0.25 mm. in diameter

Rate of application— Tons per acre	Per cent of soil aggregates exceeding 0.25 mm. in diameter for			
	Wheat straw	Rye and vetch	Alfalfa	Sucrose
None	37.6	37.6	37.6	37.6
1	38.4	38.4	39.3	44.0
2	41.0	41.8	42.0	48.9
4	44.0	47.0	48.5	61.0
6	46.1	51.2	54.2	70.5
8	46.4	56.6	60.0	75.5

The figures in Table 14 show that both the quantity and kind of organic matter affect the aggregate structure of the soil. The percentage of aggregates exceeding 0.25 mm. in diameter increased with each of the four organic materials used in ratio to the amount applied. The quality of the organic matter was even more important than the quantity, as shown by the contrast between the effects of wheat straw and alfalfa and sucrose. One ton of wheat straw or of rye and vetch increased the aggregation by 0.8 per cent compared with the untreated soil, whereas the increase due to alfalfa was 1.7 per cent and that from sucrose was 6.4 per cent. The increase from alfalfa was more than twice that from wheat straw or rye and vetch and the increase from sucrose was eight times as great. These effects continued with the 2-, 4-, 6-, and 8-ton rates of application but in different degrees.

The degree of aggregation in soil is also influenced by those factors that determine the rate of microbial activity. Before organic matter is effective as an aggregating agent, it must be decomposed. The more rapid the rate of decomposition, the higher the state of aggregation.

Since different crops produce different amounts as well as qualities of organic matter, a wide variation is to be expected in the aggregating effect of the residues produced by various crops. For example, alfalfa or clover residues are more effective in producing aggregates than are those of wheat or grass.

The importance of the quality of organic matter and its rate of decomposition (as measured in terms of microbial population) on soil aggregation may be illustrated further by comparing sucrose with more slowly decomposable materials. The addition of sucrose to soil in South Carolina caused a marked increase in microbial activity and soil aggregation. Bacterial numbers increased rapidly following the sucrose treatments, reaching a peak in about four days. They then decreased rapidly to approximately four times the number in the untreated soil at the end of 24 days. At the end of four months there were only about twice as many bacteria in the treated as in the untreated soil. The percentage of large aggregates increased rapidly following the sucrose treatments and coincided approximately with the increase in numbers of bacteria, although the improved aggregation persisted long after the bacterial population declined. Aggregation was not affected when sucrose was added to a sterile soil which was kept free of microorganisms.

Aggregation was increased in a soil inoculated with bacteria and fungi following the addition of sucrose and ground straw over similar soil receiving the sucrose and ground straw but not the bacteria and fungi. Inoculated soils to which neither oat straw nor alfalfa was added underwent only a slight to moderate degree of aggregation whereas a similar soil to which oat straw and alfalfa had been added had a considerable increase in aggregation.

The higher the percentage of readily decomposable constituents in the organic matter, the greater is its effect on soil aggregation. Composted organic matter, in addition to losing some of its aggregating effect, requires a longer period to attain its maximum effect, whereas fresh straw mulch is an active aggregating agent, particularly effective in producing large aggregates. The kind of crop or organic matter is more important to aggregation than the organic carbon, nitrogen, carbon-nitrogen ratio, or lime.

Decomposing organic matter concentrates in and around soil aggregates. As a result, well aggregated material has relatively higher carbon and total nitrogen content than unaggregated soils. They also possess a higher content of slowly oxidizable organic carbon and a wider carbon and a wider carbon-nitrogen ratio than poorly aggregated material.

CROPPING SYSTEMS AND AGGREGATION

Cultivation and other practices that influence the continuity and organic matter content of the soil affect both aggregation and crop production. This also applies to those practices that eliminate or reduce the plant cover to the point where it is no longer effective in protecting the soil against the damaging action of falling raindrops or freezing and thawing. As soon as land is taken out of sod and cultivated, the soil starts to deteriorate physically. For example, in Iowa, cultivation reduced the aggregation of Alba soil 88 per cent and Weller soil 65 per cent. However, aggregation in soils supplied with sucrose, cornstalks, and alfalfa increased 720, 335, and 335 per cent, respectively, within 30 days. These organic substances were added at the rate of 50 tons of dry matter per acre. Samples taken 84 and 168 days after the organic matter was added showed that the soils were again losing their structure. An application of eight tons of manure per acre showed little effect on soil aggregation six months later.

Soil and crop management practices produce significant differences in aggregation of the soil. Soil aggregates under four different cropping systems in Kansas increased in this order: continuous corn $<$ corn in rotation $<$

meadow in rotation < continuous bluegrass. Soils cropped to continuous small grain, continuous row crops, and rotations, including fallow, had only about 20 per cent as many aggregates as buffalo grass pasture. The amount of aggregates more than one mm. in diameter was 162 per cent higher in six virgin soils than on adjacent cultivated sites in Iowa. The size and distribution of soil aggregates was influenced materially by the cropping system, with the greatest number of large size aggregates under continuous bluegrass. For crops grown in a rotation the order of aggregation was clover, oats, corn rotation, and continuous corn, respectively. This also coincides with the amount and continuity of soil organic matter supplied.

The amount of aggregates differed strikingly in Ohio under sod, mulch, and cultivation. The mulch showed the greatest amount of aggregates among the larger sizes; sod resulted in about as much aggregation; and the cultivated soil contained only small aggregates. The state of aggregation was in fairly close relationship to the percentage of soil organic matter, except for high aggregate formation under wheat straw mulch. The most rapid rate of aggregation occurs the first few years after land is planted to permanent sod. Red clover in the rotation maintains a loose, granular structure, whereas continuous corn leaves the soil cloddy and difficult to work.

Those cropping systems which cause great reductions in aggregation are also destroyers of soil organic matter. Organic matter decreased on continuous corn plots in Iowa from 3.39 per cent in 1931 to 2.86 per cent in 1942. No significant change occurred in the organic matter content of soil where bluegrass was grown continuously or where a rotation of corn, oats, and clover was grown during the 12-year period. The aggregate state of the rotation plots was at a lower level than on the sod. Aggregation was approximately twice as high under corn in a corn, oats, meadow rotation as under continuous corn. It dropped rapidly when corn followed sod crops and increased when continuous corn was changed to rotation corn. A highly significant positive correlation was found between aggregation and corn yields.

Growing corn and wheat continuously in Virginia reduced both the percentage of soil aggregates and that of aggregates above one mm. in diameter. The addition of manure to land cropped continuously in corn or wheat increased soil aggregation temporarily. Aggregation remained the same during a 4-year rotation of corn, wheat, clover, and hay. The soil of the hay plots contained a higher percentage of aggregates exceeding one mm. in diameter. This showed that aggregates increased in size when the land was left in sod. When all crops in the rotation were fertilized or manured, the soil of the clover and hay plots had a higher percentage of soil aggregation and of aggregates exceeding one mm. in diameter than the soil under corn and wheat. Soil that had been in sod for 30 years contained more aggregates than soil cropped continuously in corn or wheat. This soil compared favorably with the soil of fertilized or manured plots of clover hay in a 4-year rotation.

After 32 years of cropping of Wooster silt loam in Ohio, the amounts of both organic carbon and nitrogen on plots of 5-year rotation experiments were found to be highly and positively correlated with the total crop production of the plots. The estimated annual losses of organic carbon and nitrogen from variously cropped plots are shown in Table 15.

TABLE 15. Estimated percentage annual losses from Wooster silt loam of organic carbon and nitrogen under different cropping systems for the period 1894–1925

Cropping System	Organic carbon	Nitrogen
Continuous corn	3.12	2.97
Continuous wheat	1.44	1.56
Continuous oats	1.41	1.45
5-year rotation	0.85	1.06
3-year rotation	0.60	0.69

Even though there were heavy losses of organic carbon and nitrogen during the years corn, wheat, and oats were grown in the rotation there was a slight increase in both items for each rotation when the rotation periods are considered as a whole. The losses sustained when these crops were grown were more than offset by gains made during the years the land was in hay. In the 5-year rotation the soil gained an average of 1.36 per cent organic carbon and 0.64 per cent nitrogen annually when the land was in hay (mainly timothy). The gains were higher in the 3-year rotation when the land was in clover hay. They were 3.25 per cent organic carbon and 2.87 per cent nitrogen.

The loss of organic matter is much higher the first few years after sod is put into cultivation. The loss is directly related to the cropping system used. Losses of organic matter and nitrogen were less for 3- and 5-year rotations during the 20-year period 1917-1937 than for a 2-year rotation in Iowa. The average loss of organic matter in Iowa, on Clarion loam where manure was not applied, was 16.2 per cent for a 2-year rotation, 11.7 per cent for a 3-year rotation, and 10.2 per cent for a 5-year rotation. The loss of nitrogen from this soil was 21.5 per cent for the 2-year rotation, 13.4 per cent for the 3-year rotation, and 10.0 per cent for the 5-year rotation. Crop residues were returned to the land in all of the rotations.

Where corn was grown continuously for 20 years on Clarion loam, the loss of organic matter amounted to 18.3 per cent. When grown in a 3-year rotation of corn, oats, and clover the loss was reduced to 11.7 per cent. In a similar experiment on Marshall silt loam the difference was even greater. Where corn was grown continuously for 10 years, 15.6 per cent of the organic matter was lost while the loss was only 0.9 per cent where a 3-year rotation of corn, oats, and clover was followed. In most cases, there were found to be highly significant correlations between the original organic matter and nitrogen contents and the losses of these constituents. The higher the original contents, the larger were the losses.

SOIL STRUCTURE AND CROP YIELDS

Correlations have been noted between various indexes of the natural physical state of a soil and productivity. Page and Willard, and van Bavel and Schaller found a highly significant positive correlation between the degree of soil aggregation and corn yields. Rynasiewicz established a straight-line relationship between onion yields and soil aggregation. Baver and Farnsworth found that sugar beet yields in Ohio were markedly reduced when the soil air space capacity fell below 12 per cent. Yoder observed that high yields and early maturity of cotton were associated with high noncapillary porosity.

In Iowa, land planted continuously to corn for 13 years produced an average of 31.8 bushels per acre, while corn grown in a 3-year rotation averaged 54.0 bushels—an increase of over 22 bushels an acre for the rotation. The soil on the rotated plots was more highly aggregated than that on the continuous corn plots. Moreover, the difference in yield between the two treatments is rapidly increasing. In five years (1940-44) the corn grown in the rotation averaged 71.2 bushels per acre while that grown continuously averaged 23.9. Variously aggregated soils produced highly significant differences in the yield of wheat under greenhouse conditions. Coarsely aggregated soils produced much better growth than finely aggregated soils.

Similar correlations between physical soil conditions and crop yield do not always follow the use of soil conditioners. The use of synthetic soil conditioners frequently improves soil structure and increases crop yield, but improved soil structure and increased crop yields do not always result from the use of these materials. Neither are all soil conditioners equally effective on the same soil. They are most effective on well dispersed soils. Even though the physical condition of a soil is improved the moisture equivalent and crop yield may not be increased. In some cases crop yields are actually reduced.

Soils treated with soil conditioners have been found to be more resistant to splash erosion than similar soils untreated.

SYNTHETIC SOIL CONDITIONERS

As a result of the studies of Ruehrwein and Ward reported in the preceding chapter, a number of investigators have studied the possibility of using synthetic polyelectrolytes to condition soil under field conditions.

Hendrick and Mowry found that water-soluble polyelectrolytes were extremely effective aggregating agents. When a polyanion, such as a hydrolyzed polyacrylonitrile, was applied at rates of 0.01 to 0.1 per cent to soil of poor structure, the aggregate analysis as determined by wet-sieving was increased, the working properties were improved, and other characteristics commonly associated with good structure were developed.

The treatment increased infiltration and percolation of water and thus reduced runoff. The moisture equivalent of the soil was increased, the wilting point was unchanged, so that the soil held water available to plant growth and the rate of evaporation from the soil surface was increased.

Taylor and Martin produced changes in soil aggregation and in such related characteristics as pore-size distribution, water infiltration, and hydraulic conductivity by applying several synthetic soil-aggregating chemicals to fine-textured Miami, Crosby, Brookston, and Paulding soils. The chemicals were used at rates varying from 0.05 to 0.15 per cent in both powdered and liquid forms.

Allison made laboratory tests on several saline and alkali soils to determine the aggregating effectiveness of synthetic polyelectrolytes CRD-186 and CRD-189. In all cases, the conditioners were applied in solution at rates of 0.025 and 0.1 per cent by spraying the solution into dry soil, followed by mixing to facilitate aggregation. Aggregate analysis by wet-sieving indicates that these two soil conditioners are about equally effective in producing a high water-stable aggregation. Alkali soils low in permeability treated with CRD-186, as indicated, gave marked increases in permeability in proportion to rate of treatment.

Sweet corn was grown on treated and untreated field plots representing normal, nonsaline-alkali, and saline-alkali soil conditions, the last at two levels of salinity. The CRD-186 was applied in solution (by spraying) at the rate of 0.1 per cent to a depth of 6 inches while the soil was being mixed with a small power-operated cultivator. This treatment gave manyfold increases in irrigation water infiltration on the alkali soils but had little or no effect on the normal soil.

Alderfer studied the influence of structure on yields of agricultural crops, using different types and amounts of synthetic conditioning materials. Fifteen separate experiments were conducted at seven locations on six representative field soils and two greenhouse soils in Pennsylvania. Several types of conditioning materials were used in attempting to stabilize a given structural condition throughout the whole 6-inch layer of surface soil, in a section of soil 6 inches deep and 6 inches wide in the row, and in a ¼-inch layer of soil over the row after seeding. The synthetic polyelectrolyte soil aggregate stabilizing used in these investigations made it possible to bring about marked changes in the physical condition of that portion of the soil to and with which these materials were properly added and mixed.

In soils with poor tilth, improvement in the structure of the whole 6-inch surface layer with the use of synthetic conditioners was accompanied by an increase in production of sweet corn, tomatoes, peppers, potatoes, lima beans, snap beans, carrots, table beets, turnips, and tobacco.

Crop yields in such soils were most closely related to aggregation and to a lesser extent to aeration porosity and permeability, measured at the end of the growing season.

On limestone soils, the greatest increase in crop production occurred with an increase in the percentage of soil stabilized into aggregates >0.25 mm. up to 35 per cent. For the loess-derived Ewingsville soil this value was 42 per cent.

Improvement of the structure of a 6-inch by 6-inch section of soil in the row increased the yield of table beets, carrots, turnips, snap beans, and lima beans. The yields of cucumbers, sweet corn, snap beans and turnips was increased by a liquid application of soil conditioners over the row after seeding.

The resistance to compaction of previously uncompacted special turf soils was found to be increased by stabilizing a favorable structural condition with the liquid application of a synthetic conditioner (HPAN).

Both field and laboratory studies revealed that soils may differ in the degree to which their finer particle fraction can be stabilized into aggregates >0.25 mm. The aggregates produced in Cavoda silt loam subsoil were very weakly stabilized compared with the aggregates produced by mixing the same quantity of synthetic soil conditioner with Hagerstown silt loam surface soil. The soils in the field experiments all showed marked response to the use of synthetic polyelectrolytes. The percentage of soil stabilized into aggregates and the size of these aggregates increased with the amount of active synthetic polyelectrolyte mixed with the soil.

DECOMPOSITION OF SOIL CONDITIONERS

The resistance of soil conditioning polyelectrolytes such as hydrolyzed polyacrylonitrile (HPAN) and vinyl acetate-maleic acid compound (VAMA), to decomposition is of particular importance to their economy of use as soil aggregate stabilizers. It is also evident that such compounds must not interfere with beneficial biological activity.

Ruehrwein and Ward showed that the adsorption of such polymers on clay is practically complete in 24 hours. Hedrick and Mowry found that VAMA-treated crumbs remained stable in moist soil for 32 months at 76°F. Field tests by Martin, Mortensen, and others also showed aggregates formed by soil conditioners were stable. *The Modern Plastic Encyclopedia and Engineering Handbook* and Greathouse and his associates report that vinyl-type plastics and resins are good to excellent in resisting microbial attack. Wellman and McCalla showed that vinyl plastics are resistant to fungal attack.

Laboratory techniques, evolution of carbon dioxide, nitrification rate, and plate counts indicated that HPAN and VAMA, at normal rates of application, are not toxic to soil microflora.

REFERENCES

1. *A Handbook in Agronomy.* 1942. Agron. Dept. Iowa State Coll.
2. Ackerman, F. G., and Myers, H. E. 1943. *Some factors influencing aggregation of claypan soils.* Soil Sci., 55: 405-513.
3. Alderfer, R. B. 1950. *Influence of seasonal and cultural conditions on aggregation of Hagerstown soil.* Soil Sci., 69(3): 193-203.
4. ———. 1954. *Soil structure studies with synthetic soil conditioners.* Unpublished data.
5. Allison, L. E. 1952. *Effect of synthetic polyelectrolytes on the structure of saline and alkali soils.* Soil Sci., 73(6): 443-454.
6. Atkinson, H. B., and Bay, C. E. 1940. *Some factors affecting frost penetration.* Paper presented at the Western Interstate Snow-Survey Conference, Seattle, Washington.
7. Baver, L. D., and Farnsworth, R. B. 1941. *Soil structure effects in the growth of sugar beets.* Soil Sci. Soc. Amer. Proc., 5: 45-48.
8. Bolton, E. F., Fulton, J. M., and Aylesworth, J. W. 1955. *The effect of two soil conditioners on some physical properties of a Brookston clay soil.* Canadian Jour. Agr. Sci., 35: 51-57.
9. Bolton, E. F., and Webber, L. B. 1952. *Effect of cropping systems on the aggregation of a Brookston clay soil at three depths.* Sci. Agr., 32(10): 55-558.
10. ———. 1944. *Effect of different types of organic materials and lime on soil aggregation.* Soil Sci., 57(2): 91-106.
11. Browning, G. M., and Milam, F. M. 1941. *Rate of application of organic matter in relation to soil aggregation.* Soil Sci. Soc. Amer. Proc., 6: 96-97.

12. Elson, J. 1940. *A comparison of the effect of certain cropping and fertilizer and manure practices on soil aggregation of Dunmore silt loam.* Soil Sci., 50(5): 339-355.

13. Gilmour, C. M., Allen, O. N., and Truog, E. 1948. *Soil aggregation as influenced by the growth of mould species, kind of soil, and organic matter.* Soil Sci. Soc. Amer. Proc., 13: 292-295.

14. Gish, R. E., and Browning, G. M. 1948. *Factors affecting the stability of soil aggregates.* Soil Sci. Soc. Amer. Proc., 13: 51-55.

15. Greathouse, G. A., Wessel, C. J., and Shirk, H. G. 1951. *Microbiological deterioration of manufactured materials.* Ann. Rev. Microbiology, 5: 333-358.

16. Hagin, J. 1952. *Influence of soil aggregation on plant growth.* Soil Sci., 74(6): 471-478.

17. Haise, H. R., Jensen, L. R., and Alessi, J. 1955. *The effect of synthetic soil conditioners on soil structure and production of sugar beets.* Soil Sci. Soc. Amer. Proc., 19: 17-19.

18. Havis, L. 1943. *Aggregation of an orchard and a vegetable soil under different treatments.* Ohio Agr. Expt. Sta. Bull. 640.

19. Hedrick, R. M., and Mowry, D. T. 1952. *Effect of synthetic polyelectrolytes on aggregation, aeration, and water relationships of soil.* Soil Sci., 73(6): 427-441.

20. Hely, F. W., and Bonnier, C. 1953. *Influence of soil aggregating substances on the population of gum-producing bacteria in a loess soil.* Antonie van Leeuwenhock, 19.

21. Hide, J. C., and Metzger, W. H. 1939. *Soil aggregation as affected by certain crops and organic materials and some chemical properties associated with aggregation.* Soil Sci. Soc. Amer. Proc., 4: 19-22.

22. Jamison, V. C. 1954. *The effect of some soil conditioners on friability and compactibility of soils.* Soil Sci. Soc. Amer. Proc., 18: 391-394.

23. Johnson, J. R., Browning, G. M., and Russell, M. B. 1942. *The effect of cropping practices on aggregation, organic matter content, and loss of soil and water in the Marshall silt loam.* Soil Sci. Soc. Amer. Proc., 7: 105-107.

24. Laws, Derby. 1954. *The influence of soil properties on the effectiveness of synthetic soil conditioners.* Soil Sci. Soc. Amer. Proc., 18: 378-381.

25. Martin, J. P. 1942. *The effect of composts and compost materials upon the aggregation of the silt and clay particles of Collington sandy loam.* Soil Sci. Soc. Amer. Proc., 7: 218-222.

26. ———. 1945. *Microorganisms and soil aggregation: I. Origin and nature of some of the aggregating substances.* Soil Sci., 59(2): 163-174.

27. ———. 1953. *Status report of soil conditioning chemicals: I.* Soil Sci. Soc. Amer. Proc., 17: 1-9.

28. ———, and Jones, W. W. 1954. *Greenhouse plant response to vinyl acetate-maleic acid copolymer in natural soils and in prepared soils containing high percentages of sodium or potassium.* Soil Sci., 78: 317-324.

29. Martin, J. P., Taylor, G. S., Engibous, J. C., and Barnett, E. 1952. *Soil and crop responses from field applications of soil conditioners.* Soil Sci., 73: 455-471.

30. Martin, J. P., and Waksman, S. A. 1941. *Influence of microorganisms on soil aggregation and erosion.* Soil Sci., 52(5): 381-394.

31. McCalla, T. M. 1955. *The influence of synthetic polyelectrolytes on nitrification rate.* Soil Sci. Soc. Amer. Proc. (on press).

32. McHenry, J. R., and Russell, M. B. 1943. *Elementary mechanics of aggregation of puddled materials.* Soil Sci. Soc. Amer. Proc., 8: 71-78.

33. McNaught, K. J. 1955. *Effect of synthetic soil conditioners on plant nutrient uptake.* New Zealand Jour. Soil and Technol., Ser. A, 36: 450-453.

34. Metzger, W. H., and Hide, J. C. 1938. *Effect of certain crops and soil treatments on soil aggregation and the distribution of organic carbon in relation to aggregate size.* Jour. Amer. Soc. Agron., 30(9): 833-843.

35. *Modern Plastics Encyclopedia and Engineers Handbook.* 1952. Plastics Catalogue Corp., New York.

36. Mortensen, J. L., and Martin, W. P. 1954. *Decomposition of soil conditioning polyelectrolytes, HPAN and VAMA in Ohio soils.* Soil Sci. Soc. Amer. Proc., 18: 395-398.

37. Neher, D. D. 1950. *The effect of cropping systems and soil treatment on the water-stable aggregates in claypan soils in southeastern Kansas.* Agron. Jour., 42(10): 475-477.

38. Nickell, L. G., and Burkholder, P. 1947. *Inhibition of azotobacter by soil actinomycetes.* Jour. Amer. Soc. Agron., 39(9): 771-779.

39. Norman, A. G., and Newman, A. S. 1941. *Some effects of sheet erosion on soil microbial activity.* Soil Sci., 52(1): 31-46.

40. Olmstead, L. B. 1946. *The effect of long-time cropping and tillage practices upon soil aggregation at Hays, Kansas.* Soil Sci. Soc. Amer. Proc., 11:89-92.

41. Page, J. B., and Willard, C. J. 1948. *Cropping systems and soil properties.* Soil Sci. Soc. Amer. Proc., 11:81.

42. Pearson, R. W., and Jamison, V. C. 1953. *Improving land conditions for conservation and production with chemical soil conditioners.* Jour. Soil and Water Cons., 8: 130-135.

43. Peele, T. C. 1940. *Microbial activity in relation to aggregation.* Jour. Amer. Soc. Agron., 32(3): 204-212.

44. ————. 1941. *Effect of runoff and erosion on improved aggregation resulting from the stimulation of microbial activity.* Soil Sci. Soc. Amer. Proc., 6: 176-182.

45. ————. 1944. *Microbial activity and soil aggregate formation during decomposition of organic matter.* Soil Sci. Soc. Amer. Proc., 8: 254-257.

46. ————, and Beale, O. W. 1940. *Influence of microbial activity upon aggregation and erodibility of lateritic soils.* Soil Sci. Soc. Amer. Proc., 5: 33-35.

47. Pearlkamp, P. K. 1950. *The influence on soil structure of the "natural organic manuring" by roots and stubbles of crops.* 4th Internat. Conv. of Soil Sci. Trans., 1: 50-54.

48. Peevy, W. J., Smith, F. B., and Brown, P. E. 1940. *Effects of rotational and manurial treatment for twenty years on the organic matter, nitrogen, and phosphorus contents of Clarion and Webster soils.* Jour. Amer. Soc. Agron., 32(10): 739-753.

49. Peters, D. B., Hagan, R. M., and Bodman, G. B. 1953. *Available moisture capacities of soils as affected by additions of polyelectrolyte soil conditioners.* Soil Sci., 75: 467-471.

50. Pierre, W. H., and Browning, G. M. 1945. *Let's examine crop rotation.* Iowa State Coll. Farm Sci. Reporter, 6: 3-6.

51. Retzer, J. L., and Russell, M. B. 1941. *Difference in the aggregation of a Prairie and a Gray-Brown Podzolic soil.* Soil Sci., 52(1): 47-58.

52. Richards, S. J., Neal, O. R., and Brill, G. D. 1948. *Aggregation of the silt and clay soil separates in relation to yields and runoff on Coastal Plain soils.* Soil Sci. Soc. Amer. Proc., 13: 23-26.

53. Ruehrwein, R. A., and Ward, D. W. 1952. *Mechanism of clay aggregation by polyelectrolytes.* Soil Sci., 73: 485-492.

54. Rynasiewicz, J. 1945. *Soil aggregation and onion yields.* Soil Sci., 60: 387-395.

55. Salter, R. M., and Greene, T. C. 1933. *Factors affecting the accumulation and loss of nitrogen and organic carbon in cropped soils.* Jour. Amer. Soc. Agron., 25(9): 622-630.

56. Sherwood, L. V., and Engibous, J. C. 1953. *Status report on soil conditioning chemicals: II.* Soil Sci. Soc. Amer. Proc., 17: 6-16.

57. Stallings, J. H. 1954. *Soil-produced antibiotics—plant disease and insect control.* Bact. Rev., 18(2): 131-146.

58. Strickling, E. 1950. *The effect of soybeans on volume weight and water stability of soil aggregates, soil organic matter content, and crop yields.* Soil Sci. Soc. Amer. Proc., 15: 30-37.

59. Taylor, G. S., and Baldridge, P. E. 1954. *The effect of sodium carboxy methylcellulose on some physical properties of Ohio soils.* Soil Sci. Soc. Amer. Proc., 18: 382-385.

60. Taylor, G. S., and Martin, W. P. 1953. *Effect of soil-aggregating chemicals on soils.* Agr. Engin., 34: 550-554.

61. Thom, C. 1941. *Out of the furrow.* Jour. Bact., 41(1): 1-15.

62. Van Bavel, C. H. M. 1949. *Mean weight-diameter of soil aggregates as a structural index of aggregation.* Soil Sci. Soc. Amer. Proc., 14: 20-23.

63. ――――, and Schaller, F. W. 1950. *Soil aggregation, organic matter, and yields in a long-time experiment as affected by crop management.* Soil Sci. Soc. Amer. Proc., 15: 399-404.

64. Van Doren, C. A., and Stauffer, R. S. 1944. *Effect of crop and surface mulches on runoff, soil losses, and soil aggregation.* Soil Sci. Soc. Amer. Proc., 8: 97-100.

65. Weeks, L. E., and Colter, W. G. 1952. *Effect of synthetic soil conditioners on erosion control.* Soil Sci., 73: 473-484.

66. Wellman, R. H., and McCallan, S. E. A. 1945. *Fungus resistance of plastics,* OSRD Report 5683.

67. Wester, R. E. 1953. *Response of vegetable crops to soil conditioners.* Agr. Chem., 8: 48-50, 125-127.

68. White, J. W. 1931. *Crop yields in relation to residual soil organic matter.* Jour. Amer. Soc. Agron., 23: 424-434.

69. Wilson, H. A., and Browning, G. M. 1945. *Soil aggregation, yields, runoff, and erosion as affected by cropping systems.* Soil Sci. Soc. Amer. Proc., 10: 51-57.

70. Yoder, R. W. 1936. *A direct method of aggregate analysis of soils and a study of the physical nature of erosion losses.* Jour. Amer. Soc. Agron., 28: 337-351.

7

Soil Surveys

Soil is the natural medium for the growth of land plants. It covers the earth as a continuum, except on rocky slopes, in regions permanently covered with ice, in very salty playas, and elsewhere that the cover of soil disappears. There are many forms of soil. The characteristics of soil in any particular place result from the combined influence of a number of factors. These include climate and living matter acting upon the parent rock material, as conditioned by relief, over periods of time, and the effects of the cultural environment and man's use of the soil.

Soil must be broken down into individual kinds to study the characteristics and predict the potentialities for use. A classification of soil must make use of experience and results of research. Classification is the tool we use in organizing our knowledge and remembering it. Classification helps us to see relationships among soils and between them and their environment, and to formulate principles of production value regarding them.

An individual unit of the continuum is a dynamic three-dimensional place of landscape that supports plants. This unit has a combination of both internal and external characteristics which have definite ranges of expression. Each individual kind of soil has a modal set of characteristics. Its upper surface is the surface of the land; its lower surface is marked by the lower limits of soil-forming processes; and its sides are boundaries with other kinds of soil.

Many hundreds of kinds of soil occur in the United States. The characteristics of each kind can be learned through observation and investigation. The history and potentialities of soil are contained in these characteristics, considered collectively. The influence of any one characteristic on soil behavior, or of a variation in any one, depends upon the others in the combination.

Soils, then, are both landscapes and profiles. This is why the detailed soil mapper draws soil boundaries. Examination of soil profiles is used to verify the location of boundaries.

The Soil Conservation Service is responsible for the Department of Agriculture soil survey. Soil surveys are made cooperatively with the State Land-Grant colleges and other agencies. They are designed to aid farmers and to assist in other programs dealing with soils and soil use.

Soil surveys cover a number of activities. They include mapping, classification, interpretation, field and laboratory characterization for soil mapping and correlation, map compilation, and publication. They also include investigations of soil genesis, morphology, and classification. Soil surveys furnish soil maps and interpretations needed in research and educational programs. The work is done according to specific standards. The survey includes a nationwide system of soil classification, nomenclature, interpretation and publication.

The purpose of the survey is to determine the nature and location of each kind of soil. Each soil is studied in relation to research and experience. It is studied with a view toward predicting yield and quality of crops, forage, and trees that may be obtained under defined systems of management. It is designed to predict the effects of such use on the soil. These predictions are used to make practical recommendations for the use and management of specific fields or tracts with the highest efficiency. Capability groupings of soils are used for convenient arrangement for prediction about similar soils.

Close working relations are maintained between those who make and supervise soil surveys, and those who use and apply the results. These in turn work closely with those who conduct the investigations essential for sound soil classification and interpretation. Close cooperation is maintained with all research groups dealing with soils, plants, and economic conditions —when these conditions relate to the scientific basis of the soil survey or its interpretation.

A work plan and a descriptive mapping legend is prepared for each survey area. The area may be a county or a soil conservation district. The work plan contains facts about the survey to be made, including plans for publication. The descriptive mapping legend contains a description of each soil mapping unit. This includes the range of surface slope and degree of soil erosion.

TYPES OF SURVEYS

Soil surveys are classed as either detailed surveys or reconnaissance surveys. These differ in the method and resulting precision of mapping.

Detailed surveys. A detailed soil survey is one in which the location of each boundary plotted on the map is observed throughout its course.

Reconnaissance surveys. A reconnaissance soil survey is one in which the boundaries between mapping units are plotted from observations made at intervals. Boundaries are not necessarily made throughout their whole course. The scale of the reconnaissance survey is often smaller than that of a detailed survey. However, the method of mapping, rather than scale or type of legend, is the basis for distinction.

Most of the surveys made for use in planning farms are detailed. Reconnaissance soil surveys may furnish all the soil information needed in some areas. This is true of areas suitable only for range or woodland use. However, care must be taken to see that the soil information obtained is adequate for the program to be carried out.

STANDARD SOIL SURVEYS

A standard soil survey is one in which the soil mapping units are defined in terms of the nationwide system of soil classification. The scale and intensity of mapping are such that soil boundaries are shown in correct location with respect to field boundaries or other landmarks. The work is done under an approved work plan.

SOIL SURVEY WORK PLANS

Soil survey work in each survey area is preceded by a survey work plan. Some standard soil surveys are covered by work plans. These are mapped according to legends of named soil units. As far as possible, they are mapped progressively. These work plans are prepared on a standard form.

MAPPING LEGENDS

The lines on soil maps represent boundaries between significantly different kinds of soil. In order to facilitate use of maps, it is necessary to keep a correct record, or legend, of the symbols. This legend shows the meaning of the symbols placed on maps. These are keyed to the descriptions of the units.

At the beginning of each soil survey report there is a descriptive legend. This is the initial part of a soils handbook for the appropriate geographic area. The descriptive legend has four sections: (a) the identification legend of mapping units and the symbols by which they are identified, (b) a description of each mapping unit, (c) a table showing the characteristics and genetic relationships of each of the units, and (d) explanation of principal geologic and topographic features of the area.

SOIL MAPPING UNITS

Mapping units are selected so that all mappable soil conditions can be adequately delimited. Mapping conditions are those significant to conservation, use management, yield potentials, responses, and conservation needs of the area. These units are consistent with a scientifically sound classification. The principles followed in the design of mapping legends is the same for all surveys. This way the units recognized in different surveys can be fitted into a national classification. The units are large enough for reporting research findings. They are also large enough for extending and applying what is known about a soil at one place to similar soils at other places.

A uniform approach is made in the classification of soils in all surveys. This way the mapping units can be properly identified in the nationwide system of soil classification. This usually requires a definition of each mapping unit in terms of soil types or phases. Mapping units may be soil associations on lands capable of only extensive use. These may be defined in terms of two or more soil taxonomic units. The greatest usefulness of mapping requires that legends of detailed surveys consist chiefly of mapping units which are subdivisions of soil types.

In reconnaissance surveys, mapping units consist mainly of combinations of soil types. These need not be alike in their properties. However, they must occur in characteristic patterns. Reconnaissance mapping units are related to the nationwide system of soil classification by the soil types occurring within a mapping unit.

Interpretation of each mapping unit includes basically the alternate system of management. Yield estimates and the effects of the alternate systems of management on long-time productivity are also given. These materials are basic for capability and other groupings of the soils. The descriptive legends include a record of research applicable to each soil unit and its interpretation for using the survey.

The soil survey is basic in carrying out a sound farm program. Many of the applications of soil science are made through the soil survey. These are especially made through capability groupings of the soil mapping units, which include forest and range sites.

Competently prepared descriptions are the basic data for soil classification and correlation. These consist chiefly of field observations and measurements. However, more and more laboratory data are being used. Adequate characterization of a soil consists of several features. It consists of a description of a typical profile, a statement of the allowable variations from the typical in profile features, and descriptions (including ranges) of slope, erosion conditions, stoniness, salinity, and other pertinent features. These are in standard terminology.

Key soils are extensive. They are major elements of the soil pattern in large soil associations or conservation problem areas. Key areas are agriculturally important. They represent samples of large soil associations or conservation problem areas. Key soils or key areas qualify on at least two counts.

SOIL SURVEY METHODS

Soil surveying consists of the examination, classification, and mapping of soils in the field. The soil scientist samples the soil at intervals not more than one-quarter mile apart. This is done by either boring into the soil with an auger or digging holes with a spade. This sampling shows the soil to consist of several distinctly different layers, called *horizons*. The horizons taken collectively make up the *soil profile*. Each of these layers is studied carefully to determine the characteristics that affect plant growth.

The color of each horizon is noted. The topmost horizon is usually darker than the others. The intensity of color in this layer denotes the amount of organic matter present. The lower layers have streaks or spots of gray, yellow, and brown which generally indicate impeded drainage and restricted aeration. Texture, or the proportionate content of sand, silt, and clay, is determined by the "feel" and is checked by mechanical analysis in the laboratory.

Texture determines to a large extent the productivity of a soil. It does this by determining how much moisture the soil will hold available to plants, whether plant nutrients or fertilizers will be held by the soil in forms available to plants or will be leached out, and how difficult the soil will be to manage.

Structure, or the state of aggregation, determines the amount of pore space between particles and how easily plant roots and moisture can penetrate the soil. Consistence, or the tendency of the soil to crumble or stick together, indicates how difficult it is to keep the soil open and porous under cultivation.

The kinds of rock material from which the soil developed, or its parent material, affects the natural fertility of the soil. The chemical reaction of the soil is determined by simple tests. The depth to bedrock or to compact layers is determined. External features, such as quantity of gravelstones or rocks that may interfere with cultivation, the steepness and kind of slope, the quantity of soil lost by erosion, and other external features are observed.

Soils much alike in the characteristics as kind, thickness, and arrangement of layers are mapped as one soil type. Some soil types are mapped in two or more phases. For example, soil types having slopes ranging from 2 to 14 per cent may be mapped in two phases—an undulating phase and a rolling phase. The undulating phase includes that part of the slope ranging from 2 to 7 per cent. The rolling phase covers that portion of the slope ranging from 7 to 14 per cent. Likewise, a soil that has been eroded in places may be mapped in two or more phases, an uneroded (or normal) phase, an eroded phase, and perhaps a severely eroded phase. Soil types are usually broken into phases because of differences other than kind, thickness, and arrangement of layers.

Soils having similar profile characteristics other than texture of the surface horizon are put in the same series. A soil series, therefore, includes all soil types having about the same kind, thickness, and arrangement of layers, except for texture of the surface layer, whether the number of such soil types be only one or several.

A soil series takes the name of the place where it is first found. For example, Culpeper is the name of a series first found at Culpeper, Virginia. The Culpeper series consists of acid, friable to moderately friable, well-drained soils with light-brown or yellowish-gray surface layer and a reddish-brown or light-red subsoil. Culpeper soils are developed on undulating to hilly topography and are underlain by mixed arkosical sandstone, quartzite, and granite-gneiss materials.

The following illustrates the grouping of the Culpeper series into types, and the types, in turn, into mapping units (phases):

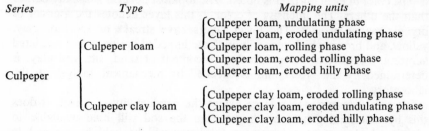

Series	Type	Mapping units
Culpeper	Culpeper loam	Culpeper loam, undulating phase Culpeper loam, eroded undulating phase Culpeper loam, rolling phase Culpeper loam, eroded rolling phase Culpeper loam, eroded hilly phase
	Culpeper clay loam	Culpeper clay loam, eroded rolling phase Culpeper clay loam, eroded undulating phase Culpeper clay loam, eroded hilly phase

When two or more kinds of soil are so intricately mixed that they cannot be shown separately on a map of the scale used, they are mapped together. The areas of the mixture are called a *soil complex.*

Areas that have little true soil, such as bare rocky mountainsides, coastal beach, or dune sand, are not designated with series and type names but are given descriptive names.

The soil type is usually the unit of mapping in soil surveys. However, where the type is subdivided, the soil phase is the unit mapped. The unit, or the kind of soil, is most nearly uniform and has the narrowest range of characteristics of the subdivisions. Consequently, land use and soil management can be more definitely specified for the unit than they can for broader groups of soils that contain more variation. As a result, we can usually say, for example, that soils of the Davidson series need lime for alfalfa. On the other hand, Davidson clay loam, undulating phase, has very mild slopes and, though needing lime, is suited to general farm crops grown in a rotation with alfalfa or other hay. The eroded hilly phase of Davidson clay loam, however, has slopes that fall from 14 to 25 feet in 100, is hard to work with heavy machinery, erodes easily, and should be used principally for permanent pasture. Both phases are included in the Davidson series, as are other types and phases, even though each has specific differences in land use and soil management.

The soil survey of Culpeper County, Virginia, presented in Table 16, shows how the soils are classified.

SOIL SURVEY INTERPRETATIONS

The purpose of soil survey interpretations is to organize and present knowledge about soil properties, qualities, and behavior so that users of soil maps can make intelligent choices among alternative uses and combinations of those practices related to soil conditions. The main use of these interpretations is in the development of sound soil and water conservation plans on individual farms and ranches. However, they can also be used for watershed planning and for many other purposes.

A knowledge of different kinds of soil is necessary to accurately predict the behavior and response to management. Results of field and laboratory research and experience of qualified individuals related to soil behavior and use, once interpreted, can be applied to similar kinds of soil wherever they occur. However, it is impossible to carry out detailed research on each different soil area. But, by using all available classification data and soil

TABLE 16. Soil series of Culpeper County, Va., arranged by geographic position, and their principal characteristics (1)

Series	Parent rock	Profile description		Subsoil consistence	Drainage
		Upland			
		Color [1]			
		Surface soil	Subsoil		
	Acidic rocks:				
Cecil	Granite, granite gneiss	Yellowish gray	Moderate reddish brown	Firm	Good.
Appling	"	"	Brown to reddish brown	Friable	"
Culpeper	Arkosic sandstone and quartzite; some granite gneiss.	"	Moderate reddish brown	Friable to firm	"
Albemarle	"	"	Yellowish brown	Friable	"
Louisburg	Granite and granite gneiss	"	Shallow, has no subsoil	Friable to loose parent material	Good to excessive.
Halewood	"	Weak yellow	Moderate yellowish brown	Friable	"
Hayesville	Granite and inclusions of granodiorite.	Light yellowish brown	Strong brown to moderate reddish brown.	"	"
Yadkin	"	Moderate brown	Moderate to dark brown	"	Good.
Hazel	Mica schist, arkosic sandstone, and quartzite.	Brownish gray to dark yellowish brown.	Shallow, has no subsoil	Firm parent material	Good to excessive.
Elioak	Granite gneiss and mica schist.	Light yellowish brown	Brown to moderate reddish brown.	Firm	Good.
Manor	Mica schist	"	Light yellowish brown.	Friable	Good to excessive.
Watt	Graphitic schist	Light olive gray	Shallow, has no subsoil	Friable to firm parent material.	"
Tatum	Sericite schist	Weak yellow	Strong brown to moderate reddish brown.	Firm	Good.
Nason	"	"	Strong yellowish brown	"	Moderately good.
Lignum	"	"	Dusky yellow	Friable to firm.	Fair.
Manteo	"	Yellowish gray	Shallow, has no subsoil	Firm parent material	Good to excessive.
Bucks	Reddish-brown Triassic shale and mudstone (with a purplish cast).	Light brown (with a purplish cast).	Pale reddish brown (with a purplish cast).	Firm	Good.
Penn	"	Pale brown with a slight purplish cast.	Shallow, has no subsoil	Firm parent material	Good to excessive.
Wadesboro	Light-brown to reddish-brown Triassic shale and mudstones.	Yellowish gray to weak yellow	Strong brown to moderate reddish brown.	Firm	Good.
Lansdale	Light-brown and yellow Triassic shale.	Weak yellow	Light yellowish brown	Firm; slightly compact.	Moderately good to fair.

TABLE 16. (Continued)

Upland (Continued)

| Series | Parent rock | Profile description | | Subsoil consistence | Drainage |
| | | Color 1 | | | |
		Surface soil	Subsoil		
Brecknock	Baked moderate-gray Triassic shale and mudstone.	Light olive gray.	Light olive gray.	Friable to firm.	Good to fair.
Catlett	Baked dark-gray Triassic shale.	.....	Shallow, has no subsoil	Firm parent material.	"
Croton	Gray, green, yellow, and brown Triassic shale and mudstone.	Yellowish gray mottled with light yellow and light gray.	Mottled.	Firm.	Poor.
Stanton	Mixed acidic and basic rocks:	Mottled.	"	Very firm.	Poor to very poor.
Zion	Triassic shale and diabase	Dusky yellow.	Yellowish gray	Firm to slightly plastic	Fair.
Kelly	.....	Light brownish gray	Mottled.	Tough, plastic.	Fair to poor.
Wilkes	Granite gneiss mixed with any basic rock.	Weak yellow.	Shallow, has no subsoil	Variable parent materials.	Good to excessive.
Helena	"	Yellowish gray	Light yellowish brown.	Plastic.	Fair.
Lloyd	Dark-colored greenstone or diabase mixed with granite or arkose sandstone.	Moderate brown.	Moderate reddish brown.	Firm.	Good.
Rapidan	Dark-colored trap conglomerate consisting mostly of greenstone.	Moderate reddish brown.	"	"	"
	Basic rocks:				
Davidson	Dark-colored greenstone, diabase, or diorite.	Moderate brown.	Moderate reddish brown to dark red.	Firm.	"
Mecklenburg	"	Moderate yellowish brown.	Dark yellowish brown	Firm to slightly plastic	Moderately good.
Fauquier	Dark-colored greenstone (schisty in places).	Light yellowish brown.	Strong brown to moderate reddish brown.	Firm.	Good.
Aldino	Light-colored greenstone.	Yellowish gray	Light yellowish brown.	Friable to slightly plastic.	Fair.
Catoctin	"	.....	Shallow, has no subsoil	Firm parent material	Excessive.
Iredell	Diabase	Light gray	Light olive to light olive brown.	Plastic.	Fair to poor.
Elbert	"	Mottled.	Mottled.	.....	Poor to very poor.

TABLE 16. (Continued)

Series	Parent rock	Profile description		Subsoil consistence	Drainage
		Color¹			
		Surface soil	Subsoil		
Terrace Land					
Hiwassee	Old alluvial deposits from — Acidic and basic rocks	Moderate brown or dusky yellow to light brown.	Moderate reddish brown.	Firm	Good.
Altavista	Acidic rocks	"	Light yellowish brown	Friable to firm.	Fair.
Masada	"	Weak yellow.	Light brown	"	Good.
Roanoke	"	Very pale brownish gray highly mottled with light gray.	Mottled.	Plastic.	Poor.
Colluvial Land					
Starr	Local alluvial and colluvial deposits from— Reddish upland soils	Moderate reddish brown.	Moderate reddish brown.	Friable	Good to moderately good.
Seneca	Light-colored upland soils	Yellowish gray.	Light yellowish brown, slightly mottled.	"	Moderately good.
Worsham	Local thin colluvial deposits from granite, gneiss, and schist.	Light gray (mottled)	Highly mottled	Firm to slightly plastic	Poor to very poor.
Bottom Land					
Buncombe	Recent alluvial deposits chiefly from granite, gneiss, and schist.	Very pale brown	Pale brown	Loose	Excessive.
Congaree	"	Light yellowish brown	Light yellowish brown	Very friable	Good.
State	Moderately old alluvial deposits from acidic rocks.	"	Moderate yellowish brown	Friable	"
Chewacla	Recent alluvial deposits chiefly from granite, gneiss, and schist.	"	Mottled.	"	Fair.
Wehadkee	"	Light gray (mottled)	Highly mottled	Firm to slightly plastic	Poor.

¹ Soil color names used throughout the report are from U. S. Dept. Agr. Misc. Pub. 425(4); color of soil when moist unless otherwise stated.

maps, it is usually possible to make predictions that apply to each kind of soil.

A knowledge of the characteristics of individual soils in relation to their effects on plant growth and combinations of farming practices is necessary for such predictions. This knowledge may be gained from basic soil investigations, data from experimental fields, long-time farm records, and from less formal experiences and observations made and recorded in the field. Interpretive data will apply to similar soils regardless of where they are found.

ALTERNATIVE USES OF SOIL

There are a number of possible uses for most kinds of soil as well as different management levels within each use. The "best" use of any kind of soil may depend upon other characteristics of the farm or ranch, such as location and size of unit, the amount of land suitable for different uses, climatic conditions, availability and location of water, and the skill, resources, and desires of the operator. For each kind of soil we need to know the kinds of crops, including forage and trees, that can be grown; their expected yield; and the long-time effects of a practice, or, more commonly, of a combination of practices, on soil behavior and productivity. Consequently, several interpretations may be needed for each kind of soil in farm and ranch planning. Each of these interpretations should be as accurate as possible.

PERMANENCY OF SOIL INTERPRETATIONS

Some soil interpretations are subject to frequent change whereas others are relatively enduring. Interpreting a combination of soil characteristics, rather than individual ones, provides a more lasting basis for making predictions relative to soil behavior. Broad general use patterns of soils in most well-developed areas have been fairly well established. However, there are marginal soils between those definitely suited to cultivated crops and those definitely not suited, which are used differently under various local conditions.

Interpretations relating to specific soil management practices are temporary. Suggested uses of soils for various crops, estimated long-time yields, practice opportunities and limitations, and similar qualities are subject to frequent change.

Soil survey results, to be effective, must be accurately interpreted at the beginning and constantly improved as new information is developed. Soils carefully defined in the field and accurately mapped make an enduring basis for reinterpreting as needed. Soil surveys meeting these requirements and permitting interpretation under different conditions are complicated, and presentation of the results is difficult.

INTERPRETIVE SOIL GROUPS

Soils should be arranged in groups for specific purposes without omitting or concealing significant details. Thus, by grouping many kinds of soil, the capabilities of the basic soil classifications can be reduced. Groupings and summary tables showing dominant characteristics of the soils, together with statements of significant problems or limitations in use, provide the user with an indication to the soil classification and map and the most highly significant predictions. However, the user must learn to grasp the details before he can make effective use of the soil survey.

Basic data for most agricultural groups include a number of items. They include soil characteristics that reflect important differences in use and management and response to treatment on arable land. They also include estimates of crop yields on the various kinds of soils under physically defined systems of soil and water management, and the effects of these systems on long-time productivity. Soil characteristics and qualities that reflect differences in rate of growth of trees and that influence the kind and amount of natural vegetation on rangeland are considered, too.

CAPABILITY GROUPINGS

Kinds of soils are first grouped into capability units. These include soils nearly homogeneous in respect to major crop adaptability, tillage practices, water management practices, general levels of yield responses, or ability to produce similar kinds and amounts of vegetation. The kinds of soil within a capability unit may differ from one another in the details of practice application, especially lime and fertilizer responses, and in crop yields, within the limit permitted for the unit.

OTHER INTERPRETIVE SOIL GROUPINGS

Soil mapping units may also be grouped in many other ways. Soil mapping units may be grouped and interpreted according to their arability with irrigation or following drainage; according to productivity for individual crops or groups of crops; and according to such special qualities as erosion hazard, response to lime, fertilizer response, and so on. Soil mapping units may be grouped into productivity classes according to current practices as a basis for appraising land for tax assessment or mortgage risk. They may be grouped according to their ability to store water. Important groupings are made in accordance with their engineering properties, as subgrades for highways and airports, for example. Other groupings are made according to suitability for various kinds of terraces, grassed waterways, and other structures.

ASSEMBLY OF DATA A CONTINUING PROCESS

Soil survey interpretation is no better than the information upon which it is based. To be most useful the data should be diverse and applicable to specific kinds of soil and organized for effective use. The data should cover such items as yield estimates of adapted crops under defined systems of management, research data, and the recorded experiences of those concerned with the soil. These data should be assembled by named soil types and phases. If properly organized this information can be used to predict the behavior of individual soils and to group soils into capability units and in other ways for various purposes.

Grouping soils according to capability implies the prediction that the soil can be used according to the recommendations made for the class, sub-class, and unit into which it is placed. The soil survey interpretation gives alternative possibilities for productive, sustained use, rather than "recommendations." Predictions are implicit in all recommendations to farmers. The same is true in the grouping of soil mapping units into capability classes, subclasses, and units. In recommendations made to farmers, there is an implicit prediction. It is that he will maintain or improve yields or quality of crops and conserve his soil if recommendations are followed.

STATUS OF MAPPING

Surveys adequate in scale and detail for farm planning have been made of about 425 million acres. In addition, adequate maps are on hand for about 13 million acres not yet within soil conservation districts. Range surveys suitable for ranch planning were made on about 2.3 million acres.

TABLE 17. Soil surveys within soil conservation districts to June 30, 1953

State or Territory	Acres	State or Territory	Acres
Alabama	17,752,889	New Hampshire	1,035,097
Arizona	878,699	New Jersey	2,724,155
Arkansas	16,550,410	New Mexico	5,596,051
California	7,020,986	New York	8,455,546
Colorado	5,371,317	North Carolina	12,024,262
Connecticut	608,539	North Dakota	13,557,873
Delaware	525,147	Ohio	6,617,884
Florida	8,976,559	Oklahoma	26,052,088
Georgia	23,270,231	Oregon	5,207,650
Idaho	7,216,756	Pennsylvania	3,575,496
Illinois	12,643,890	Rhode Island	377,882
Indiana	4,015,920	South Carolina	12,905,779
Iowa	12,125,890	South Dakota	16,383,869
Kansas	18,373,175	Tennessee	6,305,938
Kentucky	9,998,073	Texas	41,227,927
Louisiana	8,691,679	Utah	1,139,927
Maine	2,776,982	Vermont	2,125,938
Maryland	4,487,513	Virginia	9,605,697
Massachusetts	810,806	Washington	10,859,286
Michigan	4,338,009	West Virginia	8,910,776
Minnesota	6,587,809	Wisconsin	10,000,579
Mississippi	13,164,233	Wyoming	3,320,944
Missouri	3,021,279	Alaska	916,020
Montana	9,686,892	Hawaii	254,647
Nebraska	13,281,018	Caribbean area	1,095,534
Nevada	1,027,481		423,478,628

THE SOIL PROFILE

The characteristics of the profile of a soil determine its value for agricultural use. In studying soil profiles the major horizons and their subdivisions should be located first. If the different layers are well enough defined they should be given letter designations as A, B, and C. Often some laboratory study is required before this can be done.

With the horizon boundaries located, the depth and thickness of each are recorded, together with the character of the boundaries between them. The zero point for measurement is usually the top of the A_1. After measurement, each horizon is described with special attention to the major characteristics that determine the soil's productive value.

Effective depth of soil. Effective depth of soil refers to the depth to which plant roots can penetrate readily in search of water and plant nutrients. It is the depth or layer of soil most favorable for growth of roots and for the storage of moisture that plants can use. Effective depth may be limited by underlying material that, because of certain physical or chemical properties, prevents or seriously retards the growth of roots. For example, a soil may be described as shallow over rock, hardpan, claypan, caliche, gravel, or other distinctive material that limits the effective depth. This conservation aspect of depth connotes something different from just a profile layer in soil-type classification. It carries a utilitarian meaning— about drainage, ease of cultivation, resistance to erosion, available moisture capacity, and soil material available for plant-root development. Effective depth should not be confused with such measures as thickness of surface soil, or depth to water table.

If the layer that limits effective depth is rock or other hard material, the effective depth is also the practical limit of excavation. Where a limiting layer such as claypan or gravel, however, does not hamper excavation, the depth suitable for excavation should be described and mapped if the information is needed, for such purposes as building a dam or leveling land for irrigation.

A shallow soil has limited amounts of plant nutrients and small water-storage capacity. Generally speaking, crops suffer from lack of water more quickly on shallow than on deep soil. Land leveling for irrigation may be impractical on shallow soil. The gradients of terraces, or whether terraces can be used, may depend on the effective depth of soil. Application of other soil and water conservation measures also is affected by the effective soil depth.

The following descriptive terms and ranges are used to define effective depth of the root zone:

Deep	36 inches or more
Moderately deep	20 to 36 inches
Shallow	10 to 20 inches
Very shallow	Less than 10 inches

In some localities it may be necessary to distinguish (a) soils either without layers limiting root growth at any depth, or at some depth below 60 inches, from (b) those soils with inhibiting layers at depths of 36 to 60 inches. The term *very deep* could be used for the first, and *deep* for the second.

In some areas information about layers within the effective depth of soil may also be needed, such as (a) thickness of the surface soil, (b) thickness of subsoil, or (c) thickness of sandy soil over a layer of much lower permeability. The following terms will probably fit most conditions:

Thin .... 0 to 6 inches
Moderately thick .... 6 to 12 inches
Thick .... 12 to 18 inches
Very thick .... 18 to 36 inches

The terms *thick* and *thin,* with appropriate modifiers, are to be used in describing soil layers other than effective depth. *Deep* and *shallow* are reserved for expressing effective depth. For example, it is *thin* surface soil, not *shallow* surface soil.

Soil textural classes. Based on the texture of soil horizons, soils have been grouped into a large number of textural classes. We frequently speak in terms of a broad group of textural classes. Even though the terms *heavy* and *light* have been used for many years, they are confusing, since the terms arose from the power required in plowing, not the actual weight of the soil. In a few places "light" soils are referred to as those low in productivity. This includes soils of clay texture.

The U.S. Department of Agriculture divided soils in three classes on the basis of general textural terms. They were divided into five classes in relation to basic textural class names. This classification is as follows:

GENERAL TERMS		BASIC SOIL TEXTURAL CLASS NAMES
Sandy soils	Coarse-textured soils	{ Sands Loamy sands
Loamy soils	Moderately coarse-textured soils	{ Sandy loam Fine sandy loam
	Medium-textured soil	{ Very fine sandy loam Loam Silt loam Silt
	Moderately fine-textured soils	{ Clay loam Sandy clay loam Silty clay loam
Clayey soils	Fine-textured soils	{ Sandy clay Silty clay Clay

Permeability. In simplest terms, permeability of a soil may be defined as its capacity to transmit water or air. It can be expressed quantitatively, in terms of rate of flow of water through a unit cross-section of saturated soil in a unit of time under specified hydraulic conditions.

In mapping, it is necessary to determine the permeability of each horizon within the effective depth of soil and, in most instances, the permeability of the layer that limits effective depth. The permeability of all significant soil horizons and their relation to each other and to the entire profile must be considered. Often, the chief concern is with the one or two least permeable horizons.

Permeability of the surface layer of soil affects the rate of infiltration of water into the soil. Actually, the permeability of the first one or two inches of soil fixes the maximum rate of infiltration. The highest rate is attained under ideal cover and soil structure conditions. Because of the wide variations, the rate of infiltration is not considered in setting up soil mapping units. It usually can be inferred, however, from the mappable soil characteristics when the cover and surface conditions are known.

Sets of relative classes of soil permeability are as follows:

	POSSIBLE RATES IN INCHES PER HOUR*
Slow:	
1. Very slow	Less than 0.05
2. Slow	0.05 to 0.20
Moderate:	
3. Moderately slow	0.20 to 0.80
4. Moderate	0.80 to 2.50
5. Moderately rapid	2.50 to 5.00
Rapid:	
6. Rapid	5.00 to 10.00
7. Very rapid	Over 10.00

Available moisture capacity. Available moisture capacity of a soil is its capacity to store water that is usable for plant growth. Actually, it is the difference between moisture equivalent and wilting coefficient.** When two or more soil layers are within the effective depth, the total available moisture capacity of the soil is the sum of the capacity of different layers. This capacity is a measure of soil's ability to supply plants with moisture during droughty periods.

When moisture equivalent and wilting coefficient are expressed in the usual way, as percentages of oven-dry soil, available water may be calculated if the bulk density and thickness of the horizon are known:

$$\text{Inches of available water} = \frac{(Pm—Pw) \times V \times D}{100}$$

where

Pm equals moisture equivalent
Pw equals wilting point
V equals apparent specific gravity (volume weight)
D equals thickness of soil horizon in inches

* Very tentatively suggested rates through saturated undisturbed cores under a ½-inch head of water.

** The *moisture equivalent* is the percentage of water held after subjecting a sample of wet soil held in a vessel of specified dimensions to a centrifugal force of 1,000 times gravity, equivalent to a pF value of approximately 2.7. The *wilting coefficient* is the percentage of water present in a soil when plants permanently wilt. This occurs at about pF 4.2. These values and the energy relations of soil water are discussed in any standard textbook on soils.

The following terms and ranges are suggested for five degrees of available moisture capacity:

DEGREE OF AVAILABLE MOISTURE CAPACITY	AVAILABLE MOISTURE CAPACITY IN INCHES OF WATER PER 60 INCHES OF SOIL DEPTH
Very high	12 inches or more
High	9 to 12 inches
Moderately high	6 to 9 inches
Low	3 to 6 inches
Very low	Less than 3 inches

The "face" of the soil is a helpful indication for one making field estimates of the available moisture capacity. Texture and organic matter content are probably the most important distinguishing characteristics. Silt loams, for example, hold more available water per foot than sandy loams; loamy sands hold less than fine sandy loams. Structure and consistence may also prove useful indicators. Occasional laboratory checks may be desirable to ensure uniformity of results.

Soil reaction. Soil reaction receives special emphasis in soil classification. This is partly because of its direct importance. However, it is mainly because of other qualities, less easily determined. These may be inferred from soil reaction.

The intensity of soil acidity or alkalinity is expressed in pH—the logarithm of the reciprocal of the H-ion concentration. With this notation, pH 7 is neutral. Lower pH values indicate acidity; higher values show alkalinity. Soil horizons range in pH from a little below 3.5 to a little above 9.5.

The corresponding terms to use for ranges in pH are as follows:

	pH		pH
Extremely acid	Below 4.5	Neutral*	6.6-7.3
Very strongly acid	4.5-5.0	Mildly alkaline	7.4-7.8
Strongly acid	5.1-5.5	Moderately alkaline	7.9-8.4
Medium acid	5.6-6.0	Strongly alkaline	8.5-9.0
Slightly acid	6.1-6.5	Very strongly alkaline	9.1 and higher

Soil-drainage classes. On the basis of internal drainage soils are grouped into seven classes. Each of the seven drainage classes is defined on two bases. First, in broad general terms and, second, in terms of the morphological relationships existing among podzolic soils and among the dark-colored soils of the grasslands.

0. *Very poorly drained.* Water is removed from the soil so slowly that the water table remains at or on the surface the greater part of the time. Soils of this drainage class usually occupy level or depressed sites and are frequently ponded. Very poorly drained podzolic soils commonly have dark-gray or black surface layers. They are light gray, with or without mottlings, in the deeper parts of the profile. Very poorly drained grassland soils com-

---

* Strict neutrality is pH 7.0, but in field work those soils between pH 6.6 and 7.3 are called *neutral.* Where significant, the terms *very slightly acid* and *very mildly alkaline* may be used for soil of pH 6.6 to 6.9 and 7.1 to 7.3, respectively.

monly have muck surfaces with distinct evidences of gleying (formation of gray colors in a wet soil).

1. *Poorly drained.* Water is removed so slowly that the soil remains wet for a large part of the time. The water table is commonly at or near the surface during a considerable part of the year. Poorly drained podzolic soils may be light gray from the surface downward, with or without mottlings. Poorly drained grassland soils commonly have slightly thickened dark-colored surface layers.

2. *Imperfectly or somewhat poorly drained.* Water is removed from the soil slowly enough to keep it wet for significant periods. They commonly have a slowly permeable layer within the profile, a high water table, additions through seepage, or a combination of these conditions. Podzolic soils in this group are uniformly grayish, brownish, or yellowish in the upper A horizon. They commonly have mottlings below 6 to 16 inches in the lower A and in the B and C horizons. Grassland soils in this group have thick, dark A horizons. They are high in organic matter content and have faint evidences of gleying immediately beneath the A horizon.

3. *Moderately well drained.* Water is removed from the soil somewhat slowly. The profile is wet for a small but significant part of the time. Podzolic soils in this class have uniform colors in the A and upper B horizons. They have some mottling in the lower B and in the C horizons. The grassland profiles have thick, dark A horizons, and yellowish or grayish, faintly mottled B horizons.

4. *Well-drained.* Water is removed from the soil readily but not rapidly. These soils are commonly intermediate in texture. However, soils of other textural classes may also be well drained. Podzolic soils in this class are free of mottlings, and horizons may be brownish, yellowish, grayish, or reddish. They may be mottled deep in the C horizon or below depths of several feet. The grassland soils have thick, dark A horizons, reddish, brownish, or yellowish B horizons, and C horizons that may or may not be mottled.

5. *Somewhat excessively drained.* Water is removed from the soil rapidly. Some of the soils are lithosolic.* Many of them have little horizon differentiation and are sandy and very porous. Podzolic soils are free of mottling throughout the profile and are brown, yellow, gray, or red. Grassland soils have relatively thin A horizons, with brownish, yellowish, grayish, or reddish thin B horizons. They have no mottling within the solum (profile).

6. *Excessively drained.* Water is removed from the soil very rapidly. They are commonly lithosols or lithosolic. They may be steep, very porous, or both. Shallow soils on slopes may be excessively drained. Podzolic soils are commonly brownish, yellowish, grayish, or reddish in color. They are free of mottling throughout the profile. Grassland soil profiles commonly have thin A horizons.

Inherent fertility. Inherent fertility is an important factor in the selection of soil mapping units where the difference may have significant implications as to proper use, management, and protection. Such characteristics may be of a sufficiently permanent nature to be mappable within at least helpful limits.

Inherent fertility, or nutrient level, is difficult to evaluate on any national scale except with a very large number of fertility ranges. It is not

* Consisting of freshly and imperfectly-weathered mass of rock fragments.

necessary, however, to compare inherent fertility of soils in different regions. For these and other reasons, this factor generally should be used as a mapping criterion only when it is necessary to separate mapping units that are alike in other characteristics.

Usually four degrees of inherent fertility—high, moderate, low, and very low—will be sufficient.

Organic matter content. The organic matter content of a soil usually is a fair index to its durability and productive capacity. Often it can be determined satisfactorily on the basis of observable characteristics, especially color and sponginess. Organic matter needs frequently can be determined roughly by the tendency of soils to crust or "bake." Organic matter content, like inherent fertility, generally should be used only to differentiate mapping units that otherwise are similar.

Three broad classes will commonly suffice—high, medium, and low.

Underlying parent material. Character of underlying or parent material is often a significant indicator in setting up mapping units for soil conservation surveys. Soils developed on calcareous glacial drift may be more desirable for some crops than those developed on acid glacial material. Soils of limestone origin usually are more productive than those derived from noncalcareous sandstones, acid shales, or granitic rocks. Parent material may give some indication of outstanding soil deficiencies, such as lack of copper or manganese, or the presence of toxic elements such as selenium.

Organic soils. Properties of organic soils most likely to be significant in setting up mapping units are: 1. Thickness of organic materials; 2. Kind and thickness of underlying material, and especially its permeability; 3. Reaction (pH range); 4. Texture or structure of the surface layer—*peat* or *muck* (If muck, an estimate of the amount of mineral matter will be helpful.); 5. Character or composition of organic material, such as sphagnum peat, sawgrass peat.

Use of the term *shallow* should be avoided unless the characteristics of the profile add up to the equivalent of a shallow soil. For example, 18 inches of peat over sandy clay may have the crop-response value of a deep soil. On the other hand, 18 inches of peat over limestone may be properly described as shallow.

If organic soils are covered with an overwash of mineral soil, the necessary significant mapping units should be determined, described, and given descriptive titles.

Other characteristics. Soil characteristics other than those enumerated may be found significant in land use and management. They should be considered in setting up soil mapping units.

Names and descriptive titles for soil units. After the soil units are determined, suitable names or descriptive titles should be prepared. Where the information is available, the important soil types occurring in each mapping unit should be listed.

Table of soil characteristics. A table of significant soil characteristics will be helpful in (a) selecting soil maping units for a new survey, (b) appraising the significance of soil units shown on a survey, and (c) writing clear descriptions of soil mapping units or groups.

ASSOCIATED LAND FEATURES

Associated land features, such as slope, erosion, wetness, salinity overflow hazard, and susceptibility to streambank cutting, are significant in farm conservation plans. There may be still other features that can be classified and mapped.

Soil slope gradient classes. In defining soil classification units soil slope is given special attention. Within the permissible slope ranges of many soil types, units are defined in terms of slope gradient indicating differences significant to use and management.

Soil slope is normally measured by the hand level. It is expressed in terms of percentage, or the difference in elevation in feet for each 100 feet horizontal. Thus, a soil slope of 45° is one of 100 per cent since the difference in elevation of two points 100 feet apart horizontally is 100 feet.

Soil slope classes are established with alternative minimum and maximum limits in terms of gradient. Soils are divided into six slope classes:

1. A *Class*. This includes level or nearly level soil areas on which runoff is slow or very slow.

LIMITS	NAMES
Lower—0 per cent	Single slopes—level; or level and nearly level.
Upper—1 to 3 per cent	Complex slopes—level; or level and nearly level.

2. B *Class*. This class consists of gently undulating, undulating, or gently sloping soil areas on which runoff is slow or medium for most soils.

LIMITS	NAMES
Lower—1 to 3 per cent	Single slopes—gently sloping; or very gently sloping and gently sloping
Upper—5 to 8 per cent	Complex slopes—undulating; or gently undulating and undulating

3. C *Class*. In this class are gently rolling, rolling or moderately and strongly sloping soil areas on which runoff is medium to rapid for most soils.

LIMITS	NAMES
Lower—5 to 8 per cent	Single slopes—sloping; or sloping and strongly sloping
Upper—10 to 16 per cent	Complex slopes—rolling; or gently rolling and rolling

4. D *Class*. This class is made up of very strongly sloping or hilly soil areas on which runoff is rapid or very rapid on most soils.

LIMITS	NAMES
Lower—10 to 16 per cent	Single slope—moderately steep
Upper—20 to 30 per cent	Complex slope—hilly

5. E *Class*. In this class are steeply sloping or very hilly soil areas on which runoff is very rapid on most soils.

LIMITS	NAMES
Lower—20 to 30 per cent	Single slopes—steep
Upper—45 to 65 per cent	Complex slope—steep

6. *F Class.* This class is used where the soils are usually fertile and permeable and distinction in soil slope above the E class therefore may be needed.

LIMITS	NAMES
Lower—45 to 65 per cent	Very steep
Upper—None	

Internal soil drainage. That quality of soil that permits downward flow of free water through it is known as internal drainage. Six relative classes of internal drainage are recognized and defined.

0. *None.* No free water passes through the soil mass. In humid regions, the water table is at or near the surface most of the year.
1. *Very slow.* The rate of internal drainage is much too slow for optimum growth of the important crops in humid regions. It may even be too slow for optimum growth of crops on soils in semiarid regions.
2. *Slow.* In slow internal drainage, the rate of movement of water through the soil is not as fast as in medium drainage but faster than in very slow drainage.
3. *Medium.* Internal drainage is not so free as in rapid drainage but is freer than in slow drainage. Saturation with water is limited to a few days.
4. *Rapid.* The horizons somewhat restrict the movement of water through the soil as compared with very rapid drainage. Saturation with water is restricted to a few hours.
5. *Very rapid.* The rate of movement of water through the profile is very rapid. This is usually because of high porosity. The soil is never water-saturated.

Erosion. Erosion is the movement of soil and geologic material by natural agencies—primarily wind, water, and gravitational creep. Geologic erosion is normal—not a result of human activity. Erosion mapping in soil conservation surveys for farm planning is concerned with accelerated, or man-induced, erosion (or *soil erosion*).

Erosion consists of two distinct processes—detachment and transportation. Raindrops that fall on unprotected soil or in shallow water supply energy for the process of detachment. Flowing water is the transporting agent that completes the process of water erosion. Also, both wind and flowing water may detach and transport soil particles. If detachment occurs without transportation, there is no erosion.

The purposes of soil erosion mapping are to (a) give a quantitative estimate of the changes that have occurred, (b) give an indication of the rate of past and possible future damage, and (c) show what is left in the way of productive topsoil.

Erosion classes are given in the *Soil Conservation Survey Handbook,* USDA Miscellaneous Publication No. 352. In surveys for farm-planning purposes, however, erosion classes frequently can be generalized somewhat from those given in the *Survey Handbook.* Whenever this is done, an erosion legend is to be set up and each class defined. They should be denoted by standard erosion symbols from the *Handbook.* Erosion mapping units should be numerous enough to show differences that are significant for the land-capability classification.

Saline and alkali classes. Soils with harmful amounts of soluble salts and those with a high degree of alkalinity are shown separately on detailed soil maps from nonsaline or nonalkali soils. Each subdivision of a soil is defined according to salinity or alkalinity. Predictions for its use and recommendations for its treatment are given. The definition of mapping units varies. It varies with the character and condition of salt accumulations, the physical character of the soil, the possible utilization of the soil, and the objectives of the survey. Soils are grouped in terms of the agronomic significance of salt and alkali, as follows:

Class 0. Soils free of excess salt or alkali. Practically no crops are inhibited by or show evidence of injury from excess of salts or alkali.
Class 1. Soils slightly affected by salt or alkali. The growth of sensitive crops is inhibited but that of salt-tolerant crops may not be.
Class 2. Soils moderately affected by salt or alkali. Crop growth is inhibited and no crop does well.
Class 3. Soils strongly affected by salt or alkali. Only a few kinds of plants survive.

Salinity classes. Standards for converting measurements for conductivity of the soil saturation extract into salinity classes have been established. The interpretation is in terms of milliohms per centimeter.

TABLE 18.   Approximate limits of salinity classes (3)

Class	Percentage of salt	Conductivity of extract in milliohms per centimeter
Class 0: Free	0 -0.15	0-4
Class 1: Slightly affected	0.15- .35	4-8
Class 2: Moderately affected	0.35- .65	8-15
Class 3: Strongly affected	above .65	above 15

Soil color. Color is the most obvious and easily determined soil characteristic. It has little direct influence on the functioning of soil. However, we may infer a great deal about a soil from its color—provided the color is considered along with the other features. The significance of soil color is almost entirely an indirect measure of other, more important characteristics or qualities not so easily and accurately observed. Color is one of the most useful and important characteristics for soil identification. This is especially true when color is combined with soil structure.

Organic matter is not an exact measure of soil color. This is because organic matter is neither all of the same color nor is it the only coloring matter in soils.

Color patterns. Nearly every soil profile consists of several horizons differing in color. The complete color profile should be presented for every soil profile examined in the field. A single horizon may be uniform in color or it may be streaked, spotted, variegated, or mottled in many ways. Accumulations of lime or organic matter may produce a spotted appearance. Streaks or tongues of color sometimes result from seepage of colloids, organic matter, or iron compounds from overlying horizons. Certain combinations of mottled colors, mainly grays and browns, indicate poor drainage. The word *mottled* means marked with spots of color. Since mottled colors occur unassociated with poor drainage, a mottled or variegated pattern of colors occurs in many soil horizons. They especially occur in parent materials that are not completely weathered.

Mottling in soils may be described by noting the color of the matrix and color, or colors, of the principal mottles, and the pattern of mottling. The color of the mottles may de defined using the Munsell notation, as with other soil masses. However, it is even better to use the standard linguistic equivalents. This is because the precise measurements of the color of the mottles is rarely significant. In fact, descriptions of soil horizons containing several Munsell notations are difficult to read rapidly.

Other factors. Bottomlands subject to streambank cutting need to be indicated and identified. Occasionally the topographic position will have significance enough to warrant expression. Character of the substratum can be covered in the characterization of soil mapping units. A separate symbol may be desirable in some legends.

MAPPING PRESENT LAND USE

Information on present land use (or land cover in the case of land not used for crops) is needed for farm conservation planning and other purposes. Each legend should provide for these main classes of land use or as many of them as are present: Cropland (L); idle land (X); pasture or grazing land, or grassland (P); woodland (F); and possibly brushland. Others may be set up if needed, but each should be clearly defined.

ESTIMATED YIELDS

After the soil survey is completed yield estimates are made for each of the major crops grown for two levels of management practices. They are made for common management practices and for best management practices. Yield estimates are made on these two bases for each major crop grown and for each soil type phase.

RELATIVE SUITABILITY OF SOILS FOR FARMING

When soil units are differentiated on the basis of both internal and external characteristics significant to land use, each unit possesses individuality significant to land use and to management requirements. When these data are assembled for individual units, the units may be grouped for specific purposes. This grouping is done on the basis of three factors—productivity, workability, and conservability. This grouping indicates the relative suitability of soil units for crops, grazing, and forestry.

REFERENCES

1. Basiden, A. M., Coleman, C. S., Dantzler, W. D., Henretty, L. B., Hurley, F. W., Moore, J. R., Perry, E. A., Perry, H. H., Vessel, A. J., Watkins, T. R. 1952. *Soil survey of Culpeper County, Virginia.* USDA Ser. 1941, No. 3.
2. *Guide for the Federal Part of the National Cooperative Soil Survey.* 1954. USDA, SCS.
3. Hockensmith, R. D. and Steele, J. G. 1943. *Classifying land for conservation farming.* USDA Farmers' Bull. 1853.
4. Soil Survey Staff. 1951. *Soil Survey Manual.* USDA Handbook 18.

8

Soil Testing

The need of soil testing has increased with the increased use of fertilizer. Rapid chemical soil tests for determining lime and fertilizer needs are widely used.

The purpose of soil testing is to determine the available supply of the major plant nutrients in soil. Since there are no reliable natural indications of available supplies, laboratory tests have been developed. The accuracy of a particular soil test can be determined only by comparing its value with results obtained with field fertilizer experiments.

Soils vary widely in chemical nature. Consequently, a soil test that gives good results in one area may give poor results in another. It is thus necessary to try each test in the soil area for which it is to be used. Even then, there may be individual cases in which a test fails to show what is expected. However, if the test is standardized on the basis of field experiments, its limitations recognized, and is not used as the sole guide, it can be a reliable aid in measuring the fertility status of a soil.

Soils vary greatly in fertility levels—amount of plant nutrients they contain. Much of this difference is due to past management practices as related to cropping, liming, and fertilization. However, these past practices have varied so greatly from farm to farm that a fertilization and liming program that does well on one field may not be satisfactory on another.

140

DETERMINING SOIL FERTILITY

Several approaches have been used in determining the fertility levels in soils. This has been done to make sure the proper rates and kinds of lime and fertilizer are applied. The most important of these approaches are discussed below.

Knowledge of the liming, fertilizing, and cropping history. Lime and fertilizer requirements, due to lack of accurate information, can be only approximately predicted. It is often difficult to obtain accurate cropping histories from farmers, and the losses of plant nutrients due to crop removal, soil fixation, and erosion are difficult to measure.

Observation of deficiency symptoms of growing plants. Plants show symptoms of nutrient deficiency, if the lack is severe enough. These deficiency symptoms give good leads as to the fertilizer requirements. These symptoms are often complicated, however, both by disease and by insect damage. Consequently, absolute identification of deficiencies may be difficult. In most instances, by the time the deficiency occurs it is too late to obtain full benefit from fertilizer additions to that particular crop. In addition, plants may be mildly deficient and not show characteristic symptoms, yet yields might be increased by proper fertilization.

Tests of fresh plant tissue. The plant is the end product of all the factors in the environment. Therefore, much information can be obtained from tests made directly on the growing plants. Of course, as in the case of deficiency symptoms, if the plant is found lacking in a given nutrient it usually is too late to obtain the greatest benefit from fertilization.

Soil tests. This method permits the soil to help answer the question as to plant-food deficiencies—and in time to permit correction before the crops are planted. However, soil tests are most effective when used in conjunction with tissue tests, observation of deficiency symptoms, and study of management history. The coordinated and careful use of these four tools should make for more effective and more efficient use of lime and fertilizer.

It must be remembered that poor crop yields are not always due to plant-food deficiencies. Merely applying the right amount of lime and fertilizer will not ensure good crop yields. Careful attention must also be given other management practices if maximum benefits are to be realized from the lime and fertilizer applied. These include good crop varieties, proper cultural practices, correct seeding date, and control of weeds and insects.

SOIL FERTILITY NOT SAME AS PRODUCTIVITY

Although we know a great deal about soil, we cannot tell much about its fertility simply by looking at it. However, we can determine its productivity fairly accurately from visual observations.

For example, if soil is well drained, most crops will grow well. But if water stands on the land much of the time, the land is saturated and too wet for best crop growth. If stony, it is difficult to work. If the topsoil is thick, the plant roots have a larger storehouse from which to get their food and moisture. A soil may be well drained and stone-free with thick topsoil, but still poor in fertility—because it is low in plant food.

The chemical or fertility status of a soil is not visible, however. It is best learned by chemical analysis. Intensive research on methods for determining the fertility status of a soil have produced the commonly known quick tests.

A lime and fertilizer recommendation based on a reliable soil test is therefore important in profitable crop production.

SOIL AND PLANT TISSUE TESTS

Soil and plant tissue tests are valuable aids in the diagnosis of plant nutrient deficiencies in the soil and plant and as a basis for making fertilizer recommendations. However, they cannot be applied arbitrarily if good results are to be expected. Due regard must be given the differences in plant requirement and the ability of various soil types to satisfy these requirements. The plant and the soil in which it grows form a closely-knit living unit.

The complexities of the soil and the plant are comparable in many ways to those of the human body. A doctor observes the patient's symptoms before diagnosing the illness. So should the farm manager examine the soil and the sick plant growing on it before diagnosing the case and prescribing treatment. The farm manager should proceed as the doctor. He should obtain information on the history of the soil and plant.

The doctor obtains all the information possible by questioning and observing the patient. He checks such items as the pulse, temperature, blood pressure, and blood count. This information is helpful in diagnosing a case. These tests give the doctor added information to complete the history of the illness.

In a similar way, the farm manager can use plant and soil tests. Success with these tests depends on knowing a few fundamentals and applying a few important rules. The medical doctor's interpretation of the answers to these questions and tests is based on an understanding of the "workings" of the human body. Likewise, the farm manager's success as a "trouble shooter" or diagnostician depends on his understanding of the "workings" of the soil and the plant.

We need not become fearful of the job of diagnosing plant nutrition problems. On the contrary, we should make an effort to understand a few basic concepts. As the family doctor can take care of the usual run of sicknesses by use of his tests, so can the user of these soil and plant tests take care of the usual run of soil and crop problems. In unusual cases a specialist must be called.

SOME BASIC CONCEPTS

The plant. The plant is a biological factory. It converts simple plant nutrients into complex materials such as straw, grain, and forage. The plant nutrients are nitrogen, phosphorus, potassium, calcium, carbon, oxygen, and other essential elements. The plant obtains these nutrients from the soil and air. Sunlight is the source of power that runs this great biological plant. Nutrient needs of different plants and different parts of plants vary. The larger the yield, the greater is the demand for nutrients.

The elemental needs of a 100-bushel corn crop are given in Table 19. Here are listed the 14 nutrient elements required by the crop. Nitrogen (N), phosphorus (P), and potassium (K), are the primary fertilizer elements. They are the nutrients most likely to be found deficient in cases of malnutrition of plants. Consequently they are the nutrients with which we are primarily concerned in the soil and plant tests. Table 20 gives the nitrogen (N), phosphate (P_2O_5), and potash (K_2O) needs of various farm crops. These figures are averages. The composition of a crop is subject to variations dependent upon the soil and climatic conditions under which the plant is grown. These averages, however, are useful in considering the plant food problems on the farm.

TABLE 19. The elements essential for plant growth and their weight per acre in the stems, leaves, grain, and roots of a 100-bushel corn crop (21)

Element	Symbol	Primary source	Pounds per acre	Approximately equivalent to the amount of the element in
Carbon	C	Carbon dioxide of air	5,360	4 tons of coal
Hydrogen	H	Water	740	810 gallons water[a]
Oxygen	O	Air and water	5,480	740 gallons water
Nitrogen	N	Nitrate and ammonia in soil	160	800 lbs. 20% ammonium sulfate
Phosphorus	P		25	300 lbs. 20% super phosphate
Potassium	K		130	260 lbs. 60% muriate potash
Sulfur	S		20	20 lbs. yellow sulfur
Magnesium	Mg		25	250 lbs. Epsom salts
Calcium	Ca		35	90 lbs. of limestone
Iron	Fe		6	6 lbs. of nails
Manganese	Mn		2	6 lbs. potassium permanganate
Zinc	Zn		0.20	Shell of 1 flashlight battery
Copper	Cu		0.03	9 inches of No. 9 copper wire
Boron	B		0.06	½ pound borax
Total element weight			11,883.11	
Total dry weight of roots, grain, stalks, leaves			12,000	
Difference[b]			116.89	

[a] Water is 11 per cent hydrogen and 89 per cent oxygen on a weight basis.
[b] Consists of ten or more other elements which are at present not regarded as essential for plant growth.

The plant reflects the level of nutrition in many ways. The type of growth and yield are variable indications of levels of soil productivity. Plants, like animals, develop characteristic symptoms of disorder when they are poorly nourished. Many of these deficiency symptoms have been identified and described for both the major and minor elements for various crops. In some cases the deficiency symptoms are specific for different elements and are easily identified. In other cases, these symptoms are mixed and overlapping, and may be confused with insect injury and the effects of diseases. When the professional diagnostician cannot positively identify the symptoms, he finds plant tissue tests useful in eliminating several nutrient factors as possible causes of the symptoms.

Plant roots penetrate the soil and absorb nutrients into the sap. These nutrients are transported in the cell sap to the portion of the plant where

TABLE 20. Average nutrient content of field crops (21)

Crop	Yield per acre	Part of crop	N	P₂O₅	K₂O
			Lbs. per acre		

Crop	Yield per acre	Part of crop	N	P_2O_5	K_2O
Corn	80 bus.	Grain	60	25	18
	4,000 lbs.	Fodder	35	8	52
	1,200 lbs.	Stubble & Roots	9	2	10
		Total	104	35	80
Soybean	30 bus.	Grain	115	26	30
	3,000 lbs.	Straw	36	9	15
	900 lbs.	Stubble & Roots	10	3	4
		Total	161	38	49
Wheat	35 bus.	Grain	32	20	11
	3,000 lbs.	Straw	18	7	31
	1,100 lbs.	Stubble & Roots	6	2	5
		Total	56	29	47
Oats	50 bus.	Grain	37	14	10
	2,500 lbs.	Straw	16	4	35
	900 lbs.	Stubble & Roots	4	1	7
		Total	57	19	52
Alfalfa	6,000 lbs.	Hay	180	20	120
(2 yrs. old)	4,000 lbs.	Stubble & Roots	100	15	40
		Total	280	35	160
Sweet Clover	3,000 lbs.	Tops	100	10	45
(biennial)	2,000 lbs.	Roots	60	8	20
1st yr. growth		Total	160	18	65
Red Clover	4,000 lbs.	Hay	100	14	60
	1,500 lbs.	Stubble & Roots	40	4	14
		Total	140	18	74
Lespedeza	4,000 lbs.	Hay	80	10	40
	1,200 lbs.	Stubble & Roots	15	1	10
		Total	95	11	50
Ladino Clover	4,000 lbs.	Hay	110	15	55
	1,500 lbs.	Stubble & Roots	35	6	18
		Total	145	21	73
Timothy	3,000 lbs.	Hay	30	9	55
(2 yrs. old)	1,500 lbs.	Stubble & Roots	9	4	20
		Total	39	13	75
Brome Grass	3,000 lbs.	Hay	37	10	52
(2 yrs. old)	1,500 lbs.	Stubble & Roots	10	4	20
		Total	47	14	72

they are converted from raw materials to intermediate and finished products. Concentration of nutrients in the cell sap is usually an accurate indicator of how adequately the plant is being fed. If an element is low in supply in the soil, the cells of the conducting tissue will be low in that element. Since this element limits growth, the other elements may "pile up" in the cell sap because they cannot be used. Efficient functioning of plants depends on an adequate supply of nutrients in proper proportions. This concept is the key to plant tissue tests.

Factors other than the proper supply of nutrients can slow down the rate of plant growth. They may cause an increase in the concentration of the nutrients in the cell sap. Examples of such factors are unfavorable weather, insect and disease injury, poor cultural practices, and root injury caused by deep cultivation.

Plant tissue tests are used to determine the amount of nutrients in the cell sap. This reveals the nutritional status of the plant at the time of testing. The average farm crop grows over a period of 80 to 120 days or longer. The nutritional status of the plant during the growing period changes constantly.

The soil. The first requirement of a productive soil is an adequate supply of plant nutrients throughout the plant's life. Such a soil meets all the plant's demands for food. It is obvious the full capacities of crops are never realized if "starvation" occurs any time during their growth, even though plants are capable of outstanding recovery from short periods of nutrient starvation.

A soil with an abundant supply of the mineral foods is not necessarily productive. The second requirement of a productive soil is that it provide a satisfactory environment for root growth. Major environmental factors are water supply, temperature, aeration, and soil structure. A man can die in a room abundantly supplied with food and water if the air lacks oxygen, or in an unheated room during freezing weather. So can a plant die in a soil adequately supplied with water and plant food, but lacking in oxygen in the soil air, or in a soil that is too cold.

A favorable environment is essential throughout the root zone of the plant. Conditions that restrict root development restrict normal development of the plant.

Soil productivity is ensured by maintaining an ample supply of plant food and a favorable environment for root growth. Unproductive soils are made productive by corrective measures—measures that bring about favorable environment and an adequate supply of nutrients. Soil exhaustion results from the use of practices that permit erosion or that deplete the supply of available nutrients, or from cultural practices that create poor environmental conditions by destroying the soil structure.

Good root environment results from the maintenance of ample supplies of active organic matter. Organic matter may be supplied by using good cropping systems and cultural practices that improve soil structure. The plant food supply is maintained by using fertilizer and manure. Enough fertilizer and manure should be used to replace the nutrients removed in the harvested crops or lost through leaching and erosion. The surface of the ground must be protected from the bad effects of erosion at all times.

HOW SOIL TESTS CAN HELP

Soil tests can assist farmers in several ways. They indicate the amount and kind of fertilizer and lime that should be applied to a certain crop when grown on a certain soil. Often they can be used to determine which of two or more available fields are best suited to the growth of a specific crop. Combined with plant tissue tests, soil tests are excellent diagnostic tools for trouble shooting when a crop fails to grow satisfactorily.

The value of soil tests was illustrated with alfalfa in New Jersey by Purvis. In a mixed seeding with brome grass, on a Norton clay loam soil, alfalfa produced very poor growth during the first season. Soil tests indicated an available potassium level of only 60 pounds to the acre. Replicated plots were treated with muriate of potash at the rate of 200 pounds of K_2O to the acre during the early spring of the second year. The increase in yield due to the treatment was over 400 per cent.

Soil tests also afford an excellent control for determining erosion losses during hard rains. In such instances nutrients lost from the soil can be replaced before the crop begins to suffer from such deficiencies. Potato growers in New Jersey have profited greatly from such use of soil tests in recent years.

Forsee found it possible to make accurate fertilizer recommendations for celery grown on organic soils on the basis of careful tests made on representative soil samples collected from the proposed site of the crop. The same method of approach holds for other crops. Tissue tests proved an invaluable tool for diagnosing differences on a growing crop. This was especially true in those cases where representative soil samples were difficult to obtain. Forsee found that to obtain maximum celery yields the potassium level as determined by the soil test should be about 250 pounds per acre, and water-soluble phosphorus, approximately 30 pounds. The pH should be adjusted to a value of approximately 5.5. Where the phosphorus and potassium levels in the soil are optimum for maximum yields, the fresh stem tissue may analyze approximately 0.3 and 11 per cent phosphorus and potassium, respectively.

Lynd, Turk, and Cook made tissue tests and foliar analyses on corn grown in a Brookston soil following 7 years of continuous fertilizer and rotation experiments to determine the nutritional status of the corn plant as affected by the experimental treatments. A partial chemical analysis was also made on the soil. Analysis of soil samples taken at the beginning and after 7 years of continuous experimental treatment did not show differences sufficiently great to account for the differences in corn yields. Tissue tests indicated that nitrogen was the limiting factor in plant growth and that a definite change took place in the nitrogen status of plants with the initiation of the flowering period. Foliar analysis for total nitrogen in leaf samples taken during the flowering period indicated positive correlation with corn yields.

Lynd and his associates suggested that plant tissue testing be utilized for determining the period of sampling for foliar analysis, for indicating possible limiting factors in plant growth, and for substituting in the interpretation of results from foliar analysis.

By integrating fertilizer recommendations with soil tests, Coleman materially reduced the risk in production and the resulting net returns by fertilizing the soil so that plant food was eliminated as the limiting factor in plant growth. He found soil tests made possible more intelligent deep applications of the plant food needed to bring up the level of fertility to an adequate reserve supply of the different nutrients in proper balance for maximum production of quality crops. When this was done, and this level was maintained through the use of starter or maintenance applications of fertilizer, Coleman found the calculated risk was reduced.

Coleman found the considerations which should receive major attention in reducing this calculated risk when interpreting fertilizer recommendations with soil tests are:

1. The exchange capacity of the soil.
2. The species of plant and the root surface in contact with the soil.
3. The amounts of the various plant foods that will be released from the soil during the growing season—as indicated by soil tests.
4. The nature and condition of the soil treatments applied, the soil to which they are applied, and when and how they are applied.

Since the exchange capacity of soils varies widely, consideration is given this factor in determining the release of plant food and the level to which the mineral supply should be built up. Sandy and highly leached soils have low exchange capacities. Heavy clay soils well supplied with organic matter have high exchange capacities. Soils high in montmorillonite, or swelling clays, have ample storage for plant nutrients.

The high exchange capacity of montmorillonite clay makes it possible to build back plant food reserves that have been exhausted by excessive cropping. The exchangeable nutrients—potassium, calcium, magnesium, and the adsorbed phosphorus ion—are relatively immobile. They move through this kind of soil slowly. When applying these nutrients, they should be placed well into the soil so as to be in the root zone. Since they do not leach readily out of such soils, they can safely be applied in sufficient quantities to restore deficiences and meet the major plant-food needs for several years. This is especially true when proper starter or maintenance applications are used.

Because of the relative immobility of these mineral nutrients, their availability is largely dependent upon the extent to which the plant root surface is in contact with the soil. Dittmer showed that the soybean has only 2.5 square inches of root surface in contact with a cubic inch of soil; the oat plant, 13.9 square inches; and the rye plant, 30 square inches.

This variation in root surface in contact with the soil explains why a higher level of fertility is needed for satisfactory production of soybeans and similar crops than for rye, which has a more extensive root contact with the soil. Since such plants as clovers and alfalfa have the ability to synthesize a high protein content in their tissues, they naturally have higher requirements for mineral nutrients than the more carbonaceous non-legumes. Because of this, the higher protein crops grow satisfactorily only on soils with a high mineral content. A crop such as rye, which has an extensive feeder root system and is lower in protein, does not require as high a level of mineral nutrients to produce forage of high carbohydrate and cellulose content.

A poor soil's ability to release a sufficient amount of plant food for a fair crop in a favorable growing season has erroneously been taken to mean that weather is responsible for good or poor crops. Soils with a high reserve of plant food are able to release sufficient nutrients for a fair crop even in unfavorable growing seasons. This explains why, in unfavorable growing seasons, crops on poor soils fail—chiefly because of low fertility.

Unlike mineral nutrients, nitrates are mobile and are carried down into the soil by percolating water. Because of this, nitrates cannot be stored as such in the soil and do not lend themselves so well to measures by soil tests. The amount of this nutrient present in the soil varies with bacterial activity. Bacterial activity in turn is affected by soil tilth, drainage, aeration, amount and kind of organic matter, soil texture, and other factors. Nitrogen, however, is held in the soil in a rather stable form as organic matter or humus. A much better estimate of the nitrogen that will be released during the growing season can, therefore, be made by testing the soil for its per cent of stable organic matter.

As this organic matter decomposes, it produces the mobile nitrates. The percolating water carries these nitrates through the soil to the root zone.

SOIL-TESTING PROCEDURES

There is great variation in the procedures employed by different laboratories in testing soils. However, all systems of analysis have one thing in common —each attempts to extract from a soil a definite amount of the nutrient elements available to plants. Each soil-testing procedure is established with carefully conducted field experiments. Once the critical nutrient levels of plant response are determined for a given procedure, reliable results are obtained even though they may differ markedly from equally reliable results obtained by another procedure.

Solutions of various acids and salts are commonly used as extractants and have given satisfactory results. Some laboratories employ electrodialysis to remove available nutrients from the soil. This method is believed to extract all available nutrients from both light and heavy soils.

Morgan developed a soil-testing method which was built around the use of a 10 per cent solution of sodium acetate in 3 per cent acetic acid. The acetic acid solution was buffered at pH 4.8 for the soil extraction. This solution Morgan designated as the "universal" soil extracting solution, and this scheme of testing was designated as the "Universal Soil Testing System." Morgan's system was revised and brought up to date by Lunt and others.

Major emphasis is being placed on soil tests at present. However, considerable attention has also been given to rapid tests for soluble nutrients in plants and some study given to rapid determination of total nutrients in plants. Soluble nutrients in soil have been used as an index of nutrients available for plant growth. Soluble nutrients within the plant have been used as an index of nutrients recently taken into the plant or reflecting recent metabolism. Total nutrients in the plant have been considered to picture the complete nutritional history of the plant.

More recently, attempts have been made to increase accuracy by improving the technique or better interpreting the results. Certain changes in reagents, procedure, and reading of tests by photometric means have permitted a closer calibration of results. Correlation with actual crop performance has aided in intelligent application of rapid test results and enhanced the utility of the test.

Wolf and Ichisaka presented a rapid, reliable system of analysis for soluble nutrients in soils and plants and for total nutrients in plants. Advantages of this system are use of common reagents and procedures and adaptation to readings by photoelectric colorimeter with similar standard curves for any nutrient in the three categories. Spinach was used as the test plant.

Satisfactory correlations between soil tests for phosphorus and potassium and the response of field crops to these elements as fertilizer were reported by Bray. These correlations were achieved by improved soil-testing techniques and a modified method of interpretation based on the work of Mitscherlich. Arnold and Schmidt showed a phosphorus soil test was correlated with the response of tomatoes to phosphate fertilizer. Their results were based on data from 25 field experiments carried out in Illinois.

Arnold and Schmidt found tissue tests were correlated with the soil test at a particular date. The relationship changed on different dates. Samples taken in July were most consistent in their relationship to the soil test.

Peech and English found a number of rapid microchemical soil tests in use were subject to serious analytical errors. Some of the inherent technical difficulties, and interferences by diverse ions, were found to cause errors that invalidated the results in many instances. They investigated the interferences in these tests and overcame them by development or adaptation of more specific reagents and by use of comparative complex forms.

The accuracy as well as the working range of the tests, particularly those utilizing color lake formation, were considerably increased by introduction of protective colloids. As a result, Peech and English developed accurate and related microchemical soil tests suitable for practical soil testing.

Spurway described a system of comparative soil testing which he thought gave a more complete soil diagnosis by means of simple chemical tests than had been commonly practiced. He was able to compare fertile and unfertile soil to ascertain their differences from the standpoint of their content of easily soluble components.

Hester found that by using a satisfactory procedure for extracting plant samples for analysis he obtained excellent substantiating data for nutrient deficiency symptoms in tomatoes.

SUMMARIZING SOIL-TEST DATA

The rapidly expanding soil-testing program has resulted in the accumulation of large quantities of chemical data on soils. The analytical results from a single soil sample provide specific information for only one field. However, many of the individuals engaged in soil testing believe that periodic summaries of soil-test results will provide useful information of a more general nature.

McCollum, Nelson, Miles, Parker, Welch, and others discuss the interpretation and application of information obtained through such summaries. These investigators are of the opinion that summaries of soil-test results on a state, county, or type-of-farming basis show general fertility levels. They believe such information would aid agricultural advisory agencies and fertilizer and lime industries in orienting their respective programs.

Summaries of soil-test results have been published by several states. Generally it has been urged that they be used cautiously, for little information is available concerning the accuracy with which these summaries indicate the fertility status of a given area. It is not known, for example, whether the samples are being sent in from the better farms or from a cross-section of all farms. Sampling methods are not known, and they may be biased.

Parker and others defined sample bias as the failure of voluntary farmer samples to represent average fertility conditions in an area. If the existence of sample bias could be established and its magnitude evaluated, these summaries could be more easily interpreted. Theoretically, a sufficiently large systematic sample from a given area should provide a valid estimate of the fertility status of that area. A comparison of such a sampling with the one obtained from farmers should indicate the extent of the bias involved.

McCollum and Nelson conducted a study in Duplin County, North Carolina, to obtain an estimate of sample bias. Chemical analysis of soils from 1184 systematically sampled fields were compared with results from 538 voluntary samples sent in to the Soil Testing Division. Cropping history for fields included in both samples was obtained by personal contact and by correspondence, respectively. Results were compared on the basis of the previous crop as well as on the basis of the general mean of the two samples.

The pH and content of organic matter and potassium were significantly higher in the farmer samples but the differences were small in magnitude. The calcium and magnesium were distinctly higher in samples taken by farmers. On the other hand, the phosphorus was significantly lower in the farmer sample but again the difference was small.

The tendency for higher levels of pH, potassium, calcium, and magnesium may serve to substantiate the idea that the better farmers are sending in the majority of the samples. However, the difference in results for pH, organic matter, phosphorus, and potassium is not considered sufficiently great to invalidate a summary of results from farmer samples.

Seasonal effects on values obtained for pH, phosphorus, and potassium present a problem. However, assuming the same type of seasonal distribution from year to year and the same type of farmers sending in samples, relative differences among areas, among crops, or in trends can be established.

Parker and his co-workers summarized soil-test data from North Carolina and Tennessee. The data were summarized on a county basis by computing the nutrient index—a weighted average of the percentage distribution of the soils in the various nutrient levels. The counties were averaged in order of increasing indices for phosphorus, potassium, pH, calcium, and magnesium. The counties were then divided into four equal groups and the average index for each group calculated. The phosphorus indices were related to soil associations in Tennessee but showed little correlation with fertilizer usage as given on a county basis in U.S. Census reports. In North Carolina, however, there was a very good correlation between phosphorus indices and fertilizer usage. This was explained in part by the initially greater uniformity of available phosphorus and much higher average per-acre application of fertilizer in North Carolina. The potassium indices were related to some extent with soil associations and regions in both Tennessee and North Carolina. The acidity indices were correlated with lime usage by counties as obtained from PMA records.

TAKING GOOD SAMPLES IMPORTANT

Undoubtedly one of the most important issues associated with soil testing is the matter of obtaining a soil sample that adequately and accurately represents the area to be tested. The instructions for soil sampling that follow are based on the type of procedure involving a composite sample from a given area. This is the sampling method in use by almost all states in this country.

For the purpose of sampling, the farm should be divided into areas or fields. These should not be larger than 5 to 10 acres in an area. If an area or a field is uniform in appearance, production, and past treatment, it may include as much as 20 acres. However, areas that are different in appearance, slope, drainage, soil type, or past treatment should be sampled separately even though smaller than 5 to 10 acres.

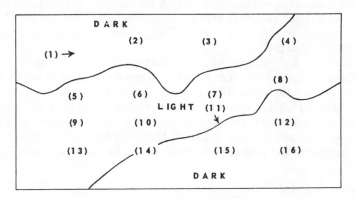

FIGURE 37. Field showing where the soil should be sampled.

Figure 37 shows the method of properly locating the areas to be sampled. Take a separate composite sample for each soil area or field. In taking samples a soil tube, soil auger, or narrow-bladed trowel are preferable, but with proper precaution a satisfactory sample can be taken with a spade and knife.

Avoid taking the sample from the fertilizer band when sampling fields in row crops. Avoid unusual spots such as old fence-rows or roadbeds, or where lime or manure has been piled or spilled. Avoid small areas that are much different from the rest of the field; if desirable these areas can be sampled separately.

The soil is easier to sample when its moisture condition is suitable for plowing. Even though the soil is too wet to plow, it can often be sampled, however, unless it is too muddy for handling. The best time to sample is after plowing, in advance of expected lime and fertilizer application.

Any clods or lumps should be broken up before they dry out. Fairly wet samples can be spread out to dry at room temperature on a clean sheet of waxed paper. Do not dry samples on a stove or radiator.

Take a uniform core (or thin slice) of soil from the surface of the plow depth (usually about 5 to 6 inches) in from 15 to 20 spots over the field. (In permanent pastures or lawns, sample only to a depth of two inches.)

If a spade and knife are used, dig a spadeful of soil to plow depth and throw it aside. Then dig a one-half inch slice of soil and keep it on the spade. Use the knife to cut from this slice on the spade a one-half inch core from top to bottom. Place the core in a clean bucket or container. Repeat this at each of the 15 to 20 spots.

If using a sampling tube or soil auger, it may be possible for the amount of soil from each spot to be such that a pint carton will hold the soil from 15 to 20 spots. If this is not practical, such as with the spade, collect it in a clean bucket. Mix well the soil from all spots, then halve or quarter as necessary to fill a pint carton.

Label each sample with a number and your name. Be sure to keep for yourself a record of the area from which the samples were taken. One way is to make a rough sketch or map of the sample areas. Fill out the information sheets as fully as possible. This will help greatly to make your report and recommendations useful.

Alkali areas are quite numerous in some localities. Alkali salts move up and down in the soil with the moisture. Therefore, alkali areas should be sampled in one-foot layers. The sampling should be done to a depth of three feet or to water table if encountered at a shallower depth. A soil auger can be used and composite samples obtained for each one-foot depth. This should be done in a manner similar to that used for surface soils. In addition a sample of the surface crust itself should be taken and submitted for analysis.

SAMPLING A FIELD

Several factors need to be taken into account in preparing to sample a field for soil analysis. Consideration is given here to each of these factors. This discussion explains and supplements the instructions for taking soil samples as presented above.

Some feel that the difficulty in getting farmers to follow the procedures presents a greater problem than the shortcomings of the existing procedures. Undoubtedly there exists a need for more emphasis on care in sampling and a need for more method demonstration by experienced persons. It is recognized that the human factor cannot be eliminated by a standard method of soil sampling. Yet the great variety of instructions available certainly contribute to the difficulty in educating agricultural workers and farmers in proper soil sampling. Some uniformity in procedures is desirable.

Among the factors that have to be considered in preparing to sample a field for soil analysis are:

1. The decision as to the area to select for soil sampling, i.e., what size area to sample, whether to subdivide the field into smaller fields.
2. The number of borings, the distribution of the borings, and the relation of the size of the area to be sampled.
3. The sampling tools to be used.
4. Depth of sampling.
5. The size of the final composite sample (one pint usually) and whether this should result from subdivision of a larger sample.
6. The moisture status of the area—is it too wet or too dry?

SELECTION OF AREA TO BE SAMPLED

In most instructions the area to be sampled is designated as a "field." This implies an area confined to one crop or bounded by a fence, stream, ditch, road, or some other line. Frequently the instructions suggest that a separate composite sample be taken for every 5 to 10 acres—thus restricting the size of the field. Actually there is no good basis for such a restriction. Soil type and past management should be the chief factors in deciding the size of the area. It is conceivable that a 20-acre field relatively uniform in soil type and in past management could be sampled better as a unit than a 5-acre field that varies in topography, degree of erosion, soil type, treatment, and other factors.

From a practical standpoint it may be argued that there is little to be gained by dividing a 5-acre field for sampling. This is particularly true if the field is to be fertilized or limed as a unit. There is, however, the advantage that some information is obtained on the variation within the field.

Some farmers may prefer to concentrate their sampling sites in the poorer parts of the field. Then the entire field can be treated. This brings the poorer areas up to maximum production, even though the better areas may receive a slight excess. In still other instances both good and bad areas within a field may be sampled separately. This enables the farmer to find out by comparison the cause of these differences within the field. Thus the purpose for which the samples are taken will influence the selection of the area to be sampled.

Admittedly the usual instructions dealing with field size are conservative, and on two counts. They both restrict the size of the area represented by one composite sample and specify the omission or separate sampling of smaller areas that differ in topography, position, or past management practices.

SAMPLING TOOLS

A great variety of equipment is used for sampling soils. To a certain extent this will continue to be true. Some tools lend themselves better to sandy soils, others to clay soils, and still others to wet or dry soils. Some are useless where many rocks are in the soil. Even so, it would be helpful if some uniformity in sampling tools were effected.

MOISTURE STATUS

One other factor that deserves mention is the moisture status of the field when sampling soils. Little information is available on this. Most instructions do not recommend sampling fields that are very wet, since it is difficult to sample and properly mix wet soils. In addition, wet samples sent in to the laboratory may easily be contaminated en route. When they dry out in the container they may be difficult to handle. In spite of this, to avoid conflict with other farm work, it is sometimes necessary to sample fields too wet to plow. Such samples should not be dried artificially. If possible they should be allowed to air dry so they can be broken up by hand and halved, if necessary.

INCLUDE INFORMATION ABOUT THE SOIL

Any information supplied with the sample is helpful to the person making the test. The soil type name, if known, helps characterize the soil. It tells something about its physical and chemical properties useful in the interpretation of the tests. The past cropping history and soil treatment for the past 3 to 5 years provide useful information. Has the soil ever been limed, have fertilizer and manure been used? Do you know the kinds and amounts? Do you have manure available now for use on your soil? Also, what crops are you going to grow?

Other factors on which information is useful include drainage, whether the land is hilly, rolling, or level, and whether there is material underlying the soil, such as sand, gravel, or bedrock, and the approximate size of the area represented by the sample.

TIME OF SAMPLING

The soil is constantly changing. It is teeming with millions of microorganisms. Their activities vary from day to day and from season to season, with changes in temperature, moisture, and food supply. A rapidly growing crop drains soil of nutrients required for plant growth. Thus, at the end of the growing season, soils show high tests for nitrates and potassium only when the amounts of these materials added in the fertilizer, or becoming available in the soil, are in excess of crop demands. Seasonal fluctuations in soil acidity influence the availability of plant nutrients to some extent. Acidity is normally at a minimum in early spring and at a maximum in midsummer.

For general soil diagnosis, tests on samples taken in early spring are most reliable. Tests made in the autumn after the crop is harvested best indicate whether or not the fertilizer has been in excess of crop needs. Fall testing has the added advantage of allowing ample time in which to obtain materials and lay plans for spring work. The choice of time when the sample is to be taken depends, therefore, upon the purpose for which the test is made.

INTERPRETING SOIL TESTS IMPORTANT

Simple chemical soil tests can often provide us in a few minutes with more useful information about the fertility of a soil than can be learned by several days of detailed laboratory analysis. The results of the tests can be used to good advantage by a person competent to give sound soil-management recommendations. They are often misleading to those who have little understanding of the relationships between soil chemistry and plant nutrition.

Soil testing is only another tool used in diagnosing soil ills. It is not infallible. In the hands of inexperienced persons, great harm may be done soils from an incorrect interpretation of the tests. For example, they might recommend liming when actually sufficient calcium was available in the soil. Overliming may produce minor element deficiencies.

Practical interpretation of soil tests should be considered with reference to known limiting factors on crop growth for the soil being tested. These limiting factors include poor soil aeration, poor soil structure, deficient drainage, low organic matter content, unfavorable seasonal conditions, plant pests, and plant diseases.

HOME SOIL TESTING

Portable kits for testing soils are available for home use. Generally they will do a good job of testing. But most people do not have the experience or training to interpret the tests for best results. Results with home kits may often be disappointing, especially for the garden variety of soil-testing amateurs.

Soil testing need not be done in the home, however. Nearly all the State Experiment Stations, a few County Extension Directors, and some commercial firms, like fertilizer and seed companies, farm-management specialists, commercial laboratories and canneries, make tests. A small charge is made for this service by some. Usually the people in charge of the testing are competent soil scientists well qualified to make reliable interpretations of the test results and suggestions for treatment of the soil.

Soil samples may be taken to a soil-testing laboratory or mailed. In either case, be sure to give as much information about the soil as possible. This will ensure the best possible interpretation of the test results so that reliable treatments can be suggested by the soil specialist.

DETERMINATIONS

If the soil tests are to be really used as a basis for recommendations, it is important to make the reading as quantitative as possible. This is desirable from the standpoint of accuracy of the lime and fertilizer recommendations.

Lime requirements, pH, calcium, phosphorus, potassium, and organic matter usually are determined on all samples. In some laboratories, pH and lime requirements are obtained on the glass electrode, calcium and phosphorus on the photelometer, potassium on the flame photometer, and organic matter by titration.

Since soil testing on a service basis means handling relatively large numbers of samples, improved laboratory equipment and devices are extremely valuable. Many laboratories are using such special equipment with greatly increased efficiency but yet are not sacrificing accuracy.

REFERENCES

1. Arnold, C. Y., and Schmidt, W. A. 1950. *Soil tests as a measure of phosphorus available to tomatoes on heavy soils.* Soil Sci., 71: 105-115.
2. Baver, L. D., and Bruner, F. H. 1939. *Rapid soil tests for estimating the fertility needs of Missouri soils.* Mo. Agr. Expt. Sta. Bull. 404.
3. Bishop, W. D. 1951. *Soil Testing summary.* Tenn. Agr. Ext. Spec. Circ. 375.
4. Bray, R. H. 1944. *Soil-plant relations: I. The quantitative relation of exchangeable potassium to crop yields and to crop response to potash additions.* Soil Sci., 58: 305-324.
5. ————. 1944. *Soil-plant relations: II. Balanced fertilizer use through soil tests for potassium and phosphorus.* Soil Sci., 60: 463-473.
6. ————, and Kurtz, L. T. 1945. *Determination of total, organic, and available forms of phosphorus in soils.* Soil Sci., 59: 39-45.
7. Coleman, O. T. 1951. *Fertilizer recommendations based on soil tests.* Better Crops with Plant Food, 35: 16-22, 45-47.
8. Dittmer, H. J. 1940. *Quantitative study of the subterranean member of the soybean.* Soil Cons., 6: 33-34.
9. Forsee, W. T., Jr. 1950. *The place of soil and tissue testing in evaluating fertility levels under Everglades conditions.* Soil Sci. Soc. Amer. Proc., 15: 297-299.
10. Gohlston, L. E., and Miles, I. E. 1950. *Are your soils lacking?* Soil testing summary, Miss. Agr. Ext. Serv., July, 1949 to June 30, 1950.
11. Harrington, J. F. 1944. *Some factors influencing reliability of plant tissue testing.* Proc. Amer. Soc. Hort. Sci., 45: 313-317.
12. Hester, J. B. 1941. *Soil and plant tests as aids in soil fertility programs.* Commercial Fertilizer Yearbook, 31-39.
13. Lunt, H. A., Swanson, C. L. W., and Jacobson, H. G. M. 1950. *The Morgan soil testing system.* Conn. Agr. Expt. Sta. Bull. 541.
14. Lynd, J. Q., Turk, L. M., and Cook, R. L. 1949. *Application of soil tests, tissue tests, and foliar analysis to field experiments.* Soil Sci. Soc. Amer. Proc., 14: 236-241.
15. Maine Extension Service. 1949. *Summary of Maine soil test results, 1948 crop.* (Mimeo.)
16. McCollum, R. E., and Nelson, W. L. 1954. *How accurate is a summary of soil test information?* Soil Sci. Soc. Amer. Proc., 18: 287-292.
17. Miles, I. E., and McLaurin, J. T. 1948. *Soil testing and soil conservation.* Better Crops with Plant Food, 32: 19-22 and 40-41.
18. Morgan, M. F. 1941. *Chemical soil diagnosis by the Universal Soil Testing System.* Conn. Agr. Expt. Sta. Bull. 450.
19. Nelson, W. L., and Miles, I. E. 1949. *Summary of North Carolina soil test results, July, 1947—June 30, 1948.* Soil Testing Div., N. C. Dept. of Agri., Raleigh, N. C.
20. Nelson, W. L., and Welch, C. D. 1951. *Soil-testing reduces guesswork.* Better Crops with Plant Food, 35: 6-10.
21. Ohlrogge, A. J. 1952. *The Purdue soil and plant tissue tests.* Ind. Agr. Expt. Sta. Bull. 584.
22. Parker, F. W., Nelson, W. L., Winters, E., and Miles, I. E. 1951. *The broad interpretation and application of soil test information.* Agron. Jour., 43: 105-112.
23. Peech, M., and English, L. 1944. *Rapid microchemical soil tests.* Soil Sci., 57: 167-195.
24. Purvis, E. R. 1953. *Soil testing in New Jersey.* Better Crops with Plant Food, 37: 19-21, 43-45.
25. Scarseth, G. D. 1942. *Plant tissue testing in diagnosis of nutritional studies of growing plants.* Soil Sci., 55: 113-120.

26. Shear, G. M. 1943. *Plant tissue tests versus soil tests for determining the availability of nutrients for tobacco.* Va. Agr. Expt. Sta. Tech. Bull. 84.
27. Spurway, C. H. 1933. *Soil testing a practical system of soil diagnosis.* Mich. Agr. Expt. Sta. Tech. Bull. 132.
28. Uhlrich, A. 1942. *Potassium content of grape leaf petioles and blades contrasted with soil analysis.* Proc. Amer. Soc. Hort. Sci., 41: 204-212.
29. ―――. 1942. *Nitrate content of grape leaf petioles as an indicator of nitrogen status of the plant.* Proc. Amer. Soc. Hort. Sci., 41: 213-218.
30. Welch, C. D. 1952. *Use of soil test summary in agronomic programs.* Better Crops with Plant Food, 36: 15-20, 39-41.
31. ―――, and Nelson, W. L. 1951. *Fertility status of North Carolina soils.* Soil Testing Div., N. C. Dept. of Agri., Raleigh, N. C.
32. Wolf, B. 1943. *Rapid determination of soluble nitrates in soil and plant extracts.* Indus. and Engin. Chem., Analyt. Ed., 15: 248-251.
33. ―――. 1947. *The rapid photometric determination of inorganic nitrogen in soil and plant extracts.* Indus. and Engin. Chem., Analyt. Ed., 19: 334-335.
34. ―――, and Ichisaka, Vernon. 1947. *Rapid chemical soil and plant tests.* Soil Sci., 64: 227-244.

9

Plant Cover
and Conservation

Nature performs her marvelous feat of building soil
by means of "holding" and "developing" actions.
These actions are performed simultaneously, mostly
by the many thousands of types and species of plants
that inhabit the earth. In the process, Nature develops
progressively the suitable plants for each combination
of soil and climatic conditions.

Soil building is a complex, ages-long process that
begins with rock. It involves weathering of rock, frag-
mentation of rock by roots of growing plants, grinding
and transportation of rock fragments by streams,
wind, and glacial action, growth and decay of plants
and animals, and the activity of small mammals and
microscopic organisms. As plant life becomes established on the surface, organic residues begin to accumulate. These are broken down by rainfall and
heat and the activity of mammals, fungi, and insects.
The soluble portions are leached downward by rain
and water from snow, and the soil becomes darker in
color. At first, the layer of soil is very thin. It becomes
thicker as plant residues and other substances accumulate on the surface, and the humus they produce penetrates deeper into the soil. Humus accumulates faster
at the surface than at lower depths, hence the upper
part of the soil is the most productive.

Throughout the soil-building process, the surface is protected by a blanket of plant growth which holds the soil in place. Lichens are specially equipped for this job. They are flat rootless plants that cling to existence in areas where no higher forms will grow. Halted only by the barrier of perpetual snow, they thrive anywhere on earth and can even subsist on naked rock. Among the more primitive living things, lichens are usually the first members of the plant community to appear in barren ground, and as they propagate they provide an initial foothold for higher forms of vegetation.

The lichens' ability to live on rock derives from their dual nature. Lichens are composite entities, made up of two separate and dissimilar organisms, an alga and a fungus, united in an inextricable partnership. The fungus produces acids that disintegrate the rock, supplying necessary materials to the alga; in return the alga supplies organic materials to the fungus, which would die without them. This organic matter also becomes mixed with the disintegrating rock to form soil.

Lichens form a protective covering over the rock surface to catch and hold dust. This cover also holds the soil in place as it develops from the

FIGURE 38. Formation of residual soil. Generations of liverworts growing on solid rock have gradually brought about decomposition of the surface portions of the rock. The addition of organic matter in the form of decaying remains of liverworts has caused the formation of about one-half inch of soil. Peeling back the liverworts from the rock surface picks up the soil. (Ottawa, Illinois)
(Soil Conservation Service)

surface downward. As soon as the rocky surface has changed sufficiently to support higher forms of plant life, the lichens are gradually replaced by the next higher plant form in the ecological scale. Further improvement is followed by the invasion of still higher forms of plant life until the climax species is reached.

If this plant cover is removed, or is reduced so that there is not enough to protect the surface, the soil begins to erode and deteriorate. The succession of plant life that was active in building the soil may be thrown into reverse if erosion is permitted to progess far enough. Thus, lower forms of plant life would follow in succession.

The "holding" action of plant cover on the soil was not appreciated until after Nature's balance between soil-building and soil-destroying forces had been upset by its removal, which exposed the bare soil to the full force of wind and water. The erosive action that followed stopped the soil-building process and began a trend toward soil deterioration. Even now, too few people realize that the "holding" action is essential for soil and water conservation, and, in turn, for soil improvement.

The part played by wind in the soil erosion process, and methods for its control, are presented in Chapter 13.

FUNCTION OF PLANT COVER IN WATER-EROSION CONTROL

The major role of plant cover is to protect the soil from the force of falling raindrops. We know now that raindrop impact is the primary cause of erosion on cultivated land. The raindrops have the energy, in striking bare soil, to dislodge soil particles from the soil mass. They can move some soil downhill by their splashing during hard rains. Nearly all the sediment removed from fields by water erosion, however, is the result of the combined action of surface flow and raindrop splash. The raindrops dislodge soil particles and feed them into the surface flow. The splashing also gives to shallow surface flow the turbulence it needs for transportation of the dislodged soil particles. The force generated by surface flow is determined by its concentration and speed of movement downhill. Owing to the nature of the source of its energy, surface water does not flow evenly over the surface of a field, but rather causes the formation of rills and gullies.

Plant cover controls splash erosion by intercepting the raindrops and absorbing their kinetic energy. It also protects the infiltration capacity of the soil. On bare land, the beating action of raindrops during all but light rains breaks down clods and soil aggregates, and forms a tight layer at the surface. This sharply reduces the infiltration capacity of the soil and increases runoff. Plant cover prevents the formation of this tight surface layer.

Effectiveness of the cover is proportional to its amount and distribution. Weight, in terms of pounds per acre, and coverage, in terms of per cent of the ground surface that is covered, are practical measurements of effectiveness that are of about equal value. The closest indication of effectiveness is obtained, however, when weight is multiplied by coverage to give an index of "effective weight"—combination of total weight and soil coverage.

The growth forms of the different crops influence their effectiveness in protecting the soil from raindrop impact. Close-growing crops of medium

FIGURE 39. Where the ground surface is protected by low-growing plants or by a cover of mulch, it is shielded against the impact of falling raindrops and puddling is prevented. The raindrops are intercepted by the plants and yield up most of their kinetic energy before they reach the ground surface. (*Soil Conservation Service*)

height, such as oats, wheat, and vetch, have almost identical values for the same weight of cover. Tall-growing crops, such as sweet clover and cotton, provide less protection than close-growing crops for the same weight of cover in amounts above 1,000 pounds per acre. Tall, coarse crops provide less protection than close-growing crops because of their more open canopy and because their foliage intercepts raindrops some distance above the ground. When these drops fall to the ground, they still can attain erosive velocities.

For 90 per cent effectiveness, approximately 2,500 pounds (dry weight) per acre of close-growing crops or 4,000 pounds of tall, coarse crops are required. Below this point, effectiveness declines rapidly as the amount of cover is reduced and the difference between growth forms becomes less important. At 1,000 pounds per acre there is no significant difference in the two kinds of crops; both are 60 per cent effective.

It is generally recognized that, under most systems of management, land cropped to grass and trees does not present as serious an erosion problem as land devoted to cultivated crops. In fact, erosion is practically nonexistent on land protected by ample plant cover, regardless of the kind and nature of the cover. Likewise the loss of water as runoff is directly affected by the plant cover. As plant cover decreases or deteriorates, erosion and runoff losses become progressively higher.

TABLE 21. Soil loss and runoff over a 14–year period in Missouri, as influenced by plant cover (21)

Treatment	Soil	Runoff
	Tons per acre	Per cent
Continuous bluegrass	0.34	12.0
Rotation: corn, wheat, clover	2.78	13.8
Continuous wheat	10.09	23.3
Continuous corn	19.72	29.4
Fallow	41.65	30.7

EFFECT OF PLANT COVER UNDER CROPPING SYSTEMS

The effectiveness of any cropping system in reducing soil and water losses depends largely upon the proportion of close-growing vegetation used, and the length of time and season of the year when it occupies the land. Crops that provide protective cover during the months of erosion-producing rains are especially valuable for conserving soil and water.

A crop rotation of cotton, wheat, and sweet clover reduced annual soil loss by 74 per cent and annual runoff of water by 34 per cent, compared with continuous cotton, during a 21-year period at Guthrie, Okla. Both wheat and sweet clover greatly reduced erosion, but the amount of soil removed from the wheat plot was 6 times as great as from the sweet clover. During a 1.69-inch rain on July 21, 1950 (with 5-, 15-, and 30-minute intensities of 5.64, 3.84, and 2.30 inches per hour, respectively), the continuous cotton plot lost 41.65 per cent of the rain water as runoff and 1.835 tons of soil per acre. The wheat plot lost 47.51 per cent of the rainfall as runoff and 0.098 ton of soil per acre. The sweet clover plot lost no water or soil, and a

Bermuda grass sod plot lost only 0.47 per cent runoff and no soil.

In Nebraska, land that had been fall plowed and then planted to corn the following spring lost almost twice as much water and four times as much soil as land that had been sub-surface tilled at the same time and was protected with wheat residues. Combined wheat stubble and straw, left undisturbed on the soil surface, reduced the loss through runoff to 2.39 per cent of the rain that fell, and the soil loss to 1 per cent of that on bare land. Land that had been disked and planted to oats, after the corn had been harvested and the stalks removed, lost 10.852 tons of soil per acre from January 1 to June 30, 1942. Adjacent plots, protected by cornstalk residue and sub-surface tilled before the oats were planted, lost 0.613 ton of soil. Plots planted to corn, after the preceding sweet clover crop had been turned under, lost 12.364 tons of soil from one rain. An adjacent sweet clover plot, which was sub-surface tilled before being planted to corn, lost only 1.152 tons of soil.

In Wisconsin, green manure was 65 per cent less effective in controlling erosion when it was plowed under in the fall than when it was left on the surface and the land cultivated with sweeps. The soil loss was 57.8 tons per acre where the green manure was plowed under, compared with 20.22 tons where the vegetation was left on the surface. Adjacent land that was planted continuously to corn lost 111.7 tons of soil per acre annually during the 6-year period. The annual soil loss on land under small grain was 16.8 tons per acre, but only 0.68 ton on land under grass grown for hay.

Land in Georgia that was planted continuously to cotton lost an average of 24.95 tons of soil per acre annually during the period 1940-47. This rate of soil loss was reduced to 15.39 tons by using a 2-year crop rotation consisting of corn-crotalaria and cotton-vetch. A 3-year rotation of oats-lespedeza, lespedeza, and cotton reduced erosion still further to 3.38 tons per acre annually. Of the 10.15 tons of soil lost per acre during the 3 years of the crop rotation, 7.08 tons per acre were lost during the year the land was cropped to cotton. Only 0.25 ton per acre was lost during the year this land was in lespedeza.

From April to September, 1940, unmulched land in Georgia lost 12.57 tons of soil per acre, compared with 0.2 ton lost from mulched land. During this period, 32.75 per cent of the rain that fell was lost as runoff from the unmulched land, compared with 1.43 per cent lost from the mulched land. A plot which had been disk-harrowed, planted to Kobe lespedeza, and mulched with straw lost as runoff only 1.2 per cent of the rain that fell and 0.24 ton of soil per acre from April, 1940, until the end of that year. A companion plot, similarly handled except for being mulched, lost 24.2 per cent of the rain as runoff and 12.62 tons of soil per acre during the same period.

A plot in Mississippi, planted continuously to cotton, lost as runoff 58 per cent of a total rainfall of 130.7 inches during a 2-year period. The runoff amounted to as much as 96 per cent of the precipitation from individual rains. Soil loss on this plot exceeded 195 tons per acre for the 2-year period. The runoff from broomsedge in an old field was only slightly more than 1 per cent of the rainfall, and from an oak forest it was even less. Runoff from these 2 classes of cover during individual storms did not exceed 5.05 and 3.10 per cent of rainfall, respectively, and erosion was almost negligible. The cultivated land lost 4,300 times as much soil per acre as the forested plot.

It was found in Idaho that a wheatgrass type of vegetation minimized flash runoff and erosion even under conditions of torrential rainstorms and steep slopes. As long as the character of the cover was unchanged and its original density maintained, it could be grazed by livestock and wild game without greatly reducing its effectiveness in controlling erosion and runoff.

In Virginia, mature stands of close-growing crops prevented excessive rates of runoff from Dunmore silt loam on slopes up to 25 per cent, but high rates of runoff occurred on plots planted to corn. Serious soil losses occurred when corn was planted on slopes exceeding 10 per cent. Hay crops provided almost complete protection against both runoff and erosion.

Plots of Houston clay in Mississippi were covered with straw at the rate of 2 tons per acre immediately after cultivation. They lost only 0.1 ton of soil per acre from July 1 to December 31, 1942. An adjacent plot, which was cultivated but not covered with straw, lost 21 tons of soil per acre during the same period. The straw-covered plot lost 6 per cent of the 14.83 inches of rain that fell, whereas the unmulched plot lost 44 per cent.

In South Carolina, Cecil clay loam mulched with Kobe lespedeza and crimson clover hay at the rate of 4 tons per acre lost only 0.75 ton of soil during the period August, 1939, to January, 1942. This compares with 89.15 tons of soil lost per acre from adjacent land that was not mulched. An excellent demonstration of the effect of plant cover as an erosion-control measure occurred on August 21-22, 1946, when a 4.64-inch rain fell. A plot that had been disked so as to leave as much as possible of the residues from the preceding crop on the soil surface lost 275 pounds of soil per acre. But a similar plot which had been plowed and was without plant cover lost 1,767 pounds.

Erosion losses were as much as 149 times greater from unmulched plots than from plots protected by straw mulch in Illinois. During these tests 91 per cent of the ground surface of the plot mulched with straw was protected from the direct impact of raindrops. Corn stover was found more effective as a mulch than soybean residues. The corn stover left only 13 per cent of the ground surface unprotected from raindrop impact, in contrast to 27 per cent for the soybean residues.

In Missouri an average of 51 tons of soil per acre was lost annually from Shelby silt loam that was planted continuously to corn. But the rate of soil loss was reduced by 80 per cent to an average of 9 tons per acre annually when corn was grown in a 3-year rotation of corn, wheat, and red clover-timothy. During the same period, an adjacent plot of bluegrass sod lost practically no soil.

The addition of wheat, red clover, and timothy to the cropping system provided better plant cover during the time they occupied the land. Here, the land was protected by plant cover except for the portion of the year when corn was grown. Corn was followed by wheat in October. Timothy was either planted in the wheat in the fall or the next spring, and red clover was planted in the spring. After the wheat was harvested, the clover and timothy continued to furnish good cover throughout the remainder of that year, all through the third year of the rotation, and until April of the corn year when the ground was plowed. The effectiveness of plant cover in controlling erosion is illustrated in Figure 40.

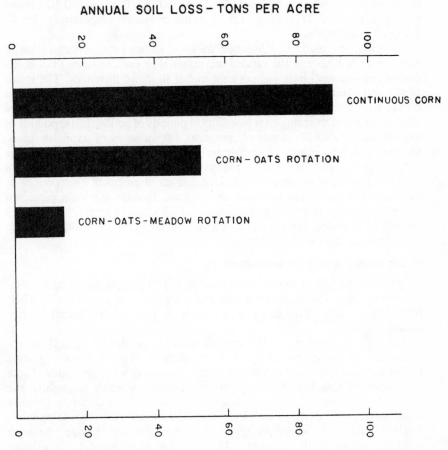

FIGURE 40. Effect of cropping practices on erosion of Shelby silt loam.

Pine and hardwod litter applied as mulch gave almost complete control of runoff and erosion over an 11-year period in North Carolina. Both forest cover and permanent sod were equally effective in controlling runoff and erosion. The use of wheat and lespedeza in a 4-year crop rotation with cotton and corn reduced soil loss to an annual average of 14.4 tons per acre for the rotation, compared with 31.2 tons from bare land.

Semiannual burnings of a forest plot over a period of 7 years increased runoff more than a hundredfold, or nearly twice the amount lost from either cotton or corn in a 4-year rotation. Burning increased runoff losses from 0.03 to 22.0 per cent of the rainfall. The amount of soil loss increased from practically none to nearly 8 tons per acre. The water drained faster from the cultivated watershed than from the protected, forested watershed.

The effectiveness of plant cover in controlling erosion and runoff is further emphasized by comparing soil and runoff losses from 1-, 2-, and 3-year old stands of hay in Wisconsin. These losses were 6.53, 0.39, and 0.10 tons of soil per acre and 3.24, 0.38, and 0.12 inches of runoff, respectively, for 1-, 2-, and 3-year stands.

Examinations made in Wisconsin in 1950 showed the concentration of nitrogen to be higher in the eroded soil material in each instance than in the parent soil—several hundred per cent higher in many instances. The losses of soil and plant nutrients were closely related to the amount of plant cover on the land during the critical erosion-hazard period. For example, Fayette silt loam planted to spring oats lost 47,000 pounds of solids, 1,100 pounds of organic matter, 63.7 pounds of nitrogen, 4.05 pounds of available phosphorus, and 7.6 pounds of exchangeable potassium per acre. During the same period, a plot of Almena soil planted to corn lost 18,000 pounds of soil, 760 pounds of organic matter, 41.3 pounds of nitrogen, 1.43 pounds of exchangeable potassium per acre. In contrast, Fayette silt loam protected by a hay crop lost only 120 pounds of soil, 15 pounds of organic matter, 1.3 pounds of nitrogen, 0.48 pounds of available phosphorus, and 2.9 pounds of exchangeable potassium per acre.

PLANT COVER AND SOIL AGGREGATION

Aggregates are the structural elements of soil. Their presence and maintenance are essential to good soil tilth and a high state of productivity. Their formation in soils depends upon adequate supplies of biologically active organic matter.

The humate fraction of the organic colloids produced by soil microorganisms, in the course of the decomposition of organic matter, appears to be the major factor contributing to the formation of soil aggregates. These organic colloids, or binding agents, are distributed uniformly throughout the soil and are adsorbed to colloidal clay particles. They effectively produce stable aggregates, perhaps by electrochemical union with organic colloids. Evidently they are bound through the carbon linkage "bridge" between reactive groups on the polymer. This reaction is believed to take place mainly by polar adsorption, resulting from the decomposition of fresh organic matter. Joined to the soil particles, the humate fraction or hydrophyllic colloids serve as bridges between the particles, keeping them from separating yet at the same time holding them apart so they will not pack down tight.

Since certain other groups of soil microorganisms break down these organic colloids as they are formed, it is necessary to keep a continuous supply of fresh organic matter in the soil if a high state of aggregation is to be maintained. This can only be accomplished by using sod or mulches, to which fresh materials are added frequently to produce continuous plant cover.

Over a 4-year period, surface application of organic material caused a greater increase in the size and number of large water-stable soil granules in

Hagerstown silt loam in Pennsylvania than did incorporation of the same materials in the soil. The increase in the soil organic matter content that resulted from the surface application of these materials was most pronounced in the 0 to 1-inch surface layer. Cornstalks and soybean residues used as mulch in Illinois increased the number of all sizes of aggregates in the soil. Straw mulch was particularly effective in promoting the formation of large aggregates.

The amounts of aggregates of various sizes were strikingly different under sod, mulch, and cultivation treatments in the soil of a peach orchard on Wooster silt loam in Ohio, which had been under treatment for 28 years, and an apple orchard on the same type of soil, which had been under treatment for 44 years. Three types of cultural treatments were used on each orchard. One series of plots was planted to cover crops, a second was left in bluegrass sod, and the third was mulched with straw. The cover crops were plowed down and renewed in accordance with usual practices. The straw mulch was renewed frequently enough to maintain a thick covering.

The mulched plots showed the greatest amount of aggregates among the

FIGURE 41. Plant cover aids the formation and maintenance of aggregates which are essential to good soil tilth. The photographs above are of two samples of Muskingum silt loam taken just across a fence from each other: *Right*, from an orchard that had been in bluegrass sod for a number of years; *Left*, from a field that had been in cultivation for more than 40 years.
(Soil Conservation Service)

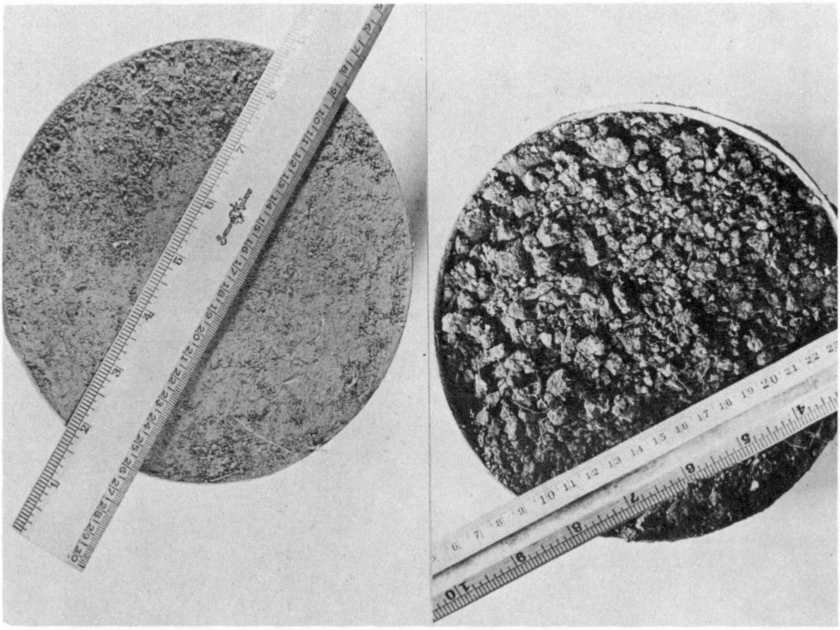

larger sizes. Sod resulted in almost as much aggregation but the cultivated soil contained only small aggregates. Even in the A horizon there were few soil aggregates over 1 mm. in diameter under the cultivation treatment. In contrast, approximately 28 per cent of the dry weight of the soil under mulch and 23 per cent under the sod in the apple orchard were composed of aggregates over 1 mm. in diameter. The same general trend occurred in the peach orchard. The state of aggregation was in fairly close relationship to the percentage of soil organic matter except for the high aggregate formation under wheat-straw mulch in another series of treatments which had been under way for 7 years.

PLANT COVER AND INFILTRATION

The sharp impact of raindrops, as they strike bare earth during heavy rains, shatters the clods and soil crumbs and breaks down the soil structure. The beating, churning action of these drops compacts the fine particles into a

FIGURE 42. Plant cover preserves the open porous structure of the surface of the ground, which favors rapid infiltration. Equal amounts of soil were placed in the cup on top of each jar. Mulch cover was placed on the soil in the cup to the left; the other was left bare. Rain was then played on the soil in the two cups for about 7 minutes. The greater amount of water in the jar with the mulch cover shows how the mulch cover increased water intake.
(Soil Conservation Service)

nearly impervious layer of surface mud, to cause "puddle erosion." The compacted surface layer becomes denser and more nearly impervious as it strains colloids and other particles from the turbid rain water that filters down from the surface. This layer is the most important factor affecting the intake of water by the soil. It decreases infiltration, increases runoff and soil loss, and paves the way for gully formation. Puddle erosion can be prevented by maintaining enough plant cover on the surface to shield the soil. This cover may be composed of growing plants or plant residues, or both. It is extremely important to have ample cover well distributed over the surface of the ground, so that the beating raindrops cannot break down soil structure and form a nearly impervious layer of soil at the surface.

Studies conducted in Missouri indicate that plant cover in the form of crops is another important factor in maintaining favorable moisture conditions in the subsoil. The beneficial effects of sods turned under for corn crops have usually been ascribed to an improved supply of nitrogen. Possibly, however, the important factor has been the accumulated moisture in the subsoil. Grass crops absorbed 87.4 per cent of the rainfall and a 3-year crop rotation with one year of sod absorbed 85.5 per cent, but the land continuously in corn absorbed only 69.6 per cent, according to trials extending over 14 years. This was the equivalent of an increase in rainfall of 7.2 inches for land in grass and 6.4 inches for land under the crop rotation, as compared with land continuously in corn. The difference in crop yield was more significant than these figures indicate, since two-thirds of the annual rainfall occurred during 6 months of the growing season—or the period when differences in rainfall mean differences in yields.

Much of the extra water absorbed by the soil protected by plants moves beyond the zone of consumption by the shallow grass roots and is stored there. Thus, the deeper soil layer (such as the 24- to 36-inch layer) under sod contains more water than the same layer under tilled soil. Moisture in two similar soils, not far from those in the erosion study cited above, are interesting from this standpoint—especially for the years 1934 and 1936, which were seasons of deficient rainfall.

TABLE 22. Moisture content at successive depths under sod and under cultivated soil (21)

Date	0–12 inch		12–24 inch		24–36 inch	
	Sod	Cultivated	Sod	Cultivated	Sod	Cultivated
	Per cent	Per cent	Per cent	Per cent	Per cent	Per cent
April, 1934	27.18	25.23	29.90	24.61	26.11	16.58
November, 1934	33.80	31.70	31.90	30.80	32.60	24.80
March, 1936	26.30	27.80	28.20	28.90	28.30	23.00
November, 1936	27.00	26.80	28.50	27.30	27.80	19.80
April, 1937	32.90	28.30	30.00	28.60	30.70	23.40

The 24- to 36-inch layer was much drier under the cultivated soil.

Since considerable time always elapsed after rain before it regained moisture, the total water content of this layer under cultivated soil never equaled that in the 24- to 36-inch soil depth under sod. The 0-12-inch layer under sod had a lower moisture content than that under cultivation during one month (March, 1936). Otherwise, the moisture supply in the 12- to 24-inch and 24- to 36-inch layers was always greater under sod. The most pronounced differences were at the 24- to 36-inch depth. These differences mean that, on the average, the 24- to 36-inch layer under sod is storing the equivalent of a 1.2-inch rain annually, which it may supply to the sod crop or to the deeper roots of the following crop in the drier summer season.

Surface mulching in Pennsylvania resulted in maintaining an optimum soil-moisture content even during the driest part of the growing season. Three and four years of mulching with manure, straw, sawdust, corn stover, oak leaves, or pine needles resulted in complete control of surface runoff and an infiltration capacity of 3 inches per hour or more. The chief value of mulch in controlling runoff and erosion was its protective effect.

An abrupt decrease in infiltration capacity followed incorporation into the soil of a heavy cover crop in orchards in Pennsylvania. Several months were required to restore a soil-plant relationship that favored a high infiltration capacity. Removal of the cover crop from the soil surface, either by incorporating it into the soil or by mowing it and removing the clippings, increased runoff. The actual ground coverage by plant material and the number of depressions for water detention were the two factors most important in controlling runoff. Wheat straw, soybean residue, and corn stover used as mulch on a permeable prairie soil in Illinois greatly increased the infiltration rate and reduced the amount of water lost as runoff.

Rothacher reports that 15 years of protection and reforestation have so improved the forest cover of 1,715-acre White Hollow watershed in eastern Tennessee that the summer peak flows have been reduced 73 to 92 per cent. At the same time, the duration of summer storm runoff has been prolonged up to 500 per cent. A more sustained flow has resulted without any material change in total water yield. The original forest cover has increased in volume from 4,444,000 to 7,104,000 board feet. Natural planted stands have so controlled erosion on open uplands that White Creek now maintains a flow of clear water suitable for rearing trout.

PLANT COVER AND FERTILIZER

Adding fertilizer to the soil aids in reducing erosion losses because it produces more plant cover. Fertilizer stimulates early growth, thus hastening the date when the cover becomes effective, and increases the amount and density of cover by increasing total plant growth. Besides helping to control erosion through the production of more vegetation, the use of fertilizer results in higher yields.

Two plots in Wisconsin were planted to a 3-year crop rotation of corn, oats, and hay. The oats in one plot were fertilized. The average annual per-acre soil loss over a 5-year period fas 47.21 tons under the unfertilized crop rotation and 13.13 tons where fertilizer was used.

The use of 200 pounds of 5-10-5 fertilizer per acre annually on land planted continuously to corn in New York reduced the loss of water by one-third and the loss of soil by two-fifths over a 9-year period, compared with unfertilized cornland. The unfertilized corn plot lost 9.5 per cent of the rainfall as runoff and 5,934 pounds of soil per acre annually. The fertilized plot lost 6.4 per cent of the rainfall as runoff and 3,552 pounds of soil per acre.

Unfertilized Shelby silt loam in Missouri, planted to a 3-year crop rotation of corn, wheat, and hay, lost an average of 8.81 tons of soil per acre annually during a 7-year period, compared with a loss of 3.69 tons for similar soil that was fertilized and planted to the same crop rotation. A comparison of soil loss while the land was in wheat and oats, both with and without fertilizer, illustrates the effectiveness of fertilizer in reducing losses by erosion. Soil loss from land in wheat was reduced by one-half, while the loss from oats was reduced more than one-half, as a result of the increased cover obtained by the use of 200 pounds of fertilizer per acre. The use of fertilizer increased the wheat yield 91 per cent and the oat yield 77 per cent on the average of a 7-year period.

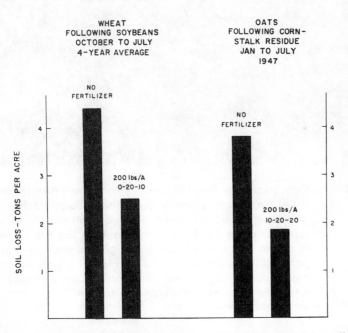

FIGURE 43. Effect of fertilizer on erosion of land planted to small grain.

PLANT COVER AND SOIL-DEPLETING AND SOIL-CONSERVING CROPS

Much has been said in recent years about soil-depleting and soil-conserving crops. Actually, the difference between the two kinds of crops is one of plant cover on the land. The soil-depleting crops do not provide enough cover

FIGURE 44. Corn plants in this Missouri field did not furnish enough cover for adequate protection of the soil against the impact of falling raindrops. Land planted continuously to cotton (another clean-tilled crop) in Oklahoma lost the equivalent of all the crop residues left on the ground and 1,860 pounds per acre annually of the soil's original supply of organic matter over a 10-year period. It also lost an average of 18.9 tons of soil per acre annually by erosion.
(Soil Conservation Service)

during the summer period of erosion-producing rains to maintain a high state of aggregation in the soil.

The plants of the soil-depleting crops take less of the minerals from the soil than do the soil-conserving plants. But the cultivation that is needed and the way that the soil-depleting plants grow encourage erosion, so that the total loss of nutrients from the soil is high. Soil-conserving plants, on the other hand, provide good plant cover once they are established. Although these plants use more of the nutrients from the soil, they prevent losses through erosion and also add enough organic matter to improve the soil's fertility.

The comparative amounts of plant nutrients removed by hay crops and the grain of the corn and oats crops in a 5-year crop rotation with 3 years of hay and in a 3-year crop rotation are shown in Tables 23 and 24.

TABLE 23. Average pounds per acre of plant nutrients removed annually by the grain of corn and oat crops and alfalfa-brome hay in a 5-year rotation of corn, oats, hay, during 1947-50

Crop	Calcium	Phosphorus	Nitrogen	Potassium
	Pounds	Pounds	Pounds	Pounds
Corn	0.35	9.46	52.55	10.86
Oats	2.01	7.36	42.82	8.92
Hay	42.90	13.52	109.31	103.43

TABLE 24. Average pounds per acre of plant nutrients removed by the grain of corn and oats and by hay in a 3-year rotation of corn, oats, and hay

Crop	Calcium	Phosphorus	Nitrogen	Potassium
	Pounds	Pounds	Pounds	Pounds
Corn	0.31	8.40	46.67	9.64
Oats	1.68	6.15	35.81	7.46
Hay	32.85	7.55	65.27	65.27

As previously stated, soil at Guthrie, Oklahoma, with a sod cover of Bermuda grass accumulated organic matter at the rate of 1,700 pounds per acre annually from 1931 to 1940. In contrast, plots that were planted continuously to cotton during the same period lost the organic matter returned as crop residues and also 1,860 pounds of the original organic matter reserve each year.

One of the most important benefits derived from maintaining enough cover is the preservation of this organic matter. It has been generally believed that oxidation was responsible for the major losses of soil organic matter. It is now known, however, that soil erosion enjoys this distinction. Investigations in Missouri showed the loss of soil organic matter by erosion to be 25 times as great as that by oxidation. Since organic matter is the source of the soil's nitrogen, the loss of the nitrogen in the organic matter removed by erosion is a controlling factor in crop yields. This was illustrated by results from the project at Clarinda, Iowa, where the addition of 180 pounds of nitrogen per acre in 1952 to plots that had grown corn continuously for the past 20 years eliminated the trouble that caused low yields. Since 1932, corn had been grown continuously on one series of plots and in a 3-year rotation of corn, oats, and meadow on another. The corn in each series received the same fertilizer treatment until 1952. The fertilizer treatment was the same again in 1952 except for the fact that the continuous corn plots received 180 pounds of nitrogen per acre. The yields in 1952 were 103.0 bushels per acre on the continuous corn plots and 98.4 on the rotation plots.*

These results suggest that if erosion losses are prevented, it will be feasible to grow corn or other soil-depleting crops successfully year after year by proper use of fertilizer and plant cover. The heavy stalk production accompanying high corn yields should provide enough cover if properly utilized. Elimination of fertility losses by erosion will plug the greatest drain on plant nutrients and make soil building a relatively simple process either with or without the use of crop rotations.

The average annual yields of corn in bushels per acre by 5-year periods and for 1952 for both series of plots are given in Table 25.

TABLE 25. The average annual yield of corn in bushels per acre by 5-year periods and for 1952 for corn grown continuously and in a 3-year crop rotation during the period 1932 to 1951, inclusive, and 1952

Croppings systems	Average annual yields in bushels per acre				
	1932–36*	1937–41	1942–46	1947–51	1952
Continuous corn . . .	23.9	32.5	23.9	17.8	103.0
Rotation	25.8	57.0	72.0	83.9	98.4

*Includes the drought years 1934 and 1936 when the crop was a failure.

Beginning the second 5-year period, the yield on the continuous corn plots declined from 32.5 bushels per acre to 17.8 for the fourth 5-year period. During this time the yield on the rotation plots increased from 57.0 bushels per acre for the second 5-year period to 83.9 for the fourth. The difference between the yields of these two series of plots also became greater with time. This difference was 1.9 bushels for the first 5-year period, 24.5 for the second, 38.1 for the third, and 66.1 for the fourth.

Except for nitrogen, the figures presented in Table 23 do not show corn to be soil-depleting in comparison with hay. Since the hay crop contained alfalfa, it is presumed that the nitrogen removed in the harvested hay was approximately equal to the amount taken from the air by the crop. Thus the original supply of nitrogen in the soil was not changed. However, the nitrogen removed by the corn crop was a net loss to the soil's supply.

* Personal communication with F. W. Schaller, dated Oct. 31, 1952.

Similar figures are given in Table 24 for the crops grown in a 3-year crop rotation.

REFERENCES

1. Albrecht, W. A. 1938. *Loss of soil organic matter and its restoration.* USDA yearbook, Soils and Men, 347-360.
2. Alderfer, R. B., and Merkle, F. G. 1943. *The comparative effect of surface application vs. incorporation of various mulching materials on structure, permeability, runoff and other soil properties.* Soil Sci. Soc. Amer. Proc., 8: 79-86.
3. Alderfer, R. B., and Shaulis, N. J. 1943. *Some effects of cover crops in peach orchards on runoff and erosion.* Amer. Soc. Hort. Sci., 42: 21-29.
4. Borst, H. L., and Woodburn, R. 1942. *The effect of mulching and methods of cultivation on runoff and erosion from Muskingum silt loam.* Agr. Engin., 23(1): 19-22.
5. Carreker, J. R., and Barnett, A. P. 1949. *Runoff and soil loss measurements by cropping periods.* Agr. Engin., 30: 173-176.
6. Coply, T. L., Forrest, L. A., Augustine, M. T., and Lutz, J. R. 1944. *Effects of land use and season on runoff and soil loss.* N. C. Agr. Expt. Sta. Bull. 347.
7. Craddock, G. W., and Pearse, C. K. 1938. *Surface runoff and erosion on granitic mountain soils in Idaho as influenced by range cover, soil disturbance, slope, and precipitation intensity.* USDA Cir. 482.
8. Daniel, H. A., Elwell, H. M., and Cox, M. B. 1951. *Progress report, 1951—soil and water conservation research at the Red Plains Conservation Experimental Station.* Okla. Agr. Expt. Sta. Cir. M-219.
9. Duley, F. L., and Russell, J. C. 1942. *Effect of stubble mulching on soil erosion and runoff.* Soil Sci. Soc. Amer. Proc., 7: 77-81.
10. Free, G. R. 1952. *Soil movement by raindrops.* Agr. Engin., 33: 491-494.
11. Havis, L. 1943. *Aggregation of an orchard and a vegetable soil under different cultural treatments.* Ohio Agr. Expt. Sta. Bull. 640.
12. Hays, O. E. 1951. *Summary of the nineteenth annual report of the Upper Mississippi Valley Soil Conservation Experiment Station.* USDA, SCS.
13. ————, McCall, A. G., and Bell, F. G. 1949. *Investigations in erosion control and the reclamation of eroded land at the Upper Mississippi Valley Conservation Experiment Station near La Crosse, Wis., 1933-43.* USDA Tech. Bull. 973.
14. Hendrickson, B. H., Carreker, J. R., and Adams, W. R. 1943. *Stubble mulch in the Southern Piedmont.* Soil Cons., 9: 139-141.
15. Hendrickson, B. H. and Crowley, R. B. 1941. *Preliminary results with mulches applied to eroded wasteland sown to lespedeza.* Jour Amer. Soc. Agron., 33: 690-694.
16. Kidder, E. H., Stauffer, R. S., and Van Doren, C. A. 1943. *Effect on infiltration of surface mulches of soybean residues, corn stover, and wheat straw.* Agr. Engin., 24: 155-159.
17. Lamb, J., Jr., Andrews, J. S., and Gustafson, A. F. 1944. *Experiments in the control of soil erosion in southern New York.* New York Agr. Expt. Sta. Bull. 811.
18. Lillard, J. H. 1941. *Effect of crops and slopes on rates of runoff and total soil loss.* Agr. Engin., 22: 396-398.
19. Meginnis, H. G. 1935. *Effect of cover on surface runoff and erosion in the loessial uplands of Mississippi.* USDA Cir. 347.
20. Mihara, Y. 1951. *Raindrops and soil erosion.* Natl. Inst. of Agr. Sci., Ser. A: 1-59.
21. Miller, M. F., and Krusekopf, H. H. 1932. *The influence of systems of cropping and methods of culture on surface runoff and soil erosion.* Mo. Agr. Expt. Sta. Res. Bull. 177.
22. Osborn, B. 1950. *Range cover tames the raindrop—Summary of range cover evaluations, 1949.* USDA, SCS, Ft. Worth, Tex.
23. Peele, T. C. 1943. *Influence of mulches on runoff, erosion, and crop yields.* S. C. Agr. Expt. Sta. 55th Ann. Rept., 30-32.

24. ———, Nutt, G. B., and Beale, O. W. 1946. *Utilization of plant residues as mulches in the production of corn and oats.* Soil Sci. Soc. Amer. Proc., 11: 356-360.

25. Rothacher, J. S. 1953. *White Hollow watershed management: 15 years of progress in character of forest, runoff, and streamflow.* Jour. Forestry, 51(10): 731-738.

26. Slater, C. S., and Carleton, E. A. 1938. *The effect of erosion on losses of soil organic matter.* Soil Sci. Soc. Amer. Proc., 3: 123-128.

27. Smith, D. D., Whitt, D. M., and Miller, M. F. 1948. *Cropping systems for soil conservation.* Mo. Agr. Expt. Sta. Bull. 518.

28. Stallings, J. H. 1949. *Keep crop residues on the surface of the ground.* USDA, SCS-TP-80.

29. ———. 1952. *Raindrops puddle surface soil.* Jour. Soil and Water Cons., 7: 70-74, 88.

30. ———. 1952. *Soil aggregate formation.* USDA, SCS-TP-110.

31. ———. 1953. *Continuous plant cover the key to soil and water conservation.* USDA, SCS-TP-121.

32. Van Doren, C. A., and Stauffer, R. S. 1943. *Effect of crop and surface mulches on runoff, soil loss and soil aggregation.* Soil Sci. Soc. Amer. Proc., 8: 97-101.

33. Whitt, D. M., and Swanson, C. L. W. 1942. *Effect of erosion on fertility changes in the Shelby loam profile.* Jour. Agr. Res., 65: 283-298.

34. Woodburn, R. 1943. *Reduced loss of soil, less runoff when mulch used.* Miss. Agr. Expt. Sta. Farm Res., 6(8): 7.

Interrelationship of
Land, Plants, and Animals

The interdependence of plants and soils was discussed in the preceding chapter. Now, animals are added to make this a triumvirate. Proper management of land or plants cannot be achieved without some attention to the equally important role of animals.

Land furnishes nourishment in the form of mineral elements for plants. It also provides a growth medium —a place for plant roots to take hold. Plants, however, are equally important to the land in that they contribute to soil formation. A good vegetative cover provides complete protection to the soil from the erosive forces of wind and water. Decaying plants produce organic matter to increase the soil's ability to absorb rainfall. The same organic matter increases the fertility of the land and further improves its ability to grow plants. Plant roots increase the aeration of the soil.

In a somewhat different way the land provides a place for animals to "take root" when they use the land for their burrows. Animals, in turn, exert an influence on the land. Witness the soil mixing and aeration accomplished by earthworms and burrowing animals and the increase in organic matter and consequent fertility caused by the decay of animal bodies— from the tiniest insects to the largest mammals.

177

The major contribution of the land to animals, however, is indirect. It is through the plants that grow on the land and furnish food and cover. Without plants, animals could not exist.

But, conversely, many plants such as hickory trees would disappear were it not for animals. The pollination by insects as with alfalfa and the seed distribution as with mulberry by many birds and mammals are examples of the virtually indispensable functions performed by animals. These functions are being fostered when a living fence is planted between cropland and pasture, thus providing a habitat for bumblebees, solitary bees, and other insects useful in pollinating red clover, sweet clover, alfalfa, and other legumes.

NATURE'S BALANCE

Plant and animal populations progress to a state of give-and-take adjustment, which is generally referred to as Nature's balance. It is a dynamic balance, however, which changes as the productive capacity of the soil is altered by the interaction of the plants and animals, including man, living on it.

This "balance of Nature" is not confined to wild plants and wild animals. A system of farming that supports a family at a suitable standard of living without depleting its basic resources is as much at balance as are the plants and animals of a virgin forest. Conversely, a system of farming that depletes these resources and is plagued with insects, weeds, and crop diseases is "out of balance" with Nature.

Adjustments to make proper use of the land can do much to make a farm biologically balanced. In adjacent grazed and ungrazed woods in northeastern Ohio, for example, insect-eating shrews are less than half as abundant in the grazed as in the protected woods. Shrews are small, short-tailed, mole-like animals that maintain numerous path-like runways in the loose, upper layer of forest soil. These runways, which are used by the shrews in their search for food, help to aerate and incorporate organic matter into the soil, and serve as reservoirs for water. Heavy grazing destroys these runways and packs the soil so that the shrews cannot re-establish them.

Strip-cropping brings an increase in ground-nesting birds. A study by the Soil Conservation Service in southwestern Ohio furnished the following information:

AVERAGE NUMBER OF PAIRS OF BREEDING BIRDS
PER 100 ACRES OF CROPLAND (*10*)

Crop	Open fields	Strip-cropped fields
Corn	3	4
Small grain	10	27
Meadow	48	93

Living fences provide homes for insect-eating birds such as brown thrashers, catbirds, and cardinals, and predaceous insects like lady beetles, assassin bugs, and damsel bugs. Field shelterbelts do the same thing.

Streambank planting not only aids in the control of bank erosion but shades and cools the water, thus improving conditions for fish. At the same

FIGURE 45. Streambank improvement in Chittenden County, Vermont. Willows, sod, and riprap used.
(*Soil Conservation Service*)

time, game birds, songbirds, and furbearing animals find cover there.

Biologic balance is also fostered in the management of farm ponds for fish production. This involves what is known as a "food chain." The chain begins with water and mineral elements necessary for the production of microscopic plants known as algae. Small crustaceans and insect larvae feed on the aglae. These small plants and animals are collectively known as plankton. Plankton is the chief source of food for bluegill sunfish, which are in turn fed upon by large-mouth black bass. Both the sunfish and the bass are used as food by man.

When large-mouth bass are absent from the pond, the bluegill sunfish, which have a tremendous reproduction capacity, become so numerous that there is not enough plankton to feed them properly. The result is a stunted population of bluegills. The pond is "out of balance" so far as man is concerned because he cannot harvest fish of sufficient size to use for food.

An odd area, be it a bare knob, blow-out, sinkhole, or small oddly-shaped area isolated by a gully or stream, can be made to contribute to the biologic balance on the farm by planting them to appropriate plants.

The farm that keeps all natural nooks intact, and produces wildlife food and cover that is widely distributed and abundant as is compatible with successful farming, will come nearest to attaining the biologic balance that is so necessary to wild creatures and enlist all the aid Nature can give for maintenance of the farm.

ECOLOGY

The principles of ecology, dealing as they do with the effect of the total environment (soil, climate, man, etc.) on plants and animals, and with the effect of plants and animals on the environment, are basic to sound land management.

Communities. Plants and animals do not live alone. They live in definite communities, or mixtures. Many factors determine what species of plants and animals will be found in any given community. Some of these factors are soil, climate, physiography, and biota. Biota means simply all the plants and animals of a community and their effect on each other and on the site.

The importance of soils in determining the composition of any community can be illustrated by the growth of alfalfa on calcareous soils and its failure to grow on acid soils. Similarly, pheasants, for some reason yet unknown, thrive in areas of glaciated soils but do poorly in loessal or residual soil areas.

Climate exerts its influence on plant and animal communities largely through length of growing season and annual rainfall. But even the amount of daylight has its effect. Red clover, for example, thrives best where the day is long, while tobacco does best with a short day. Climatic factors also govern the migration, hibernation, and breeding of animals.

North slopes support different plants and animals from south slopes. In prairie areas trees are restricted to river valleys and to moist slopes bordering drainages.

Effects of the biota may be less noticeable than effects of the factors discussed above, but are equally important. In most cases, communities are mixtures of plants and animals. When a farmer attempts to grow a 40-acre "community" of a single species, such as corn, he is beset with competition from weeds. But when he attempts to grow an integrated community like alfalfa and bromegrass, he gets better results because these plants complement, rather than compete with, each other.

Certain plants and animals are dominant in any natural community. Others take a lesser place, or are subdominant. The result is a "layering" of plants, as in the forest, with small herbaceous plants dominated by shrubs, which are in turn dominated by young trees under a canopy of truly dominant large trees. There is a similar stratification of animals, except that animals living in the larger trees do not necessarily dominate those living on the ground. Myriads of animals, mostly insects, live in the ground near the surface. Cottontail rabbits and many birds live on the ground, others like to nest in the tops of tall trees. Some birds and animals, such as woodpeckers and squirrels, live in dens.

Succession. Communities do not stay the same forever. They are constantly changing as various factors modify the environment. This process is known as succession. Succession of animal communities usually follows succession of plant communities, For example, the birds of a prairie area will all be ground-nesting birds. As shrubs invade the prairie, or are planted there, species of birds that nest in shrubs will follow.

Succession ordinarily starts with bare soil or water. Early occupants of bare soil are aggressive annuals, such as foxtail, ragweed, or poverty grass. Their growth improves the environment so that short-lived perennials like yarrow, goldenrod, or fleabane can take over. Depending on available moisture, seed sources and other factors, the area may next be invaded by Kentucky bluegrass, native prairie grasses such as little bluestem, or shrubs like hazelbrush, sumac, or buckbrush.

Succession stopped with the native prairie grasses in the prairie areas. In other areas, the shrubs improved the environment so that pioneer trees such as bur oak, aspen, jack pine or red cedar could become established. In some cases, the succession stopped with an oak-hickory community.

Succession goes forward naturally to a climax community unless stopped by some outside influence. A forest fire can set what was a maple-basswood climax forest back to the shrub stage. Plowing returns a plant community to the bare soil stage, except that the soil may be more fertile than it was originally.

Starting with a bare water area, such as a farm pond, succession begins with submerged vegetation like algae and pondweeds. Floating vegetation, such as water lillies, soon invades the pond and shades out the submerged plants. As the accumulation of dead plants and silt is built up, the reed-marsh stage is reached, when plants like cattail and bulrush predominate. Further accumulations make conditions favorable for sedges, rushes, and spike rushes. When the pond is nearly full of decayed plants and silt, willows and cottonwoods are able to take root. These are later replaced by elm, soft maple, ash, and walnut. Lowland prairie grasses, and later upland prairie grasses, replace the sedges, rushes, and spike rushes in a climate favorable to prairie.

The water succession, like that on land, can be accelerated, stopped, or set back by outside influences. By managing a farm pond to exclude floating and swampy vegetation it can be kept in the submerged vegetation state indefinitely. Drainage and silting can change the course of succession very rapidly.

Ecotones. An ecotone is the area where two different plant communities meet. It is, for example, where prairie meets woodland, where a cornfield meets a hayfield, or where cropland is adjacent to woodland. The ecotone, or edge, is more productive of wildlife than either of the two plant communities that go to make it up. This can be illustrated with pheasants. Pheasants like to eat corn, but a cornfield is a poor place to roost at night. A hedge or cattail marsh with dense cover is much better. Therefore, the pheasant must find a place where both corn and thick cover are close together. Places where the cover types adjoin or overlap will be most used by the pheasants.

ECOLOGICAL PRINCIPLES APPLIED TO SOIL MANAGEMENT

Plant indicators. Soil surveyors have long made use of ecological principles when they used native vegetation as an indicator of the type of soil. The presence of sedges and rushes usually indicates a tight, poorly drained soil. Poverty grass, reindeer moss, and sheep sorrel usually indicate acid soils. In the present-day landscape, sweetclover indicates a pH above 6.3.

FIGURE 46. Bicolor and sericea lespedeza planted on once-useless border between woods and corn field. The two lespedezas produce food for birds and cover for birds and small animals. (Royston, Georgia)
(Soil Conservation Service)

Native legumes frequently indicate droughty, depleted sites. Broomsedge is a good indicator of poor land management rather than inherently poor soil. The absence of trees in a long abandoned field is nearly always an indication that the site is not capable of supporting trees native to the vicinity. The presence of mullein, yarrow, or vervain indicates an overgrazed pasture. On the bluffs along the Mississippi River, overgrazing is resulting in an invasion of red cedar. In other areas, thornapple follows too many cattle.

Relation to land capability classification. We are using applied ecology in the land capability classification when we say, in effect, that land in Classification I, II, and III is such that environmental conditions can be kept in the early stages of plant succession, i.e., annual and a few herbaceous perennial plants, without deterioration of the environment. In the case of Class IV, we recognize the land must be kept in herbaceous perennials, with occasional annual crops, to prevent it from eroding. Class V land must be kept in herbaceous or woody perennials because the environment is not suited to the growing of annual plants. Classes VI and VII must be kept in perennial plants to preserve the land's current productive capacity. Class VIII land calls for treatment with vigorous, hardy pioneer plants that can be established on sites usually incapable of supporting plants high in the successional scale.

Cropland. Farmers are applying ecological principles when they plan, by plowing, seeding, and cultivating, to keep cropland in the initial stages of plant succession by growing of annual or biennial crops like corn, small grain, cotton or soybeans. The same is true when lime and fertilizer are applied to permit the growth of plants that could not otherwise grow on land that is acid or of low fertility. Mulching is another practice that modifies the environment to improve conditions for desired plants.

Pasture land. On pasture land, renovation and clipping of weeds are examples of applied ecology. So is the cutting of brush and weeds at a time of year when their vitality is the lowest. The introduction of legumes that are compatible with adapted grasses actually improves the stand and quality of the grasses. Regulation of grazing to maintain the desired combination of legumes and grasses also involves a knowledge of ecological principles.

Woodland. Principles of ecology are constantly used in woodland management. When trees are to be planted, a species adapted to the environmental conditions must be selected if satisfactory results are to be expected. Protection from fire and grazing is important because it permits the woodlot to progress normally toward its climax. Improvement or harvest cuttings must be guided by a knowledge of ecology if certain desired species of trees are to be favored. For example, it is known that strict selective cutting in an oak-hickory woods will, in most areas, result in a maple-basswood climax. If oak reproduction is desired, cuttings must be made in larger blocks to afford sufficient sunlight for oak reproduction and growth. Shrub-borders around woodlands are recommended because they reduce the effect of drying winds and help maintain a desirable leaf mulch out to the edge of the woods. They tend to affect the moisture relationships within the woods to the benefit of the trees. The leaving of den trees in a cutting operation is a means of keeping several tree planters (squirrels) busy working on each acre.

Wildlife land. There are many examples of the application of ecological principles in the management of wildlife land. In drainage-ditch bank management, species of grass capable of establishment on subsoil must be used. Even then their establishment frequently hinges on adequate soil treatment. These plants should be capable of withstanding flooding, should be sod-forming to control erosion, and should be aggressive enough to offer real competition to willows and cottonwoods which are undesirable because they reduce the capacity of the ditch. The grasses should also offer food and cover for muskrats.

Fence-row management. Fence-row management illustrates a variety of ecological principles. When a farmer plants a living fence between cropland and pasture, he is creating a new environment for insect-eating birds that like to nest 3 to 6 feet off the ground. He is adding an ecotone, or edge, to be used by game birds and furbearing animals. He is developing a habitat for pollinating insects. When a farmer refrains from burning a fence-row he is well on the road to the solution of fence-row weed problems, because the weeds will eventually be replaced by perennial grasses and shrubs. Repeated burning keeps the fence-row in the annual seed stage of plant succession.

Pond management recommendations include the control of marsh plants in shallow water. This recommendation is made because marsh plants afford hiding places for small bluegill sunfish from bass. In addition, marsh plants are part of the next stage in the water area succession. Their presence may shorten the life of the pond.

Management of odd areas involves the use of ecological principles in the selection of plants suitable to the wide variety of soil conditions encountered throughout the country.

Marsh management makes use of at least two economical principles. The control of water levels provides optimum conditions for the growth of aquatic plants, thus insuring an adequate food supply for muskrats. Level ditching is designed to alter the environment by increasing the area of open water, making the habitat more desirable for muskrats.

Streambank management, if applied to a sufficient length of stream, benefits fish by reducing the silt content of the water through the control of erosion and by cooling the water by shading. Streambank management also provides an ecotone useful to birds and mammals.

Wildlife borders make their chief biological contribution through the ecotones they create.

IMPORTANCE OF WILDLIFE IN AGRICULTURE

Most forms of wildlife help farmers to produce more and better crops through their check on insects, weeds, and other pests.

The annual value of wildlife has been estimated for the Central United States at 14 cents per acre for meat and fur production, and 22.6 cents for destruction of harmful insects and other agricultural pests.

Considering only its value for control of harmful insects and other pests, wildlife is worth $36 annually on an average 160-acre farm that has adopted no special soil or wildlife conservation measures. The application of such practices have been shown to increase wildlife populations at least 40 per cent on cropland and woodland alone. Doubling the wildlife population on the average farm can probably be expected. An increase of 100 per cent would bring the annual value up to $72.

The number of beneficial forms of wildlife which a well-managed farm supports is surprising. If it were not so great, pest problems would be much more serious than they are. Dambach showed that the beneficial wildlife population on a 100-acre farm with about one-third of the fence-rows containing woody cover, fifteen acres of protected woods, twenty-five acres of good pasture, and the remaining sixty acres in a 4-year crop rotation that includes two years of meadow, would be somewhat as follows:

> Several million beneficial insects such as lady beetles, aphis lions, and syrphid flies, which feed on plant lice; chalcid flies and tachinid flies, which parasitize many kinds of insects; and assassin bugs, ambush bugs, robber flies, and nabids, which capture and feed on other insects.
>
> More than 40 kinds of beneficial birds, represented by over 400 individuals of which 80 would be associated with the fence-rows, 180 with the woods, 80 with the meadow, 9 with the small grain, and 3 with the corn.
>
> More than a thousand beneficial small mammals, principally short-tailed

shrews. About 40 per cent of these would be in the meadow, 30 per cent in the pasture, 20 per cent in the woods, and the remaining 10 per cent in the fence-rows, grain, and corn fields. Of the 20 or more kinds of small mammals commonly found in the area at least 10 probably occur on every farm.

Game birds and animals provide farmers and their friends with sport and food. Farmers having ponds, lakes, or streams also derive much pleasure and also obtain food from fish. Furbearing animals furnish recreation and cash income to many farmers.

Another important value of wildlife is found in the pollination of many plants, particularly legumes, by honeybees, wildbees, and other insects. Studies in Ohio and some of the western states showed that, with sufficient insect pollination, seed yields of alfalfa, red clover, and alsike clover can be increased as much as fourfold. Living fences, wildlife borders, and stream-bank management increase the amount of favorable environment for pollinating insects.

Some forms of wildlife, particularly some insects and mammals, are detrimental to agriculture and when overabundant may become quite harmful. One of the ways to control species that are harmful is to encourage their natural enemies. The establishment of living fences, for example, will encourage birds which will, in turn, help to control insect pests.

That wildlife is valuable to the general public is brought out by statistics from various sources. The estimated value of the wild fur and meat taken annually in the United States is $190,000,000. Commerce in furs offers employment to thousands of persons. More than 10 million persons purchase hunting and fishing licenses each year and spend $650,000,000 annually for equipment, transportation, meals, and lodging. There are at least as many people who do not hunt but enjoy seeing, hearing, studying, and photographing wildlife.

BIRDS

The food habits of some birds make them especially valuable to agriculture. According to U.S. Department of Agriculture estimates, birds destroy harmful insects to the extent that $350,000,000 in crops is saved each year. The total loss to agriculture from insects is considered to be $700,000,000 annually. By increasing the present number of birds through good land use and soil management practices, the usefulness of birds as insect destroyers can be materially increased.

Because birds have higher body temperatures and more rapid digestion and expend more energy than most other animals, they require huge amounts of food. Some insect-eating birds must fill their stomachs five or six times daily. They usually consume as much or more than their own weight in soft-bodied insects every day. Young robins have been observed to gain eight times their original weight in the first 8 days of their lives. When a young robin in captivity weighed 3 ounces, it consumed 165 cutworms weighing $5\frac{1}{2}$ ounces in all. If a 10-pound baby ate at the same rate it would have to eat $18\frac{1}{3}$ pounds of food in one day.

Although birds are of great value to agriculture, they cannot keep weeds and insects under control. Present populations of insect-eating birds could probably be doubled if every farmer did all of the practical things he could to encourage them. Even so, he still would have to exert other measures from time to time to control insects where they become overabundant.

Some birds are also valuable as enemies of mice, rats, and gophers.

MAMMALS

Production of furs, as with muskrat, and control of small rodents are probably the most important contributions of wild animals to agriculture. At least six species of wild animals are effective in reducing the numbers of frequently harmful rodents such as mice, rats, and rabbits.

Many species—five, at least—of small mammals feed extensively on insects. In field borders and woodlands their populations commonly run 100 to 300 per acre. Because small mammals feed throughout the year while most birds migrate in winter, there are more than 32,000 insect-eating-mammal-days per acre of shrub border, compared with about 13,000 bird-days per acre. It has been estimated that 100 small mammals could consume 266 pounds of insects per year—at approximately 10,000 insects per pound, that would be 2,660,000 per year.

Deer, rabbits, squirrels, and sometimes opossums, raccoons, muskrats, and woodchucks are used for food by man.

Squirrels probably planted all the hickory trees in the United States. They also planted many of the oaks, walnuts, butternuts, and the like. In spite of accelerated tree planting by farmers, squirrels are still planting more trees than man. If seed trees are nearby, squirrels will establish a forest on many acres if the land is protected from fire and grazing.

FISH

The chief values of fish are for sport and food. From 150 to 350 pounds of fish per acre can be removed from ponds and small lakes each year if they are carefully managed. Thousands of miles of streams and rivers are also producing large amounts of fish, in commercial and recreational fishing.

ESSENTIAL REQUIREMENTS OF WILDLIFE

To be suitable for wildlife, a farm must provide food, cover, and water, distributed in such a way that all are available within the distance that birds and animals will travel in one day.

Actually, the more places that can be developed on a farm where food, cover, and water are close together, the greater the wildlife population that farm will support. However, any development of cover or water at any place on the farm will be beneficial to some forms of wildlife.

Food. A large part of the farm land is devoted to the growing of corn, small grains, and legumes. Modern harvesting methods leave a good deal of waste grain in the field. In many places, wild fruits and weed seeds are also common. Thus, the amount of available wildlife food may be adequate, but because much of it is far from cover, or may be covered by snow and ice, its availability when needed is often a problem.

Wildlife food is usually adequate in late spring when insects become abundant; in summer, when insects, wild fruits, and green plants are available; and in fall, when insects, wild fruits, weed seeds, nuts, waste grain, and green plants can all be had. The critical season is winter when there are no insects, wild fruits are gone, and snow and ice cover waste grains. At the same time, the amount of cover diminishes and some food becomes unavailable because it is too far from adequate cover. Early spring is often just as critical a period.

The planting of perennial food-producing plants close to cover is one way to ensure available food supplies throughout the year. Some of the best plants for this purpose are bicolor lespedeza, sericea lespedeza, and multiflora rose. Another way to make food available, and the only way practical for the northern part of the country, is to extend cover closer to natural food sources.

Cover. Any animal, in order to exist on an area, must have cover. This must provide concealment for nest and young, shade from the hot sun, and shelter from chilling rains. It also must provide escape routes and protection from cold, wind, sleet, and snow.

If located close to food and water, most cover in many sections of the country is adequate during late spring, summer, and fall. The critical seasons are winter and early spring. The planting of locally adapted conifers close to sources of food and water is highly recommended. At least one clump of 20 to 50 conifers or other adapted trees should be included in every tree-planting area. Safe nesting cover for ground-nesting birds is often inadequate because of burning or mowing. A few areas that are never burned or not mowed until after the nesting season should be provided on every farm.

Water. All kinds of wildlife require water. They obtain it from one of the following sources:

1. Ponds, streams, springs, drainage ditches, tile outlets, marshes, and lakes or snow.
2. Food of high moisture content, such as fruits, succulent leaves, succulent sprouts, juicy insects and their eggs.
3. Dew.

Most upland wildlife can survive on water from succulent foods and dew, but the highest populations can be maintained where surface water is also available. Surface water will also make possible a greater variety of wildlife because water-loving species, such as red-wing blackbirds, muskrats, raccoons, and others, will be attracted to it.

SOIL MANAGEMENT PRACTICES THAT BENEFIT WILDLIFE

There are eight management practices that are especially important to wildlife. They are:

> Drainage-ditch bank management
> Fence-row management
> Management of odd areas
> Marsh management
> Pond management
> Shelterbelt management
> Streambank management
> Wildlife borders

The use of land for wildlife production, unlike the use of land for cereal crops, does not necessarily require that a definite area be set aside for the purpose. Wildlife is a secondary crop on lands used for growing grain and hay, for pasture, or for woodland. It is a primary crop only on wildlife land.

RELATIONSHIP OF LAND, COVER, AND WATER

Food, cover, and water distributed in such a way that all are available within the distance that birds and animals will travel in one day, are essential in developing a wildlife program.

These distances are not known for all forms of farm wildlife. A few for which the information is available are given below:

Muskrat	$\frac{1}{10}$ to ½ mile
Partridge, Hungarian	⅛ to ½ mile
Pheasant, ring-necked	½ to 1 mile
Quail, bobwhite	⅛ to 1 mile

Those are seasonal averages. The daily limit of travel will usually be no greater than the shorter distance given above.

Information is also available on the home range of a few species. They are:

Grouse, ruffed	40 acres
Mouse, field	$\frac{1}{15}$ to 1 acre
Mouse, prairie deer	½ to 1 acre
Opossum	11 to 40 acres
Rabbits	3 to 8 acres
Shrew, short-tailed	½ to 1 acre
Squirrel, fox	10 to 40 acres
Woodchuck	40 to 160 acres

It is obvious from these figures that farm wildlife species occupy relatively small areas and that the abundance of wildlife can be increased when suitable habitat is well distributed over the entire farm. Probably a combination of one permanent cover area close to food for each 20 acres of land would be ideal. Land conditions vary so widely, however, that such ideal conditions will occur on relatively few farms.

To reduce the generalization about food and cover being adjacent to each other and well distributed over the farm to a principle that can be applied rather specifically to the varying land conditions on farms, the following is suggested:

PREDOMINANT LAND CAPABILITY CLASSES* ON THE FARM	TREATMENT USUALLY MOST EFFECTIVE, MOST PRACTICAL, AND MOST ACCEPTABLE TO LANDOWNERS
I, II, III	Linear food and cover developments— fence-rows, drainage-ditch banks, field windbreaks, streambanks, wildlife borders.

* Land capability classes are discussed in Chapter 19.

| III, IV, V, VI | Area cover development—
odd areas, pond areas, and marshes, supplemented by linear food and cover developments. |
| VI, VII, VIII | Linear food development—
wildlife borders of perennial seed- and fruit-producing plants, supplemented by undisturbed small-area cover developments of grasses and conifers; marsh management. |

WILDLIFE MANAGEMENT RESOURCE AREAS

The eight management practices especially important to wildlife are not equally applicable on all farms or in all communities. Wildlife resource areas may be delineated on the basis of soil groups, erosion problems, land use patterns, and wildlife requirements.

Any line separating resource areas should be considered as the center of a transition zone between the two rather than as an absolute boundary.

Specific practices are usually applicable in each resource area. The land on which the practice is applied should be set aside for wildlife.

DRAINAGE-DITCH BANK MANAGEMENT

Water is usually present in drainage ditches and food is almost always abundant in adjacent cropland. The addition of suitable vegetative cover not only makes an ideal habitat for wildlife, but also protects and prolongs the effective life of the ditch.

Drainage ditches must be treated to protect the original channel capacity by (a) preventing siltation and bank cutting, (b) avoiding retardance of the flow of water by unsuitable vegetation, and (c) in severe climates, keeping snow and ice out of the channel. They must also be treated to facilitate cleanout and maintenance.

Ditch bank and berms should be maintained in herbaceous vegetation. This can best be done by mowing at least once a year or by restricted grazing. Mowing or grazing should be done after ground-nesting birds have left the nest, usually about grain harvest time. Avoid overgrazing so as to maintain a vegetative cover that can prevent erosion and siltation of the ditch.

FENCE-ROW MANAGEMENT

Managing fence-rows is utilizing to best advantage an area necessarily lost from cultivation. Management of fence-rows to establish or maintain desirable permanent vegetation contributes to good farming.

Living fences may also be used as contour guide lines along boundaries between crop fields. In many parts of the country multiflora rose is most useful for this purpose. It makes an effective livestock barrier in 3 to 6 years, depending on the site and treatment given. Although there is some tendency to spread by layering, indications are that it will not spread enough to be a nuisance. Reaching an ultimate height and spread of about 8 to 10 feet, multiflora rose requires no trimming.

Other plants sometimes used in fence-row management or in contour

FIGURE 47. Three-year old multiflora rose fence provides cover for birds and small animals and nesting place for a number of birds. It is a good fence for livestock. (Charlottesville, Virginia)
(Soil Conservation Service)

guide lines in various parts of the country are red cedar, blackberry, raspberry, currant, hazelnut, elderberry, panicled dogwood, and New Jersey tea. In areas where market conditions justify planting of spruce or pine for Christmas trees, single-row contour plantings can be expected to produce well-shaped trees.

None of the species listed above have wide-spreading root systems. They do not tap the soil moisture for any considerable distance. They are all low-growing; they will not shade crops.

MANAGEMENT OF ODD AREAS

The object is to develop permanent cover and prevent further erosion on small eroded areas, bare knobs, sinkholes, blow-outs, abandoned roads and railroad rights-of-way, borrow pits, gravel pits, and odd corners in cropland, and to permit utilization of these previously waste areas.

It is desirable to plant conifers, hardwoods, shrubs, and grasses, following as closely as possible the idea of having the tallest trees in the center, shorter ones next, then shrubs, and finally grass around the entire edge.

Odd areas on many farms are well suited for planting blackberry, raspberry, gooseberry, currant, wild plum, grapes, and other fruits. For sand blow-outs, jack pine, Scotch pine, red pine, or other suitable species of trees should be used. A brush mulch is usually necessary to ensure successful planting in active blow-outs. A living fence should be planted just inside the fence or brush barrier.

MARSH MANAGEMENT

For various reasons, many wet land areas on farms are not suitable for drainage. Marsh management provides an opportunity for increasing their value. Properly managed, they will produce an annual catch of 6 to 20 muskrats per acre. They usually produce waterfowl and other forms of wildlife. Recently, a market for the fruiting heads of cattail has developed.

Marshes should generally be managed for furbearing animals or waterfowl. If managed for one, they will be somewhat useful for the other, but best conditions for both cannot be maintained on the same area. In either case, two requirements must be met: (a) a dependable water supply, and (b) an abundant supply of suitable vegetation.

If practical, livestock should be excluded from the marsh; otherwise their numbers should be limited. Controlled burning may be useful in maintaining desired types of vegetation, but it is not recommended for cattail marshes. Burning should be used very sparingly, and extensive fires should be prevented.

FIGURE 48. Steep bank in cultivated field planted to attract wildlife; it also protects the soil from erosion. (Knox County, Ohio) *(Soil Conservation Service)*

The furbearer harvest should be kept low enough to ensure adequate breeding stock for the next year. In years of small muskrat populations, not more than 60 per cent of the population should be trapped. In years of high populations, 70 per cent may safely be taken. Experienced trappers know it is time to stop trapping muskrat when females outnumber males in the daily catch for several consecutive days or when females constitute more than one-third of the total catch. It is usually desirable to stop trapping when one-half of the estimated pre-trapping population has been taken.

POND MANAGEMENT

Ponds are constructed for a number of purposes. Because they provide water and cover close together, ponds are important to all forms of wildlife.

Ponds will ordinarily be supplied with water that runs off the watershed. This area should be relatively small and protected to reduce siltation to a minimum.

Ponds should not be built in running streams. The volume of water is too great, causing excessive siltation, uneconomical spillway installations, loss of desirable fish, and introduction of undesirable fish.

SHELTERBELTS AND WINDBREAKS

Shelterbelts help to control wind erosion by providing barriers against wind movement and also minimize the drying effect of wind on the soil. They also will provide cover close to cropland for insect-eating birds. Because of the large amount of "edge" in relation to acreage, shelterbelts are especially important to wildlife.

STREAMBANK MANAGEMENT

Streambank protection is undertaken to control bank cutting, protect valuable adjoining property, and reduce the silt load in streams. It also improves wildlife conditions because it usually provides food, cover, and water close together, and improves the stream for fish.

Streambank work done on any segment of a stream will be affected by the condition of the stream both above and below the segment being considered. Therefore, it is desirable to protect the entire length of stream at the same time. Frequently, it will not be possible to protect the entire stream at one time, but a plan for the entire stream can be made so that work done on any segment will later fit into the entire job.

The stream should be protected from livestock. If stock water is needed, provide watering places where cattle will not have to cross a steep bank. Often it is desirable to provide more than one watering place so they can be used alternately to prevent the stock from denuding them of vegetation.

WILDLIFE BORDERS

A wildlife border is a strip of low growing plants (herbaceous plants, shrubs, or both) along edges of woodland. They are established by planting seeds or plants or by release cutting of competing woody plants. Two types of borders are most commonly used. One type is legume-grass borders in cultivated fields and the other consists of shrub-conifer borders around woodlands.

Legume-grass borders are important in preventing erosion on the sloping ends of cultivated fields, particularly when they replace 3 or 4 rows of cultivated crops. Where cropland is next to woodland or tall shelterbelts or hedges, wildlife borders utilize the area in which satisfactory row crops are difficult to grow. Wildlife borders make farming operations easier by providing a headland in which to turn farm machinery. Both types of wildlife borders are important to wildlife because they occur where two cover types meet.

Locally adapted legumes and grasses such as alfalfa, sweet clover, lespedeza, red top, orchardgrass, bromegrass, and bluegrass may be used, and lime and fertilizer should be applied as needed.

Field borders are most easily established at the time the entire field is being seeded to meadow. When the field is plowed for row crops or small grain, field borders approximately one rod wide should be left unplowed. They can be plowed and reseeded the next time the field is seeded to meadow, or, if a good sod is established, may be left unplowed indefinitely.

Since field borders will occupy only a small acreage, it is recommended that they be left unmowed until the time of grain harvest or the second cutting of hay. By that time most young birds will be out of the nest.

Borders should be provided around existing woodlands where no natural border exists. This may be accomplished by one of the two following methods:

By occasional tree removal at the woodland edge to stimulate new natural growth.

By planting a new border around the woods margin. In a large section of the country, sericea lespedeza is useful for border planting. Direct seeding is satisfactory. Scarified seed is broadcast at the rate of 6 to 8 pounds per acre on well-prepared soil that has been allowed to settle, within 60 days after average date of last killing frost. Lime and fertilizer should be used as needed. A light mulch is beneficial on eroded soils.

REFERENCES

1. Aldous, S. E. 1947. *Muskrat trapping on Sand Lake National Wildlife Refuge, South Dakota.* Jour. Wildlife Mgt., 11: 1.
2. Allen, Durwald L. 1943. *Michigan fox squirrel management.* Game Div., Mich. Dept. Cons., Lansing.
3. ———. 1949. *The farm wildlife.* Wildlife Management Inst., Washington, D. C.
4. Anderson, W. L. 1950. *Biology handbook.* USDA, SCS.
5. ———. 1951. *Making land produce useful wildlife.* USDA Farmers' Bull. 2035.
6. ———, and Edminster, F. C. 1949. *Multiflora rose—for living fences and wildlife cover.* USDA Leaflet 256.
7. Burt, W. H. 1946. *Mammals of Michigan.* Univ. of Michigan Press.
8. Compton, L. V. 1943. *Technique of fishpond management.* USDA Misc. Pub. 528.
9. Dambach, C. A. 1944. *A ten-year ecological study of adjoining grazed and ungrazed woodlands in northeastern Ohio.* Ecological Mon., 14: 3.
10. ———. 1945. *Some biologic and economic aspects of field border management.* Trans. 10th North Amer. Wildlife Conf.

11. ———. 1948. *A study of the ecology and economic value of crop field borders.* Grad. Sch. Stu. Biol. Sci. Ser. No. 2, Ohio State Univ. Press.
12. ———, and Good, E. E. 1940. *The effect of certain land use practices on populations of breeding birds in southwestern Ohio.* Jour. Wildlife Mgt., 4: 1.
13. Dambach, C. A., and Leedy, D. L. 1948. *A recent evaluation of Ohio wildlife resources.* Trans., 13th North Amer. Wildlife Conf.
14. Davison, V. E. 1947. *Farm fishpond for food and good land use.* USDA Farmers' Bull. 1983.
15. ———. 1948. *Bicolor for quail and soil conservation in the Southeast.* USDA Leaflet 248.
16. Edminster, F. C. 1949. *Streambank plantings for erosion control in the Northeast.* USDA Leaflet 258.
17. Fisher, W. L. 1939. *Studies of the eastern red grouse in Michigan.* Mich. Agric. Expt. Sta. Tech. Bull. 166.
18. Good, E. E., and Dambach, C. A. 1943. *Effect of land use practices on breeding bird populations in Ohio.* Jour. Wildlife Mgt., 7: 3.
19. Henderson, J. 1934. *The Principal Value of Birds.* The Macmillan Co., New York.
20. Hockensmith, R. D., and Steele, J. G. 1949. *Principles of land capability classification.* USDA, SCS.
21. Hopp, H. 1946. *Earthworms fight erosion, too.* Soil Cons., 11: 11.
22. Leopold, A. 1933. *Game Management.* Chas. Scribner's Sons, New York.
23. McAtee, W. L. 1937. *Wildlife and land planning.* Pa. Game News, 8: 4-5.
24. ———. 1939. *Biologic balance on the farm.* Soil Cons., 5: 4.
25. Seton, E. T. 1938. *Lives of Game Animals.* Doubleday, Doran and Co., Inc., New York.
26. Stoddard, H. L. 1932. *The Bobwhite Quail: Its Habits, Preservation, and Increase.* Chas. Scribner's Sons, New York.
27. Swingle, H. S., and Smith, E. V. 1942. *Management of farm fish ponds.* Ala. Agr. Expt. Sta. Bull. 254.
28. Van Dersel, W. R. 1937. *The dependence of soils and animal life.* Trans. 2nd North Amer. Wildlife Conf.
29. Wandell, W. H. 1948. *Agricultural and wildlife values of habitat improvement plantings on the Illinois Black Prairie.* Trans. 13th North Amer. Wildlife Conf.
30. Weaver, J. E., and Clements, F. E. 1939. *Plant Ecology.* McGraw-Hill Book Co., Inc., New York.
31. Yeatter, R. E. 1934. *The Hungarian partridge in the Great Lakes region.* Univ. Mich. School of Forestry and Cons. Bull. 5.

11

Erosion and Productivity

Vast improvements have been made in the science of
crop production during the past 60 to 75 years. Inorganic fertilizing materials are being constantly improved in content and availability of nutrients, and in
physical properties. Rates of fertilizer application
have been increased enormously in many areas and
the number of farmers using fertilizer has increased
many times over. Better adapted and higher yielding
varieties of crops have been developed. Improved
methods of crop and soil management have been made
available. Better materials and equipment for control
of insect pests and diseases have been developed.

These and other related developments would have
brought about large increases in per-acre crop production if the fertility of the soil had been maintained.
It has been estimated that if the fertility of the nation's
soils that prevailed when the soils were first put under
the plow had been maintained at or near its former
level the average per-acre yields of most of our principal crops should have shown steady and consistent
increases of as much as 40 to 60 per cent during the
past 50 years. Actually, the increase of some crops
has been much less than this. The national average
acre-yield of corn and cotton, for example, increased
but very little up to 1938. Since then there has been
some increase in the average acre-yields of both these
crops.

195

TABLE 26. National average annual acre-
             yield of cotton and corn

Period	Cotton lint (Pounds)	Corn (Bushels)
1869–78	171.6*	25.9
1879–88	172.5	25.8
1889–98	191.3	26.0
1899–08	187.7	27.4
1909–18	183.3	25.8
1919–28	162.6	27.0
1929–38	198.0	23.0
1939–48	256.0	33.0

* Cotton now averages 429 pounds per acre.

The recent increases coincide with a combination of agricultural advances that were greatly stimulated as a result of the war effort—spread of conservation farming and, for corn, the advent of hybrid varieties.

Cotton acreage was greatly curtailed in the old cotton-growing area and expanded into new territory in the Southwest. In the Southeast, better lands were selected for cotton production, the rate of fertilization was stepped up, and the planting of legume cover-crops and application of other improved soil-conserving practices increased. Perhaps the advent of hybrid corn was the greatest single factor contributing to the recent increase in corn yield, although the amount of fertilizer used during this period was greatly increased.

A more or less steady decline in soil fertility has largely, sometimes entirely, offset the many advances made along the line of agricultural production. This is illustrated by the average per-acre yields of eight of the more important crops grown in Michigan during the period 1871 to 1940.

TABLE 27. Average annual yields of 8 crops in Michigan, in bushels per acre*

Crop	1871–80	1881–90	1891–1900	1901–10	1911–20	1921–30	1931–40
Wheat	15.0	14.9	14.0	15.6	16.9	19.5	20.4
Corn	33.4	27.5	30.0	32.2	33.3	30.4	32.6
Oats	21.9	31.9	29.7	31.3	34.0	31.0	31.0
Rye	14.4	12.2	13.6	15.0	14.4	12.9	12.3
Buckwheat	16.1	12.9	14.2	14.4	14.1	12.0	14.2
Barley	22.9	22.7	22.0	25.0	25.2	23.9	24.8
Potatoes	86.0	73.0	80.0	89.0	90.0	97.0	97.0
Tame hay†	1.21	1.22	1.21	1.33	1.28	1.12	1.27

* Data from L. M. Turk, Department of Soil Science, Michigan State College.
† Yield expressed in tons per acre.

With the exception of wheat and potatoes, there was no appreciable trend of increase in the yield of any of these crops in the 70-year period, and an actual decline occurred in some of them.

EROSION DEPLETES SOIL FERTILITY

The importance of fertility erosion is not fully appreciated. It is caused by the action of wind and water, which sorts, sifts, and removes the light-weight, fertility-bearing portion of the soil, leaving sand and other heavy material behind. The amount of topsoil may be reduced materially by the removal of the coarser material over a period of years, but the most fertile portion of the soil is usually the first to be removed by wind and water.

The soil at the surface of the ground is stirred by wind and rain water and sorted into different-sized particles. Due to its turbulent nature, the action of wind on the soil is similar to that of a fanning mill which separates chaff from wheat. It removes organic matter, fine silt, and clay particles. The

FIGURE 49. High winds are capable of lifting and transporting great distances large quantities of the organic matter and silt and clay fractions of the soil—the life-giving substances of the soil. This sorting process adds to the general sandiness and depletion of the soil productivity of the area. (Springfield, Colorado)
(Soil Conservation Service)

FIGURE 50. The wind acts as a fanning mill, removing the organic matter, silt, and clay and leaving the sand and gravel. (Redfield, South Carolina)
(Soil Conservation Service)

FIGURE 51. The portion of the field in the foreground was blown out to a depth of more than 12 inches. Sand and coarser materials were blown into drifts and dunes. (Baca County, Colorado)
(Soil Conservation Service)

lighter, more fertile fractions are lifted into the pathway of higher air currents, which often carry them for hundreds and sometimes thousands of miles. The coarser, less fertile particles skip, slide, or roll along the surface and often pile up in drifts.

Raindrops falling on bare soil splash and stir the soil particles at the surface into a muddy, watery mixture. Much of the coarser, heavier material settles out as soon as the turbulence caused by the splashing raindrops subsides sufficiently. The smaller, lighter particles, which contain the fertility elements, remain in suspension and may be floated away.

Soil erosion has played, and continues to play, a major role in impairing the productive capacity of the nation's soils. Organic matter, nitrogen, and the clay and silt fractions of the soil, which contain the life-producing nutrients, are removed by the erosive action of wind and water. The heavier, less productive material is left behind. If erosion is severe, the body of the soil itself is carried off.

Depletion of fertility in cropland is brought about by the combined action of many factors. Annual cropping removes large amounts of nutrient materials. Soluble constituents are lost through leaching processes. Organic-matter decomposition as a result of microbial activity proceeds at a rapid rate in cultivated soils. In addition to these and many other factors, the

FIGURE 52. Fertility erosion in a cultivated field in New Jersey. Organic matter, silt, and clay were splashed from the sand by the impact of falling raindrops. The washed sand, appearing as light-colored deposits between the rows, was left in the furrows. A light-textured soil in Alabama lost 60 per cent of all the phosphoric acid applied as superphosphate over a 26-year period by this process.
(Soil Conservation Service)

FIGURE 53. Organic matter, silt, and clay floated down from higher areas and formed a deposit several inches thick on this bottomland field. (Clayton County, Iowa)
(Soil Conservation Service)

process of erosion is now recognized as one of the most serious forces in the rapid depletion of fertility and productivity of cultivated lands.

Much experimental evidence is available to show the extent to which erosion carries away the life-producing part of the soil—the part that contains the nitrogen and mineral plant nutrients.

LARGE QUANTITIES OF PLANT NUTRIENTS ARE REMOVED

Analysis of old cropped or eroded Willamette Valley soils in Oregon have shown definite reductions in plant nutrients and an increase in soil acidity when compared with native sod land. The decreases in nitrogen, calcium, and sulphur were as much as 50 per cent. It is estimated that the soils of the Willamette Valley sustain a net annual loss of 29,000 tons of nitrogen and a loss of potassium, sulphur, calcium, and magnesium ranging from 2,500 to 106,000 tons annually.

The immensity of plant nutrient losses due to erosion is indicated by the amount of silt and nutrients carried in the water of the Tennessee River system. For example, on the assumption that this silt came entirely from the row crop, idle and other land subject to severe erosion, it has been estimated that the loss from each acre of such land during 1939 would average 5.2 tons of silt, 84.6 pounds of CaO, 97.9 pounds of MgO, 212.2 pounds of

K₂O, 13.0 pounds of P_2O_5, and 23.8 pounds of nitrogen. Calculated on the basis of the total acreage of the watershed, the average acre-losses of the three bases, as oxides, carried in solution were 167.0 pounds of calcium, 31.7 pounds of magnesium, and 7.1 pounds of potassium.

The estimated losses per acre from open farm land in the entire Mississippi River Basin during the same period averaged 1.9 tons of silt, 43.6 pounds of CaO, 53.8 pounds of MgO, 55.6 pounds of K₂O, 5.08 pounds of P_2O_5, and 6.64 pounds of nitrogen. On the basis of the total acreage in the watershed, the average acre losses were .6 ton of silt, 13.6 pounds of CaO, 16.9 pounds of MgO, 17.4 pounds of K₂O, 1.59 pounds of P_2O_5, and 2.03 pounds of nitrogen.

The amount of mineral nutrients contained in the drainage waters of the Tennessee River Watershed varies with the nature of the stratum from which the waters flow. The water draining the limestone areas contains the greatest amount of total mineral matter and that from the sandstone areas the least. However, the drainage waters from the sandstone areas contain more than twice as much potassium as the drainage waters from the limestone areas. The waters draining the highly phosphatic soils of the bluegrass area contained the greatest amount of phosphorus. The greatest amount of nitrate-nitrogen was found in drainage waters containing the largest amount of soluble phosphorus, thus indicating the close relation between the soluble phosphorus and nitrate-nitrogen content.

The amounts of nutrients carried annually in solution by the Mississippi and Ohio Rivers are shown in Table 28. In addition to the mineral nutrients carried by the Mississippi River in solution, this stream carried in suspension 7,469 million cubic feet of soil annually.

TABLE 28. Amounts of plant nutrients carried in solution annually in the Ohio and Mississippi Rivers (19)

Element	Ohio River*	Mississippi River†
	Tons	Tons
Phosphorus	17,199	62,188
Sodium	119,446	630,720
Potassium	396,521	1,626,312
Calcium	6,752,222	22,446,379
Magnesium	1,629,319	5,179,788
Sulphur	2,229,544	6,732,936

* At confluence with the Mississippi River.
† At Baton Rouge, Louisiana.

Leaching removes large quantities of plant nutrients from the soil. Much larger amounts are lost by this means from certain productive soils than from the less productive ones. For example, Muscatine soil in Illinois lost 311.4 pounds of calcium per acre in three years and eight months, or a little more than 27 times as much as the 11.5 pounds lost from Cowden soil in the same time. The nitrogen loss during this period was 280.9 pounds per acre from Muscatine soil but only 14.2 pounds from Cisne soil. Magnesium losses were not as high as those of nitrogen or calcium but showed the same general relation to soil types.

Numerous important depletions of organic matter, formerly attributed to oxidation, may have resulted from erosion. Loss of organic matter appeared to be a linear function of erosion. The calculated organic matter percentage of soil dropped 0.002 per cent at both Clarinda, Iowa, and Bethany, Missouri, for each ton of soil lost by erosion. The amount of organic matter removed by erosion is greater than the corresponding depletion indicated by analysis of the plot soils. Consequently, restoration of the original organic matter level does not compensate for losses of "reserve" organic matter.

Marked and significant differences in erodibility occurred in New York under a uniform treatment following treatments that permitted great differences in the rate of erosion. The calculated percentages of organic matter in the soil to plow depth were found to have dropped about 0.002 per cent for each ton of soil lost by erosion.

The losses of organic matter caused by erosion in New York vary both in amount and character. They tend to be high in proportion to the total amount of soil and the proportion of silt and clay that are lost.

Studies in Wisconsin showed that a severely eroded soil was not only lower in organic matter and nitrogen, but lost more rainfall by runoff than did less eroded soils. Severely eroded Fayette silt loam had only one-third as much organic matter and only one-half as much nitrogen as moderately eroded Fayette silt loam. The severely eroded soil, when planted to grain, lost through runoff about twice as much rainfall during the growing season as moderately eroded soil. A severely eroded soil planted to corn allowed 1.3 times as much runoff as moderately eroded soil, and severely eroded soil planted to hay allowed 2.8 times as much runoff as moderately eroded soil. With moderate erosion, such as that produced by light rains or under sod cover, the proportion of organic matter and fine soil particles in the soil removed is higher than with more severe erosion. As the rate of erosion increases in severity the eroded materials tend to become similar in composition to the eroding soil. However, the aggregate fertility losses by slight erosion may be more detrimental than those resulting from more severe erosion.

Under severe erosion, eroded materials tend to approximate the composition of the uneroded soil, and the process is in effect "removal layer by layer." With more moderate runoffs, there is a selective removal of the finer particles. Small local deposits of sand on the soil surface may be swept off by later rains, but if frequent cultivation constantly presents a fresh surface to the sorting action of running water, a continued removal of the finer particles may be expected.

The loss of organic matter by erosion on fallow soil in Iowa and Missouri was found to be 18 times as great as the normal loss by oxidation. It was estimated that in order to maintain the organic matter of these soils at their original level it would be necessary to apply as much as 9.2 tons of clover hay per acre annually. Soil at Guthrie, Oklahoma, which had an average of about 46,000 pounds of organic matter per acre in 1931, suffered an aver-age net decline of 1,860 pounds per acre when planted to cotton during the period 1931 to 1940. When planted to a 3-year rotation of cotton, wheat, and sweet clover, this rate of decline was reduced to 940 pounds per acre. Soil with a sod cover of Bermuda grass accumulated organic matter at the rate of 1,700 pounds per acre annually, instead of suffering a decline. The plots planted to cotton lost the equivalent of all the organic matter returned as crop residues and in addition 1,860 pounds annually of the original re-serves. The soil devoted to the 3-year rotation lost all the crop residues re-turned during this period plus an additional 940 pounds of its original supply. At the same time, the land devoted to Bermuda grass sod held the equivalent of its original supply of organic matter and accumulated an addi-tional 1,700 pounds per acre annually.

An inch of artificial rainfall applied to pasture land in Virginia at the rate of 3 to 3.75 inches per hour washed off 9.1 per cent of a 200-pound-per-acre application of triple superphosphate made just prior to the test. This loss was caused by only 0.2 inch runoff or 20 per cent of the water applied. Tests made at the same time with limestone of several degrees of fineness showed that the finer the material, the greater its removal by erosion.

Total losses of phosphoric acid by erosion where no cover crop or other conservation practices were used were double the quantity removed by tomatoes or sweet corn in New Jersey. Where cover crops or cover crops and manure were used annually, the loss of phosphoric acid by erosion continued to equal the quantity removed by either crop.

The removal of potassium by erosion, where no conservation practices were employed, exceeded the removal of this element by tomatoes and was nearly equal to the removal by sweet corn. Where conservation practices were employed, the potassium removed by erosion was more than half as much as that by tomatoes and continued to exceed the quantity removed from the soil by sweet corn.

The loss of organic matter and plant nutrients from the soil by erosion reduces the efficiency of fertilizers. In studies by Lamb, Carleton, and Free, several series of plots on each of the four soil types were planted to several cropping systems and given a variety of cultural practices for a period of 11 years. The different treatments permitted varying rates of erosion during the period of study. The different rates of erosion produced vast differences in yield of corn and efficiency in the use of fertilizer when the whole area was uniformly fertilized with 1,000 pounds per acre of 10-10-10 fertilizer and planted to corn.

WIND SORTS OUT MOST PRODUCTIVE PARTS FIRST

The wind tends to change the soil texture through removal of the silt frac-tion and may deplete the total fertility of the soil by sifting out the lighter and more fertile portion and carrying it away. The light-weight soil particles are the important ones in the great dry-land winter-wheat belt of the South-ern High Plains. It was the loss of such particles during the dust storms of the 1930's that opened the way for serious inroads on the fertility reserves

---

of the soils in this area.

Each shift of soil by the wind serves to remove more plant nutrients. After the soil is moved a large number of times, the remaining soil is mainly sand, regardless of the original texture. In Oklahoma, after the heavy wind storms of the early 1930's, the organic matter-nitrogen ratio in the cropped soil was 22:47, that in the virgin soil 23:30; and the average of the drifts was 24:44. As a result of cropping and wind erosion, the organic matter in the cultivated soils was decreased 18 per cent and the nitrogen was decreased 15 per cent. Very little difference occurred in the nitrogen and organic matter content of the cropped and virgin subsurface soils.

The first soil drift to lodge in a fence-row on the Panhandle Experiment Station at Goodwell, Oklahoma, in 1933 contained 24.6 per cent of organic matter. The drifted soil had been separated by wind from the surface of topsoil averaging less than 2 per cent organic matter. Removal of the rich topsoil lowered crop yields 4.5 times as fast as did later removals of surface and subsoil material. Other samples of dust collected in Oklahoma during the dust storms of the 1930's contained on the average 62.5 per cent silt and 14.3 per cent sand. The original soil, Richfield silt loam, contained 42 per cent silt and 35.4 per cent sand, whereas the drift soil contained 58.2 per cent sand and only 15 per cent silt. The effect of the sorting action of the wind on Richfield silt loam is illustrated in Figure 54.

FIGURE 54. Changes in silt and sand content of Richfield silt loam caused by the sifting and sorting action of wind in the erosion process.

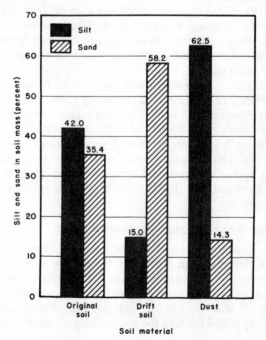

The dust contained 1.77 times as much combustible matter as the field soil and 1.47 times as much as the drift soil. The total nitrogen content of the dust was 2.15 times that of field soil and 1.88 times that of drift soil. The dust contained 1.95 times as much phosphorus as the field soil and 2.04 times as much as the drift soil, and contained 1.99 times as much base-exchange calcium as the field soil.

Samples of dust laid down on snow and ice in Iowa by a dust storm originating in the Texas-Oklahoma Panhandle early in 1937 were collected and compared with samples taken from a small dune formed by the same wind disturbance at Dalhart, Texas. The dust contained roughly 10 times as much organic matter, 9 times as much nitrogen, 19 times as much phosphoric acid, and about one and one-half times as much potash as the dune material. Analyses indicated a similar sorting effect with respect to removal of both soil particles and chemical constituents. The unaffected grass-covered soil contained 79.2 per cent coarse materials (total sands) as compared with no sand in the dust, and 19.6 per cent of fine material (silt and clay) as compared with 97 per cent in the dust. The dust contained more than three times as much organic matter and nitrogen, respectively, as the virgin soil; nearly five times as much phosphoric acid; and one and one-quarter times as much potash.

After a dust storm in Kansas in 1948 both the drift and eroding soil, which originated principally from sandstone, contained much less organic matter than similar soil in non-eroded fields. As a result of the sorting action of the wind during this storm the quantity of particles averaging 0.016 mm. and not exceeding 0.05 mm. in diameter was more than five times as great in the soil from which the drift material was derived as in dunes formed during the storm. Evidently most of the small particles in the wind-eroded soil were removed.

Wind storms removed an average of 0.85 inch of topsoil from fields near Salina and McPherson, Kansas, during March, 1950. It was estimated that about three-fourths of this soil was piled into drifts in the vicinity of the eroding field. The rest was carried away, mainly as dust particles ranging up to 0.1 mm. in diameter.

TABLE 29. Organic matter and partial chemical content of soil of unplowed grass land, dune sand, and dust

Element	Unplowed grassland, near Dalhart, Texas	Dune sand, Dalhart, Texas	Dust	
			Hays, Kansas	Clarinda, Iowa
	Per cent	Per cent	Per cent	Per cent
CaO	0.34	0.31	3.15	1.98
K_2O	2.05	1.77	2.46	2.58
P_2O_5	0.04	trace	0.14	0.19
Nitrogen	0.06	0.02	0.20	0.19
Organic matter	1.06	0.33	3.34	3.35

The data show that the original unplowed soil was much higher in essential plant nutrients and organic matter than the dune sand but much lower in these materials than the dust collected at Hays and Clarinda.

Wind erosion has reduced the productive capacity of High Plains wheat lands an average of 2.2 bushels per acre annually on land in continuous wheat culture and 4.29 bushels on land in summer fallow. Studies show that erosion during the cultivated life of a field was 4.5 times as destructive in the early stages of erosion as in the later stages. Erosion reduced the yield 0.52 bushels per acre per year for the first four years the land was subject to erosion, and at the rate of 0.11 bushels annually for the next 21-year period. Serious erosion began ordinarily two to four years after the land was first put in cultivation.

Erosion lowered the potential productive capacity of fallow land in line with the annual rate of production loss. As a result, the land capability was affected in such a way as to forecast a step-by-step loss of the productive resources of the High Plains if erosion in this area should continue at substantially the same rate that has prevailed since cultivation began.

WATER SORTS OUT THE MOST FERTILE CONSTITUENTS

Much fertile material is lost from the soil through water erosion. Material eroded from Collington sandy loam in New Jersey from June 12, 1938, to December 31, 1941, contained four times as much organic matter, 1.5 times as much phosphorus, 1.4 times as much potassim, and 2.3 times as much calcium as there was in the soil before erosion occurred. The loss per acre due to erosion was 1,149 pounds of organic matter, 67 pounds of nitrogen, 154 pounds of P_2O_5, 575 pounds of K_2O, and 141 pounds of CaO. The eroded material contained 58 per cent of materials averaging less than 50 microns in diameter compared with slightly less than 16 per cent in the original soil.

The material eroded from Dunmore silt loam cropped to corn was 16 per cent richer in total nitrogen and 11 per cent richer in phosphorus than the original soil. Water-soluble phosphorus in water extracts of eroded material from corn land contained six to eight times as much organic phosphorus as was contained in extracts of the parent soil.

The total amount of salts in runoff water from soil erosion plots at Columbia, Missouri, during the year May 1, 1924, to April 30, 1925, ranged from 166.8 pounds per acre from a plot in wheat and clover to 380.1 pounds per acre for a plot that was spaded four inches deep in the spring and fallowed throughout the season. Calcium and sulphur were lost in larger amounts than any of the other elements determined. Although the loss of potassium was rather small, the loss of this element from several plots was much greater than the amount that would ordinarily be applied in commercial fertilizer.

Soil type and cover had a marked effect on both the amounts and concentrations of the solubles lost in runoff at Geneva, New York, during the 13-month period, March, 1938 to March, 1939, inclusive. These effects appeared to be related to variations in soluble concentrations at the soil surface and to the relative rates of infiltrations and runoff.

The annual nitrogen losses from land in Missouri planted to intertilled crops on slopes averaging 200 feet in length have been found to range from 3.8 per cent of the total amount contained in the surface seven inches of soil for a 2 per cent slope to 11.1 per cent for a 12 per cent slope. The annual losses on 2 per cent slopes ranged from 3.8 per cent for slopes averaging 200 feet in length to 10.9 per cent for slopes that averaged 1,200 feet in length. Corresponding losses on a 12 per cent slope were 11.1 per cent for the 200-foot slope and 18.1 per cent for the 1,200-foot slope.

The loss of nitrogen declined with the introduction of close-growing crops into the rotation and disappeared altogether on well sodded meadows or pastures.

The depth of topsoil has been found to be less important than the selective removal of certain parts of the soil by the raindrop splash process. An eleven-year study on four soil types at Ithaca, New York, showed that soil was lost at rates varying from a trace to 138 tons per acre. Only 29 per cent of the remaining plow layer passed through a 2-millimeter screen, whereas approximately 95 per cent of the soil that was washed off passed through such a screen.

DEPTH OF SOIL AN IMPORTANT FACTOR IN CROP YIELDS

A study was conducted with corn in Iowa in 1936 and with corn and oats in 1937 to determine the relation of soil type to yields. It was found that yields vary not only with soil types but also, and more importantly, with depth of soil on the same soil type. Corn yield increased from 31 to 53 bushels per acre on Tama silt loam in 1936 with an increase in depth of surface soil from 0 to 12 inches. An even more impressive correlation of yield and soil depth was obtained in 1937, both with corn and oats. Corn yield in 1937 increased from 47 to 88 bushels per acre as the depth of topsoil increased from 0-2 to 12 inches. The average acre-yields of corn on Tama silt loam, as related to depth of topsoil during the two-year period 1936-37, and of oats in 1937 are shown in Table 30.

These data indicate that the depth of topsoil, particularly if seven inches or less, has a pronounced effect on corn yield on Tama silt loam. The results with corn grown on this soil were substantiated by data obtained on Clarion loam and Clarion fine sandy loam during 1937. Clarion loam which, after erosion, had less than seven inches of topsoil remaining produced 51 bushels of corn per acre, whereas the same type of soil with over seven inches of topsoil produced 67 bushels. Corresponding yields for Clarion fine sandy loam were 39 bushels per acre with less than seven inches of topsoil and 54 with more than seven inches of topsoil remaining.

A close correlation existed between the yield of corn, cotton, and oats and the depth of topsoil under certain cropping practices on three A-horizon depths in the 2- to 8-inch depth range of Cecil soil in Georgia during a 5-year period. The yield of cotton was 615.9 pounds per acre at the 2-inch depth, 889.1 pounds at the 5-inch depth, and 1,019.6 pounds at the 8-inch depth. The yields of corn were 18.8, 24.9, and 32.2 bushels per acre for

TABLE 30. Effect of depth of topsoil on yield of corn and oats on Tama silt loam (21)

Depth of surface soil, in inches	Corn				Oats	
	1936		1937		1937	
	No. of samples	Average yield	No. of samples	Average yield	No. of samples	Average yield
		Bu. per acre		Bu. per acre		Bu. per acre
0-2	4	31	7	47	0	0
3-4	8	28	10	69	2	52
5-6	30	39	19	77	7	61
7-8	39	49	33	82	11	70
9-10	23	50	19	88	4	72
11-12	12	50	25	82	4	70
12	11	53	19	88	2	64

the 2-, 5-, and 8-inch depths, respectively. The yield of oats was 49.6 bushels per acre for the 2-inch depth, 61.3 bushels for the 5-inch depth, and 69.7 bushels for the 8-inch depth.

These yields represent an average of a number of crop rotations. The data show an average annual decline of 64 pounds of seed cotton per acre for each inch of topsoil lost from the 8-inch to the 2-inch depth. The yield of corn declined an average of 2.2 bushels per acre for each inch of top-soil lost and the yield of oats declined 3.3 bushels per acre for each inch of topsoil lost within the same range of topsoil depth. The yields of corn and oats as correlated with the depth of topsoil are shown graphically in Figure 55.

The yield of cotton grown continuously during a 5-year period at Athens, Georgia, ranged from 405 pounds of seed cotton per acre where there was no topsoil to 985 pounds where there was 8.5 inches of topsoil. The yield of the 6.5-inch depth of topsoil was 894 pounds and the estimated yield at the 3.5-inch depth was 650 pounds. This gave practically a straight-line average increment of 70 pounds of seed cotton per acre for each added inch of topsoil depth. This straight-line relationship is illustrated in Figure 56.

A remarkably close association of yield with soil depth and crop rota-tion system was demonstrated by this study. Cotton grown in the same rotation pattern on land in capability classes II and III* yielded 1,217 and 1,213 pounds of seed cotton per acre, respectively, on the two series of plots, each of which averaged exactly 7.6 inches in topsoil depth.

Yields of corn, oats, wheat, and second-year hay were obtained over a

---

* See Chapter 20 for explanation of capability classes.

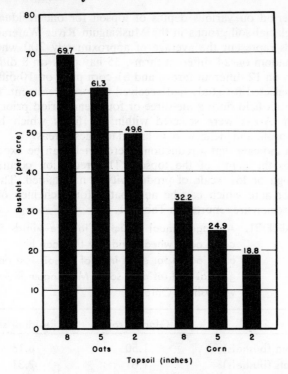

FIGURE 55. Effect of past erosion on the yield of corn and oats on Cecil soil, Watkinsville, Georgia. Average annual yield per acre for the period 1943-47.

FIGURE 56. Correlation between depth of topsoil and cotton yield on Cecil soil at Watkinsville, Georgia.

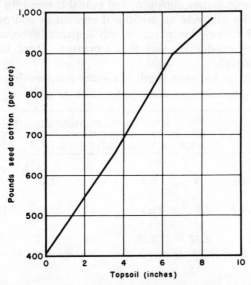

two-year period on various depths of topsoil for one residual soil group and three glacial soil groups in the Muskingum River Watershed in Ohio. These yields represent the average of approximately 200 wheat plots selected at random on 24 different farms, 35 hay plots on 8 different farms, 74 oat plots on 12 different farms, and 81 corn plots on 10 different farms. The fields selected for study had received uniform treatment, and the crop history of each field during the three-or four-year period prior to sampling was known. Areas were selected within the fields which had different depths of topsoil, and yields were obtained for these areas.

The data indicate that a reduction in crop yield can be expected as erosion reduces the depth of the topsoil. This reduction occurs whether a relatively high or low scale of productivity is maintained. The reductions in yields per acre which can be anticipated for each inch of topsoil removed by erosion are reported in Table 31.

TABLE 31. Average annual reduction in acre–yields of corn, oats, wheat, and hay that can be anticipated for each inch of topsoil lost on glacial and residual soils, Muskingum River watershed, Ohio (2)

Crop	Glacial soils	Residual soils
Corn (bushels)	1.50	3.16
Oats (bushels)	1.61	2.31
Wheat (bushels)	1.54	1.55
Hay (tons)	0.101	0.113

A pronounced relationship between depth of surface soil and grape production was observed on Chenango soil in Pennsylvania. Production varied with depth of surface soil, depth being the factor that determined the amount of organic matter, nitrogen, and available moisture contained in the surface layer. By allowing an additional amount of soil per vine, more of these essential factors for plant growth apparently became available to each plant, and production was thus increased. These findings are summarized in Table 32.

TABLE 32. Relation between depth of surface soil, pruning weight, and yield of grape vines — average for 1946-47 (1)

Pruning weight or yield	Depth of surface soil in inches					
	5.0–6.0	6.1–7.0	7.1–8.0	8.1–9.0	9.1–10.0	10.1–11.0
Pruning weight (pounds per vine)	1.0	1.8	1.8	2.2	2.3	2.6
Yield (pounds per vine)	7.9	11.3	11.4	12.5	12.5	14.1
Yield (tons per acre)	2.37	3.39	3.42	3.75	3.75	4.23

Studies were conducted in Indiana, Iowa, Missouri, and Ohio to determine the relation of the depth of topsoil to corn yields. The results of these studies are given in Table 33.

TABLE 33. Effect of depth of topsoil on yield of corn (39)

Depth of topsoil	Bushels per acre in			
	Indiana	Iowa	Missouri	Ohio
Inches				
0	19		16	
2	32	56	25	
4	41	69	38	33.7
6	48	83	46	46.4
8	54	97	54	51.1
9				59.5
10	58	102	60	
12	64	125	64	
13	67			

Information was obtained on 989 soil observations and wheat samples taken from the Wild Horse and Rock Creek sample areas in Oregon in 1939, 1940, and 1941. On the Wild Horse area the average yield of wheat on soils 48 inches or more in depth was 46 bushels per acre, compared with 22 bushels on soils less than 24 inches in depth, and with 13 bushels where the topsoil was less than 6 inches in depth. The results on the Rock Creek area show that yields of 27 bushels were reduced to 20 bushels as the total soil depth changed from more than 48 inches to less than 24 inches, and that yields of 31 bushels declined to 21 bushels with a change from 15 to less than 10 inches in depth of topsoil.

The loss of an inch of topsoil caused a reduction of 0.9 bushels per acre in the yield of wheat in the Wild Horse area, and 0.8 bushels in the Rock Creek area. The change in yield due to erosion was most pronounced on shallow soils, amounting to as much as 1.7 bushels per inch where the topsoil was less than 6 inches deep.

The corn yield for 1943 on non-desurfaced Austin clay at Temple, Texas, was 27.6 bushels per acre, whereas that for desurfaced (topsoil removed) soil, representing the marly (limestone) C horizon, was but 16.4 bushels. The desurfaced plot had been cropped to row crops during the period 1932-43 with a green manure crop that was turned under each year. In spite of this treatment, the corn yield on the desurfaced plot was but 59.4 per cent of the yield from the non-desurfaced plot where no green manure crops were grown or turned under.

Erosion has lowered crop yields throughout the country generally and has resulted in abandonment of both large and small areas. Some of the abandoned land may have been too shallow for cultivation at the time it was broken out, but much of it was reduced in depth by erosion to the point where it became too shallow for cultivation. Some soils have only about 2 to 4 inches of topsoil originally. Once reduced to a depth insufficient for adequate water storage for crop growth, such lands are virtually lost to the growing of cultivated crops except under irrigation, regardless of the inherent productivity of the soil material. Some of the deeper soils may be reclaimed—at a price. It is much more economical to keep them from eroding than to restore them.

CROP YIELDS HIGHER ON UNERODED SOILS

Experiments conducted over a four-year period on Fayette silt loam at La Crosse, Wisconsin, and on other soil types at other conservation experiment stations show that crop production was significantly higher on uneroded than on eroded soil. Moderately eroded soil with five to six inches of surface soil yielded significantly more corn, small grain, and hay than severely eroded soil which had lost all but two inches of its surface soil. This difference in yield was evident even though all plots were brought up to a similar potash and phosphorus level and planted to a 5-year crop rotation including three years of hay. The average yield of corn on moderately eroded soil was 92 bushels per acre, compared with 65 bushels on severely eroded soil. Barley produced 21 bushels per acre on moderately eroded soil, compared with 12 bushels per acre on severely eroded soil. Hay produced 3.5 tons on moderately eroded soil, compared with 3.2 tons on severely eroded soil. The severely eroded soil produced only 70 per cent as much corn, 57 per cent as much barley, and 91 per cent as much hay as the moderately eroded soil.

Field tests were made in Wisconsin on 45 farms, located as far north as Barron County and as far south as Grant County, in order to determine if erosion affected production on other soil types and under other climatic conditions in that state. Slightly eroded, moderately eroded, and severely eroded plots were selected in each field where all three stages of erosion were present. At least four plots selected at random were harvested for each soil depth, and on most fields two or three locations of similar soil depth were harvested.

Small-grain yields were obtained on 18 farms of which 15 showed a significantly higher yield on the less severely eroded soil. Three soil depths were found in the same field on 11 farms. Small grain on these fields yielded an average of 65 bushels per acre where there were six or more inches of surface soil, 50 bushels where there were four to six inches of surface soil, and 43 bushels per acre where there were three inches or less of topsoil. In other words, there was a reduction of 22 bushels per acre as a result of the loss of three inches of surface soil.

Corn yields were obtained on different soil depths on 12 farms. In each instance the yield of corn was higher on the slightly eroded than on the more severely eroded soil. On eight of the farms where all the soil depths were present in the same field, the average yield of corn was 80 bushels per acre where the soil was only slightly eroded, 67 bushels per acre where the soil was moderately eroded, and 60 bushels per acre where the soil was severely eroded.

These data indicate that the yield of a crop is significantly decreased with the loss of topsoil through erosion, and that depth of surface soil is a major factor influencing yields of crops. With few exceptions, the yield was correlated directly with the depth of surface soil regardless of soil type, variety of crop, cultural treatment, fertilizer practice, or climatic condition.

Smith reported that the average annual acre-yield of corn on certain soils in Missouri declined from 64 bushels with 12 inches of topsoil to 16 bushels where all the topsoil had been eroded away. Yields were obtained on Shelby, Grundy, and Mexico soils over the 5-year period 1940-44 on soils with 0, 2, 4, 6, 8, 10, and 12 inches of topsoil. Past erosion reduced the yield of soybeans on an average of about 1.79 bushels per acre per inch of topsoil lost on Shelby soil and 0.73 bushel on Marshall soil.

Data secured in 1938 by the technical staff of the Greenfield, Iowa, Soil Conservation Service Demonstration project showed that the average corn yield was lowered about five bushels per acre for each inch that the surface soil was lowered below eight inches by erosion.

The yield of corn in 1939 at Bethany, Missouri, ranged from 17.1 bushels per acre where only 3 inches of topsoil remained to 47.3 bushels where 13 or more inches of topsoil remained. These were the average yields of four fields, where yields were determined for different depths of topsoil in the same field. A similar study of seven fields showed a corn yield of 15.2 bushels per acre where all the topsoil had been removed by erosion, compared with a yield of 67.5 bushels per acre where 13 or more inches of topsoil remained.

Similar studies were conducted during 1939 and 1940 in Indiana, Iowa, and Ohio. In the studies carried out near Fowler, Indiana, the corn yields were determined for different soil depths in the same field. The studies were made on 16 fields in 1939 and on 18 in 1940. The depth classes of topsoil ranged from one to 13+ inches in 1939 and from 0 to 13+ inches in 1940. The average yield for the 16 fields in 1939 ranged from 49.2 bushels per acre, where topsoil was one to two inches deep, to 93.4 bushels for the 13+-inch depth. The corresponding yields for the 18 fields in 1940 ranged from 19.8 bushels per acre, where all the topsoil had been removed by erosion, to 69.5 bushels where 13+ inches of topsoil still remained. The 1939 yield data for each of the three important soil types mapped in the 16 fields at Fowler are presented graphically in Figure 57. The data show that for comparable depths the corn yields for the three soil types were fairly constant, except for the 11.5- and 13.5-inch depths of the Parr silt loam. However, in general, there was a substantial decline in the corn yield on each soil as the depth of topsoil decreased.

Approximate evaluations of the principal soil characteristics such as profile, surface texture, slope, and erosion were made for the soils of Smokey Hill and Lyon townships of Geary County, Kansas. These evaluations were tested and revised by the use of crop-yield data collected by two methods: (a) a survey of farms to obtain yield and practice data for fields of small grains, and (b) harvesting samples of corn from the different soils in fields farmed by the same operator under identical cultural practices.

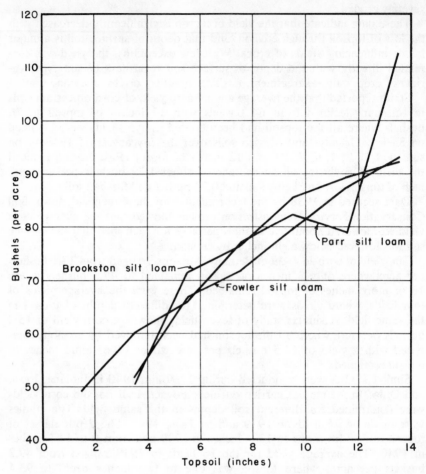

FIGURE 57. Corn yields expressed in bushels per acre for different depths of topsoils for three soil types near Fowler, Indiana, in 1939.

The results of this evaluation showed that productivity was inversely proportional to the degree of erosion. The productivity rating ranged from 95 per cent for none or slight erosion to a minimum of 40 per cent for very severe erosion, whereas moderate erosion had a rating of 85 per cent and severe erosion 70 per cent. It is of interest to consider the composite soil rating in relation to depth of topsoil alone. This relationship for the 46 samples comprising the basic data is shown in Figure 58.

Yields of wheat for 1946, as calculated from the yield and practice survey in Geary County, Kansas, are shown in Table 34.

The yields of both corn and cabbage were higher on uneroded Dunkirk soil at Geneva, New York, in 1943 than on severely eroded soil of the

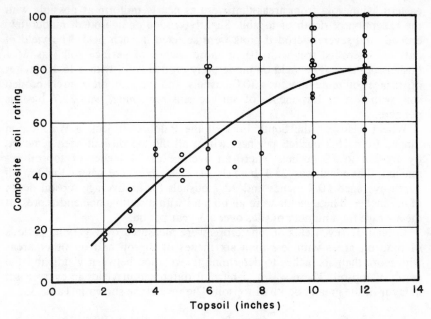

FIGURE 58. Composite soil rating vs. depth of topsoil, Geary County, Kansas.

same type despite the fact that 126 pounds of readily available nitrogen was applied per acre to the severely eroded soil and none was applied to the slightly eroded soil. The uneroded soil produced 4.7 tons of sweet corn and 16.7 tons of cabbage per acre in contrast to yields of 3.2 tons of sweet corn and 13.8 tons of cabbage per acre from the severely eroded soil. Moderately eroded soil (33 inches of soil over shale) in Ontario County, New York, produced 38 No. 1 rose stock per hundred feet of row space, whereas severely eroded soil (14 inches of soil over shale) of the same type and in the same field produced none.

Yields of oats were obtained on five widely scattered farms in south-

TABLE 34. Effect of erosion on the yield of wheat in Geary County, Kansas, 1946 (26)

Topography and degree of erosion	Yield
	Bu. per acre
Level to gently sloping—none to slight erosion	21
Undulating to sloping—none to slight erosion	18
Undulating to sloping—severe erosion	11
Undulating to sloping—very severe erosion	8

eastern Minnesota from areas that were as nearly uniform as possible with the exception of depth of topsoil. Slightly eroded or uneroded, moderately eroded, and severely eroded plots were selected in each field. The yield of oats on uneroded soil with 10 or more inches of surface soil was 36.1 bushels per acre. The yield on moderately eroded soils, with 5 to 10 inches of surface soil remaining, was 30.0 bushels; and the yield on severely eroded soil, with five or less inches of surface soil remaining, was 22.7 bushels per acre.

Wheat yields on the South Fork of the Palouse Project in Washington ranged from 15.3 bushels per acre where all the topsoil had been removed by erosion to 50 bushels where an average of 24 inches of topsoil remained. The yield was 35.1 bushels of wheat per acre where the topsoil depth averaged 10.7 inches and 22.7 bushels for an average topsoil depth of 4.7 inches. These yields were all on land with a south slope and represent the average for a number of sites over a 3-year period.

In New Jersey, yields of nine crops were measured over varying periods of time on areas with less than six inches of topsoil and on other areas with more than six inches to determine the relation between yields and the depth of topsoil. There was a significant difference in yields in every case, in favor of the greater depth of topsoil. The results are shown in Table 35.

TABLE 35.   Crop yields per acre for various depths of topsoil, New Jersey (25)

Crop	Average number locations studied	Years of study	Depth of topsoil	
			0 to 6 inches	6 inches or more
Potatoes	12	7	233 bushels	298 bushels
Corn	4	5	40 bushels	64 bushels
Wheat	4	5	17 bushels	34 bushels
Oats	2	3	21 bushels	32 bushels
Soybeans	2	3	4 bushels	18 bushels
Barley	2	3	26 bushels	55 bushels
Rye	2	3	11 bushels	37 bushels
Alfalfa	2	3	2 tons	3.3 tons
Asparagus	1	1	232 pounds	728 pounds

CROP YIELDS HIGHER ON TOPSOIL THAN ON SUBSOIL

A study was initiated in 1936 near Wooster, Ohio, to determine the relative crop production of topsoil and subsoil. Three series of plots were used. The topsoil was stripped off down to the subsoil on one series of plots. This topsoil was spread over a second series of plots where the original topsoil was undisturbed, thus doubling the depth of topsoil. On a third series of plots the original topsoil was left undisturbed. Corresponding plots in each of the three series were planted to the same rotations and given identical treatment otherwise. The average annual yield of corn, oats, wheat and hay per acre on these plots for all treatments for the 9-year period 1937-45 are shown in Table 36.

TABLE 36. Effect of depth of topsoil on the yield of corn, oats, wheat, and hay at Wooster, Ohio, over a 9-year period (39)

Crop	Average annual plot yield		
	Double topsoil	Virgin topsoil	Subsoil
Corn (bushels)	98.65	81.82	39.31
Oats (bushels)	52.12	57.24	21.37
Wheat (bushels)*	33.2	27.9	11.8
Hay (tons)	3.67	2.60	1.94

*Average for 1937-47

The yield for each kind of crop except oats was higher on the double topsoil than on the virgin topsoil, and they were much lower in every case on the subsoil plots than on the virgin-topsoil plots.

Untreated soil from which about one-half the topsoil had been removed by erosion yielded more than four times as much grain as untreated subsoil at Bethany, Missouri, over a 7-year period. Similar soils limed at the rate of three tons per acre in the beginning and fertilized with 200 pounds of superphosphate per acre produced 1.8 times as much grain where one-half of the topsoil still remained as where the subsoil had received the same treatment.

A study similar to that reported at Wooster was started at Columbus, Ohio, in 1938. The average annual acre-yield of corn for all treatments in the three series of plots for the 8-year period 1938-45 was 42.9 bushels for normal topsoil, 18.2 bushels for subsoil, and 67.0 bushels for the double topsoil. The addition of 500 pounds of 0-14-6 fertilizer per acre and enough limestone to bring the pH to 6.5 changed the yields to 48 bushels per acre for normal topsoil, 20.1 for subsoil, and 65.2 for double topsoil.

A study was made in California of the influence of soil horizons A, B, and C on the rate of growth of certain annual plants which dominate early successional stages, compared with certain perennial herbs recognized as stable or climax in grassland communities, and on the comparative plant development in horizons A, B, and C. The growth rate of both the annual and the perennial species was appreciably greater in horizon A than in lower horizons, regardless of the soil series or the species used. Likewise, the amount of plant material produced in horizon A was consistently greater than in horizon C, regardless of species or soil series. This held true, also, in horizon B with the exception of Olympic soil, in which the B horizon proved nearly as productive as the A horizon for two annual species.

This deviation from the average may be accounted for by the fact that the Olympic was formed under grassland conditions; hence the B horizon may have been subject to greater accumulation of materials from the upper horizon than the forest soil.

The A horizon of naturally eroded Cecil sandy loam produced an average annual acre-yield over a 4-year period of 939 pounds of seed cotton compared with a yield of 304 pounds for the B horizon and 81 pounds for the C horizon. The A horizon was more than three times as productive as the B horizon and 11 times as productive as the C horizon.

Manure was applied at the rate of four tons per acre to half of the plots on each horizon in 1939, the last year of the 4-year period of study. The yield of seed cotton as influenced by the addition of the manure is shown in Table 37. The addition of manure resulted in increased yields on all horizons, but its beneficial effect was relatively greater on the C horizon than on the A and B horizons. The addition of manure lifted the yield on the C-horizon plot above that for the unmanured B-horizon plot, but did not raise the yield of the B-horizon plot to that of the unmanured A-horizon plot.

TABLE 37.   Effect of the addition of 4 tons of manure per acre on the yield of seed cotton on A, B, and C horizons of Cecil soil (18)

Horizon	Yield of seed cotton per acre	
	Unmanured (Pounds)	Manured (Pounds)
A	561	845
B	348	501
C	51	426

EROSION REDUCES EFFICIENCY OF FERTILIZERS

Studies in New York showed that cropping and cultural practices that resulted in sheet erosion rapidly led to inefficient use of fertilizer. Corn was grown on four of the leading soil types of the state which were cropped uniformly and fertilized with 1,000 pounds of 10-10-10 fertilizer per acre. The per-acre yields ranged from 17 to 88 bushels on Bath flaggy silt loam at Ithaca; 62 to 100 bushels and 54 to 82 bushels, respectively, on Ontario sandy clay loam and Dunkirk silty clay loam at Geneva; and from 49 to 69 bushels on Honeoye silt loam at Marcellus, even after two years of alfalfa-clover-timothy hay.

Along with the decline of productivity chargeable to removal of soil by erosion has gone a lesser but more steady decline of fertility from the land due to crop removals. The decline of productivity in the Southern High Plains due to erosion was five times as great as that due to crop removals during the first four years of cultivation. It was only 1.5 times as great during the next 21 years of cultivation. The total decline in productivity of land that had been in cultivation 15 years or more, due to both causes, amounted to 7.01 bushels of wheat per acre.

Soil erosion has played, and continues to play, a major role in destroying the productive capacity of the nation's soils. It is now recognized as the most widespread and destructive agent involved in bringing about the rapid depletion of the fertility and productive capacity of cultivated land. This is accomplished through the removal of the organic matter, nitrogen, and clay and silt fractions, which are the life of the soil, as well as through the physical removal of the soil body itself.

The selective and sorting action of wind and water in the erosion process under some conditions may remove organic matter and essential plant nutrients without producing a significant net loss of soil from the surface of the land. This process leaves the soil in an infertile state. In order to restore the soil to its original state of fertility, the plant nutrients and organic matter thus removed must be replenished. This, if physically possible of accomplishment, would involve tremendous expense. In many instances, replacing the lost material would be completely out of the question.

REFERENCES

1. Alderfer, R. B., and Fleming, H. K. 1948. *Soil factors influencing grape production on well-drained lake terrace areas.* Pa. Agr. Expt. Sta. Bull. 495.
2. Barre, R. D. 1939. *Effect of erosion on crop yields.* Supplement to Muskingum Watershed Ohio Survey Report, *Runoff and water retardation and soil erosion prevention for flood control purposes.* Appendix X.
3. Bennett, H. H. 1939. *Soil conservation.* McGraw-Hill Book Co., Inc., New York.
4. Bryant, J. C., and Slater, C. S. 1948. *Runoff water as an agent in the loss of soluble materials from certain soils.* Iowa State Coll. Jour. of Sci., 22: 3, 260-297.
5. Daniel, H. A., Elwell, H. M., and Cox, M. B. 1943. *Investigations in erosion control and reclamation of eroded land at the Red Plains Conservation Experiment Station, Guthrie, Oklahoma, 1930-40.* USDA Tech. Bull. 837.
6. Daniel, H. A., and Langhan, W. H. 1936. *The effect of wind erosion and cultivation on the nitrogen and organic matter content of soils in the Southern High Plains.* Amer. Soc. Agron. Jour., 28: 587-96.
7. Duley, F. L. 1926. *The loss of soluble salts in runoff water.* Soil Sci., 21: 401-409.
8. Finnell, H. H. *Monthly Progress Report, Soil Conservation Service, Oct. 1949.*
9. Fippin, E. O. 1945. *Plant nutrient losses in silt and water in the Tennessee River system.* Soil Sci., 60: 223-39.
10. Fly, C. 1935. *A preliminary report of the chemical and mechanical analyses of dust deposited by wind at Goodwell, Oklahoma.* Panhandle Agr. Expt. Sta. Bull. 57.
11. Free, G. R. 1946. *Evidence of the effect of erosion on the organic matter and erodibility of Honeoye soil.* Amer. Soc. Agron. Jour., 38: 207-217.
12. ———, Carleton, E. A., Lamb, J., Jr., and Gustafson, A. F. 1946. *Experiments in the control of soil erosion in central New York.* N. Y. Agr. Expt. Sta. (Cornell) Bull. 831.
13. Hays, O. E., and Muckenhirn, R. J. 1944. *The effect of depth of surface soil and contouring on crop yields.* SCS and Minn. Agr. Expt. Sta. (Mimeo.)
14. Hays, O. E., and Rost, C. O. 1944. *The effect of surface soil and contouring on crop yields in Minnesota.* SCS and Minn. Agr. Expt. Sta. (Mimeo.)
15. Hendrickson, B. H. 1948. *Review of Principal Results—1947.* USDA, SCS, Watkinsville, Ga. (Multi.)
16. Kaiser, V. G. *Wheat yields as affected by soils, slope and erosion.* Handbook of Colfax Work Group, Oregon. SCS.

17. Lamb, J. Jr., Carleton, E. A., and Free, G. R. 1950. *Effect of past management and erosion on fertilizer efficiency.* Soil Sci., 70(5): 385-92.
18. Latham, E. E. 1940. *Relative productivity of the A horizon of Cecil sandy loam and the B and C horizons exposed by erosion.* Amer. Soc. Agron. Jour., 34: 12.
19. McHargue, J. S., and Peter, A. M. 1921. *The removal of mineral plant-food by natural drainage waters.* Ky. Agr. Expt. Sta. Res. Bull. 237.
20. Millar, C. E. 1923. *Studies on virgin and depleted soils.* Soil Sci., 16: 433-48.
21. Murray, W. G., Englehorn, A. J., and Griffin, R. A. 1939. *Yield tests and land valuation.* Iowa Agr. Expt. Sta. Res. Bull. 262.
22. Neal, O. R. 1942. *Erosion control aids fertility maintenance.* N. H. Agr. Expt. Sta., Crops and Pastures, 6: 4.
23. ———. 1943. *The influence of soil erosion on fertility losses and on potato yields.* Amer. Potato Jour., 20: 57-64.
24. ———. 1944. *Removal of nutrients from the soil by crops and erosion.* Jour. Amer. Soc. Agron., 36(7): 601-607.
25. ———, and Brill, G. D. 1948. *Annual report of research in methods of soil and water conservation in New Jersey.* SCS.
26. Pine, W. H. 1948. *Methods of classifying Kansas land according to economic productivity.* Thesis for a doctor's degree, Univ. of Minn.
27. Powers, W. L., Jones, J. S., and Ruzek, C. V. 1939. *Composition, rating and conservation of Willamette Valley soils.* Ore. Agr. Expt. Sta. Bull. 365.
28. Rogers, H. T. 1941. *Plant nutrient losses from a corn, wheat, clover rotation on Dunmore silt loam.* Soil Sci. Soc. Amer. Proc., 6: 263-71.
29. ———. 1942. *Losses of surface-applied phosphate and limestone through runoff from pasture land.* Soil Sci. Soc. Amer. Proc., 7: 69-76.
30. Sinclair, J. D., and Sampson, A. W. 1931. *Establishment and succession of vegetation on different soil horizons.* Univ. of Calif. Hilgardia, 5: 7.
31. Slater, C. S. 1942. *Variability of eroded material.* Jour. Agr. Res., 65: 209-219.
32. ———, and Carleton, E. A. 1938. *The effect of erosion on losses of soil organic matter.* Soil Sci. Soc. Amer. Proc., 3: 123-28.
33. Smith, D. D. 1946. *The effect of contour planting on crop yields and erosion.* Amer. Soc. Agron. Jour., 38: 810-19.
34. Stallings, J. H. 1950. *Erosion of topsoil reduces productivity.* USDA, SCS-TP-98.
35. Stauffer, R. S. 1942. *Runoff, percolate and leaching losses from Illinois soils.* Amer. Soc. Agron. Jour., 34: 830-35.
36. Thomas, H. L., Stephenson, R. E., Freese, C. R., Chapin, R. W., and Huggins, W. W. 1943. *The economic effect of soil erosion on wheat yields in eastern Oregon.* Ore. Agr. Expt. Sta. Cir. 157.
37. Uhland, R. E. 1940. *Field method of evaluating effects of physical factors and farm management practices on soil erosion and crop yields.* Soil Sci. Soc. Amer. Proc., 5: 373-76.
38. ———. 1944. *Rebuilding eroded soil is a slow process.* Soil Cons. 9: 276-69.
39. ———. 1949. *Crop yields lowered by erosion.* USDA, SCS-TP-75.
40. Wooley, J. C. 1943. *Fertility losses as a basis for erosion control planning.* Agr. Eng., 24: 377-79.
41. Zingg, A. W., and Chepil, W. S. 1950. *Aerodynamics of wind erosion.* Agr. Eng., 31(6): 379-82.

12

Water-Erosion Control
on Cultivated Land

As has been previously stated, water erosion on cultivated land results from the application of energy from
two distinct sources. They are, first, the falling raindrop and, second, surface flow. The energy exerted
by the falling raindrop is applied slantingly or vertically from above, while that of surface flow is applied
parallel to the surface.

Since the falling raindrop applies its energy from
above, remedial measures that are needed are entirely
different from those needed to combat the erosive
forces of flowing water. Measures aimed at controlling
the effects of the falling raindrop must be designed to
intercept and de-energize the raindrop before it strikes
the ground. Those aimed at controlling surface flow
must be designed to prevent the concentration and
retard the movement of free water over the ground.

When raindrops strike the ground surface or the
film of water covering it, they splash bits of soil and
organic matter into the air. Some of these splashed
particles may rise to a height of two feet or more and
move horizontally more than five feet on the level
surface. On sloping ground, the larger proportion of
the splashed material moves downhill. Two inches of
rain on an area produce enough energy to raise a
seven-inch layer of soil a height of three feet over the

area, if the energy could be applied at one time. More than 100 tons of soil per acre may be splashed by the most beating types of rain falling on a bare, highly detachable soil.

Control of the erosion caused by raindrops can be accomplished by the proper use of a cover of vegetation, either living or dead. Such covers, when properly used on the surface of the ground, serve as cushions to absorb the energy of the falling drops and rob them of the power to splash soil. Soil not splashed or torn loose by the falling raindrops is not likely to undergo any serious erosion.

CONTROL OF RAINDROP SPLASH

The first steps in developing a program to control erosion by raindrop splash are (a) to determine the potential erosive capacity of the rainfall during each season of the year, (b) to determine the vulnerability of the soil to this type of erosion, and (c) to plan a cropping system that will provide adequate vegetal cover to furnish protection in sufficient amounts at the proper time. The potential erosive capacity of the raindrop can be determined in a general way by reviewing the local records that show intensities. These data may be arranged in chart form showing rainfall intensities by months. The rainfall intensity data may also be expressed in terms of the number of excessive storms by months. Rains falling at the rate of .25 inch during a 5-minute period or at the rate of .35 inch during a 15-minute period may be considered, for all practical purposes, the excessive erosion-producing rains. It is likely, however, that more detailed information about the impact characteristics of raindrops will be needed as we move further into this method of studying erosion control.

The major portion of the erosion in most localities is the result of a small number of rains. In some areas, as much as 80 per cent of the annual erosion may be attributed to a half dozen or so intense storms. In practically all locations, more than half of the annual erosion may be attributed to a small portion of the total number of rains occurring during the year. It is possible to identify through the records of individual rains the season or seasons when the erosion-producing storms occur.

Records from the Arnot Soil Conservation Service Experiment Station at Ithaca, New York, illustrate this point. Twenty-one rains, or less than 12 per cent of the total of 177 that cause .5 ton or over of soil loss per acre each, accounted for 65 per cent of the total soil loss during a period of eight years and seven months ending December 31, 1943. Two of these rains caused 17.7 per cent of the soil loss.

A breakdown of the 177 rains at the Arnot Station into intensity groups illustrates the importance of the rainfall intensity in the erosion process. Records of these rains have been assembled in eight different groups based on the maximum intensity for a 15-minute period. The amount of soil lost by erosion during each group of storms is presented in Table 38.

The character of the rainfall is more important in causing erosion than the total amount of rain falling, when other conditions remain constant. A slow, gentle rain is not nearly so destructive as an equal, or even smaller, amount of rain falling in only a small fraction of the time. A greater portion

TABLE 38. Number of rains causing .5 ton or over of soil loss per acre, average rainfall, maximum rainfall intensity for 15-minute periods, and soil loss per acre at Ithaca, New York (6)

Number of rains	Average rainfall	Average maximum rainfall	Soil lost
	Inches	Inches per hour (Intensity)	Pounds per acre
55	.54	.50	8
29	.59	.62	57
33	.68	.77	232
12	.77	1.14	721
27	.94	1.50	1,594
9	1.12	2.16	3,527
10	1.73	2.73	5,704
2	1.35	4.00	14,427

of the water that falls during slow rains enters the ground surface. It is only during intense rains that the combined effect of raindrop splash and surface flow, acting as a team, exert their maximum influence in the erosion process.

Other rainfall data from the Arnot Station show that the greatest erosion hazard from rainfall occurs during the period June to September, inclusive. During this same period of eight years and seven months, the average annual numbers of excessively heavy rains were: eight during June, eleven during July, fourteen during August, four during September, and one during October. No excessively heavy rains occurred during any of the other seven months.

Total rainfall by months is not as reliable as rainfall intensity data or the number of excessive storms by months. It may serve, however, in the absence of the more reliable data, in developing a rainfall hazard chart. This is illustrated by data obtained at Guthrie, Oklahoma, where the period of greatest total rainfall runs from April to November, inclusive. This coincides only roughly with the period of highest 15-minute maximum intensities, which extends from April to October, inclusively. The months of April, May, June, August, and September are the months having a large number of excessive storms (high-intensity rainfall).

The advantages of using the number of excessive rains per month, in preference to the use of the total rainfall, in establishing the rainfall hazard chart is illustrated by the data obtained at Tyler, Texas, during the period 1931-1940. Soil loss from continuous cotton plots during this period was more closely related to the number of excessive storms than to the total rainfall.

TABLE 39. Average annual rainfall, 15-minute intensities, and total rainfall by months at Guthrie, Oklahoma, 1930-1940 (1)

Month	Rainfall	Maximum 15-minute intensities	Excessively heavy storms*
	Inches	Inches	Number
January	1.45	.31	0
February	1.44	.87	.1
March	1.87	.93	.3
April	2.60	1.67	.9
May	4.37	2.45	1.6
June	3.73	2.08	1.6
July	1.63	1.72	.5
August	3.42	2.08	.9
September	3.67	2.13	1.1
October	1.97	1.15	.5
November	2.56	.60	.2
December	1.50	.33	0

*Average annual for 17-year period

TABLE 40. Average annual rainfall, number of excessive storms, and soil loss by erosion on continuous cotton land at Tyler, Texas, 1931-1940 (7)

Month	Rainfall	Excessive storms	Soil loss
	Inches	Number	Tons per acre
January	4.17	.5	.52
February	3.92	.4	.22
March	3.55	.8	.60
April	3.95	1.5	1.85
May	3.40	1.2	4.61
June	2.67	1.6	1.99
July	2.87	1.5	1.45
August	2.34	1.5	.54
September	2.04	1.0	.35
October	2.82	.4	.49
November	4.11	.8	.76
December	5.45	1.0	.97

Table 40 shows that the three months November-January, inclusive, record the highest total rainfall. But the period April-August, inclusive, includes the largest number of excessively heavy storms, causing the greatest soil loss by erosion. During June and July, the total rainfall was relatively small compared with that of November, December, and January, when the loss was considerably lower than during the April-July period. It should be noted, however, that there was both a substantial rainfall hazard and soil loss during each month of the year at Tyler.

The occurrence of such erosion-causing storms is not necessarily the same from month to month in different areas. This is shown by the data in Table 41, giving the number of excessive storms by months for varying period of time at five different locations. For the most part, however, the period May-September, inclusive, includes the months of the greatest rainfall hazard at these localities.

TABLE 41. Average number of excessive storms by months for varying periods at five different locations (7)

Month	Bethany,[a] Mo.	Clarinda,[b] Iowa	Hays,[c] Kans.	La Crosse,[d] Wis.	Statesville,[e] N. C.
January	0	0	0	0	.3
February	0	0	0	0	0
March	.1	0	.1	.1	.8
April	.1	.8	.1	.5	.3
May	1.4	1.1	.8	.7	.7
June	1.8	2.1	1.4	1.3	1.7
July	1.0	2.0	.6	1.5	2.0
August	1.3	1.0	1.1	1.2	3.0
September	.9	.8	1.0	1.1	.3
October	.4	.5	0	.3	.8
November	.1	0	.1	.1	.5
December	0	.1	0	0	0

[a] Average annual for 10 years.
[b] Average annual for 8 years.
[c] Average annual for 9 years.
[d] Average annual for 15 years.
[e] Average annual for 6 years.

We have seen that rainstorms vary widely in their capacity to erode soil. We find, likewise, that soils differ greatly in their stability or their capacity to withstand the erosive forces set in motion by falling raindrops. Soils deficient in those properties that impart stability are more vulnerable to the raindrop impact than those that are high in such properties. Soils having low resistance to the raindrop impact usually require more intensive protective measures than those possessing high resistance. Even with those soils highly resistant to splash erosion, the impact of falling raindrops puddles the surface soil, causes fertility erosion, and reduces infiltration into the soil.

The difference between the forces supplied by the raindrops and the resistance offered to those forces by the soil represents the energy remaining to be absorbed by vegetal covers, if erosion is to be controlled successfully. As is to be expected, the values of plant covers in shielding soil from the pelting by raindrops vary widely. The kind, amount, and uniformity of distribution of plant cover influence its effectiveness. Dense, low-lying covers are more effective than coarser covers resting either on or some distance above the surface of the ground. Other things being equal, the protective value of plant cover in controlling raindrop splash varies more or less directly with the amount of cover. Even small amounts of plant cover exert a worth-while influence.

Tests conducted on shallow, mixed-range soils, to determine the effect of plant cover on reducing raindrop splash, show that 657 pounds of range-forage cover per acre reduced the amount by 73 per cent from what it was on bare soil. The same tests show that 1,292 pounds of range-forage cover reduced the raindrop splash by 93 per cent, 1,865 pounds of cover reduced it by 96 per cent, and 5,592 pounds reduced it by over 99 per cent. Corresponding figures obtained from similar tests conducted on hardlands (Pullman soil) show a reduction of 52 per cent of raindrop splash by 704 pounds of range-cover per acre, a 90 per cent reduction with 2,016 pounds of cover, a 96 per cent reduction with 3,307 pounds, and over 99.5 per cent reduction with 4,785 pounds of cover per acre.

The use of 750 pounds of buckwheat straw per acre as a mulch at Ithaca, New York, reduced the soil loss to less than one-fourth of the amount from bare land. Present indications are that from one to two tons of plant cover (dry-weight basis) per acre, uniformly distributed over the ground surface at the time of the storm, are needed for effective protection against raindrop impact.

The adequacy of vegetal cover produced by the cropping system in use, in absorbing the raindrop impact, is illustrated graphically by comparing a chart that shows the extent of the rainfall hazard by months with another that presents a combination of resistance offered by the soil to the hazard and the amount of protection supplied by the cropping system in use. The chart in the upper part of Figure 59 shows the raindrop hazard by months, as measured by the number of excessively heavy rains, for the period March-October, inclusive. No excessively heavy rains were recorded during the months omitted from the chart. The lower half of the figure indicates the estimated protection against the raindrop impact supplied by the foliage of the crops used in the rotation.

It may be seen that the major rainfall hazard occurs during the months of June-August, inclusive, with a fairly high degree of hazard occurring in September. The peas that occupy the ground during the first part of the year supply adequate protection during May and the first half of June. The peas are harvested for canning and the top growth is removed from the field at the beginning of the high-rainfall hazard period, June-August. The removal of the peas exposes the bare ground to the impact of raindrops until the cover crop of rye-vetch can become established and produce sufficient cover to absorb the impact. Since the cover crop is not seeded until July, and some weeks elapse after the planting date before adequate plant cover is pro-

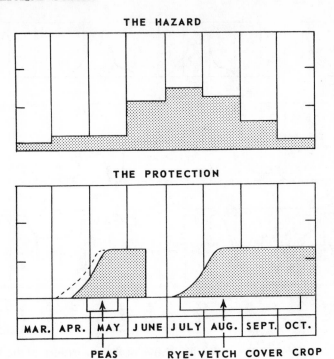

FIGURE 59. Schematic outline illustrative of a gap in the protection provided by a crop in a rotation and the following winter
cover crop.

duced, the land is without satisfactory protection during most of the
period from mid-June to mid-August. It is evident that the system in use
does not meet the requirements of a conservation cropping system.

The same method may be used in determining whether a given crop rotation meets conservation requirements. It is necessary, however, to prepare
the two charts so they will cover the full period of time occupied by the rotation. The rainfall hazard chart will be the same for each year of the rotation, but the protection chart should reflect the protection provided by the
crops used in each season of each year of the rotation. This is illustrated
graphically in Figure 60 by the use of two distinct types of crop rotations
which have the same rainfall hazard.

The rainfall hazard begins in early spring and increases steadily until it
reaches a peak in June. It declines somewhat after reaching a peak, but remains high throughout the summer. It declines gradually during the early
fall and disappears during the latter part of the season. Farm A is cropped
to a 4-year rotation consisting of fallow-wheat-kafir-fallow. The two fallow
years provide no protection against the raindrop impact, except the little
that is provided by kafir stubble during the second year. The wheat year,
when stubble mulch tillage is practiced, provides fair protection throughout

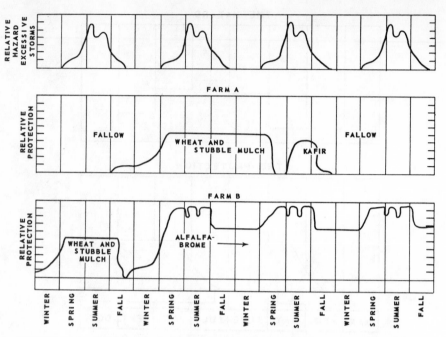

FIGURE 60.   Schematic outline illustrative of the occurrence of the hazard
(excessive storms) and the protection (obtained from agronomic practices) on two different farms in the same area
during a 4-year period.

the year, whereas the kafir does not develop any degree of protection until
after the peak of the rainfall hazard has been reached and passed. The
maximum protection supplied by the kafir during the latter part of the summer is inadequate.

The four-year rotation practiced on Farm B supplies protection much
superior to that on Farm A. Again a four-year rotation is used, but this
time it consists of one year of wheat and three years of alfalfa-bromegrass
hay. Stubble mulch tillage is practiced during the wheat year and, as a result,
fairly adequate cover protection is supplied during the entire rainfall hazard
period. The alfalfa-bromegrass hay supplies ample protection during the
last three years of the rotation.

It is evident that the cropping system shown in Figure 59 and the four-
year crop rotation used on Farm A in Figure 60 fail to supply the plant
cover needed to protect the soil against the ravages of falling raindrops. Under field conditions it may be found impossible or impractical in many instances, especially where row crops are grown, to develop crop rotations
that will in themselves provide adequate amounts of cover at the proper
time. In such cases, the crop rotation must be supplemented by the use on
the ground surface of crop residues and mulches, if raindrop splash is to be
controlled. The major portion of the available evidence shows that the best

FIGURE 61. Stubble-mulch tillage leaves the crop residues on the surface of the ground. The residue provides protection against falling raindrops and improves the soil in a number of ways. (Sherman, Nebraska)
(Soil Conservation Service)

FIGURE 62. When the cropping system includes clean-cultivated row crops, the residues of the preceding crop should be left on the surface of the ground. A 36-inch stand of sweet clover is here being chopped up and spread over the ground by an Edwards Culti-cutter. With the clover chopped up and mashed down by this tool, sub-surface tillers and planters operate in the mulch with little trouble. Splash erosion is eliminated. (Pendleton, Oregon)
(Bureau of Plant Industry, Soils and Agricultural Engineering)

way to utilize crop residues in cropping systems is to leave them on the surface.

PREVENTION OF SPLASH EROSION BASIC TO SOIL IMPROVEMENT

It was pointed out in Chapter 3 that splash erosion accounts for the major losses of organic matter from the soil. Larger amounts of plant nutrients are removed from the soil by this process than by crops. It was also shown that much of the plant nutrients added to the soil in the form of commercial fertilizers are removed by splash erosion before the crops could utilize them. It will be pointed out in a later chapter that splash erosion is active in destroying the physical properties of the soil as well.

This being the case, it must be assumed that the control of splash erosion holds the key to any soil improvement program. Those farm practices that provide effective plant cover throughout the year are most effective in laying the basis for permanent soil improvement programs.

CONTROL OF SURFACE FLOW

That portion of the rainfall which does not find its way into the soil by percolation, or is not impounded in depressions on the surface of the ground, or

FIGURE 63. Heavy wheat stubble being broken, shredded, and scattered evenly over the ground by a machine using rotary knives. Once the ground is in this condition, planting and cultivating can be done through the mulch. Effective erosion control is provided. (Pendleton, Oregon)
(Bureau of Plant Industry, Soils and Agricultural Engineering)

is not intercepted by plant canopy, escapes from the field as surface runoff. As has been stated previously, the chief role of surface flow in the erosion process, before concentrating into rills and gullies, is transporting soil material. It has been stated also that soils which are protected from splash erosion by falling raindrops are not likely to undergo serious erosion as a result of surface flow outside of rills and gullies.

The force of surface flow is applied parallel to the surface. The amount of force it generates is definitely related to the concentration and velocity with which it moves down the slope. The secret of reducing the damage caused by surface flow, then, is to control its concentration, and to retard, or regulate, its velocity.

When runoff water from one small area is allowed to run straight down the slope, it joins with the runoff water from other areas and soon attains great volume as well as high velocity. Since an acre-inch of water weighs more than 113 tons and the ability of flowing water to move objects varies approximately with the sixth power of its velocity, it is easy to realize the tremendous power exerted by runoff water and visualize what is required to stop a load of this magnitude once it gets under way. Doubling the degree of slope increases the total soil loss 2.8 times. It is small wonder that tons

FIGURE 64. Stand of wheat seeded in stubble mulch with McCormick and Beilke drills. The residue from the preceding crop provides ample protection from splash erosion. The soil benefits in many other ways from leaving the trash on the surface. (Pendleton, Oregon)
(Bureau of Plant Industry, Soils and Agricultural Engineering)

upon tons of topsoil may be rolled, or suspended and carried from a cultivated field, leaving eventually but a small amount of either soil or moisture on the field for plant growth.

The regulation of both the concentration and velocity with which free water moves over the surface of the ground may be accomplished by controlling the length of slopes over which the water moves. Where slopes are steep or long enough to favor damaging concentrations and velocities, they need to be shortened by establishing appropriate mechanical barriers at strategic distances. The most popular mechanical barriers now in use for shortening slopes include the terrace, contour cultivation, and contour strip-cropping.

By terracing, the field slope is divided into several small watersheds. The short slopes thus formed, plus the use of a cropping plan, soil treatment, and cultural practices fitted to that field, will allow only a minimum of runoff water to attain scouring velocity. By controlling the velocity of flow, soil loss by scouring is reduced and more runoff water may be absorbed as it moves slowly from the field.

TERRACING

Terraces may logically be divided into two types of classes—level and gradient—on the basis of their primary function. Both types are alike in that they are used to control water and reduce scour erosion. They differ in that the level terrace is used to conserve moisture, whereas the gradient terrace is used for the orderly disposal of surplus water during times of excess rain-

FIGURE 65.   Terraces are useful as a link in the water disposal system but do not protect the soil from raindrop splash erosion. From 6 to 8 inches of topsoil were removed from this terraced field in a period of eight years. (Guthrie, Oklahoma) *(Soil Conservation Service)*

fall. Since one of the major functions of the level terrace is the conservation of moisture, its use naturally would be restricted to those areas where the rainfall is inadequate for maximum crop growth and where conservation of moisture is of primary importance. The gradient terrace, on the other hand, is recommended for humid conditions where, under an ideal conservation program, the only time we could tolerate graded terraces functioning as water diversion structures would be during periods when the soil is fully charged with water or during peak rainfall intensities of excessive duration. Terraces do not protect the soil from splash erosion, however.

CONTOUR STRIP-CROPPING

One means of utilizing the high erosion-control value of close-growing crops is to adopt a contour strip-cropping pattern. Instead of planting a field solidly to erosion-inducing crops, such as cultivated row crops, alternate strips of row and close-growing or sod crops should be planted. Once established, the sod crops usually provide ample protection from erosion, both by raindrop splash and surface flow, to land planted to them. They provide no protection from raindrop splash for the strips planted to clean-tilled crops, however. During rains of light to moderate intensities and amounts, the soil on the sod strip may be able to absorb the water that flows onto them from the clean-tilled strips immediately above. They thus prevent

FIGURE 66. Once established, close-growing crops in contour strip-cropping patterns protect the soil on which they grow from both splash and scour erosion. However, they do not protect the strip planted to clean-tilled crops. (Bell County, Texas)
(Soil Conservation Service)

FIGURE 67. This is a part of a 150-acre field planted to a rotation of corn, small grain, hay, hay in alternate strips. Unless the strips are laid out practically on the contour much of the advantage is lost. (Greene County, Virginia)
(Soil Conservation Service)

any water from flowing off onto the clean-tilled strip immediately below. But during extremely heavy rains or rains of long duration, large quantities of water may flow from the sod strips to the clean-tilled strips.

During rains of the last two named types, strip-cropping may actually increase the rate of erosion by surface flow on the strips planted to clean-tilled crops. Under these conditions, flowing surface water moves from the clean-tilled strips onto the sod. It immediately loses its turbidity (because the plant cover intercepts the falling raindrops which impart turbidity to shallow sheets of surface water) and deposits its load of debris. When it leaves the sod strip on the lower side (usually channelized) to enter the cultivated strip, it will be practically clear and thus have higher eroding capacity.

Various width strips of the soil-protecting crops are effective in reducing erosion and decreasing the distance of soil movement on between-terrace slopes. Under some conditions, little or no soil moves from cultivated strips, while under other conditions large colluvial fans accumulate in meadow strips. Some of these colluvial fans are of sufficient size and extent to indicate that there is continuous severe erosion from the cultivated strip. In consequence, the quantity of vegetation in the meadow strip decreases and its quality deteriorates. The volume and distribution of the colluvial fans appear to be affected by variations in physiographic, pedalogic, and agronomic factors.

No one combination of crops or width of strips of the crops employed will be universally satisfactory. One prerequisite for the success of the strip crop pattern, according to Gerdel, is that the strips be laid out and maintained on the contour. If they diverge from the contour more than four or five per cent, for distances as little as 100 feet, much of the erosion-control effectiveness of strip-cropping may be lost even on the least erosive soil types.

The effectiveness of strip-cropping, when the strips are laid out with varying divergences from the contour, is influenced by soil type, degree and length of slope, previous erosion, and other factors. Gerdel found a wide variation in the effectiveness of a given strip-crop pattern when applied to soils with varying water-intake capabilities. The loss of soil from some soil types remained within safe limits when the strip diverged as much as 5 per cent from the contour, whereas the loss was excessive on other types under similar conditions. Even a divergence of as much as two per cent from the contour permitted heavy soil losses with some soil types. A divergence of not more than four or five per cent under the most favorable conditions is considered the maximum allowable.

Gerdel also found a definite relation between the degree and length of slope and the effectiveness of strip-cropping, when the strips were laid out with varying divergences from the contour. Soil losses were two to three times greater from soils with moderately heavy to heavy subsoil than from soils with light-textured subsoil, where the slopes were similar and the watershed above the strips comparable in length.

The amount of erosion that has occurred on a field before it is strip-cropped directly affects the amount of erosion from the cultivated strip. Approximately twice as much erosion occurred on the cultivated strips from which more than 75 per cent of the topsoil had been removed before strip-cropping as on those from which only 50 to 75 per cent of the topsoil had been removed.

Even though erosion may be controlled on the areas planted to the sod crops, it does not mean that no erosion is taking place on fields planted in strips. Soil continues to erode on that portion of the field planted to row crops, even though it may be practically eliminated on the sod areas. The eroded soil on the clean-tilled areas moves downhill and is deposited on the sod strips. As these strips are alternated with row crops, the soil will eventually reach the bottom of the hill and escape from the farm into drainage channels. It should be remembered that the soil is on the move on the clean-tilled areas, and eventually will reach the bottom of the hill. With strip cropping, it simply takes longer for it to get away.

Even though the soil may not actually be carried off the field, it is changing locations on the field. This may result in damage as serious as though it were carried away.

CONTOUR CULTIVATION

Contour cultivation, like terracing, is effective only in controlling erosion by surface flow. It, more accurately, is a part of the water-disposal system. When properly carried out, it is one of the most effective mechanical control measures for cultivated cropland. Generally, it is effective from the stand-

FIGURE 68. Contour cultivation is effective only in controlling scour erosion. It is an effective means of conserving moisture during
seasons of low rainfall. It also shortens downhill slopes over
which surface flow is free to move. (Monona, Iowa)
(Soil Conservation Service)

point of increasing crop yields, reducing runoff, and reducing scour-erosion
losses. Like other measures, it has its limitations. Maximum results may be
expected only when it is used in conjunction with other good farming practices. Surplus water from contour-cultivated fields should be emptied into
grass waterways to prevent gullying.

Factors such as soil type, soil conditions, and amount of slope modify the
effectiveness of contour cultivation. In the semiarid areas, where the conservation of moisture is of primary importance, contour cultivation by
listing (throwing up a high bed but planting in the furrow) may be sufficient.
In the more humid areas, contour cultivation may be adequate during
periods of heavy rainfall for the orderly disposal of surplus water, and during the drier growing seasons for the conservation of moisture. It is in those
areas where contour cultivation serves this double function that appropriate
supplementary measures are essential for maximum results. Contour cultivation should be used as a supporting measure, not as a substitute for plant
cover.

REFERENCES

1. Daniel, H. A., Elwell, H. M., and Cox, M. B. 1949. *Investigations in erosion control and reclamation of eroded land at the Red Plains Conservation Experiment Station, Guthrie, Oklahoma, 1930-40.* USDA, Tech. Bull. 837.
2. Dieseker, E. G., and Yoder, R. E. 1936. *Sheet erosion studies on Cecil clay.* Ala. Agr. Expt. Sta. Bull. 245.
3. Ellison, W. D. 1948. *Experiments in soil erosion and infiltration on range lands in the High Plains.* USDA, SCS, Fort Worth, Texas. (Mimeo.)
4. Gerdel, R. W. 1940. *Soil losses from cultivated strips in strip-cropping fields in the Ohio Valley Region.* USDA Cir. 588.
5. Lamb, J., Jr., Andrews, J. S., and Gustafson, A. F. 1944. *Experiments in the control of erosion in southern New York.* Cornell Univ. Agr. Expt. Sta. Bull. 811.
6. Musgrave, G. W. 1949. *Designing agronomic practices to meet specific erosion hazards.* USDA, SCS-TP-84.
7. Pope, J. B., Archer, J. C., Johnson, P. R., McCall, A. G., and Bell, F. G. 1946. *Investigations in erosion control and reclamation of eroded sandy clay lands of Texas, Arkansas, and Louisiana at the Conservation Experiment Station, Tyler, Texas, 1931-40.* USDA Tech. Bull. 916.
8. Potter, W. D. 1949. *Normalcy tests of precipitation and frequency studies of runoff on small watersheds.* USDA Tech. Bull. 985.
9. Zingg, A. W. 1940. *Degree and length of land slopes as it affects soil loss and runoff.* Agr. Eng., 21(2, 3).

13

Wind-Erosion Control

Wind is the most active factor in destroying fertility on most of the Great Plains soils. It is also active in other areas. It is a natural hazard in the spring and winter wheat areas. Great Plains soils are noted for their high fertility; but this fertility, as in all soils, is largely bound up in the upper, humus-bearing zone. It has taken Nature centuries to create this rich top-soil. To lose it during a storm or a series of storms is to lose from immediate crop production the fruits of all Nature's efforts.

Soil blowing has become a greater problem in Plains agriculture as new areas have been brought into cultivation. This is not necessarily because the hard sweeping winds have become more intense, but because the new areas have poorer soils and thinner crop cover.

The greatest danger from soil blowing is in early spring, when the highest monthly velocities of the year are encountered and the land is bare or nearly so. Soil blowing may be serious any time of the year if not stopped by the use of appropriate control measures or prevented by a suitable cover of vegetation.

Any comparatively level field devoid of a covering of vegetal matter may blow if the soil is finely pulverized or tightly and smoothly crusted. The more sand the soil contains, the greater is the likelihood of blowing. Once a field has started to blow, the condition will normally grow worse unless control methods are used. During hard sweeping windstorms, "eternal vigilance" and prompt action are necessary to detect blow spots and prevent them from spreading over vast areas.

The lands of the Plains region originally were occupied by vegetation that over the centries had proved best equipped to thrive under each particular soil and climatic condition. Under natural conditions, soil was less exposed to wind action, even during prolonged droughts. This was because the residues of the previous season's growth remained as a protective covering until rains, however long delayed, came to stimulate new growth. Wind erosion also is a serious problem on many of our muck lands and in many areas along the Atlantic and Pacific coasts as well as along the Great Lakes and other places.

The destruction of natural cover incident to placing the land in cultivated crops or to overgrazing makes it necessary to maintain an effective substitute for the original cover. If this is not done, exposure of the soil to the wind for even short periods may allow severe erosion to take place.

FIGURE 69. Cotton on sandy, tightly crusted field badly damaged by wind erosion. In some sports the topsoil is blown out to the subsoil. Soil excellent for range grasses but unsuited for cultivated crops. (Texas)
(Soil Conservation Service)

The maintenance of an adequate vegetal cover, therefore, becomes the primary goal of all wind-erosion control efforts. The soil-blowing hazard has always been greatest in seasons of drought, after crop failures, and in places or on soil types poorly adapted to accumulate moisture. The wind-erosion hazard is greatest in those areas where erosion-producing rains are less frequent, and is less of a problem as a rule where such rains occur frequently.

SOIL BLOWING

The rate of soil flow under a wind force varies inversely with the roughness of the surface. Surface roughness in turn is dependent on the height and lateral frequency of the surface obstructions.

The initial rate of soil flow over cultivated soils is less when such soils are ridged than when the soil surface is smooth. This is because ridges reduce the wind velocity for some distance above the average surface of the land and trap soil on the leeward side. Ridges, however, produce greater velocities of wind flow over the crest of the ridge, and also greater eddying. This results in a more rapid rate of erosion at the crest of the ridge. The initial net effect of ridging on these two sets of opposing forces is a reduction in the rate of erosion. As the field surface becomes leveled again by the trapping of soil in the furrow and the wearing down of the ridge crests, the effect of these two sets of forces tends to become reversed. The ridges

FIGURE 70. Newly constructed ridges trap eroding soil on leeward side. As the field becomes leveled by the filling of the furrows and the wearing down of the crest of the ridges erosion continues as though the field had never been ridged. (Oklahoma)
(Soil Conservation Service)

lose their effectiveness and erosion is resumed as if the ridges had not been formed.

Listing the soil at right angles to prevailing winds, either solid or every other row, or in strips in conjunction with planting to corn or other row crops, was tried at Colby, Kansas, in 1914 during a devastating dust storm. This listing was followed by a rainy period after the first week in May, during which it rained 9 out of 11 days. These showers brought up the seeds that had been planted, sprouted the weed seeds which were abundant everywhere, and kept the soil from blowing long enough to give crops and weeds a chance to become established.

That fall an abundance of moisture enabled fall wheat to make a good growth before winter set in. The following spring there were only a few bare fields, mostly where the wheat was sown too late to make enough growth to cover the ground. Most fields were covered with growing wheat, heavy stubble, corn or sorghum stalks, or weeds. Although high winds were frequent during the spring months, the only serious blowing was on the late-planted wheat fields where the vegetation was not sufficient for protection.

The absence of vegetal cover was responsible for the serious soil blowing that occurred in the Colby, Kansas, area in 1935. The lack of rain during the fall of 1934 made it impossible to secure stands of wheat over most of the territory. In areas where moisture was enough to start the crop, lack of precipitation during the winter months resulted in not enough moisture to

FIGURE 71. Sudangrass stubble left anchored at the top of the ground provides excellent protection against wind erosion. (Big Springs, Texas)
(Soil Conservation Service)

sustain the plants. Practically all fields that had been prepared for wheat were without a protective cover of vegetation when the strong winds started to blow in the spring of 1935. Furthermore, because the drought of 1934 caused a shortage of fodder for livestock, wheat stubble, corn stalks, and Russian thistles and other weeds were grazed off closely or harvested for feed. Even native buffalo grass pastures were so heavily overgrazed that the remaining vegetation was not enough to protect the soil.

Although almost any soil will blow if the physical conditions are right, the sandy soils are perhaps the most susceptible. The soil conditions most favorable for blowing are a smooth, finely-pulverized surface free from a growing crop, weeds, or crop residues. A soil is least subject to blowing when it is covered with growing vegetation, weeds, or crop residue or, if without cover, when it is rough and cloddy.

In the Great Plains, sandy and very sandy soils offer so little resistance to blowing that they cannot be safely cultivated and should be kept in or put back to grass. Heavy soils that form tenacious lumps and clods are least subject to blowing, and on them ordinary tillage practices can usually be employed with safety. Between these extremes is a large acreage of soils that are highly productive but on which special precautions and treatments are necessary to prevent soil blowing.

Experience over the last 20 to 30 years in the 14-20 inch rainfall belt has revealed the dangers of farming these soils. It has shown that on gentle and

FIGURE 72. Sandy soil, unfit for growing cultivated crops, should be returned to grass. Here sand lovegrass is being seeded in a stubble of sorghum and rye which will hold the land from blowing until the grass gets started. (Seminole, Texas) *(Soil Conservation Service)*

steeper slopes none of the shallow, moderately sandy and deep, loose sandhill soils can be kept productive under cultivation. Shallow hardlands,* both flat and sloping, have undergone severe erosion in all areas of less than 18-inch average rainfall. Nearly level, medium-textured, moderately sandy lands, on the other hand, have resisted erosion under rainfall as low as 16 inches when suitable wind-erosion control practices were used.

Medium-depth hardlands have a fair to good record of performance, but where the rainfall is less than 17 inches a program of alternate cultivation and restoration under sod is required to avoid the severe damage.

Experience indicates that the hardlands deteriorate more slowly than the sandy lands. On such lands the difficulty of maintaining crop residues and of producing crop stands are reliable signs of overuse.

The length of safe periods of cultivation necessarily varies with soils and climatic conditions. Deep, loamy sands in areas of 18 to 20 inches of rainfall offer fair possibilities of maintaining fertility and stabilty against wind erosion when green manure crops are used in the rotation. The deep, nearly level hardlands, the best of the High Plains wheat soils, can be safely farmed with appropriate precautions.

These findings parallel very closely the observations made in the Prairie Provinces of Canada, where it was found that regardless of conditions in different localities there are some definite principles that have general application. Among these are that summer fallow may be used on medium loam soils under proper conditions, but sandy or clay soils require the protection of vegetal cover. This means that plowed fallow, though suitable on loams, is not safe on sand or clay unless protective cover crops are planted. These more difficult soil types, therefore, should be protected with a crop or trash cover, or both.

It is generally true that wind with a wide, unbroken sweep carries more drifting material than it does over narrow strips and therefore its sand-blast action is greater on unstripped land. This seems to be at least one reason why strip-crop farming assists in control in most if not all localities.

In solving the soil-drift problem, one of the first requirements is to determine the soil types and past cropping history and remove from cultivation as soon as possible such areas as are not suited for cultivation.

It is important to note that, although any fallowed piece of land may drift, some fallows have remained remarkably stable. Soils do not all erode with equal ease. For example, medium-textured soils do not erode as readily as others. Medium-textured loams that are not extremely high in organic matter do not drift readily unless improperly managed, but sandy soils and some clays are difficult to manage.

Soil that has never been deprived of its native vegetal covering by cultivation, or is being cultivated for the first time, is fairly resistant to wind erosion.

Light sandy soils are extremely subject to drifting. It is practically impossible to summer-fallow this type of land, even in strips as narrow as 4 rods, without serious danger of drifting. Furthermore, records show that

* Clay soils.

FIGURE 73. The cotton plants on the left have trapped soil blown in from unprotected field at far left. Once the soil is trapped it remains in place as the wind cannot set it in motion again. (Kern County, California)
(Soil Conservation Service)

because of the low water-holding capacity of such soils and the frequent damage from soil drifting, yields on fallow generally are no higher and may even be lower than yields on stubble land. Consequently, fallowing this type of soil for moisture conservation is of questionable value. If done, it should be confined to those seasons when the moisture in the soil is not enough to justify seeding a crop. These soils should be seeded to grass and kept in pasture permanently where feasible. Where planted to grain continuously, a rotation of wheat and fall rye is commonly used in the spring-wheat area, with the rye drilled directly into the wheat stubble. The rye stubble should be left until the following spring. The wheat may then either be seeded with a oneway disk with seeder attachment, or the land may be plowed, packed, and seeded immediately. Both crops are cut as high as possible so that the stubble may be left to collect snow and protect the soil against wind erosion.

Soil drifting may occur on sandy soils despite these measures. It is essential, therefore, to observe conditions in the fields at all times and, when necessary, plow furrows through danger spots at the first signs of drifting. Knolls that are highly subject to drifting should be seeded permanently to grass.

Clay soils are subject to drifting. They are usually uniform in texture, and drifting may start in any part of a field or even an entire field at one time. Once started, drifting is severe even in narrow strips. There is a rapid increase in intensity of soil drifting near the windward edge of a field of highly calcareous heavy clay soil followed by a nearly constant rate of flow along the remaining part of the field, as compared with a relatively uniform rate of increase of erosion across the whole length of the field on loam or clay loam soil. Drifting frequently piles the soil in the stubble at the edges of each strip to as great an extent as on the edge of a large field. Strip-cropping on this type of soil, therefore, has definite limitations.

Crops on clay soil are usually fair to good, especially if the crop is seeded on well-prepared fallow or on stubble land that has a good reserve of moisture. To prevent soil drifting, every effort must be made to keep this stubble anchored at the surface of the soil.

Although loam soils show a wide variation in their susceptibility to drifting, they are as a class the least susceptible. The actual damage is by far the most serious when wind erosion occurs in these soils, however.

Once drifting starts, there is a gradual separation of the fine soil particles

FIGURE 74. Sand dunes formed on overgrazed rangeland. Once drifting starts, there is a gradual separation of the fine soil particles and organic matter from any coarse sandy material, and as drifting continues the soil becomes progressively lighter in texture. (Crane County, Texas)
(Soil Conservation Service)

and organic matter from any coarse sandy material, and as drifting continues the soil becomes progressively lighter in texture. The greater the distance the material is moved, the more complete is the separation. It is extremely important, therefore, to check drifting at its source. Drifting usually starts at a few vulnerable spots and spreads over the entire field. For this reason strip-cropping has proved to be a valuable aid in controlling soil drift, especially on the loam soils.

Loam soils have a fairly good moisture-holding capacity and, under normal conditions, the stubble from crops is enough to form a good trash cover. In addition, these soils tend to retain a cloddy structure which helps to resist wind erosion. Soil drifting on loam soils is relatively easy to control. The damage caused by drifting, however, is so severe that extreme precautions to prevent soil drift are justified.

By maintaining a trash cover or a cloddy condition at the surface, it is possible to control drifting in fields up to 40 rods wide. If the stubble is light, however, a sound precaution is to seed a narrow strip of grain about 3 to 4 rods wide down the center of the field before starting to summerfallow. This temporarily reduces the width of the crop strip to 20 rods or less. As conditions improve, these narrow strips can be eliminated.

Since soil drifting on loam soils can be prevented by creating a lumpy surface, by maintaining a trash cover, or by a combination of these measures, a much wider range of cultural practices is possible on such soils than on the light sandy or heavy clay soils.

WIND EROSION REDUCES CROP YIELDS

Topsoil to an average depth of about 9 inches has been removed from certain fields in western Kansas, mainly by wind erosion, during the 19 years the fields have been devoted to the production of wheat. The loss included all of the fertile A horizon. This land is now much less productive and contains substantially less organic matter and undecomposed crop residue than when newly broken. Owing to lower amounts of crop residue this "old" cultivated land is less protected from erosion by wind and water. The soil itself, however, is more resistant to wind erosion now than when it was first brought under cultivation. This is due to the presence at the surface of the finer texture of the original B horizon. When the protective influence of crop residues was discounted, the old cultivated land was less than half as erodible as land broken out of virgin sod between 1946 and 1948. With crop failures, such as occur on all types of land in dry years, the recently broken land apparently would be most vulnerable to erosion by wind.

Wind erosion in the Great Plains has reduced the annual potential production capacity of the land 7 bushels of wheat per acre since the land was first put into cultivation more than 30 years ago. Four and two-tenths bushels of this 7-bushel loss in yielding capacity are due to removal of fertility by wind erosion. The other 2.8 bushels are due to the removal of fertility by the crops harvested.

Soil fertility was removed much faster by the wind during the first 4 years after active erosion started than during any like period later. The

FIGURE 75. Soil fertility is removed much faster by the wind when wind erosion first becomes active. The dust removed by storms during this rapid phase of fertility decline consists mainly of the rich, black organic matter and silt and clay of the topsoil. These dust storms are known as "black rollers." *(Soil Conservation Service)*

rate of loss for this period was from 4 to 5 times that of later losses. The dust removed by storms during this rapid phase of fertility decline consisted mainly of the rich, black organic matter and the silt and clay of the topsoil. These dust storms are known as "black rollers." Materials composing the dust are the more fertility-bearing portions of the topsoil. Erosion reduced crop yields more rapidly during this early period of active erosion that later. Fertility elements removed by crops were in direct proportion to crop yields.

The effects of lost fertility have been masked or offset by improved crop yields resulting from the use of improved varieties of wheat, and by better tillage. It has taken new, higher-yielding wheats and better cultural practices to make up for the 7-bushel decline in yield caused by loss in soil fertility.

CROPPING PRACTICES AND WIND-EROSION CONTROL

The best means of preventing wind erosion on cropland is to keep a vegetal cover on the land continuously. The effectiveness of plant cover in preventing wind erosion was amply demonstrated during a dust storm at Salina and McPherson, Kansas, in March 1950. During the storm, wind erosion occurred only on fields which did not have enough vegetal cover. Wherever the crop residue on the surface amounted to a ton or more per acre, little or no erosion occurred; but where the vegetal cover was not enough, topsoil to an average depth of about 0.85 inch was removed.

The effectiveness of organic residue retained at the surface to prevent wind erosion is due mainly to the reduction in wind velocity, and, to a lesser degree, to the high capacity of the residue to trap the eroding soil.

The amount of wheat stubble or straw required to prevent erosion by wind varies with the relative erosiveness of the soil and the velocity of the wind. The higher the velocity of the wind, the greater is the amount of crop residue required. Studies in Canada have shown that the amount of stubble needed to give equal protection had to be doubled to withstand an increase of 5 miles per hour in wind velocity at the 1-foot height. Short stubble provides less protection to the soil than an equal amount of longer stubble.

Stubble provides less ground coverage than an equal weight of straw, but is less subject to removal by high winds. The combination of straw scat-

FIGURE 76. A cover that furnishes a high degree of protection to wheat land against wind erosion is provided by leaving a high stubble and spreading the chaff during combine harvesting. This practice is more effective than using either stubble or chaff alone. (Curry County, New Mexico)
(Soil Conservation Service)

tered on the ground and stubble provides more protection against the wind than equivalent amounts of straw or stubble alone.

Cropping systems and cultural operations should be directed toward the maintenance of surface covers of growing crops or undecomposed residues. The condition of the soil surface as to roughness, coarseness, and cover—all of which help the soil to resist blowing—is determined to a large extent by the method of tillage.

Row crops may place the surface in condition to blow. When such crops as corn and sorghum are harvested, either the stubble should be left about a foot high or higher or at least 2 rows in 20 should be left standing. If these crops are pastured, the stock should be removed while there are still enough stalks with leaves attached to furnish protection. Strip-cropping aids in the control of soil blowing by shortening the distance that loose soil can move. If the strips are laid out on the contour, water also is conserved, which in turn helps prevent blowing.

The soil-blowing hazard on summer-fallowed land may also be reduced by carrying on cultural operations in the manner that results in a minimum of soil disturbance—for example, controlling weed growth with sub-surface tillage or by chemicals, cultivating wherever possible only when the ground

FIGURE 77. Corn and sorghum stubble should be cut at least a foot high for effective wind-erosion control. If stubble of this height contains a large amount of leaves it is even more effective. (Brownfield, Texas)
(Soil Conservation Service)

is moist, and using types of tillage tools that do not pulverize the soil. Cutting corn and sorghum stubble so as to leave a fairly large amount of leaves usually will protect the soil from blowing. Land left over winter in grain stubble or with a cover of weeds will not blow, and winter wheat with a good fall growth usually protects the soil sufficiently.

Because of climatic conditions the lands of the central Great Plains, if not protected by vegetal cover, are more subject to severe wind erosion than almost any other agricultural area of the world. In this area, both drilled and row crops should be planted in rows running at right angles to the direction of the prevailing winds or on the contour. Land in wheat 2 to 4 inches high lost 2.5 times as much soil by wind erosion when planting was in rows parallel to the direction of the wind as when planting was in rows at right angles to it. The additional obstruction presented by the wheat in rows at right angles to the wind direction accounted for a large part of this difference. The safest practice is to return all fields west of the 20-inch rainfall belt in the Great Plains to grass, at least on a rotation basis, for a period of 5 to 7 years. Such a rotation is more likely to maintain the much-needed crop stubble and other residues for wind-erosion protection, to

FIGURE 78. The haze in the background is caused by the dust from an unprotected wheat field. The land in the foreground is protected by sorghum stubble and the soil is not blowing. (Tulia, Texas)
(Soil Conservation Service)

improve soil structure, and to promote other favorable conditions than is the conventional cropping system.

The wind-erosion problem is so complex that only by a combination of measures can a successful program of wind-erosion control be provided and maintained and future serious damage prevented. To completely repair erosion damage, even if it were possible, would be costly and uneconomical. In the struggle against wind erosion, preparations 10 to 20 months in advance of probable hazard condition can be made in connection with productive crop management and will not only protect the capital investment but prevent expensive repair operations later.

Among the crops adapted to southern Great Plains conditions which have erosion-resisting residues are the winter and spring grains—wheat, barley, and rye. Of these, winter wheat is of foremost importance. Grasses grown for seed, hay, or pasture are excellent erosion-control plants. The row crops which leave erosion-resisting residues are all of the sorghum family, among them milo, kafir, hegari, broomcorn, and sudangrass. The mere growing of any of these crops does not necessarily give erosion protection to the soil in which they are grown. The ideal system of management for wind-erosion

FIGURE 79. Preparations made 10 to 20 months in advance often prevent costly wind-erosion control in the future. On this field milo has been seeded for stubble in which to seed sideoats grama in following spring. (Dalhart, Texas)
(Soil Conservation Service)

FIGURE 80. Ground cover can be perpetuated by seeding new crops through the stubble and other residue of preceding crop. (Montana)
(Soil Conservation Service)

control requires that the surface residue be returned. It is best to leave the residue cover on the surface and to plant through the residues for the next crop. The growing crop then perpetuates the ground cover and provides a renewal of the residue supply at the close of the season.

The practices of burning stubble and overgrazing stalk fields have no place in a wind-erosion control program. Some of the most severe wind erosion in the Panhandle area of the southern Great Plains is attributable to these two destructive practices. Rank wheat stubble has often been burned because of the mechanical difficulty of working it into the soil and because of the temporary fertility depression that often follows when the stubble is retained. These are more than compensated for by the protection provided the soil when the stubble is left unburned and by the ultimate increase in productiveness. Methods have been developed for leaving this straw on the surface of the ground and planting through it. The temporary depression in crop yields can be overcome by proper use of nitrogen. In addition, the use of crop residues on the surface of the ground increases the rate of water absorption and the water-retention capacity of the soil. If a droughty season follows, this advantage more than offsets the fertility depression. The reverse may be true, however, if another favorable season follows, but the odds against two bumper crops in succession are too high to risk exposing soil to wind erosion by burning the straw. Another practice that has resulted in just as disastrous consequences is that of renting stalk fields to outside herdsmen, who almost invariably leave the cattle in the field until the last scrap of vegetation has been consumed. Moderate stalk-field grazing benefits farm livestock, but the livestock should be removed when the effectiveness of the ground cover is threatened.

Where sorghum crops are cut with a binder for fodder, either a uniform stubble at least one foot high should be left, or regular strips 4 to 6 rows wide should be headed and the intervening space of 20 to 30 rows harvested for forage. A good stand of any of the sorghum varieties will protect the soil from the wind if this rule is followed.

Heavy wheat stubble and thick stubbles of close-growing sorghums left one foot high or higher may be worked into the surface soil as soon as convenient. Still better, plantings of the next crop may be made in the standing stubble and surface residues.

When corn and other clean-tilled crops which provide little protection against erosion are grown, strip-cropping with sorghum or suitable grass is necessary. On light sandy soil, the rows should run about at right angles to the direction of the prevailing winds. The erosion-resisting strips should be spaced closely enough to protect the non-erosion-resisting crop. The wind-break strips should be not less than 4 rows wide, and may be wider depending on the number of rows listed or cultivated at one time. Under severe blowing conditions, the width of main crop strips generally should not be greater than 20 rows, although the actual width will depend on soil type, direction of rows, and type of crops involved. Under severe erosion conditions, strips as narrow as 5 rows may be practical.

FIGURE 81. Wheat planted in this stubble was well protected from wind erosion. (Dalhart, Texas)
(Soil Conservation Service)

Where both drilled crops and row crops are grown on terraced fields, and it is desired to strip-crop, winter grains and other drilled crops can be planted in the irregular "point-row" areas between strips. This not only makes it possible to lengthen the row-crop strips but improves conditions for crop diversification as an aid in the control of wind erosion.

No rigid system of either continuous culture or rotation has been devised that can equal a flexible cropping plan in economy of production. Such a plan takes into consideration the soil moisture and fertility conditions of individual fields at each successive planting period of the year. Crops should be selected that will provide the maximum cover under these varying conditions.

The dependability of crop production under the variable system assures a continuity of plant cover. The need for emergency crops depends on the success attained in producing and maintaining the residues.

The normal residues of cultivated crops in the winter-wheat areas, if properly managed, should provide ample cover except during periods of prolonged drought. Where no vegetal cover is produced because of crop failure, measures should be taken to make sure that the maximum possible amount of precipitation enters the soil for use by the next crop. Emergency cover crops may be planted when normal moisture-saving practices fail to

FIGURE 82. Beans, potatoes, cowpeas, and similar crops should be grown in strips between strips of sorghum, sudangrass, or corn. (North Dakota)
(Soil Conservation Service)

produce enough crop growth to supply the needed cover. If the summer has been too dry to produce a crop and the surface residue has disappeared and rains occur in late summer, a stooling sorghum such as sudangrass or dwarf milo should be planted to renew the ground covering for the winter. When winter wheat fails and the land is still bare as the summer season approaches, a dual-purpose planting of wide-row sorghum for grain is in order as a substitute for summer fallow. Milo or similar crops grown in rows 10 to 15 feet apart provide a desirable partial fallow effect and at the same time give stubble protection against blowing until wheat is again planted the following fall to provide a ground cover.

Beans, cowpeas, and similar crops should be grown in strips between the strips of sorghum, sudangrass, or corn.

Adequate supplies of soil moisture hold the key to the successful maintenance of ample crops and crop-residue cover. Those practices that are most effective in controlling wind erosion are also effective in getting greater amounts of rainfall into the soil. The use of vegetal cover, contour cultivation, and level closed-end terraces is important in this connection. These practices are effective in reducing runoff even during the hardest rains.

In the spring-wheat areas, the practice of fallowing, generally assumed to be essential for the conservation of moisture, provides large areas of bare land. The practice of a plowless fallow to leave all residues on the surface has been assumed to be one of the most effective methods for protection against wind. However, under certain conditions this practice breaks down. Under this system, 21 months or more must elapse between the harvesting of one crop and the initial growth of the next. Near the end of this period, when protection is most needed, residues may be so decomposed as to be of little value for protection against wind.

In some spring-wheat areas, strip-cropping with maintenance of as much crop residue as possible has been adopted as a regular practice to reduce the hazards of wind erosion. Cover crops are seeded on fallow usually about August 1 as an additional protection. Experiments have indicated that if the cover crop does not exceed 6 inches in height, little reserve moisture is lost from the fallow. The moisture used up by the cover crop may be regained by additional amounts of snow trapped. Thus, yields on cover-cropped fallow are often about equal to those on bare fallow, although some decreases and some increases in crop yields have been recorded. Cover crops may be pastured as long as their protective value is not destroyed.

Considerable acreages of land now in cultivation in the southern Great Plains, especially along the western edge, either are too sandy or have too little rainfall for dependable annual crop production. These lands should be put back to grass. Other parts of the western sandy lands are capable of producing excellent crops, especially sorghums. If they are farmed in large blocks, however, soil drifting may, at critical times, spread quickly from one field to another and involve whole sections. Farmed fields should be small and guarded by permanent plantings of grass or browse plants. With reasonably-sized holdings, there is no reason why soil blowing cannot be controlled, even in years of drought, by the proper management of crop cover and proper methods of cultivation. Regrassing by natural or artificial means on the shallower, sandier slopes of the Plains is important.

Legumes and grasses used in rotation with field crops have been found to be effective in reducing the wind erodibility of irrigated soils. For example, land in potatoes after 40 years of cropping to a 3-year rotation of potatoes, beets, and barley lost 74,000 pounds of soil per acre by wind erosion that will spread to or menace well-watered parts of the same or the crop rotation, the soil lost from the land in potatoes was only 970 pounds per acre. Land cropped to wheat continuously was 4.4 times as erodible as wheat after second-year sweet clover. The yields were 19 and 45 bushels per acre, respectively.

TERRACES SUPPORT CROPPING IN THE WIND-EROSION CONTROL PROGRAM

Uniform distribution of the moisture supply within a field is essential to the establishment of adequate vegetal cover and a wind-erosion control program. For example, a droughty knoll or slope of only a few acres may start erosion that will spread to or menace well-watered parts of the same or adjacent fields.

Level terracing (except on the heavy soils) and contour tillage, which have demonstrated their effectiveness in increasing the average soil-moisture supply by about 25 per cent under High Plains conditions, have become a very material support to the vegetative program. This type of soil management results in saving water for productive purposes, which is needed to help bridge droughty periods in the maintenance of a vegetal cover for erosion prevention. Level closed-end terraces are of doubtful value on the heavy soils. The infiltration rate of these soils is so low that the water would stand in the fields long enough to damage the crops.

In the area of 20 inches average rainfall or less, it was formerly believed that all terraces built on gently rolling and nearly level land should be level with closed ends and high enough to back water to the next terrace above. Recent studies, however, indicate that open-end terraces may be best where stubble-mulch tillage and other conservation practices are used. The most practical terrace interval can be determined by linear spacing of terrace area rather than by vertical spacing. The average distance between terraces on silty clay loam wheat lands in the Plains should be 125 to 150 feet.* On typical areas of this kind of soil the vertical interval can range from 0.4 to 1.0 foot, the effective height of the terraces being adjusted accordingly. Where small areas of a field are very uneven, splice terraces should be built if the uneven distance exceeds about 250 feet, and terrace sections should be eliminated where the distance falls below 75 feet. Terraces ending in midfield or abutting the edge of the field should have closed ends.

It sometimes becomes necessary to change the vertical interval within a field. On the High Plains, terraces are designed to retain the water that falls within a given area. Use of a fixed vertical interval on land with slopes that

---

* *Soil Conservation Service Regional Engineering Handbook.*

average less than 1 per cent causes extremely wide variations in linear spacing where relatively small variations in slope occur. This fact, together with the importance of getting water to all parts of the field, makes adjustment of vertical interval and terrace height necessary.

The terrace cross-section best suited to wheat farming is low and broad. A broad crown facilitates the use of machinery in maintaining the terraces. A properly built wheat-land terrace can be cultivated and planted the same as any other part of the field. It can be maintained with one round of a one-way disk plow around the terrace annually.

Loam soils used for diversified farming should be terraced in the manner described for wheat land, except that the distance between the terraces should be 150 to 200 feet. A narrower base may be used, if row-crop production alone is to be practiced on loam soil, but in all cases under semiarid conditions a terrace base of 30 feet or more is desirable.

WINDBREAKS

Windbreaks can be used to control wind erosion where the rainfall is enough to support trees. The utilization of trees as windbreaks in humid areas where wind erosion constitutes a problem is relatively simple. Since moisture is not a limiting factor, the trees can be planted in accordance with a standard pattern. However, standard patterns are not always feasible in areas of limited rainfall. Occasionally, the pattern of tree planting in such areas must be made to conform to the topography of the land rather than to a standard pattern. By conforming to the topography, better advantage can be taken of the limited amount of water available. This plan provides for planting trees in low places where water tends to accumulate during rains—drainageways and similar places—or where snow accumulates in the winter.

The principal value of trees in wind-erosion control is in the broader protection they give to cultivated fields which may start to blow as a result of exposure to dust swept from bare roadways. Windbreaks scattered over a wide area help to break up the surface wind currents which otherwise would sweep the ground without obstruction.

Along highways where snowfall is heavy, tree windbreaks should be placed on the lee side of the road. Naturally favorable sites exist along level stretches of the roadway where surface waters collect, stand in the ditch, and soak into the soil, thus providing an important additional moisture supply to enable tree maintenance without cultivation or irrigation. Other naturally favorable locations occur along drainageways and small lakes in pasture areas along farm roads. The control of erosion by appropriate vegetation may also help to improve conditions for planting on adjacent areas. Sites of this type should be developed with strict regard to the availability of water from the drainage area. In some areas, it may be possible to obtain water for the trees by means of diversion structures.

Species suitable for windbreak plantings which have proved their hardiness in the Panhandle area include Chinese elm, Russian olive, green ash, cottonwood, and tamarisk. The suitability of trees for windbreaks varies with soil type, moisture supply, and other functions. In general, tall-growing trees should stand from 8 to 10 feet apart in the row and should be interplanted with the more shrublike species.

Temporary protection against rabbit injury is necessary for tree stock until the trees are large enough to withstand attacks. A permanent rabbit guard of wire netting is preferable.

Wind-tunnel studies of the flow pattern of wind over model barriers and windbreaks show that the sharper the barrier the more complete is the protection provided. Rounded shapes have a lesser zone of influence than narrow vertical shapes. The porosity of a barrier decreases the degree of protection downwind but at the same time extends its zone of influence.

The prevailing ratio between ground wind and standard velocity in the open is about 0:07, although this changes somewhat with the velocity and is about 0:01 higher at 20 inches than at 16 inches above the ground surface. The ratio between the wind velocity at the surface of evenly mowed grass and standard velocity is about 0:50—a clear indication of the extent to which the frictional drag of even vegetation tends to reduce velocities. The ground wind is constantly lagging because of ground friction, but it is ultimately set in motion again by the "pull" of the more rapidly moving currents above it. Since the stilled air mass has depth, the pull of free-moving currents that have passed the ends of the shelterbelt, and can act on the sides of this mass, also is important. Thus the ground pattern to tangible reductions due to a windbreak is never rectangular, but tends to be narrowed toward its outer limit at the same time that the block of stilled air is being thinned to a wedge by the overhead current.

If the wind is diagonal to the barrier and the breadth as well as distance from the belt is calculated, so as to obtain an area measure expressed in area units of height times length of barriers (HL), the summation of all wind reductions give the "HL units."

On the basis of this approach, a 15-mile-per-hour wind has from 11 to 12 units for a single barrier. Higher wind velocities have more units and lower velocities will have fewer units, but aside from this, an expression results by which we can directly compare in a single term the effectiveness of two barriers differing widely in dimensions, proportions, or composition.

The value of four wind barriers separated respectively by distances of 25, 20 and 30 times their common height is approximately the same as four barriers of equal length and type acting independently.

In addition to protecting the soil from erosion, windbreaks planted around farmsteads render another valuable service. By reducing wind velocities in the winter, they reduce the fuel requirements for the farmer and the feed requirements for the livestock. They may reduce fuel requirements from 25 to 34 per cent, depending on the way the windbreaks are laid out, their height and density. Livestock that have the advantage of protection by windbreaks require less feed and gain weight more rapidly than those not protected.

TILLAGE AND WIND-EROSION CONTROL

As previously stated, the best way to prevent wind erosion is to keep the surface of the ground covered with vegetal cover at all times. It follows

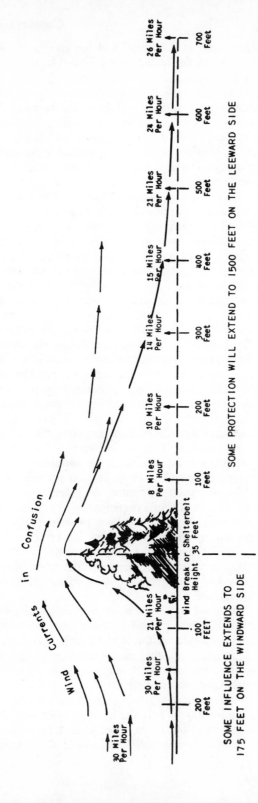

EFFECT OF TREE PLANTINGS ON WIND VELOCITY

FIGURE 83. Windbreaks break up the surface wind currents which otherwise would sweep the ground without obstruction. They provide some protection on the windward side but the greatest protection occurs on the leeward side. *(Soil Conservation Service)*

that the more often a soil is cultivated and the greater the length of time it lies bare and exposed to the action of the elements, the more apt it is to be damaged by wind erosion.

It is equally true that the system of managing land which results in keeping the most residue on the surface will generally be most desirable from the standpoint of erosion control. Stubble-mulch tillage makes it possible to carry heavy residues over into the second year. This is important in years when the crop fails or does not produce an appreciable amount of protective cover. Tillage operations aimed specifically at erosion control alone should be used only as a last resort.

Delayed stubble-mulch tillage—leaving stubble mulch undisturbed until weed growth is sufficient to require cultivation the following spring—is the most effective method of controlling wind erosion. It is also as satisfactory as other methods of tillage from the standpoint of wheat production. At Amarillo, Texas, for the 8-year period 1943-50, for example, average annual acre-yields of wheat were identical for early and delayed fallow. The yield in each case was 20 bushels. With delayed fallow, all of the crop residues can be left on the surface of the ground for protection during the winter and spring months.

Residues left standing, as with delayed fallow, are more effective than plowed residues for controlling wind erosion during the winter and spring blowing season. This is especially true following years of low crop yields or crop failures, when only small amounts of crop residues are produced. Even with stubble-mulch tillage following harvest, as practiced with early fallow, some of the effectiveness of the stubble for controlling wind erosion is destroyed.

When the soil is bare, any tillage that roughens the surface gives temporary protection from erosion. This can be done by ridging or clodding the surface soil, or by raising subsoil material to the surface.

Among the implements which have been used for ridging and clodding are the lister, shovel or sweep cultivator, deep-furrow drill, spring-tooth harrow, plow, and pocket digger. Implements that have been used for bringing subsoil to the surface are the subsoil plow, moldboard plow, lister, disk plow, and grading machine. If considerable crop residue is present, drifting can generally be controlled by sub-surface tillage. If crop residue is lacking, however, the land is more likely to drift when sub-surface tilled than when it is plowed or listed, because sub-surface tillage does not leave a sufficiently cloddy surface.

Shallow tillage when the soil is moist increases clodding of sandy loam soil. The object of raising heavier soil material from the subsoil is to produce a more cloddy structure in the surface soils that have become unstable. Although operations of this character may do permanent good, under certain conditions they are costly and should be considered only as a temporary substitute for measures that provide vegetal cover. The organic matter produced in the soil by a vegetal cover serves the same purpose, provides certain other advantages, and the method costs less. Vegetal cover renewed once a year gives more lasting protection than mechanical control measures. It aids in maintaining soil fertility and in keeping the rate of moisture absorption at a high level.

Tillage methods at best offer only temporary relief and, if used, must be repeated at intervals during the season. They are usually uneconomical. In no case should they be substituted for vegetal cover, once conditions become favorable for starting either a regular crop or an emergency cover crop. Tillage practices should be employed to the maximum when all other measures have failed.

Where erosion-prevention tillage can be performed in conjunction with necessary soil preparation or moisture-saving practices, its usefulness is much increased. For maximum moisture conservation, it should be carried out on the contour.

RECONDITIONING LANDS DAMAGED BY WIND EROSION

The most common effect of wind erosion consists of removing the topsoil to plow depth and piling it up in hummocks or drifts. Many hummocked fields are so rough that equipment cannot be driven over them.

The first goal in reconditioning wind-eroded soil is the establishment of vegetal cover over the area affected. This must be preceded, where necessary, by leveling to permit ordinary farming operations and accumulation of sufficient moisture to support the crop to be grown.

FIGURE 84. The soil of this field was stabilized by seeding sudangrass and sorghum. The area was badly eroded when the planting was made. (South Dakota)
(Soil Conservation Service)

The leveling operation may be carried out by the use of wind intensifiers, drag poles, or tractors and road graders. Burlap bags filled with sand and placed at different spacings on the crest of dunes are effective wind intensifiers. After the sandbags are in place, channels about 3 feet wide and 4 feet deep should be dug across the dune and the sand carried out beyond the crest. The sandbags are lowered as the wind moves the sand from around them. Instances have been observed where this method has lowered a dune about 2 feet during a single storm, flattening the crest and forming a small dune 6 to 10 feet farther on.

A drag pole, 8 by 8 inches and sufficiently long to extend down the leeward slope of a dune from the crest to the base, may be dragged along the sharp edge at right angles to the crest. A tractor and road grader may be used to level up the field directly or to cut wind channels in the dunes parallel to the direction of the wind. One or more turns over the highest points remove enough soil to give the wind a chance to continue the process. A 20-foot dune, prepared for wind-blast action by this method, was leveled to 5 feet during a 6-month period, putting it in condition for planting. Deep listing may also be beneficial.

Broomcorn and sudangrass are satisfactory plants for use in stabilizing dunes. These plants are more resistant to wind action than a number of other crops grown.

Hummocks and drifts usually form about weeds and contain a relatively high amount of unrotted organic matter, though much of this may be in a finely pulverized condition. An ample moisture supply is necessary to return areas of this kind to crop use. Until enough moisture is available to start plant growth, further erosion should be prevented by appropriate tillage treatment. This should be supplemented by vegetal-control measures at the first opportunity.

Similar treatment should be given to areas where the topsoil has been removed. The greatest need on such areas, however, is a renewed supply of organic matter, which can only be accumulated from successive crops.

Needed moisture-conservation measures may be combined with reconditioning operations. By increasing the moisture supply and improving the natural moisture distribution, they aid materially in hastening an opportunity for the first crop. Field tests indicate that badly wind-eroded areas may be reclaimed for agricultural use in relatively short periods.

WIND-EROSION CONTROL ON MUCK LAND

Wind, besides causing direct soil loss on muck land, may cause widespread damage to growing crops. Some of the major damage involved in this type of wind erosion occurs in Michigan, New York, and California. In Michigan and New York, the major damage occurs in late spring. During this period, the wind picks up large quantities of finely divided material as well as sharp pieces of muck and wood and hurls them against the tender stems of the young vegetable plants. A few days of active blowing may be enough to cut off effectively the above-ground growth of the young plants.

The critical period in the San Francisco Bay area in California is April, May, and June. Here the major damage is done to lands planted to white asparagus, although the production of any crop which does not provide a vegetal or residue cover during the summer is susceptible to damage.

The use of windbreaks is the most effective means of controlling the velocity of the wind, and hence the damage, from the blowing muck in Michigan and New York. They should be placed in rows at right angles to the direction of the prevailing wind.

Tree planting is relatively inexpensive and easy. Dense masses of trees deflect the wind currents upward and off the surface of the land. For each foot of the tree height, one-half to one rod of protection on the leeward side is obtained. Three rows of trees with a row of taller-growing species in the center serve to accentuate the upward deflection. Thus, by proper selection of varieties of trees and proper spacing of distances and observation of direction of wind, areas can be made relatively free from wind damage. Decreasing the wind velocity prevents blowing out of the crop and erosion of the soil. Tall-growing trees that are hardy, long-lived, and rapid in growth

FIGURE 85.   The main defense lines of trees are located at right angles to the direction of the prevailing wind. The secondary defense lines of trees should be run at right angles to these at intervals of about 20 to 30 rods. (Foard County, Texas) *(Soil Conservation Service)*

should be selected. Low-growing shrub hedges are not desirable nor effective for such purposes.

After the outside boundaries of the area have been determined, the rows of the tallest varieties are planted. The main defense lines should consist of 3 rows at least 8 feet apart with the trees 6 feet apart in the row. The row spacings should be adjusted to the type of cultivating equipment available on the farm. The tallest-growing variety should be planted in the middle.

The secondary defense lines should cross the fields every 20 to 40 rods at right angles to the primary strips. The rows may be single or double, 6 feet apart with the trees 4 to 5 feet apart in the row.

Trees may be planted beside the roadways if they are not set closer than one rod from the road. They should not be planted where the roots can penetrate tile lines and choke them up. The potential possibilities of muck-land soils cannot be fully realized until sufficiently large plantings of trees are established to break the wind and prevent it from damaging crops and soil.

Rye seeded in the fall may be used as a temporary windbreak under certain conditions. A few drill rows of rye seeded at the usual time and allowed to grow into the following spring ordinarily make enough growth by late May or early June to provide considerable protection. A few drill rows of rye seeded immediately adjacent to a row of newly-started willows make an effective windbreak. The rye should preferably be on the windward side of the permanent windbreak. Oats or barley seeded in the early spring in the manner indicated for rye may be used if rye could not be started the previous fall. These will probably not grow as high as rye but if thickly seeded they may make a denser windbreak at the immediate surface of the muck. The use of these grains, or wheat, greatly improves the effectiveness of recently-started windbreaks.

Oats may be used in single drill rows between rows of onions seeded in the usual manner. The oat rows may be placed from 6 to 14 rows apart.

It is estimated that the windbreak on muck soils protects or checks the velocity of the wind for a distance to the leeward of about 20 times the height of the windbreak.

Cover crops are highly desirable when there is any likelihood of blowing during winter. Under favorable conditions, a cover crop of rye or wheat, planted in pure stand or mixed with oats or barley, covers the soil completely and protects it from the action of the wind.

In addition to providing winter protection, the roots of a cover crop, especially of fall grain, when plowed under for the succeeding crop serve to hold the muck. Moreover, the fresh organic matter provided by the cover-crop materials tends to increase the size of the muck granules. These larger granules are not so easily moved as the smaller ones.

The soils of the Great Plains have been found to be highly erodible by wind when 50 per cent of the total material is less than 2 mm. diameter. By comparison, an average of 74 per cent of the peat-soil materials of the San Francisco Bay area is less than this size and, since the specific gravity of the muck material is only about one-third that of sand, these muck soils are extremely susceptible to erosion by wind. It has been estimated that soil loss by wind in this area may be as much as one-fourth to one-half inch per year.

In the Delta area of the interior valley of central California, the normal movement of the cool, moist winds from the Pacific across the ground surface is upset by the upward movement of heated air rising from the dark ground surface of the muck lands. The result is a turbulent mixing process. The extremes of heat exchange are manifested by the formation of rotating columns of air masses which funnel the lighter, heated air from near the ground surface to higher elevations.

It is estimated that approximately 40 per cent of the dust movement is due to direct blowing of the wind, 30 per cent to dust whirls, and the other 30 per cent to factors related to crop culture.

Satisfactory methods of wind control have been developed for some of the conditions prevailing in the San Francisco Bay area. They reduce the direct and rotational wind force originating from the bare cultivated ground surface during April to July, the period of highest wind movement. They include the use of protective mulches, residues, strip-cropping, or wind barriers in the form of trees, shrubs, or crops. Farmers, however, are reluctant to adopt them as they involve the use of new types of farm machinery and in some cases call for an outlay of considerable sums of money.

Introduction of crop residues as a protective surface cover may require changes in cultivating equipment. A modified system of strip-cropping could be carried out in conjunction with the growing of asparagus—the principal crop grown. Such a system should provide either a live or dormant crop growth considerably higher than the crowns of the asparagus ridges during the period April through June.

COASTAL-DUNE STABILIZATION

In many coastal areas, the sand washed ashore by wave action is blown inland after drying and is deposited in dunes of various types. Usually the initial product of this process is the formation of a foredune just beyond the high-tide watermark on the shore. As the size of the dune increases, the sand at the crest is blown farther inland where it accumulates and is shaped into another dune. Soon additional dunes are built—one behind the other. Since these dunes are by no means stable, they may level off gradually and supply material for the building of new dunes.

The only permanent solution to this type of problem is the establishment of vegetal cover over the entire surface of the dune. The windward side, being the active part of the dune, should be stabilized first. After this side has been stabilized, the rest of the dune can be brought under control.

Three principal steps are usually required to establish a permanent vegetal cover on coastal dunes. The initial step consists of planting beachgrass and dunegrasses to arrest sand movement. Then, intermediate seedings or plantings of leguminous species are necessary as soon as the beachgrass has stilled the moving sand. This step may be combined with the seeding or planting of permanent grasses and legumes or shrubs and trees, if the initial sand-stilling plantings are sufficiently vigorous to have com-

FIGURE 86. The first step in stabilizing beach sand is the planting of beachgrass and dunegrass. (Ottawa County, Michigan)
(Soil Conservation Service)

pletely stilled the sand and eliminated the possibility of movement.

In establishing initial grass plantings, the order of planting should be from the windward to the leeward side. Plantings should be uniform, without unprotected gaps or strips; otherwise, pockets will be blown out in the dune which may result in the loss of all that has been achieved by previous stabilization activities.

Permanent control of sand dunes can be accomplished only by establishing on them a vegetal cover, either by natural succession or by seeding. Mechanical structures that stop sand movement only temporarily are costly and, if not properly placed, may cause turbulences that make the dune difficult to stabilize.

Records running back for centuries tell of attempts to hold drifting dunes and prevent the destruction of fertile lands back of them. Before the Christian era, the Pharaohs built great walls along the edges of the plains on either side of the Nile Valley to prevent wind-blown sand from covering fertile fields and orchards. For many centuries, the people of Holland have planted and cared for the dunes along their coasts, and have even promoted the formation of dunes to keep back the sea from their homes and fields. The first authentic accounts of successful dune stabilization report the work done by French engineers, who reclaimed the dunes and extensive sand plains along the southwest coast of France. As early as 1778, the

French Government sent an engineer, Baron de Villiers, to Gascony to study conditions and prepare plans for reclamation. The system proposed by him and later perfected by engineers Chambrelent and Bremontier was the formation of protective dunes on the shore just above high watermark, followed by planting of the dunes with sand-binding grasses and a final planting of maratime and other pines.

The work of planting dunes and sand wastes in this country has been limited. In Massachusetts, from 1826 to 1838, numerous plantings of beachgrass were made on Cape Cod by the Federal Government and by the town of Provincetown. As constant care was not given these plantings, and fishermen and laborers cut the sod and removed the woody growth, the dune lands reverted to their original conditions. Attempts have been made to stabilize dunes along the coasts of Long Island, New Jersey, and the Carolinas. Examples of successful dune control are on the Clatsop Plains at the mouth of the Columbia River in Oregon, in Golden Park in San Francisco, and along the Michigan shore of Lake Michigan.

The usual method of starting the grass is to set out plants of beachgrass or marram grass in groups or rows, the spacing depending upon the severity of the wind and on whether the aim is to build up a dune or to still the sand in place. The beachgrass grows vigorously, putting out rootlets at the nodes as these become covered. Care and attention in maintaining sufficient density, and the immediate replacement of plants that have failed, are the chief requisites in the preliminary holding of the dune. After the grass has become well established, seedlings of coniferous trees are planted among the grass. On sand areas leeward of dunes, the usual method is to cover the surface with brush arranged like shingles on a roof and held down with a shovelful of sand here and there. Seeds of the desired conifers are then sown among the brush.

On active dunes, the planting of grass or other herbaceous plants is necessary for temporarily holding the sand, but forest trees or shrubs must be planted to bring about final stabilization.

Initial sand-stilling plantings of beachgrass were not sufficient to permanently stabilize eroding coastal sand dunes in the Pacific Northwest. Seeding of permanent grasses and legumes was necessary to provide a close permanent vegetal cover over that loose, moving sand. Once the dunes became stabilized the beachgrass died.

The dune stabilization work on the Pacific coast has shown that seeding of grasses and legumes can be made for permanent dune stabilization into one-year-old plantings of beachgrass if they are vigorous and have stilled the sand. Mixtures of commonly available tame grasses and legumes were better than native grasses and legumes for permanent dune stabilization. The most satisfactory mixture contained hairy vetch, common ryegrass, purple beachpea, Clatsop red fescue, and tall fescue. On rough, undulating dune areas, plantings of pine and Scotch-broom are made instead of these grass-legume seedings, as the herbaceous plants are more difficult to maintain.

On Cape Cod, control measures for small dunes include the spreading of brush on the windward side of the dune. The branches serve as a barrier against the wind and as a trap for catching beachgrass seed. The grass becomes established the following season. Once the grass becomes established well enough to prevent further serious blowing, pine trees are planted. Three to five-year-old pine trees planted in rows about 3 feet apart and with 3-foot spacing in the row are used. The common practice is to plant the trees in early spring, the season when moisture in the sand is most likely to be enough for plant-growth requirements.

In stabilizing sand dunes on Cape Henry, it was found necessary to supplement other practices by construction of groins at about 100-yard intervals. These structures consisted of two-strand barbed wire fences and driftwood posts with barberry brush interwoven into the wire. The brush was arranged with the butts placed alternately up and down. The fence, a little over 4 feet in height, extended from the foredune across the foreshore down to the average high watermark. The seaside end was divided into a short wye, with wings 15 feet long, to protect it from erosive wave action. A short ell projecting upward at the upper end served to protect the structure and prevent scouring of the foredune by oblique winds.

Sandblow areas in Vermont were laid out in alternate 12- and 24-foot strips at right angles to the direction of the prevailing wind. The 12-foot strips were planted to weeping lovegrass and black locust and the 24-foot strips to red pine. The lovegrass seed was broadcast at the rate of 3 pounds per acre and raked in. The black locusts were set at 6-foot intervals in 2 staggered rows in the grass strips. Early the second spring, or during the fall after planting the lovegrass, red pine was planted in the 24-foot space between the grass-locust strips, using a 6-foot spacing in 4 staggered rows. Ample fertilizer and lime were applied for both grass and trees at the time of planting the grass.

REFERENCES

1. Bates, C. G. 1945. *Shelterbelt influence: I. General description of studies made.* Jour. Forestry, 43: 88-92.
2. ———. 1945. *Shelterbelt influence: II. The value of shelterbelts for house heating.* Jour. Forestry, 43: 176-196.
3. Brown, R. L. 1948. *Permanent coastal dune stabilization with grasses and legumes.* Jour. Soil and Water Cons., 3: 69-74.
4. Call, L. E. 1936. *Cultural methods of controlling wind erosion.* Amer. Soc. Agron. Jour., 28: 193-201.
5. Chepil, W. S. 1944. *Utilization of crop residues for wind erosion control.* Sci. Agr., 24: 307-319.
6. ———. 1946. *Dynamics of wind erosion: V. Cumulative intensity of soil drifting across eroding fields.* Soil Sci., 61: 257-263.
7. ———, and Englehorn, C. L. 1951. *Report on causes and effects of wind erosion in east central Kansas in March 1950.* Kans. State Coll. Dept. Agron. (Mimeo.)
8. ———, and Zingg, A. W. 1952. *The effect of cultivation on erodibility of soils by wind.* Soil Sci. Soc. Amer. Proc., 16: 19-21.
9. Chepil, W. S., and Milne, R. A. 1941. *Wind erosion of soil in relation to size and nature of the exposed area.* Sci. Agr. 21: 479-487.
10. ———. 1941. *Wind erosion of soil in relation to roughness of surface.* Soil Sci., 52: 417-431.
11. Finnell, H. H. 1950. *The plowup of western grasslands and the resultant effect upon Great Plains agriculture.* Paper presented at the Southwest Social Sci. Assoc., Houston, Texas.

12. ———. 1950. *Upkeep of Southern Great Plains wheat lands.* Okla. Agr. Expt. Sta. Cir. M-204. (Mimeo.)
13. Guild, E. R. 1938. *Land whoa! The migration of Cape Henry.* Mil. Engin., 30: 81-85.
14. Hopkins, E. S., Palmer, A. E., and Chepil, W. S. 1946. *Soil drifting in the Prairie Provinces.* Can. Dept. Agr. Farmer's Bull. 32.
15. Kelly, J. B., Midgley, A. R., and Varney, K. E. 1948. *Revegetation of sandblows in Vermont.* Vt. Agr. Expt. Sta. Bull. 542.
16. Kucinsky, K. J., and Eisenmenger, W. S. 1943. *Sand dune stabilization methods on Cape Cod.* Econ. Geog., 19: 206-214.
17. Van Doren, C. E., and Johnson, W. C. 1952. *Fallow and the wind erosion hazard.* USDA, SCS-TP-111.
18. Weir, W. W. 1950. *Subsidence of peat lands of the Sacramento-San Joaquin Delta, California.* Hilgardia, 20(3).
19. Whitfield, C. J. 1938. *Crop production on land badly damaged by wind erosion.* Amer. Soc. Agron. Jour., 30: 461-464.
20. ———. 1939. *Sand-dune reclamation in the Southern Great Plains.* USDA Farmer's Bull. 1825.
21. Woodruff, N. P., and Zingg, A. W. 1952. *Wind tunnel studies of fundamental problems related to windbreaks.* USDA, SCS-TP-112.
22. Zingg, A. W. 1950. *Report on the investigations of the wind-soil movement problem in the Sacramento-San Joaquin Delta region of the Central Valley of California.* Kans. Agr. Expt. Sta. and USDA, SCS. (Mimeo.)
23. ———. 1950. *Investigations on the mechanics of wind erosion.* USDA, SCS Research Ann. Rept.
24. ———. 1951. *Investigations on the mechanics of wind erosion.* USDA, SCS Research Ann. Rept.

14

Mulch Farming
for Row Crops

A quiet revolution is taking place on a few farms in the Corn Belt and other sections of the country. A new method that bids fair to alter our method of growing row crops is emerging. Used primarily on corn to date, it is based on sound and well-proved principles. It all but eliminates erosion, conserves water, increases crop yields, lowers crop production costs, and improves the soil.

The foundation for all versions of the new method is the way in which crop residues and other organic materials are being managed. Other building-blocks appear in the form of wider row-spacings, increased number of plants per acre, liberal use of fertilizer, and less disturbance of the soil.

The new method of farming makes use of crop residues as mulch on the surface of the ground and, in some cases of wider rows, of growing sod crops on the strips between the corn rows during the corn-growing season. The mulch or sod crops protect the soil against the blasting action of falling raindrops and get more of the rain water into the ground.

Shielding of the surface preserves the physical structure of the soil and holds to a minimum the loss of organic matter and plant nutrients from the soil by erosion. The increased amount of soil moisture made available by this process assures larger yields of the row crops and a greater total yield where the sod strips are used between the rows of cultivated crops. The outstanding achievement of this method is that land can be heavily cropped every year, by the same crop if need be, and improved at the same time.

One variation of the new method of growing row crops is illustrated by the success of Dr. George Scarseth (formerly Head of the Agronomy Department, Purdue University, now Director of the American Farm Research Association) in growing corn on a rundown Indiana farm. The farm in Tippecanoe County, Indiana, that Dr. Scarseth bought in 1950 produced only 25 bushels of corn per acre that year. The farm had not yielded more than 30 bushels per acre for the previous ten years.

On May 24, 1951, Dr. Scarseth planted corn with a mulch planter. There was no plowing, disking, or other soil preparation—the corn simply was planted through a mulch of weeds and cornstalks.

One kernel was dropped every 8 to 10 inches in 40-inch rows, giving a stand of 17,000 stalks per acre. The planter placed fertilizer at two depths: (a) 300 pounds of 10-10-10 in a split band 3 inches deep in the row to get the seedlings off to a fast start ahead of the weeds, and (b) 800 pounds of

FIGURE 87. Corn planted in alfalfa sod. The alfalfa sod protects the soil from erosion, increases the amount of rain water that enters the ground, and improves corn yields.
(International Harvester Co.)

FIGURE 88. View of the mulch planter. Mulch planting produces cultivated row crops under soil-improving rather than soil-
depleting conditions by combining two beneficial practices:
(1) maintaining a mulch on top of the ground to retard erosion from wind and water, maintaining open surface soil
structure, increasing water intake, and making maximum
use of crop residues to improve soil tilth and fertility; and
(2) making more efficient use of soil moisture and chemical
fertilizers to increase crop yields, resulting in even greater
volumes of organic matter for further improvement of soil
tilth and fertility.
(International Harvester Co.)

10-10-10 in a band 9 inches deep to feed the corn as it grew.

Weeds were controlled, but not killed, by two shallow cultivations. To
be certain that there was plenty of nitrogen to grow both corn and weeds,
Dr. Scarseth side-dressed the crop with 200 pounds of ammonium nitrate
per acre, six inches deep, a foot from one side of the row. This was done
July 6, the time of the second and last cultivation.

Rainfall was ample early in the season, but August was very dry and
there was a severe Helminthosporium infestation in September.

Test rows in the field were given less than the full fertilizer treatment.
They demonstrated clearly the theory that to get a quick, profitable build-up
in yield there must be plenty of plant food to do the complete job.

This method of growing corn is based on well-established experimental
findings. It is well known that mulches get more water into the ground,
hold it better, and prevent erosion. Plenty of plant food was applied to

TABLE 42. Per acre fertilizer treatment, yield, and profit (13)

Amount of fertilizer	Bushels	Fertilizer cost	Production cost	Profit or loss
No fertilizer	2.5	$ 0.00	$38.45	-$ 34.70
300 lbs. 10-10-10 in row	30.0	$ 8.50	$46.95	-$ 1.95
300 lbs. 10-10-10 in row + 800 lbs. 10-10-10 at 9"	59.5	$38.12	$76.57	+$ 4.18
1100 lbs. 10-10-10 + 200 lbs. ammonium nitrate side dressing	125.5	$46.62	$85.07	+$103.18

meet the requirements of both the weeds and corn. Sufficient quantities of plant nutrients were added to grow 150 bushels of corn per acre under ideal conditions. The corn was planted thick enough to get a sufficient number of plants (17,000) per acre to produce 100 bushels or more corn per acre. Cultivation was held to a minimum in order to hold down erosion, prevent pruning of corn roots, and preserve soil tilth.

The soil on this farm was protected a full 12 months of the year. Stalks, shredded when the corn was picked, provided a mulch cover during the winter. The mulch planter did not disturb this cover. Two light cultivations

FIGURE 89. Planting with the mulch planter. Note the heavy mulch of chopped stubble on the surface of the ground between the rows.
(International Harvester Co.)

with disks knocked down and handicapped the weeds, but did not kill them. Weed growth in the spring and early summer, plus stalk mulch, held the soil despite a near cloudburst which badly eroded nearby clean-cultivated land.

Clean cultivation is a poor practice. Weeds, fed enough nutrients so that they will not rob the crop, can be almost as important as clover or grass in building fertility and preventing erosion. They supply organic matter, improve soil tilth, and provide cover. Weeds did not hurt the corn yields in Dr. Scarseth's field because the corn plants, stimulated by plenty of plant food, outgrew and finally shaded the weeds. A thick stand of corn is needed to do this.

In test rows, 1,100 pounds of 10-10-10 produced only 59.5 bushels of corn—because there was not enough nitrogen for both weeds and corn. The side dressing of an extra 66 pounds of nitrogen boosted corn yields to 125.5 bushels an acre.

Plant nutrients used by weeds—even $8 to $10 worth an acre—are stored capital in the form of organic matter (provided they are not lost by erosion), improved tilth, and fertility—extra corn the next year!

This method, with some modifications, produced an average of 98.9 bushels of corn per acre in 1953 despite the fact the growing season was dry and hot. In addition, the corn took just 3 hours of man-and-tractor time per acre, compared with 10 hours for the average—a saving of $28 per acre in man-machine costs alone.

ADJUST FERTILIZER AND NUMBER OF PLANTS TO AVAILABLE MOISTURE

This new method of growing corn is based on the assumption that, in order to get maximum yields, enough fertilizer must be used to feed the largest number of plants that the available moisture will support.

Today in the Corn Belt—and in irrigated sections—the recommendation is around 16,000 to 20,000 plants per acre, depending on the soil, fertilization, and other factors. These recommendations also hold for the northern states, with single-ear hybrids such as are used there. In the South, where prolific two-ear hybrids are used, the range is from 10,000 to 14,000 plants per acre. In the Great Plains, it runs from 4,000 to 6,000.

WIDE ROW SPACING

Wide corn rows—60, 72 and 80 inches—are gaining in popularity. By spacing the plants close enough together in the rows, wide rows will produce almost as high yields as 40-inch rows and under some conditions will permit the production of sod crops between the rows during the corn growing season. Robert Arnold of Greencastle, Indiana, harvested 75 bushels of corn per acre in 1953 from single corn rows 80 inches apart. In addition, he grew an excellent pasture crop for his hogs on the same land. Ted Funk, McLean County, Illinois, planted 200 acres of corn—a row every 60 inches—which averaged 90 bushels per acre; and he also got a good stand of legume-grass seeding.

Peterson and Engelbert obtained top corn yields without plowing the field and with only one cultivation during the 1952 season in Wisconsin. The corn was planted on a field of old legume sod which was heavily infested with quack grass. The field had been disked twice. Eight hundred pounds of 10-10-10 per acre were placed 9 inches deep, and 300 pounds of 4-16-16 were drilled in the row. The field was cultivated just once, on June 30, with an ordinary shoe-type cultivator and side-dressed with 250 pounds of ammonium nitrate per acre. It yielded 135 bushels of corn per acre, 4 bushels more than a 131-bushel yield from another part of the field getting the same fertilizer treatment, but receiving standard cultivation in place of the mulch-planter treatment.

Pickard and Bateman obtained corn yields that averaged about 6 bushels less for mulch planting than with the conventional method of planting during the years 1951 and 1952 in Illinois. The yield from the usual planting method averaged 95 bushels per acre. The comparisons in Illinois were made where the fields had been given 66 pounds of nitrogen per acre and had a corn population of 12,000 plants per acre.

Browning, Norton, and Shedd also obtained lower yields where corn was subtilled than where plowed. This work was done, however, before it became recognized that large amounts of fertilizer were necessary for high yields and before the advent of the mulch planter.

LIMIT CULTIVATION AND INCREASE NUMBER OF HYBRIDS

Louie Abbott has averaged 129 bushels of corn per acre annually over a period of 16 years on his 210-acre farm in Whiteside County, Illinois. He averaged 140 bushels per acre on 65 acres in 1952.

Abbott plows down 400 pounds of 0-48-60 and 300 pounds of ammonium nitrate per acre. He mixes three good hybrid varieties, of slightly different maturity dates. This extends the period of tasseling which gives better pollination and spreads out the "pull" on moisture and fertility. He plants 18,000 kernels and expects a 16,000-stalk stand. He hill-drops 3 or 4 kernels every 30 inches in 36-inch rows. The corn is cultivated once, when eight to ten inches high. If necessary Abbott advocates control of weeds with chemicals, but says damage from weeds even in a drought year will be in direct proportion to the good done by *not* hurting the corn with what he calls "root-pruning cultivation."

Funk's Research Acres in McLean County, Illinois, obtained 122 bushels of corn per acre in 40-inch rows; 122 bushels in 40-inch rows with every third row missing; 125 bushels per acre with corn in single 60-inch rows; and 99 bushels per acre with corn in single rows 80 inches wide.

In two years of tests, single 60-inch rows yielded more than corn planted in 40-inch rows. The 80-inch rows at Research Acres have shown about a 15 per cent decrease in yield compared with conventional 40-inch planting.

WIDE ROWS GIVE BETTER STANDS OF LEGUMES

Yields are only a part of the story. The grass-legume seedings—Atlantic alfalfa, Kenland red clover, ladino clover, and brome—have shown up well. Actually, the stand in 1953 in the 60- and 80-inch corn middles was better than where an oats or wheat nurse crop was used.

A. J. Berwick, Doan Agricultural Service, found no yield differences between conventional 40-inch planting and corn planted 72 and 80 inches apart in Kane County, Illinois. Despite a very dry August, the summer seeding of grass-legume in wide-row corn was almost as good as the seeding with oats. This makes corn superior to oats, for corn produces about 100 bushels per acre as compared with only 50 bushels for oats. In addition, the oats frequently lodge (fall down) because of high fertility and the grass-legume seeding is smothered out. By eliminating the oats, a corn-legume-corn-legume rotation can be followed. This will allow 50 per cent of the land to be in corn, 50 per cent in legumes—a higher cash return, and plenty of legumes for a livestock program.

PRESENT FARM MACHINERY INADEQUATE

The present farm machinery in the Corn Belt was designed for use on conventional 40-inch rows and clean cultivation, but it is not suitable for use with the wide rows. The mulch planter is solving the plowing and planting problem. The mulch planter and the use of chemical weed killers are practically eliminating the need for cultivation. But the corn pickers and certain other types of machinery need to be redesigned to meet the needs of the new method of growing corn.

NITRO-GRASS ROTATION FOR CORN

The Illinois Agricultural Experiment Station is developing one modification of this new method of growing corn. It provides for use of grass and the substitution of nitrogen fertilizer for legumes for soil improvement in cropping systems. It is called "nitro-grass" rotation and is expected to produce maximum corn yields and full protection against soil erosion.

CHEAP NITROGEN FORCES CHANGE

The availability of cheap synthetic nitrogen and its use in corn production assures that there will be some significant changes in corn-production practices.

Studies of the legume program for grain systems of farming reveal not weakness but, rather, limitations imposed by the nature of the program. Well-managed Corn Belt farms were so productive that yields were held back because insufficient nitrogen was fixed for the high productivity made possible by the rotation. Ordinarily half of the land remained bare and subject to erosion because it was in corn and beans. Thus, erosion control was only partially achieved and the organic matter content could not be maintained. Getting a stand of legumes is becoming most difficult due to disease, insects, and low fertility.

Some of the limitations of the legume system can be eliminated by the use of new and cheap synthetic nitrogen. One of the uses for synthetic nitrogen will be to help the legume program, especially on second-year corn, wheat, or oats, or on first-year corn when the legume fails or is not up to full expectations.

CORN BELT IS GRASS COUNTRY

The Corn Belt is grass country. Thousands of years ago, the grasses in the native prairie vegetation took over. They reduced the native legume population to around 3 per cent, once the legumes had built up enough humus so that nitrogen could be cycled from humus to grass and back again into humus.

Except for nitrogen fixation, grasses are far better than legumes for many purposes. Grass pastures do not cause bloat in cattle; pure legume pastures do. Grasses form better, tougher sods; legumes usually form relatively poorer sods, and sweet clover and soybeans actually encourage soil erosion. Grasses form a better granular or crumb structure in soils. Stands of grasses are, in general, more easily obtained than stands of legumes.

Most important in the Corn Belt, grasses can be fall-planted and amount to something for late fall, winter, and spring cover and pasture. Except for vetch, a very unsatisfactory possibility, legumes cannot be fall-planted and used for this purpose in the Corn Belt.

It seems evident that big changes in corn-production methods in the Corn Belt may be expected. With all these advantages in favor of grasses, and with ample cheap nitrogen to make the grass approach legumes in protein composition, there appears to be no good reason why grass and nitrogen cannot supplant the legume. We are concerned here only with legumes as used in grain rotations, primarily for soil improvement.

More study of the "nitro-grass" rotation in the field is needed before specific recommendations can be worked out, but this applies principally to the management and nitrogen fertilization of the grass, not the corn.

Growing grass without nitrogen and utilizing the residue for corn can reduce yields, rather than increase them. The grass, in decomposing, would use up the nitrogen needed for corn. But the result with nitrogen-treated grass can be different.

With no knowledge of how to handle the grass (rye was planted between rows in the middle of August), a total of 355 bushels of corn were produced on the same plot at the Illinois Agricultural Experiment Station in 4 years of corn (rye catch crop), or 89 bushels per acre annually. Enough nitrogen for the whole of the corn crop and for the decomposition of the rye crop was added each year.

The waist-high green rye was shredded at corn planting time, and corn was planted and fertilized in one operation, using a mulch planter. Most of the chopped rye remained on the surface as a mulch.

In addition to producing an average of 89 bushels of corn per acre, this practice increased the organic matter supply of the soil, practically eliminated soil erosion, improved the structure of the soil, provided a mulch all summer, and increased the biological activity of the soil to an all-time high. The legume rotations only partially achieve these objectives.

The only concern is whether some of the organic matter could be used more economically as feed for livestock instead of being returned directly to the soil. Eight crops (one of corn and one of rye each year) in 4 years with the vegetative parts returned to the soil is a lot of organic matter. Perhaps the rye could be used more profitably for moderate grazing in the fall and spring, or by mowing early for grass silage. The shredded corn stalks should provide adequate cover. The kind of grass to use and how it should be handled need further study.

Experience indicates that some such nitro-grass program holds the key to high production at a low cost per bushel—and with complete soil conservation.

GROW CORN OFTENER

This new cropping system makes it possible to grow corn every year on the same field and improve the yield at the same time. There is nothing to indicate that this practice will lead to increased difficulties from insects and diseases.

By using such systems, it is safe to assume that corn can be grown a lot oftener and more profitably. If the grass in such a rotation can be used as a crop, so much the better. Soil organic matter maintenance, and even its increase, will still take place. With two crops a year, competition from pasture-grown beef can be better met and returns per acre can be even higher than from just 90- to 100-bushel corn. In addition, of course, practically complete soil conservation is thrown in as a rich dividend.

ADD INSECTICIDES WITH FERTILIZER

Another noteworthy development in this corn-field "revolution" is the use of fertilizer as a carrier of insecticides. Rootworms, wireworms, cutworms, and beetles possibly may be controlled for $2 or $3 an acre, perhaps less, by using fertilizer as insecticide carriers. In Kentucky, fertilizer-mixed aldrin (1 lb. per acre) or chlordane (2 lbs. per acre) boosted corn yields as much as 19 bushels per acre under normal moisture conditions, even though checked plots showed little or no injury from corn rootworms or other insects thought to be important. The corn plants also were faster growing and earlier tasseling. At these low rates of use, Kentucky investigators say you have nothing to lose and a lot to gain; you will gain even if the Southern corn rootworm does not attack your field.

SEED WHEAT IN CORN

The Ohio Agricultural Experiment Station is finding it profitable to seed wheat in unharvested corn. The corn is planted in 70-inch rows. The wheat is seeded in the wide middles at the fly-free date. This practice delays corn harvesting until the corn crop is in condition for it. It also provides a longer growing season for the wheat.

Most of the loss in yield caused by wide row-spacing will be made up by utilizing more of the growing season. The average result should be about three bushels less of corn, three bushels more wheat, better quality of both crops and orderly sequence in fall farm jobs. The farmer who does not sow wheat after corn could profit well by planting cover or meadow crops directly in the growing corn. Experiments with row-space widths at Wooster suggest the idea that such a system can be practical, or at least as practical as any system that depends upon summer seeding of small seeded crops.

MULCH INCREASES CORN YIELD

In 1953, corn land at Wooster, Ohio, mulched with 10 tons of manure per

FIGURE 90. Interplanting in wide corn-row middles. Vetch and ryegrass in 63-inch corn rows at Wooster, Ohio. The vetch and ryegrass were seeded in late June, and the photograph taken about August 15.
(Ohio Agricultural Experiment Station)

acre, produced nearly eight bushels of corn per acre more than similar land with an equal amount of manure plowed down. In 1951 the increase was 11 bushels; in 1952 it was 10 bushels. The increase from using a two-ton mulch of straw in the summer of 1953 was 16 bushels per acre.

Soil moisture in August, 1953, was 3 per cent higher under manure mulch and 4 per cent higher under straw mulch than in unmulched soil. Four farmers who tried the practice in 1953 got increases in yields of 6 to 19 bushels.

The water-saving capacity of mulching was again shown on runoff plots at Wooster in 1953. Unmulched soil lost more than one-third of the rainfall by runoff, whereas the manure-mulched plots lost only a small percentage. It is the bedding in the manure which does the job. The more bedding in the manure the more efficient mulch it makes.

ADEQUATE USE OF FERTILIZER POINTS WAY TO HIGHER PRODUCTION

Both the science and the practice of using commercial fertilizers are undergoing radical changes. The possibilities for increasing farm efficiency through eliminating low soil fertility as a limiting factor in crop production are just now being appreciated. Recent research in the development of soil tests and the application of required nutrients permit the production of high yields on poor soils in favorable seasons.

By using appropriate soil-building programs, much land that was abandoned because of erosion or excessive nutrient removal is being made more productive than when it was first cultivated. Some fields once considered suitable only for trees or rough pasture are producing profitable yields of corn and other crops. The wide difference in the initial productiveness of many virgin soils has been almost eliminated in favorable seasons. People on many soils of low fertility need no longer be held down to a standard of living based on nutrient delivery by low-producing fields. They can now enjoy the same advantages as their neighbors who possess better land.

ORGANIC MATTER IMPORTANT

Our past agricultural production has been closely associated with the quantity of organic matter in soils. Probably over 95 per cent of the nitrogen and over 50 per cent of the phosphorus absorbed by crops on unfertilized soil come from organic matter. With soils high in humus, and conditions ideal for organic matter breakdown, yields are usually high. But in excessively dry or wet seasons, these nutrients are not released and yields are reduced. Crop rotations including legumes have been widely used as a means of restoring soil nitrogen and organic matter. The value of these legumes has been almost universally accepted, yet under practical farm conditions they actually have added only limited amounts of nitrogen and masked the fertility decline. Legumes add nitrogen and furnish soil cover, but remove more minerals from the soil than do grain crops, particularly when only the grain is removed.

TABLE 43. Yield of corn following legumes with and without supplemental nitrogen.* 3-year average, Putnam silt loam (9)

Corn following	Yields-bushels	
	No N	66 lbs. N
Red clover	74	101
Sweet clover	90	110
Lespedeza	83	96
Soybeans	82	110
Timothy	74	95

* Mineral treatments added in quantities to remove them as limiting factors in production

On Sanborn field at the Missouri Agricultural Experiment Station, 65 years of different cropping systems show soil changes from different crop sequences and soil treatments. Where legumes and grasses have been included in crop rotations without soil treatments, the soil now contains less phosphorus, potassium, calcium, and magnesium than where corn or wheat has been grown continuously. The first cropping system that failed was continuous clover without soil treatment. After 15 years, this system was abandoned—not because of accumulation of insects or diseases—but because the removal of this crop for hay removed minerals to such an extent that clover would no longer grow.

Legumes are grown as green manure crops for soil improvement on many farms. However, where livestock are produced, the use of legumes primarily for soil improvement is more an ideal than a practice. Most legumes will be used as livestock feed. It is reasoned that where manure is returned, the soil is benefited. Except in those regions where winters are so severe as to require barn feeding, however, the efficiency of manure returns is too low to be of much value. In much of the southern two-thirds of the United States, most winter feeding is done in pastures and there is little manure to be returned to cultivated fields.

Experiments show that legumes in an average rotation will not furnish sufficient nitrogen for optimum corn yields. The addition of chemical nitrogen when legumes are turned under has given profitable increases in yield.

Since chemical nitrogen is being used in ever-increasing quantity, the need for additional minerals to maintain a proper balance is a necessity for maximum yields of quality crops.

SOIL TESTS SHOW NUTRIENT NEEDS

As soils declined in fertility in the past, small additions of phosphates and then mixed fertilizers were applied to improve yields. For years both experiments and farm practice attempted to determine the minimum quantities of applied nutrients that would give a profitable response. In few cases was the quantity of nutrients added sufficient to replace that removed in crops, not to mention losses by erosion. Consequently soil fertility continued to decline.

It formerly was possible to determine nutrients needed for a given soil type through field experiments. But past management has changed soil nutrient levels to an extent that greater variations may be found on adjoining farms with similar soils than between soils with widely different characteristics. Without soil tests it is not possible to determine the limiting factors in plant growth. Addition of plant nutrients in fertilizers to bring a low-fertility soil up to high fertility that will produce top yields may in some cases involve a cost nearly equal to the value of the land. In the interest of farm efficiency and best plant growth (proper balance of nutrients is important), only those nutrients that are deficient should be added. Experiments have shown that the addition of a nutrient already present in adequate amounts may depress rather than benefit yields and quality.

INTERPRETING SOIL TEST RESULTS

Organic matter is about 5 per cent nitrogen. Under conditions in the Corn Belt, and according to soil tests now in use, from 4 to 6 per cent of this nitrogen will be released on sandy soils (depending on climatic conditions). Silt loams will release from 2 to 3 per cent, and loams about 1¼ to 2½ per cent. If a soil analysis shows 2 per cent organic matter, the surface 7 inches (2,000,000 pounds) would contain 40,000 pounds. Considering a content of 5 per cent nitrogen, this soil would contain 2,000 pounds of nitrogen, or 1,000 pounds for each one per cent organic matter. If the soil was a silt loam and from 2 to 3 per cent of the nitrogen were released annually, then this surface soil could provide a corn crop with from 40 to 60 pounds of nitrogen, or sufficient for yields of 30 to 40 bushels per acre.

These methods of calculation have given good correlations with field experiments. The high levels of release are obtained in good seasons and the low levels in excessively wet or dry years. A summary of 208 fertilizer experiments with corn conducted in all parts of Missouri showed that nitrogen applied according to soil tests (ample minerals present), which included an average of 80 pounds of nitrogen per acre, increased yields from 56.9 to 97.3 bushels. This was an increase in yield of one bushel for each 2.2 pounds of nitrogen added.

Small grains make most of their growth during the cooler season of the year when organic matter breakdown is slower. Satisfactory correlations have been obtained using values for release of nitrogen from the soil equal to one-half those used for corn.

Phosphorus becomes a limiting element when levels of available nitrogen are increased. Field results indicate that for maximum yields of wheat and clover, the soil should show a reserve of near 200 pounds of phosphorus per acre; and for corn, soybeans, and oats, at least 100 pounds.

Potash needs are increased as we remove more legumes. Best results with corn and clover have been obtained with tests showing potassium levels of near 300 pounds per acre. A 200-pound level appears adequate for soybeans, wheat, and oats. Recent experimental work suggests that it may be desirable to add quantities of potassium much greater than these, except on soils of high clay content.

There are indications that soil tests may be of more value in determining that a soil contains sufficient lime than in determining the amount to apply. Recent tests show that some soils may have been overlimed, possibly creating potassium and boron deficiencies. Where high-calcium liming materials have been used, magnesium is becoming a limiting element. Dolomitic limestone is not effective if soils are near neutrality, and soluble magnesium compounds must be applied to correct deficiencies. Soil tests for determining the liming status of the soil are probably the most dependable of all in use.

GOOD SOIL SAMPLES ESSENTIAL

Soil testing still requires some development and correlation with field experiments. Its value is attested by the number of tests being made in all parts of the country and the results that have been accomplished on farms. The weakest link in the soil-testing program is poor samples. Too many samples are inadequate, or fail to be representative of the area to be tested. A poor sample can result in improper diagnosis of nutrient reserves and cause the use of improper treatment. For best results, a composite sample of at least six borings should be taken on each five acres, smaller on an area of highly variable soils), and the average results from all samples of a field should be considered in determining the soil treatment program.

ADEQUATE NUTRIENTS REDUCE SEASONAL HAZARDS

Although interest in adequate fertilization is at the highest pitch in history, there has persisted the dread of losing both crop and fertilizer in unfavorable seasons. In 1951, some areas of Missouri experienced the heaviest rainfall on record. The State Experiment Station found that where nitrogen was plowed down and minerals had been provided, the corn outgrew grass and weeds. The added nitrogen, substituted for that normally provided by organic matter, nourished the plants, and yields were well above average.

The seasons of 1952 and 1953 were extremely dry. The favorable response in these years dispelled the fear of losses in dry seasons and promoted the use of soil testing and the application of treatments to provide adequate nutrient reserves. For example, where moisture was too scant to produce corn grain, adequate nutrients in many cases made the difference of whether there was silage and forage for winter feed, or whether a dispersal of herds for lack of feed was necessitated.

In a corn experiment at Columbia, Missouri, in 1952, where only 2½ inches of rain fell from July 3 to August 8 and the average maximum temperature was 91 degrees, adequate fertility made the difference between profit and loss. Where no nitrogen was used, the highest corn yield was 54 bushels (only 60 per cent as much as in 1951), and this was obtained with a thin stand. Where the population was increased, yields declined. Where 50 pounds of nitrogen were plowed down, the highest yield (61.6 bushels) was secured with a population of 11,000 plants. With thicker planting, the yields again went down. The addition of 120 pounds of nitrogen gave the highest yield, i.e., 86.2 bushels, at 14,000 plants. But where 250 pounds of nitrogen were used, the high yield was 97.1 bushels from a stand of 17,000 plants per acre. It is seen, under these conditions of scant rainfall, that the heavier rates of planting decreased yields only where there was a shortage of nitrogen. It might be concluded that providing plenty of plant food made a limited supply of moisture more effective.

PASTURES CAN BE IMPROVED WITH NITROGEN

No land is so extensive or so much in need of improvement as are permanent pastures. Much of this land was initially low in fertility, or has been exhausted through cultivation, and is now producing a low yield of poor-quality forage that gives land little protection. In both experiments and under practical farm conditions in Missouri, the addition of adequate nitrogen with other plant nutrients increased hay yields from less than a ton to over six tons per acre, and protection of the soil from erosion was complete. In most states, demonstrations can be found where meat production was increased from less than 100 pounds per acre to over 500 pounds. Similar increases were obtained in milk production. Attempts have been made to maintain combinations of grasses and legumes in these mixtures. Difficulty in maintaining proper balance of these plants has focused attention on applying chemical nitrogen to the grass (with adequate minerals) to obtain maximum yields of high protein forage. The nutrients that need be added can be determined by soil tests.

RESIDUAL EFFECTS OF FERTILIZER

In the past, the entire cost of soil treatment has been charged to the crop treated. With heavier treatments, residual effects are striking. In experiments where nitrogen was applied to corn at rates of 200 pounds, the yield of the following wheat crop was sufficient to pay for the entire nitrogen application with none being charged to the corn. In seasons favorable for the growth of oats, similar residual responses were secured following corn when nutrient reserves were restored according to soil tests.

TABLE 44. Rate of application and residual effect of nitrogen (9)

Nitrogen applied	Corn 2-yr. av.	Wheat 1-yr. av.
	Bushels	Bushels
0	86.2	15.7
33	95.7	18.0
66	102.5	19.0
132	114.5	22.7
200	116.7	28.0

Soil limed to pH 6.2, 2,000 lbs. rock phosphate, 3-12-12 at 150 lbs. on corn and 300 lbs. on wheat

FERTILIZE BY PRESCRIPTION

The University of Wisconsin has developed a method of fertilizing crops by prescription. The way such prescriptions are written is relatively simple and is based on the fact that plants can get certain percentages of nitrogen, phosphorus, and potassium from the soil, manure, and fertilizer.

TABLE 45. Estimated percentages of the amounts of nitrogen, phosphorus, and potassium present in available form in soils and applied as manure and fertilizer that may be obtained by a crop like corn during one season (1)

Source of N, P, and K	Percentages obtained by crop during one season		
	N	P	K
Soil (available present)	40	40	40
Manure (total present)	30	30	50
Fertilizer (available present)	60	30	50

A 100-bushel crop of corn requires 150 pounds of nitrogen. On the basis of the estimate, it can get only 40 per cent of the available nitrogen, or 80 pounds, from a soil that contains 200 pounds per acre. The difference, namely, 70 pounds, will have to come from manure and/or fertilizer. Since what is applied is also only partially obtainable, as indicated in Table 45, appropriate calculations need be made in writing the fertilizer prescription for nitrogen, phosphorus, and potassium.

Crop composition varies considerably, but for purposes of these calculations the average amounts of plant foods contained in the tops and roots of the crop at the stage of maximum uptake suffice.

TABLE 46. Pounds per acre of nitrogen, phosphorus, and potassium in corn, sugar beets, and potatoes at yields indicated (1)

| Crop | Acre yield | Pounds per acre in crop | | |
		Nitrogen (N)	Phosphorus (as P_2O_5)	Potassium (as K_2O)
Corn	100 bushels	150	60	120
Sugar beets	20 tons	155	60	195
Potatoes	500 bushels	210	70	290

The calculations involved for writing the fertilizer prescription for any particular field are relatively simple, as can be seen in the following example, where a prescription for a 100-bushel yield of corn is given.

Suppose that the tests on a sample of soil reveal pounds per acre of available nutrients as follows:

Nitrogen—200 (N)
Phosphorus—35 (P) or 80 when converted to fertilizer phosphate (P_2O_5)
Potassium—125 (K) or 150 when converted to fertilizer potash (K_2O)

Enter the results of the soil-test figures for nitrogen (N), phosphate (P_2O_5), and potash (K_2O) in a tabulation as shown in Table 47, and then calculate (using percentages in Table 45) the amounts the crop will actually get from the soil. Then estimate and list the amounts of manure and/or fertilizer that appear to be needed to give approximately the amounts of nutrients required for the 100-bushel yield. The figures for nutrients thus supplied, and the respective amounts obtained from the percentages in Table 47 that the first crop can get, are next entered. The total amount the crop can get is then determined and, if this total is close to what the farmer uses, the job of writing the prescription or formula for the 100-bushel crop is completed.

In 1952, soil samples were collected from 173 fields in 10 southern Wisconsin counties and analyzed for pH, available nitrogen, phosphorus, and potassium. Fertilizer prescriptions where then written for individual fields, using the method described above. In addition to soil-test results,

TABLE 47. Formulation of fertilizer prescription on basis of soil tests and manure applied for 100-bushel corn (1)

Source of Nutrient element	Lbs. Nitrogen		Lbs. Phosphorus		Lbs. Potash	
	Present	crop gets	Present	crop gets	Present	crop gets
Soil (available)	200	40% or 80	80	40% or 32	150	40% or 60
275 lbs. ammonium nitrate	90	60% or 54	—	— — —	—	— — —
400 lbs. 3-9-18	12	60% or 7	36	30% or 11	72	50% or 36
400 lbs. 4-16-16	16	60% or 10	64	30% or 19	64	50% or 32
Totals crop may get	—	151	—	62	—	128
Totals needed	—	150	—	60	—	120

the amount of manure applied and crop to be plowed under were taken into consideration.

It was recommended that corn be drilled or hill-dropped so as to have 17,000 plants per acre. It was also prescribed that cultivation be shallow, with only one or two cultivations, to avoid root pruning.

Yield results were obtained by harvesting four 50-foot rows, one in each quarter of the field, and weighing the ears. A composite sample of 12 ears was taken for moisture determination and dried in the oven. Yields were then calculated to a 15 per cent moisture basis. Accurate records were obtained from 173 fields on 102 farms.

TABLE 48. Yields of corn in 1952 fertilized in accordance with prescriptions for 100-bushel yield arranged according to population (1)

Yield ranges (Bu. per acre)	No. Fields in each range	Average yield for each range (Bu. per acre)	Average corn population (Stalks per acre)
Under 100	15	92	13,370
100 to 110	18	106	13,790
100 to 120	31	116	14,280
120 to 130	40	124	15,220
130 to 140	38	134	15,420
140 to 150	25	144	15,990
Over 150	6	155	16,560

Total number of fields—173. Average all fields—124.

The growing conditions in 1952 were ideal, as evidenced by an average yield in the "100-Bushel Corn Adventure" of 124 bushels per acre. The state average corn yield for 1952 was 58 bushels, about 14 bushels higher than the 10-year average. The above data show in a striking manner that the higher yields are associated directly with the higher plant populations.

The interest in fertilizer prescriptions increased and in 1953 about 1,500 were written for corn fields in 37 counties in Wisconsin. Not only were farmers very interested in this program, but the Extension Service, through the county agents, enlisted the help of fertilizer and seed dealers and through their efforts 756 fields were harvested.

TABLE 49. Yields of corn in 1953 fertilized in accordance with prescription for 100-bushel yield. Arranged according to yields and populations (1)

Yield ranges (Bu. per acre)	No. fields in each range	Average yield for each range (Bu. per acre)	Average corn population (Stalks per acre)
Under 100	332	85.8	13,900
100 to 110	166	105.1	14,960
110 to 120	128	114.6	15,260
120 to 130	73	124.5	15,880
130 to 140	41	134.0	16,640
140 to 150	12	146.2	17,050
Over 150	8	159.8	17,850

Total number of fields—765. Average all fields—102.2.

Counties in the northern as well as the southern part of the state were included in the study in 1953. As a result, yields were down slightly but still over 100 bushels per acre. Of the farmers getting less than 100 bushels per acre, the great majority did not comply entirely with the fertilizer prescription. The top-yielding field on the William E. Renk and Son farm gave a yield of 169 bushels per acre one year. The yield was obtained not only because of the fertilizer prescription, but also because of the careful planning methods and good cultural practices used by the Renks. Their stand of corn was nearly perfect, about 19,000 plants per acre. Mr. Renk calculated the cost for several of his fields. On this field, the total costs, including land rental, were $95.44 an acre. The fertilizer charge was about $28 an acre. The cost of corn in this field was $0.56 a bushel, picked and hauled to the farm. In another field on this farm, using fertilizer costing $18.00 an acre but with smaller populations, the yield was 117 bushels per acre. This corn cost $0.88 a bushel. Although the Renks did not grow any corn without fertilizer, it is estimated that their yield without fertilizer would have been about 70 bushels per acre. This corn would have cost over $1.00 a bushel to produce.

Along with fertilizer recommendations, directions are given as to desired populations, proper placement of fertilizer, weed control, and planting populations. It is necessary to plant from 10 to 20 per cent more kernels than the desired population. Farmers are enthusiastic about this type of recommendation. Although the prescription may call for 10 times as much fertilizer as many farmers are accustomed to using, they do not complain because they can easily realize that following a specific plant-food prescription gives maximum profits per acre.

INTERPLANTING DOES NOT NECESSARILY REQUIRE MORE MOISTURE

Interplanting of grass or grass and legumes in corn, as is sometimes done in this new method of growing row crops, does not necessarily mean that more moisture is required. There will be some competition, but the total draft on moisture may be no greater.

Surface mulching and sod cover have been shown to increase greatly the absorption of water by the soil during rains. The Soil Conservation Service showed that out of a total of 9.38 inches of water applied at a uniform rate over a 5-hour period, 5.38 inches were absorbed by Muscatine silt loam in bluegrass pasture and only 1.34 inches by similar soil just across the fence in corn. The bluegrass sod was instrumental in getting 4.04 inches more of the 9.38 inches of water into the soil.

TABLE 50. Total amount of infiltration during 5-hour period (Muscatine silt loam in Illinois) (4)

Soil	Bluegrass pasture	Corn land	Difference due to land use
	Inches	Inches	Inches
Muscatine silt loam	5.38	1.34	4.04
Tama	5.03	1.51	3.52
Berwick	3.48	1.21	2.27
Clinton	2.77	2.17	0.60
Viola	1.63	1.28	0.35

In addition to the low intake of bare soil, the loss of moisture by evaporation from the soil surface is relatively high. On small fallowed areas of Abilene clay loam, boarded to prevent runoff, over 60 per cent of the rain that fell during a 2-year period at Spur, Texas, was lost by evaporation. Similar, and even greater, losses by evaporation from the soil surface have been reported on the High Plains. During the hot summer, moisture losses of one-half inch or more may occur from the surface 6 inches of clay soils by evaporation within a few days after a rain. The moisture stored below a depth of 6 inches, however, is relatively stable and losses due to evaporation are negligible.

Losses due to evaporation may be reduced by increasing the depth of moisture penetration. On sandy soils, water from rainfall will penetrate to a greater depth than clay loam soils and losses by evaporation will be less. Surface mulches or sod crops increase infiltration, aid deeper penetration of moisture, and greatly increase the amount of water available for plant growth.

The Forest Service found small differences in the consumptive use of water (the amount of water used and transpired by the vegetation plus that evaporated) between plots kept bare of vegetation and those in various types of vegetation, and on significant differences in consumptive use between a watershed in good and poor grass cover in Arizona. During the 15-year period, 1934-47, vegetation density more than doubled.

TABLE 51. Tests of water use from open–top metal containers, Sierra Ancha Experimental Forest, Arizona, 1936

Conditions measures	Rain	Consumptive use	Use of rain
	Inches	Inches	Per cent
Bare soil	26.33	23.47	89
Grasses	26.33	24.27	92
Half–shrubs	26.33	25.36	96
Shrubs	26.33	25.34	96
Woody legumes	26.33	24.82	94
Winter annuals	26.33	25.75	98

WELL-FERTILIZED CORN USES WATER MORE EFFICIENTLY

It has been shown that plant cover increases the amount of rain water that enters the ground. It will now be shown how the efficiency of this water can be increased by the use of fertilizer.

In addition to sharply-increasing corn yields, full soil treatments were an important factor in materially reducing the amount of water required to produce a bushel of corn in experimental trials conducted near McRedie in central Missouri by the University of Missouri during the summer of 1953. Corn on soil with full treatment—grown in a 4-year rotation of corn, wheat, and 2 years of meadow, with grain and hay crops removed—produced 79 bushels per acre and required 16 inches of soil moisture. In terms of water use, some 5,600 gallons of water were required to produce a bushel of corn. Corn grown without soil treatment—in a corn-oats rotation with only the grain removed—produced 18 bushels per acre and required about 14 inches of soil water to raise the crop. On a per-bushel basis, some 21,000 gallons of water were required.

Soil retains water that neither drains away nor rises to the surface, by capillarity, where it would be lost by evaporation. However, this water in the soil may be extracted by plant roots when they grow into it. Medium-textured, gravel-free soils retain about one inch of water in each 6-inch layer of soil while coarse-textured, gravely soils contain about two-thirds of an inch of water in each 6-inch layer.

ROOTS UTILIZE STORED WATER

The total amount of stored water that plant roots may remove depends upon root penetration as well as upon the amount of water in each layer of soil. Some soils, such as the Hanceville and Lebanon of the Ozark uplands, are underlain by rock and cemented hardpans into which roots do not penetrate. They store a total of only three inches of water for corn use in the interval between rains.

The Putnam and Marshall soils of northern Missouri and the bottom soils throughout the state are deep, containing as much as 8 to 10 inches of water in 4 to 5 feet of soil. Corn, well fertilized, can use this as it will grow roots to reach these depths.

Leaves of unfertilized corn growing on Sanborn Field curled in 1947, although there was ample moisture in the soil at depths greater than 3 feet. Adjacent plots of fertilized corn showed no injury with the moisture depleted to 42 inches. Roots of fertilized corn penetrated the soil 4 feet in 1953 in some instances and removed over 9 inches of water from Putnam soil.

Water consumption by corn through the summer months revealed that an average of one inch of water was used a week. A deficit in excess of 3 inches during the growing period would result in complete failure on the shallow soils but would only depress the yield of corn on the deeper soils.

DATA SUPPLIES ANSWERS

The extent to which different moisture deficits will depress the yield of corn and the frequency of dry seasons are questions every corn producer would like answered. The 64 years of record at Columbia, Missouri, provide information that may be used as a fair guide for estimating the water storage capacities and for expected corn performances on other soils throughout the state.

Taking all seasons into consideration, an average corn yield of 87 bushels per acre may be expected with modern fertility practices but only 53 bushels were obtained for the period when normal rates of planting were combined with the use of legumes, manure, and small amounts of fertilizer.

Soils in which the roots of corn will not penetrate below 36 to 42 inches will store only about 6 to 7 inches of available water. Such limitations restrict the average corn yields to about 42 bushels where modern fertilization methods are practiced. However, the crop still has measurable values beyond grain production in dry years when feed is scarce. Fodder or silage produced represents the most efficient use of the available water supply by any of the crops, and unused fertility remains to nourish small grains planted following corn cutting.

Regardless of the depth of the soil, fertility is essential for the efficient use of water.

DIFFERENCES IN ROOT DEVELOPMENT

Smith, of Missouri, measured the soil moisture used by corn from the upper 3½ feet of soil. Root development under fertilized crops was greater and they penetrated more deeply into the soil. Thus, corn growing on plots with full treatment had root development sufficient to take water at a greater rate. Since the roots penetrated to greater depth, the plants had a greater water supply from which to draw than the shallow-rooted corn on the unfertilized soil. By early August, plant roots in the fertilized area had penetrated below the 3½-foot depth. These plants actually took a little more water from the soil than could be measured in this experiment.

Water removed from the unfertilized plot was about one-eighth inch daily throughout the season. This was also the approximate water removal from the full-fertilizer-treatment plots for the first third of the season. After that time, the removal was more than one-fourth inch daily. Evaporation of moisture from the soil was an important factor during the early growth stages. As the corn grew the crop required more water, but shading of the soil cut evaporation losses.

SIX-YEAR AVERAGE YIELDS

The yield differences in 1953 were quite similar to those of previous years. During the past 6 years, average yields in the corn-wheat-2 years meadow rotation were 100 bushels of corn, 23 bushels of wheat, and a little more than 2 tons of hay per acre.

In the 2-year rotation of corn and oats without fertilizer, average yields were 23 bushels of corn and 6 bushels of oats per acre. However, with a similar 2-year rotation of corn and oats, but on soil with full treatments and sweet clover for green manure, yields averaged 98 bushels of corn and 37 bushels of oats.

Not only did yields per acre increase, but shelling percentage of the grain likewise increased. Corn grown on soil with full treatment shelled 79 per cent, compared with 70 per cent for the corn on the untreated soil.

Full soil treatment on fertilized plots at the beginning of the Missouri experiment included 5 tons of lime, 1,000 pounds of rock phosphate, and 100 pounds of muriate of potash. Furthermore, in years when the 4-year rotation plot was in corn, some 300 pounds of 3-12-12 starter and 100 pounds of nitrogen were used. The 2-year fertilized area was treated in a similar manner except that only 66 pounds of nitrogen were used per acre. Additional potash and phosphate were required after the first round of the rotation—with the 4-year rotation requiring more of these elements than the 2-year rotation.

Of the small amount of rainfall received in 1953 (less than 5 inches from June 1 to September 1), nearly one inch was lost in runoff from the plot in corn on untreated soil. With full treatments the loss was only one-fourth of this amount.

Average rainfall during the corn season was 20 inches during the 6-year period. Of this amount, less than 3 inches appeared as runoff—causing 2.25 tons per acre soil loss—under corn on the untreated soil. With the 2-year system receiving full treatment, runoff was slightly less than one inch and erosion less than one ton per acre. With the 4-year system including full soil treatment, runoff was a little more than one-half inch and erosion was close to one-half ton per acre.

REFERENCES

1. Berger, K. C. 1954. *Plantfood prescription for maximum profit.* Amer. Plant Food Jour., 8(1): 4-5, 14-15.
2. Borst, H. L. 1953. *Manure mulch helps control erosion and saves rainfall on sloping land.* Ohio Agr. Expt. Sta. Farm and Home Res., 38 (282).

3. Browning, G. M., Norton, R. A., and Shedd, C. K. 1944. *Mulch culture in relation to soil and water conservation and corn yields in Iowa.* Soil Sci. Soc. Amer. Proc., 8: 424-431.
4. Holtan, E. N., and Musgrave, G. W. 1947. *Soil water and its disposal under corn and bluegrass.* USDA, SCS-TP-68.
5. Kurtz, T., Appleman, M. D., and Bray, Roger H. 1946. *Preliminary trials with intercropping of corn and clover.* Soil Sci. Soc. Amer. Proc., 11: 349-355.
6. Kurtz, T., Melsted, S. W., Bray, R. H., and Breland, H. L. 1952. *Further trials with intercropping of corn in establishing sods.* Soil Sci. Soc. Amer. Proc., 16: 282-285.
7. Peterson, A., and Englebert, L. E. 1953. *Mulched-planted corn performed well in 1952 Wisconsin test.* Crops and Soils, 5(7): 26.
8. Pickard, G., and Bateman, H. P. 1953. *Corn yields from "mulch" and standard planting compared.* Crops and Soils, 5(7): 26.
9. Smith, G. E. 1952. *Soil fertility and corn production.* Mo. Agr. Expt. Sta. Bull. 583.
10. ———. 1954. *Soil fertility—Basis for high crop production.* Better Crops With Plant Food, 38(3): 22-26, 40-41.
11. Snider, H. J. 1953. *Strong roots make high corn yields.* Better Crops With Plant Food, 37(7): 17-19.
12. Stringfield, G. H., and Haynes, J. L. 1953. *Wider corn rows.* Ohio Agr. Expt. Sta. Farm and Home Res., 38(281): 20, 34-35.
13. Strohm, John. 1952. *Revolution in your corn field.* Country Gentleman, 122(2): 26-27.
14. ———. 1953. *Four ways to boost corn yields.* Country Gentleman, 123(4): 38-39.
15. ———. 1953. *Cover crops in corn.* Country Gentleman, 123(6): 30-31, 74.
16. ———. 1953. *Mulch planting of corn pays off.* Country Gentleman, 123(12): 30-31, 45.
17. ———. 1954. *Revolution in your cornfield—He's sold on mulch planting.* Country Gentleman, 124(4): 31-33.

Wheat Production with
Stubble-Mulch Tillage

This new idea of utilizing crop residue on the surface of the ground was developed and first utilized on a large scale in connection with the production of wheat in the Great Plains. During recent years, this new system of preparing land for seeding has spread over millions of acres of wheat land. Commonly called stubble-mulch farming, it consists of leaving the residue from one crop on the surface of the ground while the land is prepared for the next crop. The residue may consist of the stubble or the stubble and combined straw that is left on the land. Weed growth also serves as residue, but care should be taken that the weeds do not deplete the soil moisture needed for the oncoming crop. The weeds should be killed before they produce seed.

WIND-EROSION CONTROL

Leaving straw and stubble on the surface in sufficient quantity is one of the simplest and surest ways to prevent wind erosion on wheat land. To be most effective, the straw should be anchored in the soil. As straw gets older and is run over by tractors and machinery it tends to get brittle and is broken into short pieces. If it does not become too short it can be partially buried at the end of the season with some

293

FIGURE 91. Straw from the preceding wheat crop is utilized as a mulch cover. Wheat is seeded through the mulch. The mulch protects the soil from erosion by both wind and water. It also gets more water into the ground and reduces loss of moisture by evaporation. (Pendleton, Oregon)
(Soil Conservation Service)

straw still sticking out of the ground. This will hold other loose pieces of straw and soil movement can be stopped. This phase of the practice is treated more fully in another chapter.

WATER-EROSION CONTROL

Water erosion as well as wind erosion is also avoided as long as there is good residue cover on the land. When wheat is harvested in July and the stubble is left undisturbed until the following May there is nearly a 10-month period when the soil is well protected against blowing or raindrop splash. The land should be fallowed in such a way that residue is left on the soil in considerable quantity until the next crop is well established, and then on through the following winter and early spring months, or another 11 months. Then the combination of the remaining residue and the growing wheat plants should protect the soil until harvest time in July. This would complete a full two years that the soil would have been protected against erosion by either wind or water. At this time, the wheat-fallow rotation would be started over again. It is thus possible to protect land against wind or water erosion continuously under this stubble-mulch system. It is particularly well adapted to an alternate wheat-fallow method.

CONSERVATION OF MOISTURE

If properly managed, stubble mulch may serve to increase the moisture content of the soil compared with plowing. This may be brought about, first, through allowing the residue to stand on the soil through the winter

FIGURE 92. Sweet clover grown in a wheat-clover cropping system is utilized as mulch cover. Compare with Figure 93 which shows an adjoining field where the crop residue was turned under. (Pendleton, Oregon)
(Soil Conservation Service)

FIGURE 93. The residue from the preceding crop was plowed under. This field was adjacent to that shown in Figure 92. Both fields were subject to the same rain. (Pendleton, Oregon)
(Soil Conservation Service)

to catch snow, and second, due to the high percentage of intake of rainfall facilitated by the mulch at all times. In the cool months of spring it reduces evaporation so that there is little drying out between rains. This permits the next water that falls to penetrate more deeply into the soil because very little of it is used to wet the dried layer at the surface. In summer, it intercepts the falling raindrops, thereby preventing or reducing their damages. The infiltration rate is kept high and runoff losses low during heavy rains. If the soil profile is already filled with moisture to some depth, the additional water saved by the mulch will push the moisture down to greater depth than will the smaller intake on plowed land. Water in the second, third, or fourth foot at seeding time does much to ensure a good yield of wheat.

The Soil Conservation Service conducted studies at Amarillo, Texas, over a period of 7 years to determine the effect of different tillage methods on the moisture content of the soil. Soil-moisture samples taken on the continuous plots failed to show moisture to be consistently higher under subtillage than under the other cultural methods. In fact, soil samples taken in October, 1948, showed that the subtilled plots in both the continuous wheat and the wheat-fallow-wheat system, after producing a crop of wheat in 1948, were somewhat lower in soil moisture than plots tilled with the oneway or moldboard plow. This might be due to the fact the larger yields produced on the stubble-mulched plots used more moisture than the wheat on the other plots.

TABLE 52. Average moisture content to a depth of 3 feet on stubble mulch plots, October, 1948, and March, 1949 (7)

Tillage method	Land in:	Moisture content, per cent	
		Oct., 1948	Mar., 1949
Continuous wheat			
Moldboard plow	Wheat	16.0	18.1
Oneway	Wheat	16.3	17.2
Subtillage	Wheat	15.1	20.1
Wheat–fallow–wheat system			
Oneway	Fallow	16.2	19.0
Subtillage	Fallow	15.3	20.1
Oneway	Wheat	18.1	17.3
Subtillage	Wheat	21.5	18.9

Since larger yields were obtained on the subtilled plots than on moldboard- or oneway-plowed plots, it would be difficult to assess the amount of moisture actually made available to the crop under different tillage systems by a consideration of soil moisture data alone, where a measure of the moisture used by the crop is not available. It is noteworthy, however, than when land was in fallow for a year, more moisture was consistently found in subtilled than in onewayed land. This is convincing proof of the efficiency of the stubble-mulch system in storing moisture. Of special interest in this connection are the data that compare moisture reserves in the stubble mulch plots in late March, 1949, about 5½ months after the October sampling. It is apparent that the subtilled fallow and continuous wheat plots were able to retain sufficient winter precipitation to more than overcome the moisture deficiencies of the previous fall, and at this season of the year were able to surpass the oneway- and moldboard-plowed plots in moisture content.

SUBTILLED STUBBLE MULCH MAKES BIGGEST YIELDS

Subtillage, as practiced in the stubble-mulch system of farming at Amarillo, Texas, produced greater yields of wheat than moldboard or oneway plowing. A comparison was made of the effect of moldboard plowing, oneway plowing, and subtillage on yields of wheat on the continuous wheat plots at Amarillo during the period 1942-48, inclusive.

TABLE 53. Average annual wheat yield per acre from stubble mulch plots in continuous wheat, 1942–48 (7)

Tillage	Yield
Moldboard plow	12.5 bu.
Oneway plow	13.2 bu.
Subtillage	15.1 bu.

An average of 2.6 bushels more wheat per acre was abtained from the continuous wheat plots that were subtilled than was produced after the moldboard plow, and 1.9 bushels more than where the oneway was used. The fact that sub-surface tillage gave increased yields during the period these tests were in operation is in harmony with the effectiveness of stubble mulch in controlling erosion. It is also interesting to note that the average annual yield on the subtilled plots was 15.1 bushels per acre.

The grain yields for the 7-year period are shown in Table 54 where two implements, the oneway plow and the subtiller, were used on plots planted to wheat one year and fallow the next.

TABLE 54. Average annual wheat yields of wheat–fallow–wheat system, 1942–48 (7)

Tillage	Yield
Oneway	18.8 bu.
Subtillage	21.6 bu.

An increase of 2.8 bushels per acre was recorded in favor of the sub-surface tillage implement over the oneway on plots in wheat and fallow. For any single crop year, wheat after a year of fallow consistently outyielded wheat planted year after year. This effect was pronounced in dry years when the moisture stored during a year of fallow meant the difference between crop success and failure. In addition, fallowing made possible the production and maintenance of a stubble mulch to protect the soil from blowing regardless of the occurrence of periods of subnormal precipitation.

STUBBLE MULCH IN A WHEAT-FALLOW SYSTEM

The stubble-mulch system is well adapted in regions where alternate wheat-fallow is a common practice. This is because the wheat and straw yields are usually high after a year of fallow. With a large amount of straw on the surface at harvest time, it is difficult to prepare a good seedbed in the course of six weeks or two months for fall seeding unless the straw is chopped into shorter lengths. If a year of fallow is to follow the heavy growth of straw, however, there will be about 14 months to prepare the seedbed. This gives time to allow some of the straw to decay and to become shortened by machinery passing over it. Some of the straw will also be buried in the process of tillage. If proper implements are used when the wheat is seeded, it is possible to leave practically all of the residue on the surface for wind- and water-erosion control and soil improvement. Ample evidence is available to show that such material produces more desirable effects when left on the surface than when turned under. A minimum of from 1 to 1½ tons per acre at seeding time are needed to protect the soil against wind erosion and raindrop splash.

During years of high wheat yields and heavy straw production, the straw should be cut into short enough lengths that it will not interfere too much with planting operations. This means that all tillage operations as well as the drilling of the grain must be done with the view of leaving the maximum amount of straw on the surface at seeding time. As farm machinery becomes designed to deal with this problem more successfully, larger and larger amounts of the straw can be left on the surface of the ground at all times. Straw mixed with the surface soil is not effective in controlling erosion. It decays rapidly and is not as effective in improving the soil as when left on the surface. Straw left entirely on the surface of the ground decays slowly and is effective over a longer period of time.

SUB-SURFACE TILLAGE ON FALLOW LAND

Sub-surface tillage is a method of tillage that is accomplished by cultivating beneath the surface of the soil. When stubble and other crop residues are present, they are left on the surface to form a stubble mulch. When this type of tillage is used on fallow land, it is referred to as *stubble-mulch fallow*.

A stubble mulch on the surface of fallow land is helpful in controlling wind erosion and water erosion. It helps control wind erosion by reducing surface wind velocity and helps control water erosion by reducing splash and runoff. Wheat yields under a system of stubble-mulch fallow have been about the same or slightly higher as on fallow cultivated by other methods. There appears to be little difference in yield of spring wheat on fallow regardless of tillage method used, provided operations are timely and erosion is kept under control.

FIGURE 94. Wheat being seeded through stubble mulch. (Pendleton, Oregon)
(Soil Conservation Service)

All methods of fallow in general use have advantages and disadvantages. The two chief problems that arise in a stubble-mulch system of fallow are in connection with the tillage operations and the seeding of the crop. With large quantities of crop residue on the land, some difficulties are encountered in cultivating through the trash. It is also more difficult to control certain weeds with a sub-surface tiller than it is with some other types of tillage equipment. If a lot of residue is present on the surface at seeding time, some difficulty may be experienced in doing a satisfactory job of drilling.

Since past experience has indicated that a farmer is apt to run into some difficulties with the stubble-mulch system of fallow, it is recommended that he start out with a small acreage and familiarize himself with the operation of stubble-mulch equipment and with the limitations of the system before trying it on a large acreage. If an operator starts out with too large an acreage before he has learned to do the job, he may get discouraged with his results and revert to some other tillage method.

Although it is true that some difficulties may be encountered when first attempting a system of stubble-mulch farming, it is also true that when stubble equipment is properly used and adjusted the operator will have little difficulty. The desirability and practicability of the system has been demonstrated through research and through the results obtained by many farm operators.

From the standpoint of erosion control and soil improvement, it is desirable to leave as much residue on the surface as possible. The amount that an operator should leave on the surface, however, should be governed by the amount of trash that his drill will go through satisfactorily.

When an abundance of stubble is present, it may be avisable to cut it into shorter lengths. Short straw can be planted through more easily than long straw. In the absence of a suitable machine to cut the straw into short lengths, a disk-type implement may be used for one or more of the tillage operations. The number of times that a disk is used will depend on the amount of residue the farmer can handle on the surface. The disk used may be any one of several types on the market; the important thing is the depth of operation.

Disking should be shallow if it is to be followed with some type of sub-surface tillage. Sub-surface tillers operate much more satisfactorily when they work below the depth of disking, and they are more effective in killing weeds if not operated too deep. If a sub-surface tiller is worked at a shallower depth than the land was disked, the stubble will catch on the sweeps or blades and the machine will tend to push soil ahead of it and will often become clogged. Disking should not be over three inches in depth, because sub-surface tillage done much deeper than that is not very effective in killing weeds.

USE OF STRAW SPREADERS

If the crop is harvested with a combine, a straw spreader should be used to

FIGURE 95. Rank growth of straw and stubble being cut into short
lengths so that wheat can be planted and leave the straw as
mulch. (Pendleton, Oregon)
(Soil Conservation Service)

prevent as excessive accumulation of straw in windrows. Heavy windrows of straw are apt to cause difficulty during fallow operations and at seeding time.

OPERATION OF SUB-SURFACE TILLERS

In order to get good weed kills with sub-surface tillers, a *uniform shallow cultivation* is necessary. A uniform depth can best be maintained if the machine is weighted enough to hold it in the ground at all times. The weight of the machine should hold the sweeps in the ground, and the wheels should keep the sweeps from going too deep. Failure to properly weight sub-surface tillers may also result in the sweeps or blades coming out of the ground. If the sweeps come out of the ground, the machine will generally clog. The variation in depth of cultivation which results from lack of weight also causes a draft problem. Without enough weight a machine set so as to penetrate the hard spots will go deeper in soft areas and the load may be greatly increased.

Better weed kills and more satisfactory operation can be expected if a sub-surface tiller is pulled at a *fair rate of speed*. The slower the rate of speed the less soil-stirring results and the greater the tendency for the machine to become clogged. About five miles per hour seems to be a desirable speed.

Sub-surface tillage done on *warm dry days* will result in better weed kills than if the weather is cool and damp. Sub-surface cultivators also operate better if the *soil is not too wet*. Since weeds as a rule are more difficult to control with sub-surface tillers than they are with some other methods of cultivation, it is advisable to do the cultivating under optimum conditions whenever possible.

REQUIREMENT FOR STUBBLE-MULCH FARMING

The equipment used in preparing a wheat seedbed under a stubble-mulch system must be carefully chosen and properly used. Keep in mind that a good seedbed for wheat is one that is in good tilth, weed-free, and with enough residue left on the surface to protect the soil and the young crop against either wind or water erosion.

There is no set of tools best for all conditions. There are many combinations of tillers, packers, weeders, and drills that may be so used as to result in a good job. Whatever equipment is used the proper job must be kept in mind at all times.

To give some practical suggestions as to different methods that may be followed to obtain a good job of fallowing with the stubble-mulch system, a few different methods are outlined below. It is important that a farmer make use of as much equipment as he may already have in doing this job.

Method No. 1. If there are few weeds in the stubble in the fall, the fallowing operation need not begin until spring. Unless there is an excessive amount of straw, the first operation should be delayed until weeds and volunteer wheat have been well started. The first operation may be with a oneway disk. It should be run at a shallow depth so as not to bury much straw. If the oneway is set at a long angle the disk will not need to go very deep to cut all the soil and kill volunteer wheat and weeds. It is better to do this first operation when weather conditions are dry. This means a better kill of weeds and volunteer wheat.

After this first oneway operation the land should be allowed to lie for a few weeks start again. At this point one of several implements may be used. One that will undercut the soil and loosen it to about the depth of ordinary plowing is usually desirable. One of several types of sweep machines will be found to do this job well.

When the weeds start again, the next operation may well be done with a rod weeder. If weeds come on too rapidly another operation with this same equipment may be necessary.

Just prior to seeding wheat, it is well to give the land a final stroke with a plain rod weeder without the shovel attachment. This tends to kill the small weeds, including downy bromegrass, that may have germinated since the last weeding. The rod weeder also tends to pack the soil, making an ideal place in which to plant the seed.

Method No. 2. Another possible procedure which, with some adjustments for conditions and equipment available, may be found suitable in certain areas, is as follows:

Suppose weeds have grown up in the stubble in the fall, it might be considered advisable to kill them. If the field were mowed or onewayed to kill weeds, the stubble would be laid flat. This would allow most of the snow to blow off the land. This can be prevented by tilling the soil with a sub-surface tiller at a fairly shallow depth that will allow the stubble and weeds to stand and catch snow. If the operation is done at proper time the weeds will be killed before the seeds mature.

FIGURE 96. One of several types of sweep machines used for stubble-mulch tillage. (Oregon)
(Soil Conservation Service)

The land may be left over winter in this condition. The procedure in the spring may then follow about that outlined in Method No. 1. However, if there is little volunteer wheat it may be desirable to omit the first operation with the oneway, and do all the tillage with sweeps, rod weeders, and possibly some type of packer or treader to be described later.

Method No. 3. Some of the most effective equipment for stubble-mulch farming has been of the heavier blade type. It is particularly good for the first or deepest operation.

Following this operation the rod weeder, or special rods attached to this same frame, may be used. The oneway or disk would be used in case of excessively heavy straw. Sometimes excessive straw in low areas may necessitate the use of disk tools. Whenever these are used care must be taken that the straw is not too completely buried. If much straw is turned under with a oneway it may affect the use of other implements. For example, a rod weeder cannot be operated satisfactorily through land that has much straw turned in below the surface.

Method No. 4. In case the ground is dry or hard it may be desirable to go through with a chisel-type implement to do a breaking or ripping job. Some difficulty may be experienced due to clogging if the residue is heavy or if the chisels are too close together. It is well to follow this chiseling operation in a short time with sweeps that undercut the entire soil. It is not advisable to attempt to use this machine for all operations during a fallow season. This invariably results in covering too much residue. After the sweeps have been used, the next operation should be with broader sweeps or the rod weeder.

DRILLING WHEAT IN STUBBLE-MULCH LAND

After land has been properly prepared using the stubble-mulch system, it is important that the right method be used in seeding. In many cases farmers have a fair amount of residue on the land up to planting time. Then by improper methods of drilling, too much of the residue may be covered. This can be avoided by use of proper drill or adjustments on the drill itself or the speed at which the drill is operated. The ordinary deep-furrow drill, or the semi-deep-furrow drill, can be made to operate satisfactorily through residue. Another drill designed especially for working through residue is being manufactured in Alberta, Canada.

The objective of drilling through stubble mulch is to make a clean furrow in which to deposit the seed, with a press wheel that will press the soil firmly down on the seed. This aids in germination. There should then be sufficient old straw on the surface and sticking out of the surface on the ridges between the rows to prevent wind erosion. This straw will also give a high intake rate in case of heavy rain and will greatly reduce runoff and erosion. Shoe-type drills have been found satisfactory for drilling through residue. They give little trouble from clogging and leave much of the residue anchored, but sticking out of the soil between the rows.

CONTROL OF DOWNY BROME OR CHEATGRASS

One difficulty some growers have had in using the stubble-mulch method is in the control of downy brome or cheatgrass in wheat. It must be admitted that this is somewhat more difficult with the stubble-mulch system than where the moldboard plow is used. However, some of our best wheat growers are using the method and are keeping the cheatgrass down to the point where they do not consider it a serious problem. In some cases they find it advisable to plow the land occasionally. Every effort should be made to kill the cheatgrass along the edges of fields, in fence-rows and along roadsides. It is from these places that much of the seed is scattered onto the fields. If care is taken to get most of these weed seeds to germinate in the fall after harvest these plants can be killed by the fallowing operations the next summer. A thorough weeding then, just before seeding, should eliminate any plants that may have germinated ahead of wheat-seeding time. Late seeding is advantageous for the control of the plant disease known as "wheat mosaic." The use of chemical sprays and special cropping practices for the control of downy brome are being studied but definite recommendations cannot yet be made.

SOIL NITRATES

There is a tendency for nitrates to form somewhat more slowly under stubble mulch than where land is plowed. However, since time between crops is longer in a wheat-fallow system, there is sufficient time for nitrates to accumulate, providing the land is thoroughly tilled. For this reason land fallowed by the stubble-mulch system will usually have an abundant supply of nitrates for the wheat crop. On some of the more sandy soils the addition of nitrogen fertilizers may sometimes be beneficial. As the heavier soils are farmed for a longer time they may reach the point where nitrogen fertilizers will prove beneficial.

MACHINERY REQUIREMENTS FOR STUBBLE-MULCH TILLAGE

As previously stated, stubble-mulch tillage is very effective in controlling both wind and water erosion. It is also new enough that development of its application and adaptability is still incomplete. Partially because of its newness and partially because its application represents a drastic change in the methods by which soil may be handled, machinery problems have been encountered in most places where it is used. Furthermore, stubble-mulch tillage differs in form from community to community, just as rotations differ between areas. Likewise, adaptation of machinery to stubble-mulch tillage will differ as the practice itself changes.

In order to evaluate the machinery requirements for stubble-mulch tillage and other conservation practices, it is necessary to understand what must be accomplished. Before the necessity for practicing conservation was recognized, farming and farm machinery had developed in such a way that adequate seedbeds could be prepared, seed could be placed in the best position in the soil, weeds could be controlled and the crop harvested, all as economically as possible, with all too often little thought as to what happened to the soil.

To control erosion and maintain productivity, other things must be done simultaneously to the soil than merely preparing seedbeds, and planting and harvesting crops. A protective cover, either in the form of growing vegetation or as a mulch, must be maintained on the surface for as much of the period when erosion losses are most likely to occur, as follows:

1. Tillage must be done in a way to keep the proper amount of residue on the surface.

2. Where adequate amounts of straw are left on the surface of the ground the soil will absorb water readily and will be protected from raindrop splash and wind erosion.

3. Moisture losses must be controlled either by drainage and aeration in wet soils or by exclusion of air in the drier areas.

Frequently the changes that come with the adoption of conservation farming are of sufficient magnitude to make the machinery in common use in the community less well adapted than other machines that are available.

TYPES OF SUB-SURFACE TILLERS

There are several types of sub-surface tillers on the market—the straight blade, wide sweep, narrow sweep, and rotary rod weeder. In selecting a sub-surface tiller it is important to consider such things as size, clearance, weed-killing ability, and sturdiness of construction.

If a machine is too wide, difficulties will be encountered on irregular ground. If a wide piece of machinery is needed, it is advisable to have it in sections so that it has flexibility. A wide machine built in sections will follow the contour of the land better than a machine of similar width built on one rigid frame. A wide, rigid sub-surface tiller results in a lack of uniformity in depth of cultivation; this in turn causes variation in draft and poor weed killing.

It is important to select a sub-surface tiller with *sufficient clearance* to go through large amounts of stubble. Stubble in which large Russian thistles are present is especially difficult to get through, and unless the machine has a lot of clearance it will not operate without clogging.

There is a good deal of difference in the ability of various sub-surface tillers to *kill weeds*. The sub-surface tillers that tend to stir the surface soil are more effective on controlling shallow-rooted weeds than the machines which depend on a shearing action alone. Shallow-rooted weeds are the most difficult to control with sub-surface tillers, and special consideration should be given to this problem when selecting a machine. A machine to accomplish this purpose should run shallow, should be set flat, and should pulverize the soil well.

Sturdiness of construction is also important in a sub-surface tiller. If the machine is not well built, breakage and bending will result. With the large sweeps generally present on sub-surface tillers it is especially important that these sweeps be kept running as true as possible. It is difficult to get a sub-surface tiller to operate satisfactorily if the sweeps or beams are bent.

TILLAGE OPERATIONS ON LIGHT STUBBLE

Often, the quantity of residue is so small that it must be handled carefully in order to maintain a sufficient quantity on the surface for the time when it is needed. An undercutting technique is then used for initial breaking of the soil in order to avoid unnecessary mixing of the soil and the stubble. In such areas, pretreatment of residues by either stubble shredding or disking should be avoided. Pretreatment performed in these areas is for two purposes only: (a) increase the intake of winter precipitation, or (b) to aid in weed control by inducing fall sprouting of weed seed. Where such treatment is desirable, it should be carried on in such a way as to disturb or break up stubble as little as possible.

The initial tillage job to be done in the light-stubble area is to establish the maximum depth of tillage by loosening soil to that depth. The standards that stubble-mulch tillage must meet are (a) minimum mixing of soil and mulch, (b) minimum breakage of mulch, and (c) minimum surface pulverization of the soil.

The following initial tillage implements are adapted to the undercutting technique:

The sweep plow. This is a heavy plow-like implement and should not be confused with the lighter type sweep used in secondary tillage. This implement cuts loose all roots and soil to the maximum depth of cultivation. The degree of loosening obtained is dependent on soil type and moisture in the soil at the time of the operation. This tool generally produces insufficient loosening of the surface soil and must be supplemented by secondary-tillage implements. It will not kill growing vegetation in the humid areas, but is well adapted to the West. There appears to be little difference in the operation of the 90- or 120-degree sweeps as long as the sweep will shed. The high-lift sweep blades loosen the soil better, but are more inclined to furrow it when it is loose at the time of operation. Nearly all the sweep bottoms now available wear out too quickly. In this operation, sweep bottoms should be made of at least as good material as plow shares. A coulter is needed on all sweeps when used in heavy stubble. In this operation a coulter is used much more severely than on a plow since it must be placed to cut ahead of the point. Thus there is no relief for the cutting blade, as it is forced into undisturbed soil by sheer weight and suck of the machine. The cone bearings used in plow coulters do not stand up for this operation, either with or without grease. This implement also needs standardization and determination of the adaptability of various shapes of sweep bottoms.

The spring-tooth plow. This machine acts as a heavy-duty field cultivator capable of working undisturbed soil to the maximum depth of cultivation and must be capable of penetrating at least 8 inches. It is excellent in its loosening ability and somewhat better than the sweep in killing surface weeds when there is moisture present, but it will not kill perennial grasses.

The tools available at present are generally used at depths beyond their structural strength in heavy soils. For areas requiring deep cultivation, this tool should be stronger. It is decidedly limited in its trash-clearing ability. Even the high-clearance machines are not generally adapted to moderately heavy stubble more than 2 feet in length. Tooth clearance and tooth chatter, structural strength and the installation of hydraulic lifts are all critical points in this machine.

*The rod weeder.** The rod weeder with shovel attachment is adapted only

* An implement with small shovels or sweeps fastened to a bar with spring connections.

to light soils when used as an initial-tillage machine. Its penetrating ability is its one limiting factor. It will rate excellent in pulverizing ability, trash clearance, trash placement, and weed control. It has ample strength for those soils which it will penetrate but this application of the tool is, however, quite hard on the rod bearings.

In light-stubble summer-fallow areas, secondary tillage is usually confined to summer-fallow operations and generally does not offer much of a problem from the standpoint of the ability to control weeds and to maintain a firm sub-surface structure in order to exclude air and preserve moisture. All of these functions must be performed while maintaining a cloddy layer at the surface and without mixing residue with the soil.

Frequently the rod weeder is the sole implement used for weed control. It performs all of the functions necessary in this operation very well in all soils that are free from stones, except that in some moisture conditions at seeding time certain small weeds will ride over the rod without being killed.

The field cultivator. Where stones are present in any quantity, the field cultivator equipped with duckfoot shovels is usually substituted for the rod weeder. It performs the same function except that it does not produce the same degree of sub-surface compaction as does the rod weeder. It is probably superior to the rod weeder in killing small weeds at seeding time during autumns favored by ample moisture. In areas where heavy mulch is brought into the summer-fallow season, it is necessary that the cultivator be equipped with spring-tooth shanks so that the tooth chatter can assist in clearing trash. With a properly set cultivator, no difficulty should be encountered with trash-clearance problems.

The rotary hoe. The rotary hoe can lessen the weakness of both the field cultivator and rod weeder. It should be used in reverse in connection with the field cultivator to assist in sub-surface compaction. When used as a hoe at seeding time it will aid the rod weeder in killing weeds, and it will also help the cultivator and rod weeder to put the mulch and the ground surface in a good seeding condition. The light-weight types of hoe are excellent for this purpose under these conditions.

In the area of heavy rainfall, straw is long and yields are heavy under both conditions of summer fallow and annual cropping conditions. Some of the residues must be broken down, either mechanically or by decomposition. This must be done to make the residue easier to handle in the preparation of a seedbed and in the planting of the crop. Under such conditions, fall pretreatment of stubble on fallow land is frequently performed. The purposes of such pretreatment are (a) to shorten the length of stubble, (b) to increase infiltration of precipitation, and (c) to induce fall germination of volunteer oats and other annual weeds. The tendency in pretreatment operations is to overdo the job. The purposes are sound but treatment to perform each of them should not be so severe or inclusive as to destroy too much mulch. The following tools are used for this purpose:

The stubble pulverizer. This tool is very much in the formative stage and the forms vary from overgrown rotary lawn-mower types to hammer-mill beater types. It is believed that the ideal stubble treatment would be merely to cut the straw into perhaps 12-inch sections without undue shredding. The stubble pulverizers, of course, perform no function on the soil. They usually overdo the job in light stubble or underdo it in heavy stubble. The need or place of such a machine is not fully established, although its use will make the use of implements poorly adapted to stubble-mulch tillage much easier.

The rotary subsoiler. The rotary subsoiler is used extensively in some areas to break the surface soil into pits of perhaps a foot deep. The aim is to obtain greater infiltration of moisture into the soil. Its effectiveness depends on the type of soil, the amount and intensity of precipitation, and the depth to which winter frost penetrates. It performs little if any work on the ground itself. It is useful on soils and in areas where stubble ground needs to be broken to absorb expected moisture.

The disk harrow. Implements of the disk type are more extensively used for stubble-mulch tillage than any other type. They may include the common tandem disk, oneway or wheatland plow, or the heavy-duty orchard-type offset disk. These implements are useful in pretreatment of the stubble. As used, however, they frequently cause excessive destruction of mulch. Because of the speeds at which they are used, they pulverize the surface soil to so great an extent as to produce conditions that cause the ground to seal over. Infiltration is thus reduced rather than increased. The disk is most effective in inducing fall germination of weed seeds and, if properly used, can do a good job of stubble-mulch tillage. In order to be most effective under varying field conditions the disk harrow should be equipped with hydraulic controls to regulate either angle or wheel-depth.

INITIAL TILLAGE OPERATIONS IN HEAVY STUBBLE

The initial tillage operation in the heavy-stubble areas is usually performed in the spring for summer fallowing and in the fall for the annual cropping. Where fall tillage is done, pretreatment usually is not done unless it is necessary to shorten the straw in order to assist tillage operations.

In heavy stubble, the functions of the initial tillage are (a) to establish maximum depth of tillage, (b) to loosen the soil without excessive surface loosening, and (c) to mix residue with the soil so that quantity sufficient for adequate control of erosion is left on the surface. All the residue possible should be left on the surface. If the planter available is not capable of planting through it, the stubble should be cut into shorter lengths.

The moldboard plow. This tool can be made to produce almost any desired condition, either as a standard plow or, by removal or modification of the moldboard, as a sub-surface tiller. In annual cropping areas, the ideal job with a moldboard plow will show a uniform feather mulch protruding from between each furrow and a minimum of soil loosening. One weakness of the moldboard plow is the excessive loosening and throw of soil at speeds at which it is usually operated. If loosening and mechanical soil movement could be reduced, the moldboard plow would produce more favorable conditions. In the summer-fallow areas, the moldboard plow is generally used with a modified moldboard or without a moldboard in order to place more mulch on the surface. The plow as usually used has a tendency to bunch loose straw or to clog, caused principally by defective coulters. A properly adjusted plow of at least 16-inch bottom, having a good, well-adjusted coulter, will handle large amounts of residue without difficulty. There are two basic causes of coulter problems: improper adjustment and care, and insufficient bearings, yokes, and shanks not quite strong enough to stand the job imposed upon them for a sufficient length of time to prevent the farmer from getting discouraged in trying to keep them in adjustment.

The oneway or vertical-disk plow. In the Pacific Northwest, where tillage is performed at depths of from 5 to 8 inches, the oneway produces excessive pulverization, throw, and cover at the speeds usually operated. At these speeds, there is also a tendency to place too much of the residue about 3 inches below the surface—a position where it is most difficult to work out with secondary-tillage implements. Certain of these undesirable characteristics possibly could be alleviated by using disks of a flatter curvature. The oneway, if used at speeds well below 2 miles per hour, will produce very satisfactory results.

The heavy-duty orchard-type disk. This tool is also apt to cover crop residues excessively but it is not as objectionable in this respect as the oneway. This is mainly because available sizes of this implement load the tractor to the extent that speeds are not generally excessive. The heavy-duty orchard-type disk also cuts the straw in shorter lengths so that subsequent operations are more easily performed. Because of these characteristics, it has replaced

FIGURE 97. If the moldboard plow is to be used it should produce a uniform feather mulch protruding from between each furrow and a minimum of soil pulverization.
(Soil Conservation Service)

large numbers of both moldboard and oneway plows in the last few years and will probably continue to replace them.

The disk plow. This tool is capable of performing probably the most ideal job of any of those previously mentioned. The soil can be thoroughly broken without excessive loosening. The mulch can be placed at almost any location or mixed as needed, and the disk plow will handle heavy stubble without trouble. In order to perform such a job, it is necessary, however, for farmers to learn how to adjust the disk plow to produce the desired condition. There appears to be an excellent field for this tool in all the heavy-stubble areas if an increased volume of production can reduce the price. The principal objection to this tool is that it is too expensive for many farmers.

The sweep plow. This is the one tool of those mentioned in this group that does not produce enough surface pulverization. It has the advantage of enabling the proper degree of loosening to be produced by the supplemental tillage operation and of causing the least amount of mechanical movement of soil downhill. It is believed that this tool will have a definite place in all areas, if for no other reason than because it is better adapted to killing sweet clover at the proper time than any of those previously mentioned. Sweet clover is grown extensively in crop rotations in some wheat-growing areas. In handling it, it is necessary that a positive kill be effected at exactly the proper time. This is impossible with any of the disk implements. The moldboard plow will do the job, but unless extreme care is used the soil is left in an extremely erodible condition. In this operation, it is necessary to leave the maximum amount of clover residue on the surface in order to provide the necessary protection against erosion. The sweep performs this function well but here again this tool needs bottoms that will stand up better.

CHOICE OF IMPLEMENT DEPENDS ON NATURE OF WORK

The most satisfactory secondary-tillage implement for heavy stubble will depend on the work to be accomplished. The jobs which must be done are (a) the preparation of a firm compact sub-surface seedbed without excessive surface loosening, and (b) lifting of the crop residue from the area being tilled, and (c) the maintenance of uniform mulch on the surface. This involves spreading of straw mulch as well as clearing stubble from the upper layer of soil. These functions must be performed with a minimum amount of clogging.

The rod weeder. The application of the rod weeder is similar to that in the light-stubble areas, except that when initial tillage has been performed in such a way as to include large amounts of stubble in the area from 3 to 4 inches below the surface, it is extremely difficult to operate the rod weeder without clogging. Usually when initial tillage operations have been done with the oneway, offset disk, or with the moldboard plow having the moldboard on, it is necessary for the first operation to be done with the field cultivator.

The cultivator. When the cultivator is properly adjusted, it will clear excessive stubble from the area at which the rod weeder operates and bring it to the surface, so that subsequent operations can be performed by the rod weeder. In the annual cropping area, the field cultivator frequently will be the only tillage tool used. It is the most satisfactory of all tillage tools now available for use in preparing seedbeds where the mulch has been well mixed with the tilled layer. It is necessary that the cultivator be so constructed that the lateral spacing can be varied to meet existing conditions. It is also necessary that there be maximum clearance both vertically and fore and aft. No tooth may be closer to a wheel than it is to other teeth. Even so, this is the most frequent point of clogging. Curved shanks are necessary to lift the residue, and the shank must be so shaped that it is reducing at the ground surface. Maximum tooth chatter must be obtained to reduce clogging. Nevertheless, some difficulty with clogging will be encountered, except under the most ideal conditions. Hydraulic lift controls are practically a necessity to make this operation successful.

The disk harrow. This tool is used in tillage operations when a condition has been produced which cannot be handled by the cultivator. It is, of course, possible to produce a seedbed with a disk harrow but in so doing the mulch is buried rather than raised to the surface. Because of the extreme fineness of the ground surface that is produced, most of the effectiveness of the mulch is lost when the disk is used for seedbed preparation.

The rotary hoe. A heavy-duty rotary hoe has been adapted from the purpose for which it was designed to be used in seedbed preparation. The rotary hoe is better than any other existing tool for spreading mulches uniformly. It will raise mulch to the surface and it will break up long straw. When properly used, it is a sufficiently drastic tillage tool for many conditions and, since it is a rotating tool rather than a toothed tool, it is self-cleaning. Furthermore, it has the very desirable characteristic of doing better work as the speed is increased. The one weakness of this tool is that presently available hoes were never designed for this use, and are not sufficiently sturdy to stand the strain imposed upon them. When used in heavy stubble, it is necessary that the tandem-gang type with overlapping hoe wheels be used in order that the two gangs can clean each other. It is believed, however, that this feature could be improved by using bar cleaners between each hoe wheel in a single-gang type. If such is the case, a more drastic tillage tool can be readily made by operating a single-gang type on a sufficient skew to provide necessary tillage by dragging each tooth through the soil a short distance before it rolls out and is replaced by another tooth. Here again, we need more strength and better thrust bearings. It is believed that a machine of this type, which we might call a rotary-toothed harrow, will eventually prove to be necessary for seedbed preparation in heavy stubble. It is believed also that, if such a tool were available and would stand up mechanically, it would supplant both the field cultivator and the rod weeder in at least the annual cropping portion of the heavy-stubble area. This tool would not only do the kind of job needed on the mulch, but it would do whatever job is necessary on the soil. By changing the direction of travel and by operating at variable angles, the type of work done on the soil could be modified to meet any condition that might be encountered.

In all areas, stubble-mulch tillage adds the job of penetrating available mulch to the job of drilling. This must be done with little if any clogging. The problem of drilling is not difficult in either the light- or the moderately-heavy-stubble areas. In the light-stubble areas, almost any type of drill can be used except that the double-disk furrow openers are not satisfactory. In the moderately-heavy-stubble areas, single-disk openers of the semideep furrow type are generally adequate.

In the heavy-stubble areas, the most satisfactory opener is either the single-disk deep-furrow type or the lister type. The relative merits of each of these seem to be largely a matter of personal preference.

Press-wheel carriages are advantageous with both types, since neither will penetrate all the mulch, and the press wheels will assist materially in obtaining germination of the seed. These two openers, when used in conjunction with the press-wheel carriage, are adequate for most conditions, but it is easily possible that improvements can be made for drilling in heavy stubble.

A drill using the rotary principle, such as mentioned in connection with a rotary hoe, may be desirable. In such applications, the seed would be planted in pockets rather than in rows. The first advantage is that no amount of mulch would be troublesome and further clogging could not occur. Such clogging is a very real problem when drills are operated in squadrons of as many as six and when conditions suitable for drilling may be of very short duration and require high-speed work when suitable conditions prevail.

In stubble tillage and all conservation work, the importance of hydraulic controls cannot be too strongly stressed. Frequently, tools which would not be at all satisfactory with either hand- or clutch-type lifts can be operated fairly well when operated with hydraulic controls. Relief of the tool can be given at the proper time to avoid incipient stoppages. In addition, hydraulic controls are a necessity for some of the very heavy tools now being used. Certainly, if we expect to protect grass waterways, terrace outlets, or other conservation structures in all large-scale farming areas we must provide positive, accurate, and easily-operated means of raising or dangling implements.

REFERENCES

1. Duley, F. L. 1948. *Stubble-mulch farming to hold soil and water.* USDA Farmers' Bull. 1997.
2. ———. 1954. *Stubble-mulch farming methods for fallow areas.* Neb. Agr. Ext. Serv. Circ. 54-100.
3. ———, and Russell, J. C. 1942. *Machinery requirements for farming through crop residues.* Agr. Engin., 23(2): 39-42.
4. ———. 1946. *Stubble mulch for wheat-fallow rotations.* Neb. Agr. Ext. Service. P. F. L-21.
5. ———. 1948. *Sweetclover in a stubble-mulch system.* Soil Sci. Soc. Amer. Proc., 13: 554-557.
6. Ryerson, G. E. 1950. *Machinery requirements for stubble-mulch tillage.* Agr. Engin., 31(10): 506-508.
7. Whitfield, C. J., Van Doren, C. E., and Johnson, W. 1949. *Stubble mulch management for water conservation and erosion control on hardlands of the Southern Great Plains.* Tex. Agr. Expt. Sta. Bull. 711.

16

Grassland Farming

Agriculture in the United States is today undergoing changes greater than any since the settlement of this country nearly two centuries ago. In the past, we have been cash- and row-crop farmers. We have emphasized corn, the cereal grains, cotton, and tobacco. We have cleared the forests, plowed the Prairies of the Midwest, turned the bunch grasses of the Palouse —all of this to produce more grain, more fiber, and more of the other cash crops. In so doing we have built the greatest nation on earth.

There once was land enough for all. There was an enormous storehouse of productivity in the soil, built and held there for uncounted centuries by continuous grass cover. There once was plenty of feed for our grazing herds on the rough, poor land unsuited for production of cash crops. Besides, everyone knew that it was the grain we fed that produced the milk and the beef—pastures and hay crops were thought of as "roughage." They were poor crops indeed; in fact, not crops at all. Certainly they did not deserve nor did they get a place on productive cropland. Neither did they warrant nor receive fertilization or other care.

But all this is changing. We are now witnessing a conversion of our agriculture from a cash- and row-crop system to a grasslands system. It is a great movement—almost a crusade. It is a movement that has been progressing gradually throughout the United States, more rapidly in some areas than in others, but nevertheless moving forward in all parts of the country.

We are driving toward a grassland agriculture for several reasons:

First, our nation's grasslands have an enormous potential of productivity if properly treated. There are almost a billion acres of permanent grasslands in the United States and most of them are unimproved. Liming, fertilization, reseeding to productive grasses and legumes, and management practices that assure optimum production and utilization would result in double and treble the present production from hundreds of millions of acres of permanent grasslands. For example, pasture renovation in the Northwest has resulted in increases in herbage production of 4 to 6 times over the unimproved pastures. In Georgia, a well-fertilized coastal Bermuda grass pasture produced in a single season 569 pounds of beef plus 2,500 pounds of high quality hay per acre. At Beaumont, Texas, proper fertilization and seeding of adapted grasses and legumes in rice stubble pastures increased beef production 300 per cent. Similar improvement could be cited from work in Missouri and elsewhere.

Second, it has been shown experimentally that on much of the present cropland of the United States, improved grasses can produce as many food units per acre, at lower cost per feed unit and with greater returns per unit man-hour of labor, as corn or the other feed grains.

Third, improved grasslands can produce, as pasture, hay, and silage, most or all of the feed required for livestock. Dairy cows can produce 80 per cent as much milk on improved pasture alone as on the best combinations of concentrated feeds. Dairy cows have produced 8,000 pounds of milk per year without any concentrates.

Fourth, large portions of our population are milk and meat hungry. It has been estimated by the Chief of the Bureau of Human Nutrition and Home Economics that 40 per cent of our families have diets deficient in calcium, and 50 per cent have diets deficient in protein. The best way to ensure sufficient minerals and protein in the human diet is through animal products— milk, meat, eggs, and so forth. But if our experience of World War II is repeated, these dietary deficiencies will be accentuated, for it was meat, butter, fats, and other livestock products that became critically short. If we are to avoid recurrence of those shortages and dietary deficiencies that will handicap us in a long struggle, we must have more livestock products at prices that place them within reach of the greatest majority of our people. By a grasslands program, we can have increased supplies of livestock products, produced at lower cost, without interfering with production of other food and fiber crops and without competing for short supplies of feed grains. Without a grasslands program, we must content ourselves with less total food supply and with diets made up of lower amounts of meat, milk, butter, and cheese.

Fifth, wool is already a critically short commodity in this country. Sheep can, and at present do, exceed other classes of livestock in the proportion of nutrients they obtain from forage. Improved grasslands are required to feed the sheep that will produce the wool so seriously needed.

Last, improved grasslands are required in our cropping systems to provide sustained maximum production of other cultivated crops. Until recently, no cropping schemes that will maintain soil organic matter had been devised except those based on adequate proportions of grasses and legumes in rotation. The so-called cultivated crops permit serious soil losses by erosion. The process of annual plowing and periodic tillage is in itself a soil-destroying process. As soil fertility and organic matter decline, soil structure is lost, tillage difficulties increase, crop yields decline, and erosion hazards increase.

Grassland farming is a system based on adequate and intelligent use of grasses and legumes, a system in which the grasslands are an integral part of the cropping scheme; a system in which some areas, unsuited for cultivation, are converted to permanent grasslands; a system in which other areas are placed in crop rotations with a sufficient proportion of grasslands to protect the soil and give profitable and sustained production of the cultivated crops. In fact—in grassland farming—pasture, hay, and grass silage are cultivated crops, receiving and warranting as much care as is lavished on what are now commonly classified as such.

SOIL FERTILITY AND PASTURES

The use of limestone and superphosphate has been recommended for

FIGURE 98. Mixture of ladino clover, tall fescue, and lespedeza in Warren County, Kentucky. Ten acres carried 120 sheep during fall grazing season.
(Soil Conservation Service)

many years as a means of increasing the productivity of permanent blue-grass pastures. Where the topography of the land permitted, disking and re-seeding with grasses and clovers were recommended. The effects of such practices were often phenomenal.

It was not until the end of the first World War, when the product of the tremendous nitrogen-fixing factories of Germany and England was diverted from explosives to agriculture, that really intensive systems of pasture man-agement came into being. One such system, which added heavy use of nitro-gen fertilizers and rotational grazing to the program, had been started at Hoenheim, Germany, in 1917. This system, fostered by the Stickstoff Syndi-kat in Berlin and by Imperial Chemical Industries in London, began to re-ceive serious consideration in this country about 25 years ago. The first ex-perimental project of this type in the United States was put into operation at the Dairy Research Farm at Sussex, New Jersey, in 1927, where it has been in effect ever since.

MANAGEMENT IMPROVES IRRIGATED PASTURES

Properly prepared and managed irrigated pastures produce two to three times as much beef as unimproved irrigated pastures. An unimproved irri-gated bluegrass pasture, operated by the Kittitas Soil Conservation District in Washington, produced an annual average of 200 to 250 pounds of beef per acre over a period of four years. At the same time a 41-acre pasture similar to the unimproved pasture, but seeded to an appropriate grass-legume mixture and fertilized with about 300 pounds per acre annually of 18 per cent superphosphate, produced an average annual acre-yield of 549 pounds of beef.

The pasture plants that predominated in the mixture at the end of the period were the broad-leaved grasses, Manchor smooth brome, alta fescue, orchardgrass, and ladino clover. Yearling steers made an average gain of 2.01 pounds per day during the 5-month pasture season.

The average feed cost per pound for producing the beef on the improved pasture during this 4-year period was 7.3 cents. This figure includes the cost for the first pasture season before the plants were fully developed. The average net income per acre from this pasture was $90.84 annually for four consecutive years.

Supplementary irrigation of a well-fertilized Bermuda-ladino clover pas-ture in Georgia increased the production of dry forage 27 per cent and the production of protein 67 per cent. The increased forage and, particularly, the increased protein production were due largely to the fact that there was a greater survival and growth of ladino clover throughout the summer with irrigation than without it.

In any irrigation program all other limiting factors in plant growth should first be corrected. Before making purchases of expensive permanent equip-ment, the farmer should be sure that his type of operation will give suffi-cient returns over a period of years to justify the cost of applying supple-mental water. In some cases, it may be more profitable to alter cropping systems or farm enterprises rather than add irrigation management to the farm plan.

THE POTASSIUM PROBLEM

Special attention is called to the potassium problem. The soils of most permanent pastures have been robbed of this element over the years. When it is finally added, a large part of that applied is often fixed by the soil. This fixed potassium is held much more tightly than that adsorbed in the exchange complex. In other words, to get the effect desired, very heavy applications may be required until the potassium level of the soil has been raised materially.

PLAN YOUR PASTURE

Modern progressive farmers have found that an abundance of high-quality forage is the very foundation of any type of livestock farming.

In developing a pasture program to obtain the best possible results on any farm, two aspects should be considered as primary objectives:

(a) Lime and fertilize according to soil test.
(b) Use the proper seeding rates and mixtures.

The pasture plan is probably the most important single step. It is the

FIGURE 99. Meadow in Halifax County, Virginia, seeded to orchard-grass, alfalfa, and ladino clover. Produced 9 tons per acre of grass silage.
(Soil Conservation Service)

"blueprint" and should be written down and kept on hand for reference. In working out the plan, such things as soil type, forage requirements, season-long grazing, erosion control, and land clearing should be considered.

The different pasture plants should be studied carefully, so that each plant or combination of plants may be put on the kind of soil to which it is best adapted.

Lime and fertilizer are the "insurance" one buys in order that the pasture plan will succeed. Soil testing is the best method to use in determining what soil nutrients are in short supply, the most beneficial kind of fertilizer, and the most profitable rates of application for it. Generally speaking, annual applications will produce the greatest returns, but occasionally it may be more feasible to provide a 2- or 3-year supply of lime, phosphate, and potash when the land is prepared for seeding.

A complete, balanced fertilizer is recommended. For clovers and legumes, heavy applications of lime, phosphate, and potash are often necessary; and nitrogen may be needed at seeding time, especially if the land is poor.

For grass, heavy rates of nitrogen fertilization are almost always necessary. In addition, lime, phosphate, and potash must be present to get the best growth of grass and cereals. Even if the grasses are in combination with clovers, nitrogen may still give good returns, if applied at the proper time in the growing season.

Small grains and grasses such as fescue, sudangrass, millet, ryegrass, oats, and rye must have plenty of nitrogen to give top production. For fescue on good soil, Dr. P. G. Hogg of the Delta Experiment Station, Stoneville, Mississippi, recommends 240 pounds of nitrogen per year, applied in four separate applications. Big profits come from giving grasses and cereal crops all the nitrogen they can use to advantage.

Mixed fertilizers, such as 0-14-10 and 0-12-12 are becoming popular for top-dressing clover and legume pastures. If plenty of "fuel" is provided, these pasture areas are ideal factories for producing grass and clover. Tests and demonstrations show that $1 invested in pastures will bring back $5 to $9 in return, according to the type of plantings, soil, and management.

Proper seedbed preparation and seeding are important. The guiding principle should be getting the right crop on the right land at the right time. Fall is the best month to seed most pasture crops in the South, whereas both spring and fall are used in the northern areas.

Many pasture crops are started in a cereal or planted in rotation with cereals. Winter grazing in the South consists of cereals, ryegrass, and fescues —usually with a legume in them for spring grazing.

Many annual legumes, such as crimson clover and lespedeza, are being planted in oats or grass. Already, crimson clover—especially the new reseeding strains—is gaining fame as the "Belle of Southern Pastures."

Another practice that is spreading throughout the country is drilling seed of an appropriate grass or legume in established sods. The seeding is usually timed so as to produce grazing when the established sod is dormant or producing minimum grazing. Such seedings are well fertilized.

Ladino clover will eventually be in almost every farm-pasture program in the entire country. In the South it will be ladino and tall fescue in most pasture plans. In the North, ladino also fits into many pasture mixtures. However, other grasses, such as bromegrass, timothy, and orchardgrass, are used with it.

Pasture plants vary in their needs for plant food, length of grazing period, and best grazing season. They also vary as to the type of mixture in which they are likely to do best. A good pasture plan, therefore, will outline (a) what is to be grazed, (b) when and how it will be grazed, (c) what is to be grazed next, and (d) what to plant on the land when the old pastures are finished.

Management enables a farmer to get the most from his land in pasture. It is not hard work, but it requires his constant attention. Good management, which involves rotational grazing, weed control, and mowing the surplus forage, makes the pasture pay off and keep paying off. Controlled grazing is perhaps the most important principle in managing pastures so as to keep them productive. To get satisfactory returns from his labor and investment, a farmer must avoid overgrazing on any of his pastures.

FIGURE 100. Oats planted in sod at Southeastern Louisiana Experiment Station. Oats grazed until March 1, 1954. Sixty pounds of nitrogen were applied and produced 6 tons of silage per acre.
(Louisiana Agricultural Experiment Station)

BALANCE PASTURES WITH LIVESTOCK

It should not be overlooked that the value of pastures depends on a farming system that includes productive livestock. The farmer must gear together or balance (a) the development of pasture, (b) the production of supplemental feeds, and (c) the improvement and increase of livestock. The farm business may become uneconomical if any one of these factors is permitted to exceed or lag behind the others.

RENOVATING BLUEGRASS

According to the Iowa Agricultural Experiment Station, renovating bluegrass has come to mean introducing clover into the grass by disking or other cultivation, with the use of lime and phosphate if the soil needs them. This procedure feeds the grass roots and results in a thick, heavy sod. The vigorous grass growth largely eliminates weeds. The growth of clover provides succulent, nutritious, palatable pasturage in midsummer when blue-

FIGURE 101. Gully near Sioux Falls, South Dakota, bladed in, leveled, and seeded to mixture of alfalfa, bromegrass, and sweet clover. The gullied land was converted to productive pasture. *(Soil Conservation Service)*

grass usually becomes dormant, hard, and unpalatable. Usually a good renovation job greatly increases the productivity and carrying capacity of the pasture.

The essentials of a successful renovation job seem to be the following:

1. If possible, lime in the fall before spring seeding if the soil is acid. A good stand and vigorous growth of sweet clover or alfalfa is thus obtained. These legumes are excellent in pasture renovation seedings.

2. Disk or tear up the grass some other way in the fall if possible. The lime can then become active immediately, and it reduces the seedbed work in the spring.

3. Apply 200 to 300 pounds of 20 per cent superphosphate (or its equivalent) in the spring and work in well when preparing the seedbed.

4. Do a thorough job of tearing up the grass sod when preparing the seedbed. Do not worry about hurting the grass, for it will come back quickly and better than ever.

5. Seed in the early spring or not at all—not later than April 15 and as much earlier as possible.

6. Seed a mixture of adapted legumes. The mixture most widely used in Iowa consists of 5 pounds of sweet clover, 3 of red clover, and 2 of alsike per acre, with 10 pounds of lespedeza also included for extreme southern Iowa counties.

LIME HELPS PASTURES

At the Pasture Improvement Farm in southern Iowa, near Albia, a series of six experimental pastures were used several years to compare the production of untreated native bluegrass pastures with that obtained from the same land when renovated, both with and without lime. The seeding mixture used was that already referred to as in general use. The pastures were grazed with native steers. The pounds of beef gained per acre for the various treatments for the seasons 1941 through 1943 are shown in Table 55.

TABLE 55. Acre production in pounds of beef on untreated pastures and pastures reseeded with and without lime (8)

Treatment	Average annual pounds gained per acre 1941-43
Untreated	108
Reseeded, without lime	143
Limed and reseeded	193

Considering both tillage and seed costs it is quite obvious that, under these soil conditions, reseeding without the use of lime is not effective. Such increase in production as was obtained on pastures reseeded without lime was due largely to the acid-tolerant Korean lespedeza, with some help from red clover. But where lime was included the stand and growth of all legumes were much better. Renovation, including reseeding and use of lime, increased the average number of pounds of beef produced per acre from 108 to 193, an increase of approximately 80 per cent.

PHOSPHATE AIDS LEGUMES

Many farmers know that the growth of legumes usually is greatly stimulated by phosphate fertilizers.

One of the most striking observations on the experimental pastures at Mt. Pleasant, Iowa, was the much thicker stand and more vigorous growth of the sweet clover on the pasture that received 150 pounds per acre of 20 per cent superphosphate in addition to lime, as contrasted with the pasture limed but not phosphated.

Beginning with the 1944 season, the bluegrass renovation experiment at Albia, Iowa, was modified to include phosphorus with lime. The sod was torn up with a weighted spring-tooth harrow in the fall of 1943, thoroughly disked in the spring of 1944 and 250 pounds of 20 per cent superphosphate applied to two of the four limed pastures. The phosphate was thoroughly mixed with the soil during the disking operation in the early spring. Two other pastures were handled in identically the same manner except that no phosphate fertilizer was used. The seeding mixture was the same as for the preceding years. Native steers were turned into all pastures in mid-May and remained on them until about the middle of October, both in 1944 and 1945. The results, in pounds of beef per acre, are shown in Table 56.

TABLE 56. Average annual production in pounds of
beef per acre during 1944–45 (8)

Treatment	Pounds gained per acre
Untreated	105
Limed and reseeded	147
Limed, phosphated and reseeded	155

MANAGE THE GRAZING

The benefits of pasture renovation can be enjoyed for several years if grazing is managed properly. A common fault is to graze so heavily in the second season following renovation that the biennial clovers fail to reseed. Reseeding is essential to success and can only be accomplished through controlled grazing during those weeks when seed heads are forming.

After the seed is developed, grazing should be heavy for the remainder of the season and even into the fall, so that the accumulated growth of grass and clover is gone from the surface by winter. This close grazing permits the legume seed to be shattered and brought in close contact with the soil. It also weakens the grass so that its undesirable competition with the seedling legumes the following spring will be reduced.

SOLVE RENOVATION PROBLEMS

Some farmers have had difficulty in maintaining good stands of clovers in bluegrass pastures through a period of years. Experienced and observing livestock men are overcoming this difficulty through good grazing management. There are renovated pastures in various parts of Iowa which have good stands of sweet clover in the grass 6 and 7 years after seeding.

Pastures that have been closely grazed the season through show a rather weak sod which can be prepared for the renovation process without excessive disking or other cultivation. When the bluegrass sod was thick and heavy, the cost of preparing the seedbed has been excessive. The disk has been used almost exclusively in Iowa in pasture renovation, but not because it is the only available tool thought suitable—some farmers know that several implements are better for renovation than the disk. Shallow plowing to set back the grass and give the clover a chance to become established is preferred in some areas. Plowing also helps control weeds. Tractor-mounted corn cultivators and sub-surface tillers also have given excellent results.

Four methods of seedbed preparation were compared at Albia in 1945. These included (a) disking, (b) plowing shallow in the fall, (c) plowing shallow in the spring, and (d) tilling with a rigid, mounted, sub-surface tiller, especially constructed for the purpose. The sod was very heavy and dense.

The fall-plowed plots were plowed about 4 inches deep in mid-November (1944), while the spring plowing was done at the end of March at about the same depth. The plots that were fall-plowed were left rough over the winter with the result that there was little or no erosion. The plowed plots were disked twice with the tandem disk just before seeding on March 28. The subtilled plot was disked twice in the spring with the tandem disk, and the disked plot was disked four times.

The degree to which bluegrass was set back or killed varied greatly between the different treatments. The grass was almost entirely killed on the fall-plowed plots. The average stand of clover obtained on these plots was estimated at 96 per cent. Considerable bluegrass came back on the plots spring-plowed. The average stand of clover seedings was 78 per cent on these plots. Kentucky bluegrass came back very strong and vigorous, both on the disked plots and on those subtilled and disked. Clover stands on these plots averaged 65 and 59 per cent, respectively.

Seeding mixtures compared on each of the plots receiving the different tillage treatments included (a) a mixture of 5 pounds of sweet clover, 3 of red clover and 2 of alsike; (b) ladino clover, 4 pounds per acre; (c) birdsfoot trefoil, 6 pounds per acre; and (d) bromegrass, 8, and alfalfa, 10 pounds per acre. The clover mixture produced the heaviest growth in the first, or seeding, year. The ladino clover also made a very heavy, vigorous growth, particularly late in the season. The birdsfoot trefoil, as is characteristic of this legume, made very little growth the first year, particularly on the plots where the bluegrass had not been sufficiently killed back.

The bromegrass-alfalfa combination made an exceptionally good growth on the plots that had been plowed in the fall, so that the bluegrass was largely killed out. The conversion of bluegrass pasture to a bromegrass-alfalfa pasture appears to be a relatively simple job. Changing bluegrass pasture into a bromegrass-alfalfa pasture would seem to be a desirable step and entirely feasible on many farms.

SHALLOW PLOWING SUPERIOR TO DISKING

It will be simpler and the labor and power costs will be less, in many cases, to prepare a seedbed from bluegrass sod by shallow plowing than by disking. The plowing job can be done in the late fall at a time when other farm operations are not particularly pressing, whereas the disking procedure must be carried out in the spring in a crowded interval. Little soil loss may be expected from shallow-plowed bluegrass sod if it is plowed on the contour and left rough over the winter. Oats should be seeded in the spring with the clover, all to be grazed. On long slopes, where the possibility of erosion may offer a problem, sod buffer strips at intervals are desirable. Any small areas particularly subject to erosion may be left unplowed.

Bromegrass yields much more feed in pasture than Kentucky bluegrass. For a long-time pasture either grass should be grown with a legume. The average yield of five varieties of bromegrass is 63 per cent greater than that of Kentucky bluegrass. In the midsummer months, when it becomes hot and dry, Kentucky bluegrass stops growing and dries up.

LONG-ROTATION PASTURES

Undoubtedly many pastures left permanently in bluegrass would be helped by cultivation, where this can be done without erosion. Such pastures can be plowed and put into corn for one year, after which the field may be seeded down to bromegrass-alfalfa with oats as a nurse crop. Such a seeding should remain productive for several years, but after it becomes sodbound it can again be plowed and another crop of corn produced while re-establishing the brome-alfalfa. The grass portions of such fields, which cannot or should not be plowed, may be allowed to grow up during the year and grazed off in the early winter after corn has been harvested.

PERMANENT PASTURES

Some pastures, because of their steepness or because of trees, rocks or ditches, cannot be plowed and must be left permanently in bluegrass. Often such pastures are badly infested with weeds and buckbrush and produce little feed. In every case these pastures can be made more productive by mowing to control weeds and buckbrush, which rob the soil and grass of needed moisture and nutrients.

MOW BRUSH AND WEEDS

Perennial weeds can best be controlled by mowing when in the bud stage, which is usually early July. Pastures with perennial weeds need to be mowed for several seasons to eliminate weeds. Annual weeds, such as ragweed, are easily controlled by mowing before they have made seed.

Buckbrush has become a serious problem on many pastures. This shrub can be controlled by mowing once each summer. The most difficult job is removing the first heavy growth. The growth in succeeding years then can easily be mowed with an ordinary horse-drawn mower. Surprisingly heavy brush can be mowed by the mower with power take-off, operating the tractor in low gear with considerable speed on the sickle.

Annual mowing of pastures should become a general practice because it so greatly improves the production.

NEW AND BETTER PASTURE CROPS

The list of new and improved varieties of forage crops is increasing. The superior southern types of bromegrass—Fischer, Lincoln, and Achenbach —are already finding a permanent place on many farms. The Ranger and Buffalo varieties of alfalfa, with their high resistance to bacterial wilt, undoubtedly will have an important bearing on the use of this crop in seeding with bromegrass for hay and pasture.

Other new forage varieties are just around the corner. These include such varieties as L6 and L39 lespedeza, Madrid sweet clover, Emerson red clover, Ioreed canarygrass, Pennscott red clover, and birdsfoot trefoil, all of which are giving very promising results in pasture seedings.

TRASH-MULCH SEEDING

The trash-mulch method of reclaiming idle or rejuvenating unproductive land with legumes and grasses fills a definite need in the hill sections of Ohio and similar areas elsewhere. This fact was shown by practical field tests

FIGURE 102. Broomsedge sod being prepared for planting to pasture the trash-mulch method way. Seeding is done in the trash. (Ohio)
(Soil Conservation Service)

conducted in 16 counties in southern Ohio from 1944 to 1948, inclusive, by the Soil Conservation Service. The trash-mulch method of preparation means working up the land with some implement that leaves the plant residues on the surface rather than burying them, as ordinary plowing does. The trials were located on private farms. In all there were 90 tests on 19 soil types.

Although the trash-mulch method of seeding is particularly desirable on slopes too steep to plow, a fairly wide range of slopes was covered by the trials in Ohio. Some seedings were made on level land. Nearly one-half of the seedings were made on idle land. Some of the areas had not been cropped for 20 years. An equal number of test seedings were made on what was called pasture land. In many cases it was equally as unproductive as the idle land. Some trials were made on old meadows. The trials were inspected each year and were rated as excellent, good, fair, or poor.

Of the 90 tests, 81 were classed as successful at the end of the first season. Their ratings were 19 excellent, 27 good, 22 fair, 13 poor and 9 failures. At the end of the second season some 3 or 4 of those previously called failures were rated as successful seedings. Yields of 2 to 3 tons per acre of high-quality legume-grass hay were reported from the test areas used for hay and many days of summer pasture for others.

The results of the field trials indicated that: (a) The trash-mulch method is a good erosion-control practice. It is especially valuable in establishing legumes and grasses on idle or unproductive sloping fields where erosion would be serious if they were plowed and prepared the usual way. (b) With the use of adequate fertilizer and lime, eroded and unproductive hill lands of Ohio will produce profitable crops of grass and legumes, including alfalfa. (c) Sowing grasses and legumes, including alfalfa, is a logical first step in restoring the productivity of eroded and unproductive hill land.

Failures or poor stands were the result of (a) inadequate preparation, (b) lack of lime or fertilizer, and (c) improper seeding methods. The chief cause was inadequate preparation.

This method of seeding is advantageous on sloping land for several reasons. Foremost is its erosion-control value. The trash intercepts the falling raindrops and preserves the open structure of the surface soil layer. The porous soil takes in much of the rain and little if any runoff occurs. Infiltration of most of the rainfall makes for a good supply of moisture for the seeding. The trashy surface also reduces evaporation and in this way improves favorable soil-moisture conditions. Furthermore, most unproductive soils are low in organic matter. When plant trash is left on the surface and is mixed with the fertilizer that is applied, it gives a shallow layer of "made topsoil" which is favorable to the growth of the seedlings of grasses and legumes.

In addition to the field trials, further experimental seedings were made in Ohio at Zanesville, at the Belmont Experiment Station Farm and at the Southeast Experiment Farm in Meigs County.

WHERE TO USE THE METHOD

The trash-mulch seeding method can be used on (a) idle or unproductive hill land, where there is a grass vegetation that is worthless as a feed; (b) on other hilly grassland now in a state of low production, where it is desired to improve grass and legume production as quickly as possible; and (c) on similar areas, where it is desired to change the species of vegetation.

In the first category are idle (sometimes abandoned) areas covered with broomsedge, poverty grass, weeds, briars, and even thorn bushes. Usually such land is too low in fertility for general cropping.

In the second category are areas now called pasture land where the desirable grass species are thin and lacking in vigor. If such areas have a fair percentage of bluegrass, they may be much improved with the least cost by adequate treatment with lime and fertilizer. If, however, there is urgent need for an increase in production and quality from the field in the shortest possible time, trash mulching comes into the picture because in a year's time (sometimes less) a trash-mulched area will be in nearly full production.

The third situation may be somewhat like the second except that a different type of forage is desired. Many hill farms need hay in addition to that produced on the rotation cropland. There is also need for hay-type summer pasture. This need is often met by dual-purpose meadows. Occasionally a farm has more permanent pasture than can be used to best advantage. Converting a part of this to a dual-purpose meadow is advantageous.

WHEN TO WORK THE GROUND

In general, spring seedings are recommended. To make a spring seeding it is best to apply the lime and start working the ground the previous fall. As early as possible in the spring complete the preparation and make the seeding. Getting some of the work out of the way the previous fall enables one to sow early in the spring, which is desirable. The soil should be dry enough so that it will work up into a good seedbed. Although early seeding is recommended, many successful seedings have been made well into May. In general, the later the seeding the greater the risk.

Many successful summer seedings have also been made. The trash-mulch method practically eliminates erosion. It also increases the amount of moisture in the soil, by increasing the amount of water absorbed and by reducing evaporation losses.

HOW TO WORK THE GROUND

The first step is the application of lime. The amount applied is more important than the method of application. Have the soil tested and apply enough lime to bring the soil reaction up to pH 6.5 or 7, depending on the plants to be sown. If ladino clover or birdsfoot trefoil is to be sown, a pH of 6.5 is sufficient. If alfalfa is sown, the reaction should be pH 7. As previously pointed out, it is desirable to apply the lime during the fall before the seeding is to be made.

Work up the old vegetation with a heavy disk, field cultivator, or similar tool, or a rotary tiller of some sort if available. If an ordinary farm disk is used, it should be weighted with several hundred pounds of stone, sand, or other heavy material, particularly if old vegetation is dense. Ordinary farm disks, heavy disks, disk tillers or oneway disks, cutaway disks, field cultivators, rototillers, and even horse-drawn cultivators were used in the trials and other work. A heavy disk, either offset or straight, or the oneway disk tiller do the job most rapidly, but they require considerable power and may cut too deeply. The oneway is a bit difficult to handle on steep slopes. On the whole, the field cultivator type of implement does the job most satisfactorily. If the old sod is heavy, this implement may leave the field rough so that disking is needed to finish the seedbed. Herbicides such as TCA do a pretty good job of killing the old sod.

The amount of working will depend much on the amount and kind of vegetation on the field. In the first place, it should be remembered that the old vegetation must be killed insofar as possible so that it will not compete with the new seeding. That means that it must be cut loose and well chopped. In the second place, a seedbed must be made. Although trash mulching with a good implement takes no more time than with plowing, many become discouraged before they have a good seedbed because they have to go over the field more times than is required for conventional working. A general opinion prevails that about all that is necessary is to loosen up the old sod enough to expose some soil for the seed to fall into. Although some excellent seedings have resulted from this sort of preparation, it is really inadequate. The preparation should be sufficient to make a fairly smooth, but not necessarily a finely-worked, seedbed. In fields where there is a fair sod of cultivated grasses, either bluegrass or hay grasses from a previous seeding, working with a disk or cultivator-type implement may be difficult. It may also be impossible to kill out the old grasses. Shallow plowing is recommended on such areas. A word of caution is needed, however, for many are inclined to think that they are not plowing right unless they cut a good, deep furrow. A furrow slice three inches or less, disked up thoroughly, makes a good trash-mulch seedbed. Cultipacking before seeding is a good practice but not as essential as cultipacking after seeding.

BROADCAST SEEDING

Of the various methods of seeding tried, broadcasting after or at the same time the fertilizer is drilled is recommended. Arranging the seeder spouts so that the seed falls back of the disk is a method of broadcasting.

Drilling usually puts the seed too deep. Band seeding has been tried but is not recommended as it requires a fine and smooth seedbed.

FERTILIZE LIBERALLY

Although many successful seedings have been made with an application of 400 pounds of fertilizer, heavier applications have paid off. One farmer accidentally put on 1,000 pounds of 0-12-12 and had an excellent meadow. An initial application of from 400 to 600 pounds per acre of 0-20-10 or equivalent is recommended. Although some excellent seedings have been made using a complete fertilizer, and there are theoretical arguments in its favor, a fertilizer carrying only a small amount of nitrogen (or none) is advisable. Nitrogen may stimulate surviving grasses so that they make undue competition for the legumes. This is particularly true if there is some bluegrass in the field. Top-dressing grass and legumes in the years following seeding, particularly to supply needed potash that cannot be stored in the soil, is a must.

USE GRASS-LEGUME MIXTURE

For hay or summer pasture, a good seed mixture for spring seeding is alfalfa, 6 to 10 pounds; ladino clover, ¼ to 1 pound; and timothy, 6 pounds, or bromegrass, 8 pounds. For a summer seeding the timothy would be cut in half. For an all-season pasture for nearly continuous grazing, the alfalfa may be omitted. However, even though the alfalfa goes out in a year or so under this management there are advantages in including it. The deep roots of the alfalfa add materially to the soil-rebuilding value of the seeding. Alfalfa will also materially increase the early production from the field. For an all-season type of pasture and for long life, birdsfoot trefoil bids fair to be the best legume. The seeding rate is 3 to 4 pounds per acre. Thorough inoculation of this legume and alfalfa is essential.

The seeding should be clipped once or twice during the first season to remove weed growth. The field may appear weedy and even unpromising until clipped. Grazing may be substituted for clipping if not overdone. In a favorable season, some hay may be made the first season. If so, the cutting should be made before early September.

PASTURES FOR THE SOUTH

Because of the mild, open winters, pastures can be utilized over a greater portion of the year in the South than in the Corn Belt. There also is a wider variety of pasture plants to choose from in the South.

The Soil Conservation Service Research Station at Watkinsville, Georgia, has been conducting extensive studies over a period of years to develop suitable pasture mixtures for a wide variety of soil conditions.

For bottomlands, a mixture of Bermuda grass, Dallis grass, and white Dutch clover has proven satisfactory. Pastures consisting of this mixture supply grazing for 7 months (April through October). They have a carrying capacity of one cow-unit per acre during this period.

Kudzu makes an excellent pasture plant for steep hillsides and badly eroded and gullied areas. It grows luxuriantly in the Southern Piedmont. With moderate fertilization and little care it covers up steep eroded and gullied hillsides with succulent and palatable herbage, rich in feed nutrients. It is a heavy mulch producer. Each year it lays down under its dense canopy a mat of dead leaves to cover the ground and protect the soil.

Established on critical areas, kudzu conserves soil and water as well or better than any other known plant. Its extensive root system reaches deep into the subsoil, making it practically drought-proof. Wherever it grows, it builds up the soil, adding organic matter and nitrogen. Fenced in, for controlled grazing, it is insurance against drought in summer and fall. It remains palatable and is relished by cattle when the grass in summer pastures gets old and tough. If not overgrazed, it soon renews its top growth.

Kudzu can be grazed down in the fall, and followed by winter annual grasses and legumes. Kudzu provides a "trashy" but rich seedbed, after disk-harrowing preparation. Some reseeding types of winter annuals do well following kudzu. Among these are ryegrass, rescue grass, vetch, and Caley peas. Oats make rapid growth, sown in disked kudzu pastures.

Tall fescue, fall-sown in disked kudzu, promises to survive under a partial canopy of kudzu and produce valuable winter grazing after the kudzu tops die down at frost. The kudzu must be control-grazed during the summer to avoid shading out the grass.

In the spring, with kudzu pastures closed, as they should be for about 2 months, the winter annuals mature seeds and die down, adding more "plant manure" to what was originally poor, eroded, depleted soil. The new growth of kudzu becomes well established again by June.

Sericea, a perennial lespedeza, is sometimes called "poor land alfalfa." Like kudzu, it has the ability to make a dense stand on poor, thin land,

FIGURE 103. Kudzu is one of the most promising pasture crops in the southeastern part of the United States. It converts badly eroded and gullied land into profitable pastures. This is a 3-year old stand in Hall County, Georgia.
(Soil Conservation Service)

with moderate fertilization and little care. Like kudzu, it is also a mulch producer and a soil-improving legume unless mowed too frequently or grazed too heavily. In addition to its value as a pasture and hay plant, it produces valuable seed crops that can be combine-harvested. After its first year of growth it may be utilized for warm-season grazing, April to October.

Young shoots of sericea are tender and palatable. As the stalks grow taller than about 12 to 15 inches in height, the foliage becomes somewhat bitter and less palatable to livestock because of the increasing tannin content. Early and consistent grazing, or clipping down the taller growth until early fall, keeps the pasture in good condition and controls weeds. Allowing the plants to make late fall growth is recommended for the purpose of maintaining the vigor of the stand.

Sericea pastures may be oversown to winter annuals like burclover, crimson clover and ryegrass. Best results with winter pastures on the same land have been secured by seeding on a disk-harrowed seedbed. Heavy disking, however, damages the next year's sericea stand.

Perennial grasses, such as the tall fescues and orchardgrass, both cool-weather growers, may be oversown in the fall on disk-harrowed sericea pastures. Once established, no further tillage appears to be necessary. This provides a summer perennial legume and cool-weather perennial grass in combination on the same land—one making its best growth when the other is relatively inactive. If necessary, controlled grazing or special nitrogen fertilizer applications may be used to stimulate the grass; and lime, phosphate, and potassium without nitrogen, to stimulate the legume.

Both kudzu and sericea are exceedingly valuable plants to use on poor, eroded lands to supply the initial build-up needed to condition the land for other valuable plants that require improved land for best growth.

To meet the need for more winter grazing crops, a separate upland pasture is designed for that purpose. It contains oats, reseeding crimson clover, and ryegrass, primarily for winter grazing. Crabgrass and Bermuda take over for a short time during midsummer. This pasture receives a heavy disk harrowing, generally in late August following a rain to soften the sod. Oats are drilled. Clover and ryegrass volunteer. Due to the fact that spring is the flush grazing season, this pasture should be closed about April 15th, and a clover seed crop may be combine-harvested about June 1st. This makes a good early-winter pasture. It produces in excess of 5 tons per acre of hay-equivalent grazing, plus the clover seed crop.

Once the rather dry fall period is past, adequate rains can be expected during the winter. This climatic condition makes it practical to use moisture-loving, cool-weather growers on fertile, well-drained upland soils for controlled winter grazing.

When a softened disk-harrowed seedbed has been prepared in the fall on eroded upland soil, in preparation for seeding winter annual pasture mixtures, it is good practice to (a) apply complete fertilizer annually (and lime every 5 years); (b) use grass-legume mixtures; (c) never graze the top growth closer than 3 or 4 inches; and (d) avoid grazing when the ground is soggy.

Overgrazing is especially bad practice during the winter. All plants require warmth and sunshine for good growth, and the cool-weather growers are no exception. In addition to a root system, they must have foliage in order to respond quickly to temperatures that stimulate growth during mild spells. During the winter, sunshine is reduced because the sun is low on the horizon; days are short; and cloudiness and long, slow rainy periods further limit photosynthesis. Occasional cold snaps and freezes stop plant growth. Overgrazing seriously retards plant growth under these conditions.

Overgrazing is actually poor practice at any time of the year. It increases runoff and erosion, shortens the life and reduces the vigor of the sod plants, and reduces the total amount of feed produced. Overgrazing also robs the soil of fertility that otherwise builds up in well-managed pastures due to more vigorous root and top growth and heavier plant and animal manuring.

Other pasture plantings that show real promise are (a) oats and annual lespedeza with biennial sweet clover, (b) orchardgrass with ladino and reseeding crimson clover, (c) sericea and orchardgrass, and (d) tall fescues with ladino clover, Kobe lespedeza, sweet clover, or alfalfa.

Upland pastures should be developed on land that has had prior conditioning. For this purpose either kudzu, sericea, or rotations based upon annual lespedezas should be used. Adequate amounts of fertilizer and lime should be applied. This procedure offers minimum difficulty in securing good stands and growth of small-seeded pasture plants that are difficult to establish on depleted cropland low in organic matter.

REFERENCES

1. Bear, F. E. 1951. *Soil fertility and pastures*. Better Crops With Plant Food, 35(10): 15-18, 46.
2. ————. 1951. *Soil nutrients build your pasture*. Crops and Soils, 3(7): 9-12.
3. Beeson, K. C. 1941. *The mineral composition of crops with particular reference to the soils in which they were grown—A review and compilation*. USDA Misc. Pub. 369.
4. Blaser, R. E., and Brody, N. C. 1950. *Nutrient competition in plant associations*. Agron. Jour., 42: 128-135.
5. Borst, H. L. 1951. *Better hay and pasture with trash-mulch seeding*. Ohio Agr. Expt. Sta. Farm and Home Res., 36(269): 19-21.
6. Eby, C., Bender, C. B., and Bear, F. E. 1950. *Fertility levels in pasture land*. New Jersey Agr. Expt. Sta. Bull. 749.
7. Hendrickson, B. H. 1950. *Preliminary results with upland pasture development in the Southern Piedmont*. USDA, SCS, Watkinsville, Ga. (Mimeo.)
8. Hughes, H. D., and Peterson, M. L. 1946. *Iowa Agr. Expt. Sta. Farm Sci. Reporter*, 7(1): 14-18.
9. McVickar, M. H. 1955. *Summer pasture on permanent sod*. Plant Food Rev., 1(3): 4-5.
10. Myers, W. M. 1951. *The grasslands program in the national emergency*. Jour. Amer. Plant Food Council, Inc., 5(1): 2-5.
11. Thompson, W. R. 1951. *Plan your pasture for profit*. What's New in Crops and Soils, 3(7): 24-26.

17

Protect the Soil and
Improve the Range

The chief cause of soil deterioration on grazing land is loss of plant cover due to overgrazing and other poor land-management practices that expose the ground to wind and rain. The impact of falling raindrops, in turn, causes soil splash, puddle and fertility erosion, heavy runoff, and other damages.

The quickest, most effective, and cheapest way to restore the range is by the use of all range practices best suited to the type of operation involved, effectively coordinated with the natural growth habits and requirements of the principal forage plants.

The state of health or productivity of a range is known as "range condition." Range condition never remains unchanged for long. It is either improving or deteriorating. Range deterioration is but the effect of a downward trend of condition—the destruction of the plant cover and soil. *Range restoration* means stopping deterioration and bringing about an upward trend from an unsatisfactory to a satisfactory condition. Four range condition classes are recognized: excellent, good, fair, and poor.

In any climate there are many kinds of soils. On a given soil may be found vegetation types representing climax or varying degrees of departure from climax. An area that is uniform with respect to climatic and soil conditions is termed a "site." Differences between sites are best measured by differences in climax vegetation.

Even in each condition class, there may be a rather wide variation in density, composition, and vigor of forage plants. Because each range has its own top condition, ranges must be classified in terms of their own best possible development as well as kind of plant cover and forage production. For example, a mountain meadow naturally has a higher rainfall, deeper and richer soil, a thicker plant cover, and much greater forage growth than semidesert grassland, even when both are in satisfactory condition. Hence, a mountain meadow cannot be judged by the same standards one would use for a desert grassland.

Overgrazing is responsible also for much of the soil deterioration that occurs on grazed woodlands. It is the litter on the ground, not the foliage on the trees, that provides the effective control of soil splash caused by falling raindrops. Actually, erosion may be more severe on wooded areas where the ground surface is kept free of litter and other low-lying plant cover than it is on adjoining, unprotected, nonwooded areas.

This effect of the removal of ground cover can be observed with individual trees growing on lawns and other places, where the ground is kept free of litter and no other plant cover is provided. The foliage of the trees inter-

FIGURE 104. The area in the foreground and to the left is in pasture. The litter has been destroyed. A layer of topsoil several inches deep has been removed by erosion—mostly as a result of splash erosion. (Ohio)
(Soil Conservation Service)

cept the falling raindrops; they form into larger drops before falling from the tips of the leaves. When they strike the ground, these larger drops are more destructive and splash more soil than drops falling directly as rain. The result is more damage.

CORRECT GRAZING MANAGEMENT PROTECTS THE SOIL

It is recognized that certain combinations of plants determine range condition on any range site. It is only when a range is managed in such a way as to build up plant vigor and to return organic matter to the soil that one can expect the combination of plants known as climax vegetation, or range in excellent condition, to become established.

The soil, where the range condition is excellent, usually is darker in color than it is on ranges in poor condition. This is because the soil on a range in excellent condition contains organic matter—the living and dead plant matter, animal life, and humus—and has more plant litter on the surface.

FIGURE 105. Range in excellent condition in the Blackland area of Texas. The soil is high in organic matter and has abundant litter on the surface. The soil has good crumb structure, absorbs water readily, and has a high water-holding capacity. *(Soil Conservation Service)*

The decay of this litter and the formation of humus improves the soil structure and increases the soil's ability to take in and hold more water for plants to use.

In contrast, the soil on poorly-managed ranges is more compact at the surface and less capable of taking in water. It supports less vigorous plant growth, has less litter on the surface, and is subject to more severe damage from raindrop splash.

Both depth of soil and soil texture have a bearing on the amount of moisture the soil can take in and hold. It takes two to three inches of water to wet a fine-textured soil to about one foot in depth. On the other hand, a coarse-textured soil requires less than one inch of moisture to wet it one foot down. The finer the soil, the greater the holding surface for the film of moisture.

RANGE CONDITION AFFECTS WATER ABSORPTION BY SOIL

The sparse growth of grass on ranges in poor condition is partly due to the lack of soil moisture, and partly to the weakening of the plants by too-heavy grazing. The surface of the ground becomes sealed and the water runs off the surface like water does from a roof. The ease with which rain enters the soil and is available to the plant, however, is a greater factor at times in grass growth than the amount of rain that falls. Just after a rain is a splendid time to show how range condition makes a big difference in moisture infiltration. A good place to make a comparison is where a fence divides ranges of different condition classes. Holes can be dug to determine the depth of moisture penetration.

In May, 1948, after a 2-inch rain at Marfa, Texas, Soil Conservation

FIGURE 106. The range to the left of the fence has been overgrazed. The one to the right has been rested for about a year. Continuous overgrazing makes the soil vulnerable to the action of both wind and rain. (Andrews County, Texas)
(Soil Conservation Service)

Service range specialists and a group of ranchers checked a site where a fence divided range in good condition from one in fair condition. They found that the soil on the range in good condition was wet to a depth of 30 inches. Across the fence, that same amount of rain had penetrated the soil only 2 inches. Three weeks later, the grasses on the range in good condition were starting to head out, while those on the other side of the fence had grown up about two inches and then "burned up" for lack of moisture.

The comparative soil-moisture relationship can also be illustrated by use of infiltration rings. These iron rings, of 10- to 12-gauge black iron, can be driven 2 or 3 inches into the ground so that water cannot seep out from under them. Two should be used—one inside a larger one. A board with two nails in it may be laid across the rings so that one nail is in the middle of the center ring and the other halfway between the inner and outer rings. The nails should be adjusted so that the points are two inches above the ground. Water is applied to the inner ring from a one-gallon glass jar or similar vessel, calibrated in tenths of inches with the size of this ring. The initial application should be two inches of water. Water is added to both rings at given intervals to bring the water level up to the points of the nails. The time of application and amount of water applied to the inner ring are recorded. Water is applied to the outer ring to make up for the sidewise movement of moisture in the soil, but no measurement of this is necessary.

Information was collected in 1947 in each of the four range condition classes on a rolling hill site in west Texas to show relationship of range condition, forage production, soil structure temperature, and rate of water intake. Range condition classes are based largely on the kinds of plants making up the forage cover, compared with the climax vegetation for the site. The most valuable plants occurred on range in excellent condition, whereas the least valuable plants predominate on the range in poor condition.

Analysis of these soils showed the per cent of organic matter in the soil by range condition class, as follows:

Excellent condition	4.6%
Good condition	3.8%
Fair condition	3.6%
Poor condition	2.1%

The amount of litter and vegetation on these soils had a great influence on surface soil temperatures, which in turn affected the temperature in the surface layer of soil. Temperature readings (in Fahrenheit) in the surface layer of soil on these range lands in August, with an atmosphere temperature of 90°, were:

Excellent condition	104°
Good condition	110°
Fair condition	114°
Poor condition	120°

Moisture losses from evaporation increases as soil temperatures increase, thus reducing the amount of moisture available for plant growth. The high temperature of the soils on ranges in poor condition also affect the plants directly. Thus, the cover not only breaks the force of the raindrops but also helps to keep soil temperatures down.

Osborn found that the rate of intake of water on the same soil was determined by the amount of plant cover on the ground. The rate of infiltration or intake of water was in proportion to the amount of cover: the greater the amount of cover, the higher the infiltration rate.

Surface cover and soil conditions accounted for the different water intake capacities in the same soil.

Permanent characteristics of the soil, such as texture, exerted less influence on the amount of water lost or held than did the differences in cover and soil conditions within the same site. However, water losses were always high on very shallow soils regardless of cover or soil condition.

The tests conducted by Osborn consisted of 20-minute applications of 2 inches of water to 12- by 18-inch plots selected to represent different cover conditions. The water was applied in the form of falling drops of controlled size and velocity by means of a raindrop applicator mounted on a truck. Water and soil leaving the plot either as splash or runoff were collected and measured. This showed the comparative effectiveness of the cover in preventing splash and water loss.

The degree to which structure within the same soil may vary with cover conditions in response to past use of the range, and how these conditions affect water intake, was determined. A series of three plots—having a medium-textured surface soil with a tough clay a few inches below—lost 21 per cent, 59 per cent, and 63 per cent, respectively, of the water applied in the test.

The plot that absorbed the most water was in fair condition but had not been grazed for several years. It was covered with a dense stand of vine-mesquite grass which provided 10,605 pounds of cover per acre. Only 21 per cent of the water applied ran off; the other 79 per cent was absorbed by the soil. The soil had a porous, granular structure and withstood the impact of the water drops during the test. This permitted free percolation of water into the soil.

Another plot was in poor condition, in an area that had formerly been cultivated. Although lightly grazed at the time of the test, with 3,520 pounds of plant cover per acre, it lost 59 per cent of the water applied. The soil was densely compacted to a depth of 1½ inches.

The third plot was in a cultivated field that had been plowed and prepared for planting a few weeks previously. Young winter peas provided 1,082 pounds of cover per acre. This plot lost 63 per cent of the water applied. Although the soil was more porous than the preceding plot when the test began, drops of water striking the surface quickly sealed it over, preventing the entry of water.

EFFECTIVENESS OF COVER

Osborn also found that the effectiveness of cover in preventing splash erosion is proportional to the amount of cover present when the rain falls. Important factors are the thoroughness with which the land surface is shielded from raindrops, and the weight or bulk of the cover present to absorb the energy of the rain.

So important is the *amount* of cover in providing protection from raindrop impact that, when the results from all the plots of either range or cropland were averaged, this factor outweighed the wide differences in type of plants, range conditions, degree of use, kind of crop, or other variables. Regardless of whether results from a single site or from all sites combined were compared, the effectiveness of cover in reducing soil splash increased as the amount of cover increased.

Differences in the growth form of the cover had some influence on its effectiveness, giving different results when individual grasses of range cover or field crops were compared. These differences, resulting mainly from varying quantities of cover produced by different grasses, were generally lost in the mixtures that make up range types.

All range plants, regardless of site or cover condition, were compared to show effectiveness in reducing erosion from splash in relation to the amount of cover. The different measurements of amount ranked in the following order of effectiveness as indicators of relative protective value: (a) soil coverage, (b) weight of total cover, (c) forage density (estimated), and (d) average height.

The completeness with which the soil surface was covered was the characteristic most closely related with effectiveness in absorbing the impact of the rain. The total weight of cover (including both green forage and litter) was an almost equally reliable measure of its protective value. Since weight of cover can be more easily measured than per cent of cover, it is used as the standard expression of amount of cover.

The density of the living stand of plants, estimated as coverage when fully developed and ungrazed, and the average height of the standing forage both provide a rough indication of the effectiveness of the cover in reducing erosion by splash. However, there was wide variation from the general trend as determined for either measurement. In either case, the measure reflected in a general way the amount of cover present, but did not take account of the litter on the ground.

The rather wide range in effectiveness of the same amount of cover, as measured by any of the four characteristics just described, suggested that more than one feature might have a bearing on the results. Two combinations of the above measurements gave closer comparisons with protective values than either of the single measurements upon which they were based. This indicated that effectiveness of cover was best indicated by a dual measurement reflecting both the thoroughness of the covering (coverage or density and its mass (weight or height).

A combination of total weight and soil coverage gave the best indication of effectiveness in controlling splash. The product of these two measurements was used as an index of "effective weight." When effectiveness was checked against this index, the range of vegetation from the average trend was less than any other comparison made.

By this index, 2,000 pounds per acre of forage and litter covering 50 per cent of the soil surface would have the same value as 4,000 pounds per acre

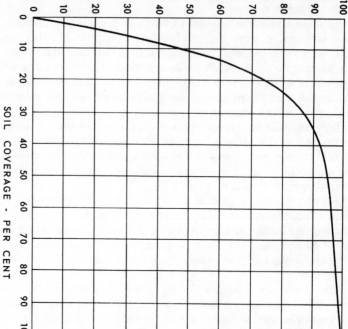

EFFECTIVENESS IN PREVENTING SPLASH - PER CENT

SOIL COVERAGE - PER CENT

EFFECTIVENESS IN PREVENTING SPLASH - PER CENT

TOTAL WEIGHT - POUNDS PER ACRE

FIGURE 107. *Left:* Effectiveness of range cover in preventing soil erosion by splash in relation to soil coverage. *Right:* Effectiveness of range cover in preventing soil erosion by splash in relation to total weight.

(Soil Conservation Service)

covering 25 per cent of the surface. Both covers would have an "effective weight" of 1,000 pounds per acre and would reduce erosion from splash by approximately 90 per cent.

AMOUNTS OF COVER REQUIRED

The results of the foregoing studies indicate the usual or average amount of cover required for any degree of control of soil erosion by splash, by whatever means the amount of cover is to be measured or estimated.

The different species of range plants and field crops can be grouped according to growth form into three classes of soil-protection values: (a) ordinary crops and grasses, (b) short sod grasses, and (c) tall crops and weeds.

Curves were plotted showing the average effectiveness of each growth

FIGURE 108. Effectiveness of different kinds of cover in preventing soil erosion by splash in relation to total weight.
(Soil Conservation Service)

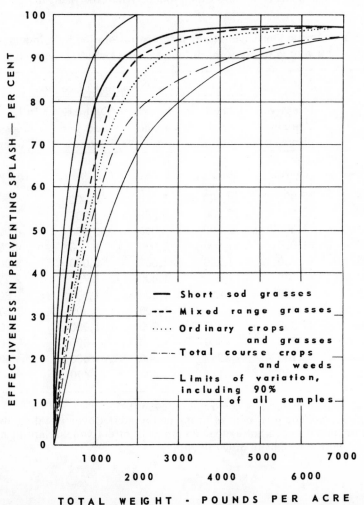

Short sod grasses
Mixed range grasses
Ordinary crops and grasses
Total course crops and weeds
Limits of variation, including 90% of all samples

EFFECTIVENESS IN PREVENTING SPLASH—PER CENT

TOTAL WEIGHT - POUNDS PER ACRE

form in relation to total weight of cover. A fourth curve is also presented, representing the average value of mixtures of species of different growth forms characteristic of the natural range vegetation judged. These curves are similar in form, and fall well within the principal limits of variation of all plots when considered together without respect to kind of cover.

The different degrees of effectiveness of the same amounts of cover of different growth forms undoubtedly reflect the natural arrangement of the foliage above the ground that is characteristic of each growth form. These differences rapidly disappear with increasing amounts of cover as effectiveness approaches 100 per cent, except that tall coarse crops and weeds were not completely effective in any amount. This is probably due to a certain amount of splash caused by drops falling from the foliage more than two or three feet above the ground surface after being intercepted. These differences in the effectiveness of growth forms essentially disappear when the amount of cover is expressed as "effective weight," which takes into account both the degree of surface coverage and the total weight of the cover.

Effective weight is especially useful in judging cover of unusual growth form or irregular distribution on the ground. When the plant materials are

TABLE 57. Amounts of cover required to control erosion by raindrops (average amounts for different degrees of effectiveness) (10)

Effective-ness	Effective weight of cover[a]	Total weight of cover			
		Short sod grasses	Mixed range grasses	Ordinary crops and grasses	Tall, coarse crops and weeds
Per cent	Lb/Ac.	Lb./Ac.	Lb./Ac.	Lb./Ac.	Lb./Ac.
98	3,000	4,000	5,000	6,000	—
97	2,500	3,000	3,750	5,000	—
95	1,500[b]	2,000	3,000	3,500	6,000
90	1,000	1,500	2,000	2,500	4,000
85	750	1,200	1,600	2,000	3,000
80	600	1,000	1,400	1,750	2,250
75	500	850	1,200	1,500	1,800
70	400	700	1,100	1,300	1,500
60	300	500	900	1,000	1,100
50	200	400	750	800	900
35	100	250	500	600	600
25	50	175	400	400	400

[a] Total weight (lb/ac.) × coverage (per cent)
[b] 2,000 lb./ac. for tall, coarse crops and weeds. Cover of this growth form ordinarily does not exceed 96 per cent effectiveness, attained when effective weight is 3,000 lb./ac.

of average form—such as the grains, fine-stemmed legumes, or mid-grasses —and uniformly spread over the ground, either weight or coverage alone is a satisfactory indicator of effectiveness in preventing splash.

The effectiveness of cover in reducing erosion by splash is a property of the cover itself, and is completely independent of the soil on which the cover occurs. These values, therefore, should be applicable to any example of herbaceous cover on any site and in any rain. Table 57 summarizes these results in terms of average amounts of cover required to provide different degrees of effectiveness in controlling soil splash.

RANGELAND

Western rangelands in the United States are usually arid, often with shallow or salty soils and steep topography. Precipitation varies from 4 to 30 inches per year, but over a large area is less than 15 inches. Evaporation rates and summer temperatures are high. These conditions frequently result in sparse plants and low grazing capacity.

Aridity makes proper grazing of fundamental importance. If plant stability is destroyed, soil erosion may increase rapidly. Once exhausted and eroded, rangeland recovers normalcy only after years of reduced use or even disuse. With proper management some ranges may recover within 10 to 15 years, but sometimes 50 to 100 years or longer may be necessary. Unfavorable plant succession results, more than from all other causes combined, from excessive livestock numbers. Since it is generally believed that ranch income is influenced more by numbers than by any other factor, operators strive for maximum numbers, risking range destruction. Thus, knowing range grazing capacity is very important.

Characteristically, livestock operations are large, and tremendous land areas are involved. Fencing of small areas generally is uneconomical; hence, it is impossible always to know the exact area from which forage is obtained.

Seasonal migration is common in the mountainous area and on public lands. On these lands range animals move to higher elevations in the summer and to lower elevations in the winter. However, year-long use is the rule in the Great Plains and humid belt of the range country. Many animals are on open rangeland throughout the year without supplemental feed, or with supplemental feed only during severe storms or just preceding calving and lambing time. Since grazing time is not readily varied as a management practice, and since supplemental feeding is often impractical or uneconomical, grazing intensity on the range is usually determined, in the main, by numbers of animals alone. Adjustment to current forage production is, at best, difficult.

RANGE CONDITION CLASSIFICATION

At one time range students judged ranges on the basis of indicator plants. Such botanical characteristics as density, vigor, reproduction, and plant age-classes of the species composing the flora (native plants) were used to determine trend and deviation from normal or climax. Where stocking history was known, estimation of correct stocking was based upon these observations. More recently, however, plant composition has been used as the primary clue to range condition.

The older method served as a basis for attempts at a more organized analysis, termed *condition classification*. Deviation from normal is classed in one of four categories, from class 1, which is virtually climax, to class 4, which is dominated almost entirely by invading species. All characters may be considered at once or separate classifications may be made for species composition, soil erosion, reproduction, and vegetation density.

Attempts have been made to interpret such data directly into grazing capacity. Again knowledge must be based upon ranges of known capabilities. Thus, if a class 2 sagebrush range is known to yield 20 animal days per acre, it is assumed that other class 2 sagebrush ranges of similar ecological nature will do likewise.

This method is subject to several objections. Among these is that it assumes knowledge of climax or normal condition. It is not always possible for inexperienced people to determine the climax with reasonable assurance. There is also the question as to whether climax is the most productive or desirable condition. Perhaps it is an uneconomical goal. Because of the number of factors involved this method is too complicated for practical use.

The plant composition method, on the other hand, contains only one factor. It is simple, direct, and easily applied; and, too, plant composition reflects the sum of the effects of all factors influencing a given site. It accurately indicates the stage in the plant succession scale. Anyone familiar with those factors can tell how good the range is.

Although plant composition is the primary clue to range condition, other factors are useful in evaluating trends. Some of the most important of these are plant density, vigor, soil tilth, erosion, livestock gains, and calving percentage.

It usually follows that ranges in top condition classes generally have better stands or densities of plants than ranges in lower condition classes. However, much depends upon the species of plants making up the range forage. Range forage of a high per cent of climax species may be more valuable even at lower densities than one with a high density composed mostly of invading species. Important changes in stand or density of vegetation aids in determining whether the trend is moving upward or downward.

Vigor, like density, can be a valuable aid in determining range condition if it is properly understood. High vigor indicates the plants are improving in growth, but vigor alone gives no clue as to the range condition. Range vegetation may be of high vigor on any range condition if the range is properly stocked.

The condition and amount of litter indicates whether a range is improving or deteriorating. If the litter is accumulating it usually is safe to assume that the range is improving. On the other hand, if there is no litter, or the amount of litter is declining, it can usually be assumed that the range is on the downgrade. The amount of litter alone, however, is not a safe basis on which to judge range condition. A properly-grazed, poor-condition range consisting mostly of invaders may have an abundance of litter.

Active erosion is usually associated with inadequate plant cover. Likewise, erosion scars usually are found where the total plant cover is increasing. The absence of erosion, however, does not necessarily indicate good or excellent condition. The plant cover may be composed mostly of annuals. It is generally true that ranges in excellent or good condition are less apt to erode than those in fair and poor condition.

The use of low-quality livestock, overstocking, or other poor management practices can easily offset the advantages accruing from excellent to good condition range. Returns may actually be greater from fair condition range where all management practices are in keeping with the condition of the forage than from good condition range where little or no attention is paid to these factors. However, when good management is practiced returns are usually greater from excellent condition range than from lower condition classes.

MEANING OF GRAZING CAPACITY

Forage production in western United States is subject to great annual variability because of weather. On perennial ranges production may vary threefold, and production of annual vegetation may vary tenfold from one year to another. Such variation requires either ultra-conservative use in productive years or flexibility in number of livestock from year to year.

Proper stocking is regarded as the largest cattle or sheep numbers that can graze each year on a given area of range, for a specific number of days, without causing a downward trend in forage production, forage quality, or soil. This is, in many ways, a wasteful method of determining rate of stocking because, if forage is to be adequate in years of low production, then there must be excessive amounts of ungrazed forage in years of high production. We have no reason to believe that overuse in one year can be compensated by underuse in another year; hence, stocking that would result in correct use in the average year does not appear to be the answer. Consequently, the general practice is to stock so as to prevent overuse of available forage in all but the most extreme drought. However, stocking should be heavy enough at all times to utilize the forage adequately.

In determining the stocking rate, it should be emphasized that some plants must remain on arid ranges when the range is fully used. This is absolutely necessary to plant welfare. Rainfall is not always sufficient to give enough regrowth of foliage to replenish food reserves. Another important point influencing grazing capacity is the lack of uniform distribution of livestock, especially cattle, over range of steep topography. Here, more accessible spots may be grazed to a dangerous degree before full use is made of less accessible forage. Hence, rate of stocking must be based upon the capacity of important accessible spots or "key areas" rather than upon the forage produced over the entire range.

RANGE CONDITION

Descriptions of range condition, which early herdsmen associated chiefly with weather, date back to Biblical times. In fact, effect of weather is so direct and obvious that other factors are frequently overlooked and even denied. Range students, of course, have recognized that long droughts cause changes, not only in the amount of but also in the botanical composition of the plant cover. They have also known and have presented evidence, both plant and soil, that ranges run down from misuse through both wet and dry years.

Stockmen have been slow to accept such evidence as a reason for adjustments in grazing, particularly since long experience has shown a constant and direct relation between weather, forage, and returns. Furthermore, with the same weather, differences in productivity were more readily charged to different kinds of rangeland than to different range conditions on the same kind of land. Acceptable evidence of improvement or decline, therefore, requires separating the effects of grazing from the effects of weather. It is also necessary to express qualitatively the effects of different grazing practices on the vegetation of different kinds of land.

DEVELOPMENT OF AN APPROACH

The effect of grazing on the condition of two kinds of ranges—an extensive natural prairie with clay soils and an extensive savannah (grassland containing scattered trees and drought-resistant undergrowth) with sandy soils —were studied over a 9-year period in the Southwest by the Soil Conservation Service. In each, comparable soils and climate made possible comparisons of undisturbed areas with areas having various grazing histories. The results, which permitted measurements of the degree of departure from climax, were used in the development of a suitable range inventory. This approach was based upon both research findings and upon tests of these findings over a wide range of conditions.

Although several methods of rating range condition have been and are used by various agencies, this qualitative-ecologic approach is now used by the Soil Conservation Service throughout the western United States in assisting ranchers to establish soil and water conservation programs.

DEFINITIONS AND APPLICABILITY

The term "rangeland" is applied to grassland areas with soil and climatic conditions which, through secondary plant succession, will lead to climax suitable for natural pasture. Thus area with prairie, savannah, or desertshrub climax are included, whereas areas with forest climax are excluded. The term "climax" refers to a relatively stable vegetation where plant succession is abreast of soil development. It is believed that classification of range conditions should be limited to ranges or natural pastures and should not be applied to tame pastures unless the object is the restoration of such areas to natural pasture. Natural plant succession operates to improve ranges, but on tame pastures the same process operates to replace the artificially established vegetation with natural vegetation. When there is not an adequate natural source of seed of successively higher species, seeding may be necessary even on natural pastures.

Wooded lands with forest climax should not be classified as *range* in various conditions but rather as *forests* in various conditions.

The term "condition" is used here as a "state of being." Because conditions may be changing, a report of condition always refers to a certain time. A practical classification of range condition must provide sufficient freedom within each class to permit inventory and mapping of range to potential condition, thus enabling a range manager to recognize an attainable goal.

Condition ratings are sometimes improperly applied to the "forage types" found. Forage types frequently themselves represent a condition. On one soil, in a given current sagebrush type, secondary succession (upward trend) may virtually eliminate sagebrush through moisture competition by climax grasses. On another soil, in the same current sagebrush type, the percentage of sagebrush may not be reduced by succession because it is the climax percentage for the site. The need for distinction between site and forage type is thus apparent. Since range condition should express departure from potential, delineation of sites must precede efforts to determine condition.

One must distinguish sharply between condition and trend. The term "trend" is used in the common sense, that is, "a general course or direction." Ecologically, upward trend is secondary succession, and downward trend is degeneration of the vegetation. Current trend must be known in order to adjust management intelligently. Thus, a change in trend due to seasonal drought may dictate an immediate but temporary reduction in livestock numbers.

Accelerated soil erosion—and conversely, soil stabilization—is generally associated with range condition. Both should be regarded, however, as features of trend rather than condition. For example, during an erosive summer rainstorm, some soil and even plants might be lost. After the storm, however, established plants might send out enough new shoots to re-establish the plants. The net change in soil or vegetation a few months after the storm might be too small to measure, and would provide no basis for a change in management; nor would a new range condition class be recognized, even though minor changes in condition would have occurred.

At the other extreme, a summer storm might erode virtually all the soil from a poorly managed mountain slope. In that case, even the basis for classifying the condition of the site would have changed. Prior to the storm a cover of perennial midgrasses might have been the climax. After the storm, the area might support little more than scattered annuals, and the presence of the annuals would represent excellent condition. Evidence of past erosion is evidence of past site modification. Range condition should be rated with respect to the greatest amount of vegetation the site can produce at the time of rating.

Current utilization has also been used as a factor in a downward trend and eventually in a lower condition class. Removal of livestock during the growing season, however, should result in an upward trend. Grazing of a pasture in alternate years will cause alternating upward and downward trends in the vegetation, but it is not reasonable to change the condition class each year.

PRINCIPLES AND PRACTICES

Under climax or original conditions, close relations existed between kinds of vegetation and kinds of soil in each climate. Now, however, the vegetation on most ranges also reflects grazing use. Under grazing, the vegetation deteriorates much more rapidly than the soil. By comparing the depth of the topsoil of grazed areas with those of areas in the same climate that retain climax or undisturbed vegetation, it is thus possible to determine the potential composition and forage production of the grazed sites.

Normally soil and vegetation develop in equilibrium up to a point limited by climate.

The interaction of soil and vegetation in normal development may be altered by grazing. The result is a "kind of vegetation" not in equilibrium with soil. The extent of this departure determines range condition. Since natural processes operate constantly to restore equilibrium, the natural processes alone, if permitted to operate, will in time restore the range to top condition.

A subsere is any completed succession after the first, or prairie. The time required for priseres (original natural succession leading to climax) is measured in centuries. Hence, the range manager is concerned primarily with subseres which restore equilibrium with soils already formed. Once equilibrium is restored, further development of vegetation is accompanied by soil development in a prairie.

A knowledge of the two extremes, of vegetation in equilibrium with the site at one end, to wholly unnatural vegetation, or bare soil at the other, is not sufficient. It is important also to measure the position of current range vegetation, i.e., range condition.

For this purpose prairie species have been divided into three groups—"decreasers," "increasers," and "invaders,"—the proportions of which provide a quantitative index of range condition. The decreasers and increasers are species found in the climax plant communities. Decreasers are those which, under grazing use, decrease from the percentage found in the climax. Increasers are characterized by a period of increase, after which they too may decrease. Invaders are species that enter plant communities as the climax vegetation is destroyed. Invaders cannot withstand the competition of the climax community. If invaders are present in the original vegetation, they occupy disturbed areas, such as mounds of burrowing animals.

Trends in relative amounts of the three groups of plants were used in developing an illustrated method of showing the course of degeneration, and hence, the nature of secondary succession to be expected on specific sites.

The course of degeneration may be arbitrarily divided into four condition classes—excellent, fair, good, and poor. The total of decreasers, increasers, and invaders is always 100 per cent. The percentage of decreasers plus the percentage of increasers up to, but not over, the percentage at climax provide a quantitative expression of current range condition. This sum is the portion of the current vegetation which is also present in the climax vegetation of the site. The sum is the complement of range condition, i.e., range deterioration. A site may have various kinds of vegetation when in poor condition, but with plant succession, these converge to the climax kind of vegetation.

In using this system, field men make a preliminary study of pastures and remains of climax species, taking advantage of such local research information as is available. For each site they prepare lists of decreasers and invaders. The increasers are then listed with their known maximum relative coverage in the climax for each site. This provides sufficient data for application of the method.

It has been found practical to estimate relative coverage of decreasers, increasers, and invaders to the nearest 5 per cent, based on the total of all foliage produced in average years. Relative amounts of various species are always more certain evidence of position in the subsere than is the density of total vegetation. It should be emphasized that annuals, as well as treetops beyond the reach of livestock in savannahs, must be included in the estimates of the relative amounts of decreasers, increasers, and invaders. Increase or invasion by annuals and woody plants are common results of range destruction.

To check forage production on range in each condition class, a two-foot quadrant can be laid out. The vegetation inside the quadrant is clipped and weighed. Litter in this same quadrant should be collected and weighed to find out how much is being returned to the soil to decay and be incorporated as humus. These weights reflect the accumulated amount of litter but not the exact amount returned in any one year.

Grass production can be increased several times by properly managing a range to bring it back to excellent condition.

CORRECT STOCKING OF RANGE IMPORTANT

Correct use of the grasslands holds the key to maximum sustained livestock production. It is also the way to obtain the forage growth needed to provide adequate protection for the land from falling raindrops.

According to a Soil Conservation Service report, a rancher in Coke County, Texas, produced more pounds of lamb and wool from 200 ewes per section than was previously obtained from 250 ewes pastured per section on the same land. The 200 ewes, managed under a system in which grazing was deferred in spring, and then pastured on a rotation system, produced lambs with an average weight of 71 pounds. This is 24 pounds greater than the average weight (47 pounds) of the lambs from the ewes grazing at the rate of 250 per section.

On a sheep and cattle ranch near Presidio, Texas, heavy stocking with light-weight ewes resulted in a low lamb crop and a lowered total production of livestock products. The rancher reduced the number of animals by approximately 30 per cent and was rewarded with higher yields, increased lamb crops (90 per cent compared with 65 per cent), and higher calf crops. The division of large pastures into several smaller pastures permits correct seasonal use, which is one of the important management practices for maintaining range in good to excellent condition.

The proportion of annual growth of forage that is harvested by livestock is an all-important factor in the maintenance of plant vigor. Plants must have adequate leaf surface and rest periods, in order to stay strong and vigorous. A vigorous growth of palatable plants gives assurance that the livestock will receive the nutrients essential for greatest growth.

Destruction of too much top growth by excessive grazing is the first step in causing range deterioration. Decadence is hurried along by other developments that make it difficult for the better forage plants to survive. The invasion by less desirable plants is an indicator of range decadence. Management practices that permit desirable plants to carry on their normal growth functions are essential to the restoration and maintenance of desirable forage species and highest sustained production of livestock.

SEASON OF USE OF FORAGE IMPORTANT

The season of use may have as important an influence on the maintenance of ranges as does the intensity with which individual species in the plant community are grazed. The danger of use too early in spring is well known. The amount of use in the fall may be equally important. Although it is generally thought that the perennial grasses are immune to damage during their period of dormancy, studies reveal that growth actually is in process throughout the year and that damage may be as extensive during the so-called dormant stage as during the early stages of seasonal growth.

In the case of blue grama, fall may be a more critical period than spring, due to the fact that the roots and buds are getting set for growth during the next season. This being the case, fall deferment assumes great importance in the management of range land. Blue grama ranges rarely have an appreciable amount of reproduction from seedlings, and the seedlings rarely develop into plants. Blue grama develops new shoots readily, however, and management should be directed at encouraging this process. Ranges in fair or poor condition should be given longer rest periods than those in good or excellent condition, in order to restore the productive capacity of the desired forage species. In many instances, even moderate grazing should be delayed through the growing season and in the fall until danger of disrupting the normal growth processes is at a minimum.

ADJUST GRAZING LOAD TO FLUCTUATION IN FORAGE PRODUCTION

Variable factors common to the range country make difficult the adjustment of grazing use currently to coincide with annual fluctuations in forage production. A system that appears to offer a practical solution to this problem is being employed by a number of ranchers. It consists of adjusting the size of the breeding herd to the forage production anticipated during a year of low rainfall, and to other factors that may contribute to below-average production. During years when a surplus of forage is produced, calves may be carried over to utilize the forage. Marketing of dry cattle and culling of inferior stock are logical steps in making the initial adjustment.

Experiences during the recent drought in the range country of the Southwest attests the soundness of such a program. Throughout the ranching country are ranchmen who have brought their herds and grass through the greatest drought in Texas history in almost miraculous manner. Table 58 gives the livestock production record of the 10,000-acre ranch owned and managed by Edwin Sawyer, at Sonora, Texas.

It is remarkable that Sawyer's lamb, wool and beef production held almost the same from 1948 to 1953. The last four years were extremely dry.

The reason for this unusal success is due, says E. B. Keng of Sonora, Area Conservationist for the Soil Conservation Service, to the kind of grassland management that Sawyer has been using for several years. Ac-

TABLE 58. Livestock production on the Edwin Sawyer Ranch at Sonora, Texas, 1948 to 1953*

Year	Inches	Number of sheep	Per cent lamb crop	Pounds of lamb (Total)	Average weight lambs (Total)	Date Sold	Total pounds wool	Cattle number	Per cent calf crop	Average weight calves (Pounds)
1948	23.33	2057	85	57420	58	6-18	16338	92	90	504
1949	36.72	1906	94	67720	62	6-14	15177	104	92	495
1950	13.15	1924	104	86144	66	8-18	13336	91	94	446
1951	8.82	1907	92	65769	61	8-1	15830	97	91	373
1952	10.92	2034	77	65089	65	7-16	16107	98	91	506
1953	6.19[a]	1647	102	74763	66	7-1	13660	92	88	460

* Keng, E. B. Soil Conservation Service. Unpublished data.
[a] 1953 rainfall: 6.19 inches late into summer.

cording to Keng, Sawyer gave his range good care prior to the drought. As a result, the range continued producing on the scanty rains that fell during the four severe drought years. Sawyer's grass was hurt during the dry spell, but sufficient good grass remained on the ground to regrass the range when good rains resumed.

DEFERRED GRAZING INCREASES FORAGE PRODUCTION

Deferred grazing, or the delayed use of forage on portions of the range, provides a practicable system of increasing forage production. Buffalo grass will yield as much as 20 per cent more forage when grazing is deferred from 6 to 8 weeks during the growth period. The additional feed resulting from this practice is a significant contribution toward the production of higher yields.

Buffalo grass and other plants of similar growth habits, such as curly mesquite, respond most favorably to relatively short periods of grazing deferment. Blue grama, sideoats, and the bluestems make their greatest contribution of forage when deferment is for a longer period.

Tobosa, threeawn, and black grama have pecularities unlike the plants mentioned previously. They are attractive to livestock for only short periods during the year. In mixtures with more palatable plants, these less preferred plants are not fully utilized. When they occur in appreciable quantities, they may be isolated for use during the brief periods when they are most succulent. Otherwise, the plants with higher palatabilities may be grazed excessively while the less preferred plants are given opportunity to increase and make up a larger part of the plant community.

Essential to good range management is knowledge of the kind and amount of forage available, the seasonal development of the forage plants, and the time and intensity of harvest to which the plants can be subjected without reducing the maximum yield of forage for livestock production. These are fundamental considerations in planning the use of the rangelands in order that the ranges may yield their highest continued production.

MANAGEMENT OF RESEEDED RANGES

Much progress has been made during the last 20 years in seeding perennial grasses and legumes on submarginal and adapted areas of rundown ranges. Unfortunately, however, the tendency to graze the grass before the seedings are well established, and to graze them too early in the season, too closely and for too long a period, causes the early loss of some good to excellent stands.

Experience has shown that, first, it pays to protect carefully new seedings from all grazing until the young plants have developed good roots to anchor themselves and effectively resist the pulling effects of grazing. Usually this will be from one to two years after seeding. Second, the seeded grasses are just about as delicate as the important native perennial bunch grasses. Neither will hold up very long under excessive use. This is true especially if grazing begins early and continues throughout the spring and early summer grazing seasons. The new growth of the more palatable grasses, closely grazed in early spring, will be repeatedly grazed throughout the growing season. This continuous grazing prevents the storage of needed food reserves in the roots, exhausts the stored food, and results in early starvation and death of the plants.

Management practices that apply equally well to seeded and native perennial bunch-grass ranges, and which together make up the range improvement program, naturally fall into three groups, i.e., grass or forage management practices, facilitating or enabling practices, and special forage improvement practices.

GRASS OR FORAGE MANAGEMENT PRACTICES

Grass and forage management practices must be used on both seeded and native perennial grass ranges if yields are to be maintained. These practices include rotation and deferred grazing, proper use of grasses, and fire prevention and control.

Rotation and deferred grazing are regarded as the most important management practices. If properly used they will (a) allow the livestock to harvest each year's forage crop with the least disturbance to normal plant growth, (b) make it possible for the plants to store up needed food reserves in their roots each year for survival during the dormant season and to permit good growth the following winter or spring, and (c) make it possible for the important grasses to produce seed.

Rotation and deferred grazing on ranges grazed during the spring and fall, or during the spring, summer, and fall, work most effectively on 3, 4, 5, or 6 pastures of equal forage-production capacity. Two-pasture systems work quite effectively on summer range.

Proper utilization of seeded and native perennial forage grasses safeguards their vigor, assures maximum production, and lessens the hazards imposed by steep slopes and unstable soils. Proper utilization levels permit the accumulation of sufficient residues to protect the soil from splash erosion and to increase water intake. This increased supply of water assures higher forage production. Benefits resulting from continued proper utilization of forage grasses are cumulative in effect. That is, they improve with time.

The occurrence of fires can easily undo all the gains made from reseeding, rotation and deferred grazing, and proper utilization.

FACILITATING OR ENABLING PRACTICES

The adoption of certain facilitating and enabling practices is essential to successful forage management programs. These include provision of an adequate water supply, fencing, and proper placing of salt.

An ample, clean, and dependable supply of stock water is of major importance in grass management. The water should be well located in each seeded and native pasture and be ample to water the herd daily during each of the grazing periods. A poor water supply in any one pasture usually complicates or prevents the use of an effective rotation-deferred system of grazing. Springs, ponds, and wells may be used to supply water.

Planned fencing, especially on cattle ranches, is the key to the control of livestock numbers on any pasture. The periods and degree of grazing in each of the rotation and deferred pastures should be governed by the condition of the forage.

New seedings must be protected from grazing until they are well established. On cattle ranches, protection usually requires the construction of either temporary or permanent fences. Permanent fences are expensive, and should be built only on pasture boundaries that are designed to fit into the desired long-time rotation and deferred grazing system. New seedings may then be protected by temporary fences wherever they cover only a part of a pasture.

On sheep ranches, new seedings can be protected by herding flocks of sheep away from seeded areas. A very effective rotation and deferred system of grazing can frequently be carried out on sheep ranches without fences. This is especially true on ranges that are divided into natural grazing units by such topographic barriers as streams and prominent ridges.

The well-known practice of placing salt away from water in the least-used parts of the range should be applied to new seedings.

Building up and using enough winter feed reserves to keep the stock off the range for about 25 days in early spring makes it possible to delay grazing of the reseeded areas each year until they are ready for grazing. Extra feed to use for about 20 days in the fall also makes it possible to remove the stock from seedings in the event early rains make the ground too unstable for grazing without damage to the grass.

SPECIAL FORAGE IMPROVEMENT PRACTICES

Brush eradication and control, range fertilization (especially annual crops), and reseeding are three special forage improvement practices that are increasing in importance.

A number of varieties of brush invade new seedings and old stands, even under light grazing. Thus far mechanical means of control have not generally proved practical. Some of the chemicals now in use offer more promise.

Successful stands of perennial grass and legumes in central and southern California have been established because good cultural practices were used and nitrogenous and phosphate fertilizers were applied after a year of establishment. Fertilization of native perennial grasses is as yet a relatively new field. It promises to become more important as the years pass.

Good production management of seedings begins before they are made.

The best sites should be selected for the first seedings. Either an existing pasture that has deep, fertile soils and is in a rundown condition, or a site that can be developed into a new and practical pasture may be seeded. Seeding of abandoned croplands has proved satisfactory in many instances. The soils usually are deeper than the average range soils and the chances for success are good. Areas for seeding should be large enough to justify establishing the facilities necessary for proper grass management.

Where new seedings are mixed with native range, they should be extensive enough for an economical unit. This will encourage the rancher to protect them in his grazing management program.

The degree of grazing use of seeded and native forage species varies from 30 to 70 per cent. The safe degree of use depends on the important (key) grass species, stability of the soil, slopes, periods of grazing, and other factors affecting the safe use of forage.

EVALUATING RANGE FORAGE

More net profit can be made from conservative grazing than from a method of grazing where the best forage plants are continually nubbed to the ground. Keeping the grazing use in line with the grass yield produces more pounds of animal products from fewer animals than when the range is overstocked. As a result of this discovery, the Soil Conservation Service developed a method for determining the grazing capacity of rangeland. This is known as the "range-condition method." Under this method, the range is classified as to range condition by ecological types.

Each major plant association generally represents an ecological climax, but all areas within the climax may not have the same production possibilities. As the classification is designed to indicate the relative productivity of different range areas, types that differ in potential productivity must be separately described.

The value of rangelands commonly varies in proportion to the amount of forage produced. This forage production can be expressed as range condition—in general the higher the forage production, the better the range condition.

Certain factors such as forage composition, erosion, litter accumulation, and forage density differ in the several condition classes. As some of these differences can readily be seen or measured, range condition is determined by analyzing and segregating these factors. A score sheet or guide has been developed for the rapid classification of all the ranges of this type.

EXCELLENT CONDITION RANGES

Ranges in excellent condition do not need restoration because they already are producing all the forage possible under the existing climate. The plant cover protects the soil from abnormal erosion and maintains the fertility. The better forage plants—particularly the deeper-rooted perennial grasses—predominate, although there are some palatable weeds and shrubs on some ranges. Better plants reproduce well in favorable years. Some litter covers the ground, and the topsoil is loose and friable, containing dark organic matter—more in areas of high rainfall than in the semideserts. The soil is

FIGURE 109. Excellent condition range in Amarillo, Texas.
(Soil Conservation Service)

FIGURE 110. Good condition range. The light-colored area in the foreground is sand that has blown in from an adjoining cultivated field. (Terry County, Texas)
(Soil Conservation Service)

porous and readily absorbs large amounts of moisture. The runoff water is clear. In other words, ranges in excellent condition serve every purpose as fully as possible.

GOOD CONDITION RANGES

Ranges in good condition are generally satisfactory although they produce less forage than those in excellent condition. The better perennial plants predominate, but there are some less palatable plants. The plant cover is thinner. Usually there is less litter and the topsoil may contain less organic matter. Erosion, if it occurs at all, is slight. Ranges in good condition offer an opportunity to increase production and value through conservative grazing and other management practices that encourage the more palatable plants. The job of restoration is not difficult or time consuming, as the better forage plants and soil are still there for quick improvement.

FAIR CONDITION RANGES

Ranges in fair condition are definitely unsatisfactory. The climax cover has been disturbed so severely that restoration may be a slow process. Valuable forage plants are considerably reduced in stand, their place occupied either by bare soil or less palatable perennial grasses, weeds, and shrubs. Annuals have usually increased. There is less total plant cover and litter. If there is not sufficient plant cover (2,000 lbs. per acre) there is likely to be active erosion, particularly on the slopes. In the latter case the dark topsoil layer may be seriously disturbed. It may contain only moderate amounts of organic matter and have only fair capacity to absorb and hold available moisture. The exposed surface of clay and silt soils may be hard and crusted. Runoff water may be loaded with silt. If neglected, fair ranges slip quickly to a poor condition. When handled carefully, they can gradually be restored. Reseeding is often practicable.

POOR CONDITION RANGES

Ranges in poor condition have lost so much of the forage stand and in some cases so much of their topsoil that they produce only a fraction of the forage grown on similar ranges in good or excellent condition. Few of the more valuable perennial forage plants remain, and low-value annuals or perennial weeds and shrubs, such as snakeweed, juniper and mesquite, may predominate. In extreme cases, removel of topsoil by washing or blowing may have exposed the subsoil or left a gravel "pavement." In this case the soil may have little organic matter and a low moisture-holding capacity. There may be active splash erosion and some gully erosion. Runoff may be rapid and heavy with silt. The job of restoring poor range to full productivity is a major one. Years, even decades, may be required gradually to build back the organic matter in the topsoil that marks satisfactory condition. Where soil and moisture conditions permit, ranges in poor condition should be reseeded to adapted forage species, to hasten recovery.

For a more rapid method of determining the composition and degree of use of range vegetation, Osborn developed the "frequency tally." The frequency tally is based on a count of a random sample of individual plants,

FIGURE 111. Fair condition range. (Pecos, Texas)
(Soil Conservation Service)

FIGURE 112. Poor condition range. (Breckenridge, Texas)
(Soil Conservation Service)

358 Conservation Practices

grazed. Composition is calculated as the percentage frequency of occurrence of each species. Percentage of use for each species is computed as the
total of the percentage of plants of this species fully grazed. Weighted average percentages of actual use and proper use are computed to indicate the
existing degree of use of the sample. Both grassland and browse, or a combination of these, can be evaluated by this method.

REFERENCES

1. Allred, B. W. 1951. *Range handbook—Series I.* USDA, SCS.
2. Campbell, R. S., Ellison, L., and Renner, F. G. 1948. *Management that restores the range.* USDA Yearbook of Agriculture: Grass, 221-226.
3. Humphrey, R. R. 1946. *Range condition: A classification of the sand-bunchgrass range in East Benton Soil Conservation District.* USDA, Pacific Coast Region. (Multi.)
4. ———. 1947. *Build your range and use it too!* Western Livestock Jour., 25(23): 28-29, 78-80.
5. ———. 1947. *Range forage evaluation by range condition method.* Jour. Forestry, 45(1): 10-16.
6. ———. 1949. *An analysis of forage utilization methods and a proposal for utilization surveys by range condition classes.* Jour. Forestry, 47(7): 549-561.
7. Marsh, V., and Humphrey, R. R. 1946. *Range conditions: A classification of the scabland bunch grass type in the Palouse Rock Lake Soil Conservation District.* USDA, Pacific Coast Region. (Multi.)
8. Osborn, B. 1947. *A guide to degree of range use in southwest Texas.* The Cattleman, 34(5): 124-126.
9. ———. 1947. *Determining range utilization by frequency tallies.* Jour. Soil and Water Cons., 2(1): 51-55.
10. ———. 1949. *Range cover tames the raindrop—A summary of range cover evaluation, 1949.* USDA, SCS.
11. ———. 1952. *Range soil conditions influence water intake.* Jour. Soil and Water Cons., 7(3): 126.
12. Pearse, C. K., Plummer, A. P., and Savage, D. A. 1948. *Restoring the range by reseeding.* USDA Yearbook of Agriculture: Grass, 227-233.
13. Smith, H. N. 1949. *Range cover evaluations in Edwards Plateau and Trans-Pecos areas.* USDA Range Memo. 37, Fort Worth, Texas.
14. White, W. T., Frandsen, W. R., and Jensen, C. V. 1948. *Planning range conservation.* USDA Yearbook of Agriculture: Grass, 217-221.
15. Woolfolk, E. J., Costello, D. F., and Allred, B. W. 1951. *The major range types.* USDA Yearbook of Agriculture: Grass, 205-211.

Woodland Farming

The increased demand for wood products, together with the pressing need for finding profitable use for much of our severely eroded and abandoned lands, is focusing attention more and more on woodland farming.

INCOME FROM FARM WOODLAND

At present, 100 million dollars' worth of wood products are sold from farm lands each year. Actual records on Norris-Doxy farm forestry management projects are beginning to show how management can increase the revenue from farm woodland. Most farms still sell standing timber, rather than processed products. Very few, even among those who are managing their woodlands intensively, have begun to cut each year or periodically as much wood as grows. Therefore, average incomes reported for farm forestry projects only indicate what farmers will receive by managing their woodlands as they do their fields. Table 59 shows accomplishments from Norris-Doxy farm forestry projects for the fiscal year (F. Y.) 1953.

Based on information now available, the Forestry Division of the Department of Conservation of Tennessee formulated the following estimates of the income that could be expected from a one-acre pine plantation where 1,000 seedlings were planted. A survival of 850 trees was expected. An additional 85 trees were expected to be lost by suppression and culling, leaving a net stand of 765 trees at 12 years of age.

All prices used represent stumpage value.

First thinning at 12 years
Total number of trees—765	Yield—430 posts @ 1½ ¢	$ 6.45	
Cut 215 trees			
			$ 6.45

Second thinning at 18 years
Total number of trees—550	Yield—200 posts @ 1¼ ¢	3.00	
Cut 230 trees	5 cds. pulp @ $3	15.00	
			18.00

Third thinning at 24 years
Total number of trees—320	Yield—100 posts @ 1½ ¢	1.50	
Cut 105 trees	8 cds. pulp @ $3	24.00	
			25.50

Fourth cut at 30 years
Total number of trees—215	Yield—4500 bd. ft. @ $15	67.50	
Cut 85 trees	2 cds. pulp @ $3	6.00	
			73.50

Fifth cut at 40 years
Total number of trees—130	Yield—6400 bd. ft. @ $20	128.00	
Cut 50 trees	2 cds. pulp @ $3	6.00	
			134.00

Final harvest at 50 years
| Cut 80 trees | Yield—21,600 bd. ft. @ $25 | 540.00 | |
| | Total gross return | | $797.45 |

Less—land purchase $15 and planting costs $10 @ 5% interest $286.69

Less—Taxes, etc.—25¢ per year at 5% interest 52.34

Total cost $339.03

Net profit . . . . . . $458.42   Annual net profit $9.17

PROTECTION AGAINST LOSS OF SOIL AND WATER

Well-managed woods help protect the individual farmer from loss of soil and water, and from loss caused by deposits of sediments. Studies by the experiment station of the Soil Conservation Service near Zanesville, Ohio, showed that the annual water loss from an acre of forested land averaged only one-ninth as much as from an acre of cultivated land. A 6-year study at the Guthrie, Oklahoma, Soil Conservation Experiment Station showed the average yearly runoff from old-growth woodland with a 5.17 per cent slope was only 0.2 per cent. From soil with a 7.7 per cent slope planted continuously to cotton, the runoff was 14.22 per cent. The yearly soil loss was 0.017 ton per acre from the old-growth woodland and 24.29 tons per acre from the cotton land.

TABLE 59. Cooperative forest management accomplishments and expenditures* (fiscal year 1953)

State	No. of projs. (Total)	Accomplishments				Expenditures		
		Woodland owners assisted	Woodland involved	Products harvested	Gross sale value	Federal	State	Total
		Number	Acres	M bd. ft.	Dollars	Dollars	Dollars	Dollars
Alabama.....	9	724	93,305	20,981	604,774	21,240	21,495	42,735
Arkansas.....	2	111	17,582	673	13,005	3,592	3,592	7,184
California....	7	645	132,666	34,346	332,143	8,293	37,759	46,052
Colorado.....	1	85	6,873	783	8,693	2,123	2,124	4,247
Connecticut...	4	586	27,724	2,816	48,752	9,800	17,876	27,676
Delaware	1	6	260	10	200	1,200	1,272	2,472
Florida......	12	1,469	748,066	36,451	618,118	22,508	41,759	64,267
Georgia	10	737	191,862	19,565	455,358	21,008	26,269	47,277
Idaho.......	3	34	7,982	38	1,140	2,500	2,580	5,080
Illinois......	12	749	24,300	2,930	95,269	24,065	83,362	107,427
Indiana......	9	985	42,203	5,744	186,144	12,552	49,798	62,350
Iowa	4	391	12,500	1,850	58,810	7,491	18,223	25,714
Kentucky	8	334	22,373	3,335	58,047	18,000	19,803	37,803
Louisiana	5	170	16,356	2,342	80,503	13,500	14,846	28,346
Maine	9	1,639	63,241	10,182	207,075	18,200	29,601	47,801
Maryland	10	1,871	34,506	12,561	280,524	18,000	46,070	64,070
Massachusetts..	2	413	14,779	4,504	66,932	5,464	7,999	13,463
Michigan	7	755	14,657	8,588	247,776	19,973	42,638	62,611
Minnesota....	6	518	15,888	4,304	145,417	9,378	22,725	32,103
Mississippi....	5	393	82,720	4,540	93,695	13,783	14,813	28,596
Missouri	12	1,393	182,764	8,582	280,189	27,174	47,959	75,133
New Hampshire	8	1,199	50,703	20,065	417,471	18,350	21,805	40,155
New Jersey...	1	538	70,151	5,474	97,133	13,099	34,030	47,129
New York....	14	2,993	216,776	31,292	768,017	19,100	99,329	118,429
North Carolina	10	1,079	98,034	27,598	802,094	24,876	38,677	63,553
North Dakota..	1	52	4,245	685	42,090	2,810	3,157	5,967
Ohio.......	12	1,286	49,716	6,394	186,034	12,445	66,794	79,239
Oklahoma....	2	104	294	—	—	632	632	1,264
Oregon......	4	647	29,732	30,657	746,902	8,478	20,772	29,250
Rhode Island ..	1	175	16,696	35	219	2,500	3,209	5,709
South Carolina	9	903	101,867	20,521	636,532	18,637	31,145	49,782
Tennessee	6	488	32,771	10,183	328,433	16,250	16,819	33,069
Texas.......	6	516	46,517	1,209	19,869	11,762	11,762	23,524
Vermont	12	3,002	77,432	26,283	662,916	28,600	54,661	83,261
Virginia	9	1,682	156,824	131,389	3,098,043	29,500	105,218	134,718
Washington ...	6	672	29,620	16,317	321,229	11,338	13,410	24,748
West Virginia..	13	1,654	46,468	6,173	156,608	18,800	34,162	52,962
Wisconsin	10	1,476	47,256	8,019	423,389	23,513	68,018	91,531
Total U.S.....	262	32,474	2,827,709	527,419	12,589,543	540,534	1,176,163	1,716,697
U.S. Summary								
F.Y. 1940 }a						4,793	8,284	13,077
F.Y. 1941 }	9	165	49,416	2,667	31,483	15,342	17,120	32,462
F.Y. 1942	10	224	92,442	10,076	125,307	18,171	19,579	37,750
F.Y. 1943	75	3,242	359,388	75,600	1,043,878	101,076	111,559	212,635
F.Y. 1944	98	8,842	742,697	323,557	3,962,784	187,316	212,209	399,525
F.Y. 1945	100	8,093	831,347	411,330	4,476,354	199,995	230,865	430,860
F.Y. 1946	156	12,083	1,321,746	452,367	6,092,499	315,441	369,065	684,506
F.Y. 1947	153	13,531	1,576,888	502,312	7,805,105	344,720	449,626	794,346
F.Y. 1948	169	14,220	1,399,971	503,641	7,668,499	353,179	467,129	820,308
F.Y. 1949	179	17,140	1,769,240	437,903	7,721,865	349,117	573,882	922,999
F.Y. 1950	227	22,828	2,542,564	518,566	9,421,220	538,812	726,973	1,265,785
F.Y. 1951	243	25,352	2,558,091	721,938	15,941,940	548,608	886,250	1,434,858
F.Y. 1952	252	27,933	2,501,317	609,562	13,924,940	537,160	985,902	1,523,062
Total		186,127	18,572,816	5,096,938	10,805,417	4,054,264	6,234,606	10,288,870

* 262 Projects

a F.Y. 1940 and F.Y. 1941 accomplishments combined.

The increased interest in woodland farming has stimulated interest in determining the factors most influential in the production of trees.

It has been found that an ample supply of moisture is a major requirement for profitable tree production. Furthermore, it has been shown that adequate moisture supplies are associated with two specific characteristics of the soil: the depth of the topsoil or A horizon, and the water-holding capacity of the subsoil or B horizon.

The depth of the topsoil determines to a large extent the area for root development. The water-holding capacity of the subsoil determines the amount of moisture, in addition to that in the topsoil, available for tree production. These two factors, when combined, determine the suitability of a given soil to the growth of trees. This is referred to as *site quality*—the potential capacity of the soil to produce trees.

SITE QUALITY

Knowledge of site quality is basic to proper management of woodland for both the establishment of new stands and the most economical management of established stands. It also enables the operator to determine intelligently where tree planting and other intensive management will be desirable and practical. Knowledge of site quality is especially needed for denuded lands and lands that may have agricultural value, so that a wise choice can be made as to their use. Knowledge of site quality of established stands enables the manager to estimate with a fair degree of accuracy the volume of wood products he may expect to harvest during a specific period of growth.

Several investigators have endeavored to develop a method for determining site quality. Some have succeeded in developing one that is applicable to establish stands of a particular species. These are only applicable to the species and conditions under which they were developed and must be used by one trained in forestry. What is needed is a method of site-quality determination applicable to any site, whether trees are present or not, and usable by a person with little or no forestry training.

SOIL PROPERTIES AND SITE INDEX*

Numerous studies have been made on the relationship between various soil properties or profile characteristics and the rate of growth or site index of forest stands. In the United States most of these studies have been made east of the Great Plains region.

NORTHEAST

Haig reported on a study of the relation between the site index of young red-pine plantations in Connecticut and the "colloidal" content of the various soil horizons. He found that the site index of red pine increased as the percentage of the finer fractions (silt plus clay) increased in the A horizon. Presumably the textural grades of the A horizons studied ranged from sands to loams, and the textural profiles of the soils were not greatly differentiated. Haig's data indicate that red pine has higher site index on sandy loam and loam soils than on loamy sand or sands in Connecticut.

---

* Total height of dominant trees when 50 years of age.

This generality also holds in the Lake States region, where it has been found that jack pine does better on the coarser soils than either red pine or white pine. Later, Hicock and his colleagues reported on another study of the relationship between soil properties and the site index of young red-pine plantations in Connecticut. The plantations were from 12 to 30 years of age and occurred on a rather wide range of soil types. They found a low degree of correlation between site index and individual soil attributes such as soil series, texture, and the character of the A_0 horizon and the subsoil. No relation was found between the acidity of any soil horizon and site index of red pine. Silt plus clay content of the A horizon showed a fairly good correlation with site index for values of silt plus clay up to 25 per cent. This was in line with Haig's results.

Total nitrogen content of the A horizon showed a better correlation with site index than did any other factor analyzed. With respect to total nitrogen content of the surface soil in this study it should be appreciated that other factors of the soil-site and vegetation complex affect it; for example, soil nitrogen should increase with increasingly favorable moisture conditions for the growth of vegetation and the subsequent decay of organic matter formed by the vegetation.

It is believed that the absence of stronger correlations between site index of red pine and soil characteristics in the studies of Haig and of Hicock was due to the age of the plantations—that is, under 30 years. It is probable that subsoil characteristics, parent material, and the moisture regimen as influenced by topography are most effective in conditioning growth of forest stands after they have reached the developmental stage when competition for growing space, moisture, and nutrients becomes marked, or after 20 or 30 years. Unless forest stands are greatly overstocked when they start, they do not develop a conspicious concentration of small roots near the surface until they are 20 to 25 years old. When this concentration of surface roots (which can be called a forest soil *root-profile*) occurs, competition for moisture and nutrients during the growing season may also occur, and trees must depend partly on roots at lower depths in the soil and substratum for the absorption of water. If subsoil or substratum characteristics or the relative topographic position is such as to be unfavorable for root growth, then the growth of the trees is reduced when the roots in the surface-soil zone compete strongly for growth materials.

Hicock also studied the relation between the composition of natural mixed hardwoods and soil types and soil properties in Connecticut. He found no strong correlation between the occurrence of the various species. and the soil factors. In the case of lesser vegetation he found that both the frequency and total numbers of plants were higher on moist soils than on drier soils. He did not find any plants that were good indicators of soil types.

McKinnon and his associates made a survey of the composition and stocking of cutover old-field white-pine lands in central New England and concluded that very light soils should be planted (presumably to pine) or allowed to grow hardwoods for cordwood, whereas the two better sites should be managed for hardwoods for sawlogs.

Lunt reported on the relation between certain chemical characteristics of the surface soil to a depth of 5 inches and the site index of even-aged stands of oak in Connecticut. Essentially no correlation was discovered between site index of the oak and various soil characteristics associated with fertility, namely: total nitrogen, exchangeable calcium, available potassium and phosphorus, and total exchangeable bases. This lack of correlation between the fertility factors and site index would be expected if no great difference between inherent chemical composition of the soils occurred. Under such circumstances, the composition of the surface soil would be conditioned primarily by the stand composition of the oak forest. In this study no observations were made on soil-profile characteristics or physical properties. Although apparently no quantitative data were obtained on topography, Lunt concluded that there was a relationship between site index and topography, the best sites being on lower slopes. That lower slopes afford better growth conditions than upper slopes or ridges is more or less true for all tree species that grow in well-drained soils, because of better moisture relations.

Donahue studied tree growth as related to soil morphology in the Adirondack region of New York. He made stand tables and collected height and radial growth data on four one-acre plots in each of four forest types: northern hardwood, spruce-hardwood, spruce flat, and spruce swamp. One soil well 10 feet long was dug to a depth of root penetration (3 to 5 feet) in each of the 16 plots. These wells afforded information on profile characteristics, texture of the various horizons, data on pH, and the amount of stone in the soil. Donahue found no difference in the mechanical composition of the mineral soil horizons in the various types. The hardwood-forest type was on Essex sandy loam, brown podsolic soil, whereas the spruce-hardwood and spruce-flat forest types were on Beckett sandy loam, a podsol. The spruce-swamp soil was peat over sand. Total height of dominant and co-dominant trees (uneven-aged stands) arranged the forest types in the following order of productivity: hardwoods>spruce-hardwood>spruce flat>spruce swamp.

Donahue's results with respect to radial growth of the important species were as follows:

Species	*Forest Type*
Sugar maple:	hardwood > spruce-hardwood.
Beech:	no significant variation with forest type.
Yellow birch:	spruce-hardwood > hardwood > spruce swamp >spruce flat.
Spruce:	spruce flat > spruce-hardwood >spruce swamp.
Balsam fir:	spruce flat > spruce swamp.

This work may not show the relationship between inherent and permanent features of the soil and tree growth in the Adirondacks. Excluding the spruce swamp, which represents a special case, the soil-profile features reported in the other three forest types are results of the presence of a combination of species whose organic matter, upon decomposing, produced characteristic soil-profile features. In the spruce-flat and spruce-hardwood types the organic matter decomposed slowly and incompletely, forming a relatively thick H layer, a podsol zone, and a zone of accumulation, presumably of humus in the B_1 and iron and alumina in the B_2; whereas the northern hardwood-forest type produced organic matter that decomposed rapidly and relatively completely with less acid decomposition products, and as a result only a relatively small amount of humus was found on the surface and a discernible podsol zone was not present.

Hall pointed out the advantages of favoring pitch pine on the sandy soil of Cape Cod because of its resistance to gipsy moth defoliation as compared with other species. Moreover, pitch pine was found to grow faster on the light, sandy soils than even Scotch pine.

Heiberg observed marked response in growth of red pine and white pine to surface applications of organic matter, both A_0 horizon material and slash, on infertile deep sands in the Adirondacks of New York. As well as increasing water-holding capacity, it is evident that the organic matter supplied some significant fertility factor because the response was evident the first year after application of green slash. Heiberg states that height growth of commonly planted forest trees in New York State is greater on mull than on mor. This relationship can best be explained by pointing out that the favorable soil-site factors conducive to mull formation are causally related to rapid tree growth—good physical soil properties, and favorable moisture and aeration. Of course, extremely sterile sands may also be deficient in mineral nutrients.

The inherent productivity of the wind-blown sandy soils derived from water-deposited sands of glacial origin in parts of the Northeast is extremely low. These soils are comparable in some respects to the sandhills of the Southeast and the deep sands of Michigan. In the Northeast, when such soils were cleared for either cultivation or pasture, wind erosion frequently developed; their productivity for forest plantations was further reduced because of the reduction in organic matter. Alpeter, working in Vermont, found mulches of organic matter such as manure, straw, hay, weeds, or tree slash to increase both survival and growth of conifers on these wind-blown sands. His observations are in accordance with those of Heiberg in the Adirondacks and of Wilde and Patzer in Wisconsin.

Diebold studied in a qualitative manner some of the relationships between soil types and forest-site quality in the Northeastern Appalachian Plateau of east-central and south-central New York. The soils of the region are derived from glacial deposits; they are genetically young and strongly influenced by the nature of the parent material, which may be acid or alkaline. Sugar maple and beech were found throughout the area along with other species. On the basis of types of humus layers and occurrence of wind throw, he concluded that deep, well-drained soils with an alkaline influence in the subsoil were best for the natural hardwood forests, whereas shallow soils and those with poor internal drainage as evidenced by subsoil mottling were of low quality for the local hardwoods. Donahue observed that poor internal drainage was related to failures or to poor growth in coniferous plantations.

Studies of the relationship of depth to water table in various soils in south-central New York as it was influenced by kinds of soil were made by Diebold and later reported by Spaeth and Diebold. Although they observed that occurrence of roots was markedly affected by the presence of a water table in the poorly drained soils, the limited data they had on heights of trees showed no apparent correlations with presence of high-water tables. On the basis of soil conditions in that area it appears likely that had proper data on height, age, volume, and stand composition been obtained, they would have discovered the expected relations between poor subsoil drainage characteristics and stand composition and site quality.

LAKE STATES

A subdivision of a part of the Upper Peninsula Experimental Forest in Michigan on the basis of soils and vegetation was made by Wilde and Scholz. They indicated that classification of forest tracts on the basis of cover types for management purposes may not be entirely satisfactory because the cover types often represent a temporary condition and thus do not give a true expression of forest productivity.

They recognized five soil and forest types, as follows:

Soil type	Forest type	Floristic type	Productivity
1. Slightly podsolized loam	Upland hardwood type (sugar maple, basswood, elm, etc.)	Acer-Nudum	High
2. Loamy podsol	Hemlock-hardwood type (hemlock, yellow birch, sugar maple, etc.)	Clintomia-Lycopodium	Medium to high
3. Swampy podsol	Lowland hardwood type (sugar maple, red maple, yellow birch, black ash, balsam fir, white spruce)	Fern type	Low
4. Muck	Hardwood-conifer swamp type (red maple, aspen, yellow birch, white spruce, black spruce, balsam fir, alder, and willow)	Urtica-Gallium	Low
5. Woody peat	Cedar swamp type (white cedar, balsam fir, spruce, and some hardwoods)	Oxalis	Very low

For the purpose of a broad correlation of soil and forest growth, Wilde proposed that the analysis of the soil may be limited to the following: (a) the consideration of topographic features and the state of the underground water; (b) the study of the soil texture and structure; and (c) the study of geological and genetic peculiarities of the soil profile. Wilde outlined the three principal types of forest soils as related to underground water that were given by Warming. They were (a) soils in which roots of the plants are permanently under influence of the water table; (b) soils in which the roots are periodically under the influence of the water table, either directly or by means of capillarity; and (c) soils in which root penetration is entirely above the water table.

The limiting factor of swamp-forest growth (under a above) is the degree of water stagnation. In the Lake States, Wilde states, fibrous peat produces no forest growth but sedges; sphagnum peat supports pure or mixed stands of black spruce and tamarack; fine woody peat supports water-loving hardwoods—black ash, red maple, yellow birch, willow, and numerous shrubs; coarse woody peat is correlated with white cedar; the typical vegetation of muck is alder.

Swampy podsols, which are developed under the partial influence of the water table, support stands of pine if they are coarse-textured, whereas if they are finer-textured (loams) the forest stand includes such hardwoods as ash, elm, red maple, sugar maple, and yellow birch, along with a mixture of conifers such as white pine, hemlock, spruce, and balsam.

If the soil mass is entirely above the influence of the water table, stand composition is primarily correlated with the texture, and in some cases the structure, of the mineral soil. In general, the sandy soils support pine, loamy soils support hardwoods, and clayey soils support both conifers and hardwoods.

The relation of soil characteristics to forest growth and composition in uneven-aged northern hardwood forests of northern Michigan was studied by Westveld. No really satisfactory methods have been devised to estimate site index of uneven-aged stands. In this study the heights of dominant trees, regardless of age, were taken as the site index. The 83 one-acre plots examined occurred on 25 soil types. Three site-index classes, 70, 80, and 90 feet, were recognized, and 92 per cent of the plots were in the 80- or 90-foot site-index classes. It may be assumed that site index was based on height at maturity rather than height at some base age, such as 50 years in the case of Eastern conifers. The narrow range in site index from the poorest to the best is not in accordance with the usual range in even-aged stands of other species. For example, site indices for various species have been found as follows: (basis 50 years) red spruce—30 to 70; southern pines—30 to 120; and (basis 100 years) Douglas fir—80 to 210.

In attempting to account for the narrow range of site indices, Westveld found in an oak-yield study in Connecticut that whereas the range in site index was from 60 to 100, 86 per cent of the plots were in the 70- to 90-foot classes. On the basis of this he believed that hardwoods have more exacting site requirements as compared with conifers, and that the poor sites in these regions are usually occupied by other forest types. It is doubtful that such a generality should be attempted, although it is agreed that certain hardwood types have relatively high site requirements. However, it is probable that in most of the earlier yield studies extremely poor sites were not sampled because of such factors as apparently abnormal stocking. Further, certain scrub-oak types maintain themselves on land of low site quality for any species.

The relation between soil characteristics and site index found by Westveld may be summarized as follows:

Soils of group 1. Loams, sandy loams, and loamy sands with yellow sand substratum 15 to 30 inches below the surface. Ordinarily occur as site index 80, although locally they may occur as class 90. Shallow or stony phases of any of these soils may occur as class 70.

Soils of group 2. Loams and sandy loams with a sandy clay till or drift substratum 25 to 30 inches below surface. Occur as site index class 90, except where stony when they will occur as class 80 and where shallowness is combined with stoniness they may occur as class 70.

Soils of group 3. Silt loams and loams with clay or sandy subsoils. Occur as site index class 90 except in the case of very stony soils.

Soils of group 4. Silt loams and loam with open coarse sand, gravel, and cobbles below 40 inches. Occur as site index class 90 except in cases of shallow or stony soils.

Soils in group 5. Shallow soils resting on bedrock. Site class 80.

The importance of soil moisture in the occurrence and growth of black spruce was emphasized by Westveld. Black spruce will tolerate wet soils, but its growth there is inferior. Westveld found that on poorly drained mineral soils (fine sandy loams) where spruce constituted about 53 per cent of the stand and 10 species were represented, the 10-year diameter and height growth was 0.9 inch and 7.0 feet, respectively. On well-drained sandy loam soils where spruce constituted only about 5 per cent of the stand, the 10-year diameter and height growth was 1.6 inches and 12 feet, respectively, with 13 species represented. On poorly decomposed peat (Spaulding peat) the growth of spruce was only 0.4 inch and 3.0 feet in 10 years, whereas on muck soil the 10-year growth was 2.4 inches and 13 feet, respectively. Because of the superior growth of spruce on soils where it constituted only a small percentage of the stand, Westveld suggested silvicultural treatment to favor spruce, especially when the associated species are of inferior commercial value.

A broad ranking of pine soils of northern Michigan into three classes was made by Donahue. Conventional soil types important in area were ranked as follows:

First-class pineland
   Ogenaw sandy loam—Low-lying, smooth, moist, sandy-loam surface soil underlain at 2.4 feet with red clay.
   Roselawn sandy loam—Sandy morainic deposits. Lens of sandy clay or clayey sand in B horizon and in the parent material.

Second-class pineland
   Roselawn sand—Coarse-textured surface and few clayey lenses.
   Rubicon sand—Flat, well-drained, with yellow B horizon 6 to 12 inches from surface.
   Bridgman fine sand—Wind-blown deposits. Fine sand.

Third-class pineland
   Saugatuck sand—Hardpan 6 to 12 inches from surface averaging 18 inches thick.
   Wallace fine sand—Wind-blown. Hardpan.
   Grayling sand—Practically no fine sands, silt, or clay, low water table. One of the first types to be planted because of ease in planting. First to revert to state for taxes.

A comprehensive study of the interrelationships of soil and site index of aspen was conducted by Kittredge in Minnesota and Wisconsin. The relation between site index of aspen and the following factors was studied: soil-texture groups, geological-formation groups, combined texture- and geological-formation groups, soil-profile groups, and natural community plant-indicator groups. Site index of aspen was found to be most closely related to soil-profile groups, to natural community plant-indicator groups, and to combinations of the two.

Conventional soil types were grouped by Kittredge into various classes on the basis of the character of the C horizon, extent of development of the A_2 horizon (leached zone), and the moisture regime under which they were developed, textural class of the A horizon, presence or absence of a gley zone, and the development of the A_0 and A_1 horizon. The correlation ratio was used as a measure of the relation between 22 soil-profile groups and site index of aspen. Observations were made on 230 sample plots. No one profile feature alone had sufficient weight to enable prediction of habitat productivity. A correlation ratio of 0.795 was found for the relationship between site index and the 22 soil-profile groups. The mean site indices of many of the groups were, however, not significantly different from each other. Xeric (dry) conditions tended to be unfavorable for the growth of aspen, especially if they were intensified by sandy surface soil and subsoil and associated with a poor development of the A_2 horizon. Mesic (median) conditions tended to be favorable. Hydric (wet) conditions tended to be favorable except where they were accompanied by deficient drainage. A strong development of the A_2 horizon was associated with good growth, and a weak A_2 with poor growth. A calcareous subsoil tended to be more favorable than a noncalcareous subsoil. A sandy C horizon combined with sandy surface horizons was unfavorable in xeric habitats but generally favorable in hydric habitats. A clayey subsoil was favorable for the growth of aspen except when associated with deficient drainage. Rock substratum at shallow depths was generally unfavorable for the growth of aspen.

Kittredge concluded that site index of aspen is a more reliable measure (of site quality) than volume growth, and may be used satisfactorily for the evaluation of the differences and relative productivity of the aspen habitats. Conversely, the habitat groups, which may be established most effectively on the basis of soil profiles, may be used within limits for the prediction of the average growth of aspen. Individual plants for the aspen community do not indicate with sufficient reliability differences either in the habitats or growth rates of aspen. Groups of plant indicators, of which the most satisfactory were those based on maximum frequencies in natural communities other than aspen, together with the soil-profile groups, are the most useful classifications for the differentiation and for the prediction of the productivity of the different aspen habitats.

From information obtained in a survey of forest soils, Gessel and Lloyd were able to predict the growth of Douglas fir. Site index increased with change in texture from coarse to light to medium. The study did not include heavy soils. There was no significant difference in site index of medium-textured soils of different profile groups. Depth of soil was an important factor for those soils underlain by hardpan or by bedrock.

Site index on the same soil profile and texture group was related to mean annual precipitation. Site index of soils increased with increasing precipitation up to 40 inches. Above this amount of rainfall site index decreased for coarse-, fine- and medium-textured soils. Site index on soils underlain by an impeding layer increased with precipitation up to 60 inches. The greatest increase was up to 40 inches. Above this amount the change in site index was small.

CENTRAL STATES

Locke reported on the relation between soil conditions and other site factors and the growth of upland oak in the Upper Mississippi Valley region. He concluded that the depth of soil horizons and their permeability, slope, and aspect were most important in determining the rate of growth under various conditions of stocking.

On the basis of a study of physical and chemical soil properties and the growth of 135 black locust plantations and 120 black walnut plantations, Auten concluded that the physical properties of the subsoil were most influential in determining site index. Plasticity, compactness, and structure of the subsoil gave the highest correlations with site index. Both species appeared to act similarly and unfavorably to insufficient or excessive drainage. Generally both species made their best growth on medium textural grades of soils such as sandy loams and silt loams. Little relationship was found between acidity or chemical composition of the soil and growth of either species.

Auten reported on a study of the site requirements of yellow poplar in the Central States. Seventy-eight sample plots in stands between 12 and 61 years of age were examined. Soil and other features examined included drainage of the site, soil texture, color of subsoil, depth of horizons, depth of organic matter penetration (thickness of A_1 horizon), replaceable calcium, available magnesium, soluble phosphorus, potassium, reaction, nitrogen, exposure, topography, and aspect. Growth of the trees was measured as average annual height growth for the most part. Many of Auten's results are of interest from the standpoint of the influence of yellow poplar on the chemical properties of the surface soil. Yellow poplar was found to make the best growth on deep, medium-textured, well-drained soils. An interesting relation between the depth of the A_1 horizon and average annual height growth was found. The range of depths of A_1 horizons was 1 to 12 inches, and the range of height-age ratio was 0.64 to 4 feet. Auten concluded that yellow poplar will not grow successfully on sites whose original A_1 horizon is less than one inch deep. It appears, however, that yellow poplar will become established and grow rapidly in old-field coves whose soil has no A_1 horizon if the soil has good physical properties and is well drained. If a soil has properties such that a luxuriant growth of yellow poplar develops, the large annual fall of litter high in calcium results in the incorporation of humus so that in time a deep A_1 horizon is formed.

SOUTH AND SOUTHEAST

Coile observed an A_1 horizon of up to 12 inches in depth under yellow poplar of site index 120 in northern Georgia. Auten found no clear-cut relationships between fertility attributes of the soil and the growth of yellow poplar. Exposure, topography, and aspect as they influence precipitation, temperature, and evaporation were related to annual growth of yellow poplar.

In a study of the highly differentiated soils derived from Triassic rocks in the lower Piedmont Plateau of North Carolina, Coile found that the site index of shortleaf pine was related to the texture-depth index of a soil profile. The texture-depth index is the ratio of the silt plus clay content of the B horizon to the thickness of the A horizon. Texture-depth indices less than 2 or greater than 8 indicated poor sites. Highest site indices were found where the texture-depth index of the soil was between 4 and 6. On the average this would represent a soil with 12 inches of A horizon and a B horizon containing 60 per cent silt and clay. On such soils shortleaf pine usually had a site index of 80 feet. Should the same kind of subsoil be covered with only four inches of A horizon, the texture-depth index would be 15 and the site index relatively low. The reasoning behind the development of the texture-depth index was based on the belief that site quality was a function of the amount and favorableness of growing space for tree roots in the soil. In the case of soils that have highly differentiated profiles with respect to texture, structure, and consistence, the depth of the surface soil and certain physical properties of the subsoil become pertinent factors in determining the volume and quality of growing space for tree roots.

Because subsoils of the same textural class may have greatly different internal drainage, aeration, consistence, and structural characteristics, all of which affect root growth, the texture of the subsoil alone or in conjunction with the depth of the surface soil is not closely correlated to site quality for a wide variety of soils.

The height growth of young black locust plantations in Mississippi was found by Roberts to be closely correlated with the depth of the surface soil. Average annual height growth was greater as the depth of the surface soil increased.

Turner studied the relation between soil types, soil-profile features, topographic features, and the site index of loblolly pine and shortleaf pine in Arkansas. He found that certain soil series usually produced pine of high site index. He concluded that height growth of the two species of pine was conditioned by the interaction of the following factors: percentage of slope as it affects surface drainage, depth of the B_1 horizon, and the mechanical composition of the soil horizons as that affects drainage and aeration. No mathematical relationships between the factors above and site index were established such that site quality could be estimated with any degree of precision.

By studying site conditions, Arend and Collins found depth of soil to be the principal factor affecting the growth and character of natural stands of eastern red cedar in the Ozarks. The sites varied from deep alluvial to shallow upland soils less than 12 inches in depth.

Coile demonstrated the existence of highly significant correlations between the site index, or height of growth, of pine stands in the Piedmont region and the depth of the surface soil or A horizon in inches and the imbibitional water value of the subsoil or B horizon. The latter value is the difference between the moisture and xylene-equivalents of a soil and it is a constant for soil series as conventionally recognized and mapped.

Coile was able to establish the site quality for loblolly and shortleaf pines of any land in the Piedmont region with an accuracy of approximately 10 per cent of the estimate for a single observation by the use of the following equations:

Site Index (Loblolly pine)

$$= 100.04 - \frac{75}{X} - 1.39\,Y$$

Site Index (Shortleaf pine)

$$= 77.32 - \frac{45}{X} - 1.00\,Y$$

Where X equals depth of surface soil in inches.
Y equals imbibitional water value of the subsoil.

These equations are based on regression analysis of soil and stand data from 156 .2-acre plots. These plots were located in well-stocked, even-aged stands of pine from 30 to 120 years of age. In addition to the conventional mensurational data on the pine overstory needed for measuring the soil-site correlation, complete tallies of the understory trees over 4.5 feet in height were made by species and diameter classes.

Analysis of this data showed that the species whose stocking was sufficiently affected by permanent mappable soil characteristics alone comprised 70 per cent of the total understory of the average pine stand.

Coile found that when natural or planted pine stands are young, it was difficult or impossible, on the basis of the vegetation, to estimate the species composition and stocking of the understory that will be present when the mature stand is removed. The correlation between soil factors and the stocking of understory species demonstrated in this study should be useful in estimating the hardwood potential of any land in the Piedmont region.

PRAIRIE PLAINS

In the drier regions of the United States it has been fairly well established that physical soil properties that allow for rapid infiltration and good water storage and low evaporation loss are associated with superior forest sites. In the Prairie-Plains region coarse-textured soils have been found superior to fine-textured soils for the survival and growth of trees planted for shelter belts.

As a result of these and other investigations there is a growing recognition of the importance of soil and the role it plays in determining the character of the tree stand and its yield in lumber or cordwood. This may seem to be a misstatement, considering the fact that where rainfall is adequate trees survive in almost any situation, including some of our roughest and rockiest land where there is little or no soil.

But the key word here is *survive*. There is a vast difference between mere survival and satisfactory growth. Where cordwood, fence posts, ties, or lumber is to be the fruit of the land, something better is needed than bare rock with a few crevices for root anchorage.

Like any farm crop, trees need moisture and plant food from the soil. And like many crops, forest stands need to be weeded and thinned if growth of crop trees is to be maintained at a maximum.

Unlike most farm crops, tree roots remain in the soil year after year, and the rate of demand for plant food during any one season of the year is rather low. Further, the amount of removal from that land is infinitely less (in undisturbed stands). Because of these facts, the rate of natural liberation of available plant food is usually ample in the forest. Hence, fertilizers are not ordinarily needed, even on soils considered to be very poor by farming standards.

However, the more favorable the moisture supply and the higher the rate of plant food liberation—other things being equal, and taking into account the differences in the requirements of various species—the better the quality of the stand and the more rapid the growth. Both moisture supply and plant food liberation are tied in with properties of the soil.

MOISTURE MOST IMPORTANT

Work at the Connecticut Agricultural Experiment Station, which was one of the first to begin research on forest soils, has shown that in most instances soil moisture is the factor of first importance. Moisture relations are indicated by the soil type. For example, Merrimac loamy sand is a drier soil than Merrimac fine sandy loam or Brookfield loam, and Leicester loam soils are wetter than Gloucester loam.

In some instances moisture conditions vary within a given soil type because of topographic position. For example, trees growing on a sandy soil with a water table averaging 5 feet deep will grow faster than they would on the same kind of soil but where the water table is 15 or 20 feet deep. Likewise, the middle or lower portion of a long slope or the north side of a hill usually has better moisture conditions and trees are likely to grow faster than on the upper portion of a slope or on the south side of a hill, although a soil map may show the same soil in all of the situations cited. This fact is indicative of some of the complications involved in determining the relationships between soils and tree growth.

One of the most striking effects of soil and moisture supply came to light when it was found that a 5-year-old planting of white pine on Hartford sandy loam was growing 27 per cent faster than an identical planting on Merrimac loamy sand not more than 350 feet away. The increase with Norway spruce was even greater—nearly 90 per cent. Here the difference was not one of soil series as such—Hartford vs. Merrimac—but rather of soil texture and moisture supply. The substratum of the Hartford sandy loam was considerably more moist and tree roots had penetrated to a greater depth than on the block of Merrimac loamy sand.

Studies conducted at Connecticut have shown that the soil in the woods is decidedly more loose and porous, contains considerably more organic matter, and has a much higher water-holding capacity than cultivated soil. Direct comparisons in nine separate locations in south-central Connecticut revealed that the topsoil in the forest, exclusive of forest litter, contained 48 per cent more nitrogen than the topsoil of cultivated fields, and was able to hold 40 per cent more water. Further, the forest soils were about 22 per cent lighter, indicating a better state of aggregation.

AVAILABLE NUTRIENTS

So far as available nutrients are concerned—especially phosphorus, potassium, and calcium—cultivated soils are usually better stocked as a result of fertilizer treatments; but in comparison with permanent pasture soils, forest soils generally have the advantage. The favorable condition of woodland soils is further enhanced by the deposition of litter and humus usually present in undisturbed forests.

RESTORATION OF DEPLETED PROFILE

Cultivation and erosion have so changed the surface soil horizon on large acreages of our land that it has lost much of its former capacity for absorbing and storing rainfall. This has greatly reduced the storage opportunity of and the transmission rate of water through the soil—the two hydrologic factors subject to modification by man. Because a larger proportion of rainfall now runs off over the land surface and less is stored in the soil, sloping lands are severely eroded and once-fertile bottomlands are frequently flooded.

Knowledge of the hydrologic characteristics of the soil is the key to understanding and solving the problems that have to be faced in restoration of these badly eroded and abandoned soils. Just as altered hydrologic processes have accelerated soil destruction, so soil rehabilitation must be based on improved water relations. Land-use practices that bring about an increase in soil permeability and large pore space offer the only permanent solution to present erosion and water problems on these soils.

Forestry practices designed for soil improvement offer the best hope for ameliorating the consequences of past land use on most of the soils no longer suitable for agriculture. This may be illustrated by examining the use of the soil in the South Carolina Piedmont as shown by a 1947 survey.

Class of use	Area (acres)	Per cent
Forest	4,035,600	59.9
Agriculture	1,896,600	28.1
Idle	635,440	9.4
Urban and other	176,100	2.6
Total land area	6,743,700	100.0

Because the forest area represents largely land that has been cultivated until erosion forced abandonment, only half of this area is suitable for good forest growth. For this better portion, vegetation develops rapidly, and restoration is assured if man does not seriously upset the natural plant succession. Improvement will be more rapid if those species known to develop better types and soil structure are favored in management.

CORRELATE SOIL WITH SITE QUALITY

Using soils and other physical features of the land, Hill and his associates developed a method of correlating soil characteristics with site quality of Douglas fir in Lewis County, Washington. The method makes possible the prediction of growth rates, within narrow limits, for this species in that area. It is thought that the method may be applicable, with slight modifications, to other areas and species.

In planning the best use of the land in the Lewis County Soil Conservation District, it was decided to attempt to correlate soil characteristics with site class. The results were striking, and useful for the area and species studied. It is believed that methods used may be of value to other workers, because of the significant relationships between soils and site quality that were found.

The age and average height of the dominant and co-dominant trees were determined by use of an increment borer and an Abney level. Sample areas were three acres or larger. In order that accurate height and age determinations could be made, only stands with homogenous composition were sampled. Because of the uniformity of the stands, five to ten age and height measurements, evenly distributed through the stand, were sufficient. Soil characteristics to a depth of 6 feet and degree and direction of slope were determined by use of a soil auger and Abney level. Notes were also taken on grazing and other land use that might have affected tree growth. This procedure was used on practically every accessible, fully stocked stand of Douglas fir of the proper age in approximately the western two-thirds of the county; 148 such stands were sampled, ranging from 25 to 150 years in age, but most of the stands were between 40 and 60 years old.

Data obtained on site classes were studied in relation to: (a) the soil series and types as mapped by the Bureau of Soils and its successors of the U.S. Department of Agriculture,* (b) the soil mapping units, and (c) the land-capability classes discussed in Chapter 7.

Soil series and types were recorded for each sample, but there were so many named soils in the area that it was impossible to obtain a statistically adequate number of samples on each of them. From the samples available, no indication of significant differences in site classes could be observed between soils of similar profile, texture, and depth, even though color, age, and morphology might differ perceptibly. Thus, the separation by series and types is unnecessarily refined and therefore undesirably complex, although by proper grouping of the soils a very satisfactory correlation was possible.

Soil-sampling units were set up in making soil surveys for farm planning as a means of recording the principal soil data needed for recommending safe use and management of the land. These units are primarily arrived at by classing together all the soils of similar profile, texture, and depth, though other physical factors may be used if necessary. Thus soils of dissimilar derivation may be classed together, and a single soil (according to the series and types system) may occasionally fall into more than one unit, depending on the depth available for roots and water.

The site indices of the Douglas fir stands growing on each of these soil

* A. W. Magnum and party. *Reconnaissance Survey of Southwestern Washington*, Field Operations, Bureau of Soils, U.S. Dept. Agric. 1911.

units showed a remarkably narrow range of values with the coefficient of variation less than 7, except on units 6Hb and 6Ha. Since these two units seemed unduly variable, other factors were tested, and it was found that site indices on these soils also fell into relatively narrow ranges if northerly slopes were separated. The average slope of these units is approximately 20 per cent. Charting the site indices of samples as they are recorded should indicate whether separation of units is adequate and if they are suitably defined.

TABLE 60. Distribution by site index of number of samples each soil group (20)

Soil group	Site Class IV			Site Class III			Site Class II			Site Class I			Average site index	Standard deviation	Coefficient of variation
	100	110	120	130	140	150	160	170	180	190	200	210			
(Lewis County, Washington)															
(1) L			1	4	3								132.50	± 7.13	5.39
(1) M					1	3	2	1					154.28	± 9.92	6.43
1L					1	4	1						150.00	± 6.32	4.21
1M								2	5	5	1		183.85	± 8.87	4.82
1H							1	1	3				174.00	± 9.43	5.41
2M								2	1	1			177.50	±10.50	5.91
2H							5	2	1				161.25	± 6.43	3.98
3M					1	3	1						150.00	± 5.00	3.33
3H				3	1	1							136.00	± 9.43	6.93
(6) H1						1	8	4	2				164.66	± 8.53	5.18
(6) H2				2	2	10	2						147.50	± 8.94	6.06
6Ha–North exposure					1	3	13	6	2				162.00	± 9.14	5.64
6Ha–South exposure				1	11	5	2						144.21	± 7.75	5.37
6Hb–North exposure						2	6	9	1				165.00	± 7.95	4.82
6Hb–South exposure				2	5	12	4	2					149.60	±10.19	6.87
(Grays Harbor County, Washington)															
6Hb–North										4	4		195.00	± 5.77	2.95
6Hb–South							1	6	4	1			176.25	± 8.69	4.93
(1)GM									2	1					
(1)GL				1	1	3	3						150.00	±10.69	7.13

It will be noted that few examples were available for measurement on some of the soil units. The danger of underestimating the standard deviation and the coefficient of variability was minimized by using the formula for small samples (using N-1 instead of N as the divisor). Larger samples would quite possibly reduce the calculated variability to some extent. Exposure on soil units other than 6Ha and 6Hb, even though some of the 1M samples were equally steep, showed no correlation with site index.

Degree of slope did not give a correlation with site index, although it may be effective, through its influence on temperatures, in the establishment and survival of seedlings of Douglas fir on south and west exposures.

Known differences in soil fertility for cultivated crops did not show any consistent influence on site index. Ability of the soil to retain and supply water for tree growth in the dry summer period is most important. This ability is a function not only of texture and profile, but also of depth to porous materials, hardrock, claypan, or hardpan.

It is reasonably certain that the *same* correlations between site classes and soil units will not hold good over wide areas, even for the same tree species. A few samples were taken on 6Hb soils in Grays Harbor County, a few miles away, where the rainfall is much higher (60 to 90 inches as against 45 to 55 inches in western Lewis County). Here the difference between northerly and southerly slopes maintained the same ratio, but the absolute values were about 30 points higher on the site-index scale.

FIT THE TREE TO THE SITE

The importance of site evaluation in the selection of tree species for planting was emphasized by observations of a large number of field and gully plantings of pines and hardwoods for erosion control in the Ohio Valley.

In general, pine is least exacting in site requirements; black locust gives good to excellent results on many sites; and hardwoods other than locust failed in practically all cases as erosion-control plantings. Locust grows best on calcareous soils, soils of good drainage, aeration, and moisture-holding capacity, and soils free from compact, impervious layers. Pine, on the other hand, thrives on soils that are more acid and less fertile than those to which locust is adapted.

On residual soils of mixed sandstones and shale origin, such as those of the Muskingum and Wellston series, pine is more reliable than locust for field plantings, especially in old poverty-grass sods and on sand and shallow and severely eroded sites. Pine is also more reliable than locust on gully bottoms where shale materials predominate. Locust fails where iron or manganese concretionary fragments are plentiful, whether on gullied or severely eroded areas. Where limestone occurs, giving rise to soils of the Brooks series, locust makes excellent growth. Soils of the Upshur series, derived from heavy nonacid shale, are generally very good locust sites.

Locust gives excellent results on well-drained soils of loessal origin such as those of the Princeton and Memphis series, and good results in gullied areas of Alford and Grenada soils. Pine also does well on loessal soils, especially for field plantings.

Soils of cherty limestone or of coastal-plain origin are very poor locust sites. Included are those of the Frederick, Bedford, Lawrence, Baxter, Dickson, Brandon, Ruston, and Atwater series. Success may be attained with locust on the better-drained cherty limestone soils if the site is mulched and fertilized, but pine is more reliable and is benefited by mulching even more than the locust. Coastal-plain soils of the Atwood series are excellent pine sites. Field plantings of pine also grew well on Brandon and Ruston soils but plantings on badly gullied areas of these soils usually give poor results.

Of the species of pine planted, the two-needle pines are found to be less exacting in site requirements than other species. In Ohio and Indiana, red and Scotch pines are best adapted to the poorer areas; white pine gives good results on the better pine sites. In Kentucky and Tennessee, loblolly and shortleaf are the species preferred for the better pine sites, and Virginia and pitch pine for the poorer ones.

PREPARE SITE BEFORE PLANTING

Observational studies made by Aikman of numerous plantings of hardwood species for shelterbelts, woodlots, erosion control, and in reforestation and afforestation projects showed that, unless soil and climatic conditions were extremely favorable, planting without some attempt at site preparation was often disappointing. This was especially true where the soil conditions were extremely unfavorable because of excessive erosion. Numerous examples were found of plantings in gullies and on badly eroded slopes that showed, after several years, a low rate of survival, poor establishment of many that did survive, and inadequate growth of the occasional, seemingly-favored tree.

Aikman found that several hardwood species planted in contour furrows on a 20 per cent slope in Iowa did much better than similar species planted on the same slope by use of a scalpel.

Although the growth response to the modification in site preparation of the 1940 experiment was least in the black locust, the growth curves of this species for a 3-year period indicated that even in this species the rate of growth difference between the two treatments was progressively greater from year to year. This divergence was greater in black locust than in most other hardwood species. Other site-preparation experiments with black locust showed that greater rate of growth differences were evident where very unfavorable site conditions were corrected by site improvement, since black locust grows quite well under moderately favorable conditions without special site preparation but showed marked response to any site preparation that improved the plant-growth conditions of unfavorable sites.

The results of this study were predominantly in favor of contour-strip planting as compared with scalpel planting. From these experiments, in which soil-moisture data to the depth of root penetration were collected, and from other experiments, designed to evaluate the relative effects of improved soil-moisture conditions and improved aeration conditions of the plowed strip as compared with scalpel planting, it was concluded that the improvement in plant-growth conditions for most hardwoods seemed to be attributable, about equally, to these two factors. However, there was evidence that in the black locust, planted on B horizon of Lindley loam, improved soil structure as a result of plowing overshadowed the increased soil moisture.

CLAY HILLTOP GROWS TREES PROFITABLY

Miller reported that a typical clay hilltop underlain by basalt on the Pullman, Washington, Soil Conservation Service Nursery was planted in the spring of 1937, to a combination shelterbelt and black locust woodlot. The area occupied by the black locust was $\frac{1}{11}$ acre. The black locust were planted on a 6 ft. x 6 ft. spacing.

Because of overcrowding, the black locust planting was thinned to a 6 ft. x 12 ft. spacing in 1945. Insofar as possible, small, overtopped, and suppressed trees were removed, but those cut were selected also so as not to impair the effectiveness of the planting for control of snowdrift.

A total of 53 trees were removed with 7½ man hours of labor for cutting, trimming, and making fence posts out of those of suitable size. Ninety-three fence posts were obtained. Forty-two were 3 inches and over in diameter at the small end, and were considered to be first-quality posts; 51 were less than 3 inches in diameter at the small end, and were considered to be second-class posts. All 93 were used in rebuilding the fence on the Nursery Farm, where they took the place of cedar posts which would have cost 35 cents each.

The value of the locust posts, because of size and lack of comparable figures, was set at 35 cents for the first class and 25 cents for those of the second class. This gave a total return of $27.45 for the materials removed by thinning from the hilltop planting. The cost of labor for thinning, trimming, and making posts was figured at $1.00 per hour, making the total cost 8 cents per post. The remaining planting was more valuable than before thinning, for both wood products and snowdrift control.

At this rate, on a per-acre basis, the gross return was $302.50 for the 8-year-period, or $37.81 per acre per year. It is evident from these figures that black locust woodlots will yield a profitable return on clay hilltops that are ordinarily farmed at a loss.

REFERENCES

1. Aikman, J. M. 1943. *The effect of site preparation on survival and growth of selected hardwood species on eroded soil.* Amer. Forester, 53-58.
2. Alpeter, L. A. 1941. *Reforestation of sandblows in northern Vermont.* Jour. Forestry, 39: 705-709.
3. Arend, J. L., and Collins, R. E. 1948. *A site classification for eastern red cedar in the Ozarks.* Soil Sci. Soc. Amer. Proc., 13: 510-511.
4. Auten, J. T. 1936. *Soil profile studies in relation to site requirements of black locust and black walnut.* Central States Forest Expt. Sta. Note 31.
5. ———. 1937. *Site requirements of yellow poplar.* Central States Forest Expt. Sta. Note 32.
6. ———. 1937. *A method of site evaluation for yellow poplar based on depth of the undisturbed A_1 horizon.* Central States Forest Expt. Sta. Note 33.
7. Coile, T. S. 1935. *Relation of site index for shortleaf pine to certain physical properties of the soil.* Jour. Forestry, 33: 726-730.
8. ———. 1948. *Relation of soil characteristics to site index of loblolly and shortleaf pines in the lower Piedmont Region of North Carolina.* Duke Univ. School of Forestry Bull. 13.
9. ———. 1949. *Effect of soil on the development of hardwood understories in pine stands of the Piedmont Plateau.* Soil Sci. Soc. Amer. Proc., 14: 350-352.
10. Diebold, C. H. 1935. *Some relationships between soil type and forest site quality.* Ecology, 16: 640-647.
11. ———. 1938. *Interrelationships between water table, soil characteristics, silvics, reforestation, and flood control in south-central New York.* Ecology, 19: 463-479.
12. Donahue, R. L. 1936. *The relation of soil character as expressed by certain soil types to the choice of land for forestry in the cut-over pine of Northern Michigan.* Amer. Soil Surv. Assoc., 17: 79-80.
13. ———. 1940. *Forest-site quality studies in the Adirondacks: I. Tree growth as related to soil morphology.* Cornell Univ. Expt. Sta. Mem. 229.
14. Gessel, S. P., and Lloyd, W. J. 1950. *Effect of some physical soil properties in Douglas-fir site quality.* Jour. Forestry, 48(6): 405-410.
15. Haig, I. T. 1929. *Colloidal content and related factors as indicators of site quality.* Yale Univ. School Forestry Bull. 24.
16. Hall, R. C. 1935. *Cape Cod pitch pine: its resistance to gipsy moth defoliation and its advantages as a forest tree.* Jour. Forestry, 33: 169-172.

17. Harper, H. J. 1940. *Relation of climatic conditions, soil characteristics, and tree development in the southern Great Plains region.* Soil Sci. Soc. Amer. Proc., 5: 327-335.

18. Heiberg, S. O. 1941. *Silvicultural significance of mull and mor.* Soil Sci. Soc. Amer. Proc., 6: 405-408.

19. Hicock, H. W., Morgan, M. F., Lutz, H. J., Bull, H., and Lunt, H. A. 1931. *Relation of forest composition and rate of growth to certain soil characters.* Conn. Agr. Expt. Sta. Bull. 330.

20. Hill, W. W., Arnst, A., and Bond, R. M. 1948. *Method of correlating soils with Douglas fir site quality.* Jour. Forestry, 46(11): 835-841.

21. Hirsh, C. R., and Hoover, M. D. 1941. *Soil profile characteristics pertinent to hydrologic studies in the southern Appalachians.* Soil Sci. Soc. Amer. Proc., 6: 414-422.

22. Kittredge, J., Jr. 1938. *The interrelationships of habitats, growth rate, and associated vegetation in the aspen community of Minnesota and Wisconsin.* Ecol. Monog., 8: 153-246.

23. Ligon, W. S. 1940. *Influence of soil type and other site factors on the success of tree plantings for erosion control.* Jour. Forestry, 38(3): 226-227.

24. Locke, S. S. 1941. *The use of soil-site factors in predicting timber yields.* Soil Sci. Soc. Amer. Proc., 6: 399-402.

25. Lunt, H. A. 1939. *Soil characteristics, topography, and lesser vegetation in relation to site quality of second-growth oak stands in Connecticut.* Jour. Agr. Res., 59: 407-428.

26. ———. 1949. *What's under the trees?* Frontiers of Plant Sci., 11(1): 3.

27. McCormick, J. F., and Cruikshank, J. W. 1949. *South Carolina forest resources.* Southern Forest Expt. Sta. Surv. Release 28.

28. McKinnon, F. S., Hyde, G. R., and Cline, A. C. 1935. *Cutover old field pine lands in central New England: a regional study of the composition and stocking of the ensuing volunteer stands.* Harvard Forest Bull. 18.

29. Miller, H. W. 1945. *Clay hilltops farmed at a profit by growing black locusts for posts.* USDA, SCS, Div. Reg. 7, Tech. Sup. 113.

30. Pearson, G. A. 1931. *Forest types in the Southwest as determined by climate and soil.* USDA Tech. Bull. 247.

31. Roberts, E. G. 1939. *Soil depth and height growth of black locust.* Jour. Forestry, 37: 583-584.

32. Spaeth, J. N., and Diebold, C. H. 1938. *Some interrelationships between soil characteristics, water tables, soil temperature, and snow cover in the forest and adjacent open areas in south-central New York.* Cornell Univ. Agr. Expt. Sta. Mem. 213.

33. Stoeckler, J. H., and Bates, C. G. 1939. *Shelterbelts: the advantages of porous soils for trees.* Jour. Forestry, 37: 205-221.

34. Turner, L. M. 1937. *Growth of second-growth pine on the Coastal Plain soils of Arkansas.* Ark. Agr. Expt. Sta. Bull. 342.

35. ———. 1938. *Some profile characteristics of the pine-growing soils of the Coastal Plain region of Arkansas.* Ark. Agr. Expt. Sta. Bull. 361.

36. USDA, Forest Service. 1935. *Possibilities of shelterbelt planting in the Plains region.* Lake States Forest Expt. Sta., U.S. Forest Service, 201.

37. Westveld, R. H. 1933. *The relation of certain soil characteristics to forest growth and composition in the northern hardwood forests of northern Michigan.* Mich. Agr. Expt. Sta. Bull. 135.

38. ———. 1936. *Soil characteristics in relation to the occurrence and growth of black spruce.* Amer. Soil Surv. Assoc., 17: 45-47.

39. Wilde, S. A. 1933. *The relation of soils and forest vegetation of the Lake States region.* Ecology, 14: 94-105.

40. ———, and Patzer, W. E. 1940. *The role of soil organic matter in reforestation.* Jour. Amer. Soc. Agron., 32: 551-562.

41. Wilde, S. A., and Scholz, H. F. 1934. *Subdivision of the Upper Peninsula Experimental Forest on the basis of soils and vegetation.* Soil Sci., 38: 383-399.

19

Surface Water
Disposal System

No matter how effective the erosion-control program may be in reducing runoff and soil loss, there will be times during heavy rainstorms or rains extending over several days when more water will fall than the soil can absorb. This presents another and, at times, a serious phase of the soil-erosion problem. At such times, the plant-cover phase of the erosion-control program must be supplemented by appropriate mechanical measures for safe disposal of the excess water.

Certain basic information is needed before establishment of any mechanical control measures to assure that the correct measures are employed. However, since any given farm as a rule comprises only a portion of a watershed—and the watershed should be considered as a whole—these data should be obtained for the entire watershed area and the measures used on the farm fitted into the over-all program.

The primary purpose of these measures is to deal with surplus water. They constitute the water disposal system. The basic information used in planning this system is obtained by means of hydrologic surveys. The data obtained from these surveys guide the planning of terraces, diversion ditches, check dams, vegetated waterways, and streambank protection, and other water-control measures.

HYDROLOGIC SURVEY

The hydrologic survey embraces a study of the rainfall, climate, and physical characteristics of the land, with emphasis on their relation to runoff and soil erosion. The completed survey should include data concerning average rainfall, maximum rainfall, flood flows, delineation of flood plains, temperatures, and growing seasons. To analyze this information properly for practical use, some data concerning the physical characteristics of the watershed must also be obtained. These should include such items as size and shape of watershed, drainage patterns, infiltration rates, slopes, soils, probable surface storage, and vegetal cover.

Analysis. These data must be gathered and analyzed to provide the information for: (a) proper design of water-disposal structures, (b) selection of types of vegetation according to flow frequencies and velocities, (c) determination of whether irrigation is required, (d) determination of runoff-control and other conservation practices adaptable to an area.

The hydrologic survey should be made before initiation of a comprehensive soil-conservation program, and in conjunction with the conservation, cover, and topographic surveys. The data concerning rainfall and climate may usually be obtained from local weather bureau records. Information concerning peak flood flows and flood plains is obtained through field investigations.

Computation of peak flows. The peak flows for these surveys are computed by treating certain of the results of field investigations according to established methods. Several methods are in general use, but none seem satisfactory unless a comprehensive survey of the area has first been made. It is also helpful to have any results of local research work. In connection with local research, emphasis should be placed on determinations of infiltration rates under prolonged rains (effects of plant cover on runoff), and effects of any proposed water-disposal structures, such as terraces, contour furrows, diversion ditches, and check dams, on the peak runoff.

The term *peak runoff* as used herein refers to the maximum rate of runoff from a given area for the frequency of occurrence that is considered. It does not mean the all-time maximum flow that may be expected over an indefinite period.

Selection of frequency for any specific job should be based on considera-

TABLE 61. Suggested flood-flow frequencies for various water-disposal structures (3)

Type of structure	Frequency
Storage and diversion dams having permanent spillways	50 to 100 years
Earth-fill dams having natural spillways	25 to 50 years
Small, permanent gully-control structure	10 to 25 years
Large, permanent, concrete gully-control structure	25 to 50 years
Terrace outlets and vegetated waterways	5 to 10 years
Diversion channels	10 to 15 years

tions such as the value of the property that would be damaged by failure, and whether or not loss of life might occur.

The rational formula

$$Q = CIA$$

is widely used to compute expected flood flows. This method can be adapted to local conditions by varying the runoff coefficient C. In this formula,

Q = rate of runoff in cubic feet per second
C = runoff coefficient, representing the ratio of runoff to rainfall
I = average rate of rainfall in inches per hour over the entire drainage area during the time of concentration
A = drainage area in acres

It is apparent that the coefficient C will vary considerably with the physical characteristics of the area. Soil conditions, vegetative cover, degree of slope, and surface detention are major considerations in selecting a coefficient. In connection with the factor of vegetative cover, proper allowance should be made for changes that may be brought about by fire, season-to-season changes in vegetation, and by any anticipated year-to-year changes in the cover.

Table 62 will aid in arriving at the C factor. If the weights given the various watershed characteristics total up to 50, the watershed would be classed as normal and the coefficient C would be 0.5. A thorough knowledge of local conditions is helpful in arriving at the correct coefficient of runoff.

Computing average maximum rate of rainfall. The time of concentration for the area must be computed, in order to determine the maximum average rate of rainfall for a given drainage area. Time of concentration of a given watershed is the length of time required for the runoff from the most remote point of the area to reach the outlet. A storm of maximum intensity continuing for the period of concentration will produce maximum runoff rates.

There are no recognized and reliable formulas for determining the time of concentration. Experience, coupled with judgment, will enable one to make a close estimate of the average velocity of flow in the main channel. Dividing this average velocity into the distance between the most remote point and the outlet produces a quotient that is a reasonably close estimate of the time of concentration for this flow. On small areas, time of the flow on the smooth slopes lying above the channel should be added to the above quotient.

Rainfall intensity and frequency data are based on weather bureau records. They show maximum expected precipitation in periods of from 5 minutes to 24 hours, with frequencies of from 2 to 100 years. The frequencies are the expected occurrence of a storm once in a stated period—for instance, once in 5 years or 10 years, or any other period of time. Some of these charts have been reproduced and are shown in Figures 113, 114, and 115. From these charts, directly or by interpolation, can be obtained the depth of rainfall for a period equal to the time of concentration for the major storms of a specific rainfall period.

A variation of this method has been widely used to compute peak flows

TABLE 62. Runoff-producing characteristics of watershed with corresponding weights (2)

Designation of watershed characteristics	Runoff-producing characteristics			
	75 to 100 Extreme	50 to 75 High	30 to 50 Normal	25 to 30 Low
	(40)	(30)	(20)	(10)
Relief	Steep, rugged terrain, with average slopes generally above 30%	Hilly, with average slopes of 10 to 30%	Rolling, with average slopes of 5 to 10%	Relatively flat and with average slopes of 0 to 5%
	(20)	(15)	(10)	(5)
Soil	No effective soil cover, either rock or thin soil mantle of negligible infiltration capacity	Slow to take up water; clay or other soil of low infiltration capacity	Normal; deep permeable soils; such as Cecil soil found in the Piedmont	High; sands, loamy sands, and other loose open soils
	(20)	(15)	(10)	(5)
Vegetal cover	No effective plant cover; bare or very sparse cover	Poor to fair; clean-cultivation crops or poor natural cover; less than 10% of drainage area under good cover	Fair to good; about 50% of drainage area in good grassland, woodland, or equivalent cover; not more than 50% of area in clean-tilled crops	Good to excellent; about 90% of drainage area in good grassland, or equialent cover woodland
	(20)	(15)	(10)	(5)
Surface storage	Negligible; surface depressions few and shallow; drainageways steep and small; no ponds or marshes	Low; well-defined system of small drainageways; no ponds or marshes	Normal; considerable surface-depression storage; drainage system similar to that of typical prairie lands; lakes, ponds, and marshes less than 2% of drainage area	High; surface-depression storage high; drainage system not sharply defined; large flood-plain storage or a large number of lakes, ponds, or marshes

from small drainage areas. Again, sound judgment is important and satisfactory results are dependent on a thorough study of the drainage area under consideration. This study will include a determination of the size of the drainage area and an examination of topography, soil, vegetal cover, surface storage, shape, and other factors thought to have an important effect on the runoff. Table 62 is then used to determine the combined weight of several of these separate factors. Five steps are involved:

STEP 1. If the watershed is hilly, with slopes of from 10 to 30 per cent, the appropriate value to assign the factor of relief is shown in column 3 of Table 62 to be 30. If the soils are composed of sands or loamy sands, or other loose, open soils, the value to assign the soil factor is shown in the right-hand column to be 5. If there is no effective vegetal cover, the second column from left shows this factor to have a value of 20. For a low, well-defined system of small drainageways, with no ponds or marshes, the surface storage factor is shown in column 3 to be equal to 15. The sum of these four factors is now $30 + 5 + 20 + 15 = 70$.

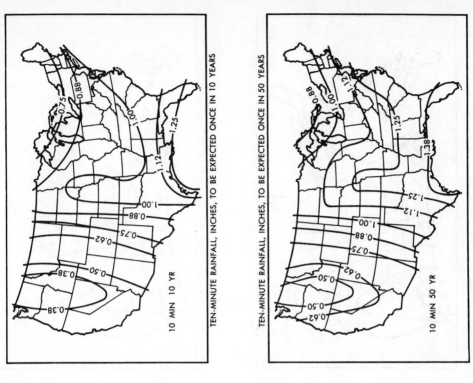

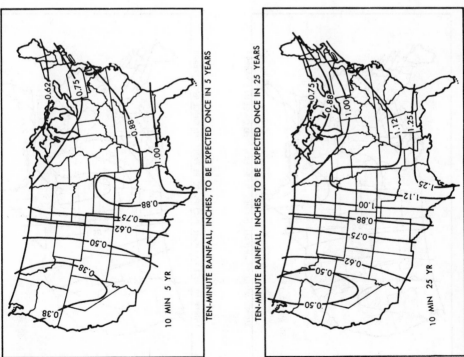

FIGURE 113. Rainfall for 10-minute periods.

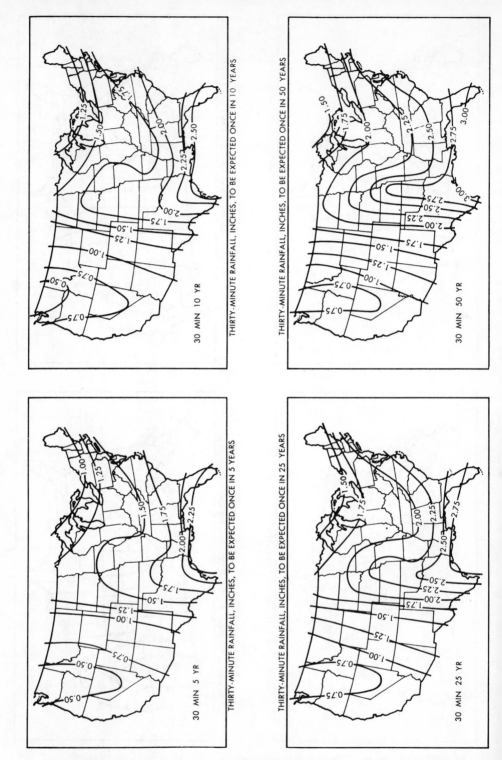

FIGURE 114. Rainfall for 30-minute periods.

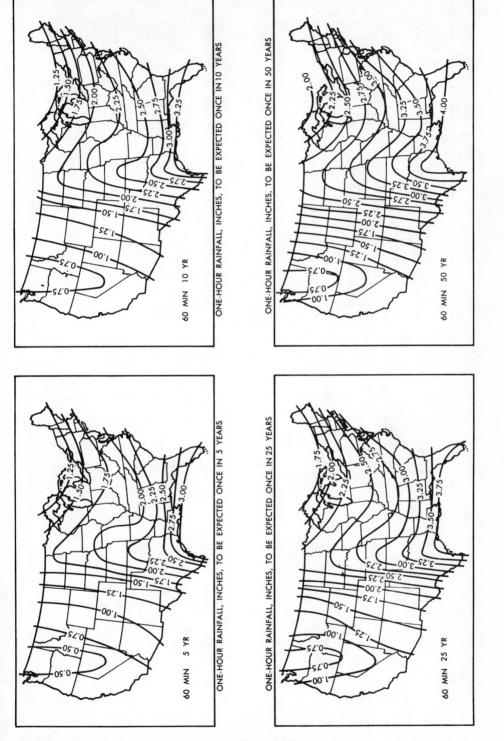

FIGURE 115. Rainfall for 60-minute periods.

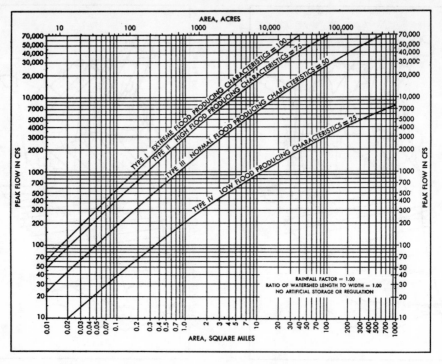

FIGURE 116. Flood-flow curves—floods of 100-year frequency.

FIGURE 117. Regional rainfall factors.

STEP 2. Now refer to Figure 116. The value of 70 is best represented by the curve for Type II. Read the peak flow from this curve, which is for 100-year frequencies.

STEP 3. The runoff is based on Yarnell's curves. Figure 117 is used to adjust this to the rainfall of each climatic region. The runoff values read in Step 2 should be multiplied by the applicable regional factor shown in Figure 117.

STEP 4. The runoff obtained in Step 3 is for 100-year frequency. If another frequency is to be used, multiply the above runoff by the appropriate frequency factor shown in Table 63.

TABLE 63. Frequency factors (factors by which 100–year flood is multiplied to estimate magnitude of flood of given frequency) (2, 3)

Frequency	Factor
Once in 25 years	0.70
Once in 50 years	0.85
Once in 100 years	1.00
Once in 200 years	1.15
Once in 500 years	1.30

STEP 5. Correct the above value for a shape factor where necessary. This shape factor is shown in Table 64.

TABLE 64. Shape factor for use with flood–flow curves* (2, 3)

Value of length/width ratio	Area in square miles					
	0.1	1.0	10	100	1000	10,000
	Value of factor					
1	1	1	1	1	1	1
1.5	0.92	0.90	0.88	0.85	0.82	0.78
2	0.87	0.84	0.80	0.76	0.71	0.65
3	0.80	0.76	0.71	0.65	0.58	0.50
4	0.76	0.71	0.65	0.58	0.50	0.42
5	0.73	0.67	0.60	0.53	0.45	0.37
10	0.63	0.56	0.48	0.40	0.32	0.24
15	0.58	0.51	0.43	0.34	0.26	0.18
20	0.55	0.47	0.39	0.31	0.22	0.15

* To estimate peak flow for any watershed multiply value taken from curves (for a length/width ratio of 1) by the factor given in this table. Length along main valley (disregarding meanders) divided by the area (in same units).

This method of computing peak flow should be restricted to runoff from rainstorms.

Peak flows obtained by this method are not generally applicable to regions having elevations greater than 5,000 feet. Other methods of determining peak flow should be used as a check when designing permanent structures having a drainage area in excess of 300 acres. To treat them according to the above methods these larger watersheds should be divided into a number of small areas.

Some information concerning peak flows from small watersheds is now available in many areas. The results of any local research should be studied prior to arriving at a peak flow for design purposes.

Any study relating to peak-flow determinations should also include an analysis of the data that are available from observed high-water marks. Statements of local residents, whose observations have covered long periods of time, should be given appropriate consideration. The data obtained from such sources often provide a check on estimates obtained through the use of accepted flood-flow formulas. One should be cautious, however, in accepting the opinions of local residents at face value.

FIGURE 118. Terraces are hillside ridges, slightly graded from the contour, which form wide, shallow, flat-shaped waterways along the uphill side of the ridge. (Coshocton County, Ohio) *(Soil Conservation Service)*

Irrigation estimates. Hydrologic surveys should contain the data required to estimate the irrigation requirements of grass, shrubs, and trees in the more arid areas. These surveys should include the mean monthly temperatures, monthly percentage of daylight hours, and average rainfall by months, which can be obtained from the weather bureau records. This information is used to determine the average monthly and seasonal water requirements for various types of vegetation. If the requirements are greater than the average effective rainfall, it is apparent that irrigation water will be required for maximum growth.

TERRACING

Terraces are hillside ridges, approximately on the contour, that form wide, shallow waterways along the uphill side of the ridge. They are used primarily to dispose of excess water and to check scour erosion caused by runoff from cultivated lands. Level terraces are sometimes used to conserve water in arid and semiarid areas, but only on soils that have high infiltration rates and are underlain by permeable sub-surface materials. They are also used on some loess soils. Those built for safe disposal of excess water have gentle grades.

TYPES OF TERRACES

Terraces may be classified into three general types: (a) bench terraces, (b) ridge terraces, and (c) channel terraces.

Bench terraces. Bench terraces are used to divide a steep hillside into a series of level or nearly level strips or benches running across the slope. The strips are separated by almost vertical risers, which are retained by rock or a heavy growth of vegetation. This type of terrace should be restricted to such uses as on vineyards and orchards planted on excessively steep slopes where frequent cultivation is practiced.

Ridge terraces. Ridge terraces are used primarily for water conservation through storage. They are constructed so as to flood collected runoff over as wide an area as possible. They are best adapted on low slopes and can be used safely only on soils with high infiltration rates and where rainfall intensities are low.

Channel terraces. The channel terrace is applicable both as a "cropland terrace" and as a "drainage terrace." The channel terrace acts primarily as a drainage channel to conduct excess rainfall from the fields at non-erosive velocities. On imperfectly drained soils the channel may also intercept subsurface flow and collect excessive ground water. Since low-velocity surface drainage is required, the channel, and not the ridge, is of primary importance. A wide, relatively shallow channel of low gradient that has gentle side slopes and ample water capacity will give the most desirable results. The excavated earth is used to bring the lower side of the channel to a height sufficient to provide necessary capacity. A ridge is not desirable since it seriously interferes with tillage operations, increases construction costs, and frequently requires, for its formation, that a large part of the topsoil be scraped from the field. In the channel terrace the ridge should be considered as supplemental to the channel and should blend gradually into the surface slopes to afford a minimum of interference with machinery operations.

There is little difference in the shape of "cropland terraces" and "drainage terraces." For the greatest drainage benefit, the channel should, in all cases, be cut into the subsoil a minimum of 6 to 8 inches. This will necessarily make this type of terrace channel deeper than the ordinary cropland terrace.

PLANNING THE TERRACE SYSTEM

In planning terraces for a field, all necessary terracing for the entire farm should be considered in order that terracing on any part of the farm may be fitted into the complete terrace system without difficulty or unnecessary expense. The possibility of rearrangement of fields, fences, and roads to conform to good land-utilization and farm-management policies should be kept in mind. Terraces should be planned according to drainage units—that is, areas that can be satisfactorily handled through one outlet or system of outlets. Such factors as ridges, drains, roads, large gullies, abrupt changes in slopes, property or field lines, and terrace lengths are some of the main determinants of boundary or division lines between terracing units. Adjacent farms may often have fields in the same drainage unit, in which case a joint terracing system may be used to advantage for both fields, provided a satisfactory agreement can be made between the two landowners for joint construction and maintenance of the terraces and outlets. These agreements must be in accordance with state and local laws.

When the field to be terraced receives any appreciable amount of runoff from an adjacent area, it will be necessary to intercept this runoff by means of a diversion terrace. If this is not done, the added water will cause overtopping of the first terrace and ultimately lead to failure of each succeeding terrace down the slope.

Terrace outlets. The first step in planning a terrace system is to select the location for the outlets or disposal areas. If protected areas or stabilized channels are not available, they must be provided before the terraces are constructed.

Vegetated outlets should be prepared one or two seasons in advance of terrace construction, depending on the length of time required to establish the cover density necessary to handle the velocity. In no case should terraces be constructed before adequate outlets are available to receive the discharge.

Locating terraces. The individual terraces on a field must be located to provide the necessary control of water, make farm operations as easy as possible, and perform satisfactorily with minimum maintenance requirements. The capacity of the top terrace must not be overtopped by runoff, or the whole system will be endangered. This means that the top terrace must be placed at a point near the top of the slope where the drainage area above is no greater than the drainage area above any other terrace of equal length.

If short, abrupt changes in slopes occur, terraces should be just above rather than on or at the foot of them. Minor adjustments should also be made in the location of successive terraces on the field in accordance with this principle. Such adjustments should not exceed 15 to 20 per cent of the applicable vertical interval of the terraces.

A short terrace is much easier to maintain than a long one and requires less channel capacity. In order to decrease the length of drainage in one direction, terraces may be crested at points about midway between outlets. The point of a ridge is an ideal location for the terrace crest and assures flow in both directions to the low points where outlets should be located. If possible, terraces should not be extended around the points of sharp ridges. If this is necessary, terraces should be strengthened at such points by enlarging the channel and increasing the height of ridge. Likewise, terraces should not be carried across depressions that collect considerable amounts of surface runoff, particularly if the terrace makes a sharp bend at this point. If it is necessary to carry terraces across such depressions, the terrace ridge and channel should be enlarged to handle the water safely.

Soil conditions. Another important factor in terrace planning is a study of the difficulties that may be encountered in terrace construction. The depth and type of soil are major considerations. In some cases, bedrock may be so close to the surface that terracing is impossible or the cost prohibitive. The type of soil may be such that the productive value of the land cannot possibly compensate for the cost of terracing.

In some cases, previous erosion may have reduced the depth of topsoil to such an extent that terracing is not feasible, or an area may be so badly gullied that the cost of constructing fills on terrace lines makes terracing impracticable.

FIGURE 119. The ends of terraces on sloping lands must outlet into especially prepared waterways that carry the water down the hillsides. (South Dakota)
(Soil Conservation Service)

TERRACE SPECIFICATIONS

Spacing. Since the need for terraces is dependent largely upon the slope of the field, the slope factor is paramount in determining the interval between terraces or their locations.

As a result of field observations and terrace-spacing studies at soil and water conservation experiment stations, Ramser established general terrace-spacing recommendations. The recommended terrace spacings for various field slopes are given in Table 65. In addition to the specified vertical interval between terraces on various slopes, this table gives the corresponding horizontal distance between terraces, the acreage of each terrace interval per mile or per 100 feet of terrace, and the feet of terrace required per acre of land.

The vertical interval in feet recommended can be determined by dividing the slope by 3 and adding 2 to the resulting quotient:

$$VI = \frac{S}{3} + 2$$

For example, the vertical interval in feet recommended for a 6 per cent slope is $\frac{6}{3} + 2 = 2 + 2 = 4$ feet.

For example, the vertical interval in feet recommended for a 6 per cent rainfall intensities are characteristic of the area to be terraced, the terrace spacing might be increased as much as 15 per cent with reasonable safety. But if rotations include a high percentage of row crops, if the soils are erodible, and if the rainfall intensities are high, terrace spacings should be decreased as much as 15 per cent. On some of the coastal-plain soils, however, where intensive cultivation is followed year after year, the minimum spacing should be used.

In spacing terraces for drainage improvement, the average or minimum vertical interval should be used as a guide. As a general rule, however, the maximum horizontal distance between such terraces should not exceed 80 to 100 feet for maximum drainage improvement.

On fairly uniform slopes, the average slope of the area can be used in computing the vertical interval for the terraces. If slopes vary considerably, the weighted average of all the slopes that a terrace is to cross should be used in computing the vertical terrace interval for each terrace.

Grades. Experimental results show that both the rate of runoff and the soil loss in runoff increases with steeper grades. Therefore, the minimum grade that will provide satisfactory drainage is desirable for both the "cropland" and "drainage" terrace. The grade should decrease from a maximum at the outlet end of the terrace to a minimum at the inlet end. Constant grade terraces are not recommended, except for drainage terraces.

In determining the final grade, the total estimated length of the terrace should be divided into increments of thirds or fourths and a variable grade established that increases toward the outlet end. The grades used depend primarily on the soils. Terrace grades should not be greater than 0.4 foot

TABLE 65. Recommended terrace spacings and related data for channel terraces—northern states (1)

$$VI = \frac{S}{3} + 2$$

Per cent slope (S)	Vertical (VI) interval			Horizontal distance			Acres per mile of terrace			Acres per 100 feet of terrace			Feet of terrace per acre		
	Minimum	Mean	Maximum	Minimum	Mean	Maximum	Minimum	Mean	Maximum	Minimum	Mean	Maximum	Minimum	Mean	Maximum
	Feet	Feet	Feet	Feet	Feet	Feet	Acres	Acres	Acres	Acres	Acres	Acres	Feet	Feet	Feet
1	1.70	2.00	2.30	170.00	200.00	230.00	20.60	24.24	27.87	0.390	0.459	0.528	256.23	217.80	189.39
2	2.27	2.67	3.07	113.47	133.50	153.52	13.75	16.18	18.61	.260	.306	.352	383.89	326.29	283.74
3	2.55	3.00	3.45	85.00	100.00	115.00	10.30	12.12	13.94	.195	.230	.264	512.47	435.60	378.78
4	2.83	3.33	3.83	70.76	83.25	95.74	8.58	10.09	11.60	.162	.191	.220	615.60	523.24	454.98
5	3.12	3.67	4.22	62.39	73.40	84.41	7.56	8.90	10.23	.143	.168	.194	698.19	593.46	516.05
6	3.40	4.00	4.60	56.67	66.67	76.67	6.87	8.08	9.29	.130	.153	.176	768.66	653.37	568.15
7	3.68	4.33	4.98	52.58	61.86	71.14	6.37	7.50	8.62	.121	.142	.163	828.45	704.17	612.31
8	3.97	4.67	5.37	49.62	58.38	67.13	6.01	7.08	8.14	.114	.134	.154	877.87	746.15	648.89
9	4.25	5.00	5.75	47.22	55.56	63.89	5.72	6.73	7.74	.108	.128	.147	922.49	784.02	681.80
10	4.53	5.33	6.13	45.30	53.30	61.29	5.49	6.46	7.43	.104	.122	.141	961.59	817.26	710.72
11	4.82	5.67	6.52	43.81	51.55	59.28	5.31	6.25	7.18	.101	.118	.136	994.29	845.00	734.82
12	5.10	6.00	6.90	42.50	50.00	57.50	5.15	6.06	6.97	.098	.115	.132	1024.94	871.20	757.56

per 100 feet of length, and in the coastal-plain areas the maximum grade should not be greater than 0.3 foot per 100 feet of length.

The application of these grades to a terrace 1,600 feet long in the Piedmont or Limestone Valley sections of the northeastern states might be somewhat as follows:

First 400 feet	0.1' per 100 feet
Second 400 feet	0.2' per 100 feet
Third 400 feet	0.3' per 100 feet
Fourth 400 feet	0.4' per 100 feet

The maximum grade should not be used except on the longer terraces. As the permeability or the erosiveness of the soil increases, greater increments of the lower grades should be used. The first 400 feet of a 1,000-foot terrace on coastal-plain soils might be given a grade of 0.05' per 100 feet, or, in some instances, established on the level or with no grade. When terraces are used primarily for drainage on imperfectly or poorly drained soils, the grades should be increased.

On imperfectly drained soils, a straight 0.4 or 0.5 per cent grade should be used. On poorly drained soils, a straight 0.6 per cent grade is best. On long terraces exceeding 1,500 feet, a variable grade of 0.4 per cent, 0.6 per cent, 0.8 per cent should be used. In some cases, where the subsoil is very heavy, grades as high as 1.0 per cent may be used safely. In no case should a grade higher than 1.0 per cent be used without a special design.

Caution. These higher grades should only be used in heavy claypan or hardpan soils. If used on light, sandy soils, serious erosion will occur in the channel when terraces are cultivated.

Lengths. In general, 1,600 feet is the maximum distance that a terrace should drain water in any one direction. On gullied land, a length of 1,200 feet should seldom be exceeded. When a few terraces in a system must exceed the maximum recommended lengths, they may be handled by draining the excess length to a convenient natural or vegetated outlet in a direction opposite to the outlet for the main part of the terrace; or the entire terrace may be drained in one direction, if the channel cross-section is increased toward the lower end to provide additional capacity. In no case should a terrace drain more than 2,000 feet in one direction. If plans indicate that all terraces in a system will have lengths in excess of 1,600 feet, two outlets should be provided.

Cross-sections. The three main requirements of satisfactory terrace cross-sections are: (a) ample channel capacity, (b) channel and ridge side slopes flat enough to permit the operation of farm machinery along the terrace without undue breaking-down of the terrace or hindrance to tillage operations, and (c) economical cost of terrace construction.

The side slopes of the channel or ridge should seldom be steeper than 4:1, and 5:1 is preferable. The water depth of a settled terrace should be from 15 to 18 inches. The minimum water cross-sectional area of the channel should seldom be less than 8 to 10 square feet. Long terraces should have a cross-sectional area greater than 8 to 10 square feet toward the lower end because there will be a greater accumulation of water in the lower reaches of the terrace.

TERRACE STAKING, REALIGNMENT, AND MARKING

Staking. The staking of terraces should always begin at the upper and of the slope, or top of the watershed. Having determined the applicable vertical interval from the average of slope readings on the area to be protected by the terrace, the rod man is sent to the top of the slope and a level reading taken on the rod held at this point. The vertical interval in feet is then added to the rod reading and the target set at the point on the rod determined by the sum of these two values. The rod is then taken to the outlet end of the terrace and moved up or down the slope until the target intersects a level line from the instrument. This point of intersection marks the outlet end of the terrace. The instrument must not be disturbed in the interval between the rod reading at the top of the slope and establishment of the end of the terrace; to do so necessitates a repetition of the process.

Having established the outlet end of the terrace, its course is then staked at 50-foot intervals on regular uniform slopes and at 25-foot intervals on irregular slopes. The distance between stakes can be determined sufficiently close by pacing. The grade of the terrace is maintained by moving the target up or down the rod a specified increment of the grade per 100 feet at each rod station. Since terraces should be staked from the outlet end toward the inlet end, the target is moved down on the rod for each station to give grade in the proper direction.

In staking out successive terraces on a field or a terrace system, the process described above is repeated, the only difference being that the staked line of the terrace immediately up the slope is used as a reference point in adding the vertical interval. The term "vertical interval" refers to the vertical distance between two terraces.

It is not always possible to secure the most satisfactory terrace layout in the first attempt. After a few lines have been staked, topographical conditions may sometimes necessitate changes in the terrace lines. If such changes are extensive, it is usually best to pull all stakes and start over again. Even experienced engineers cannot always select the most desirable starting point without first setting a few preliminary stakes and then making adjustments.

Realignment. After the terrace lines have been staked, some realignment is usually necessary on each proposed terrace in order to eliminate undesirable sharp curves, to obtain greater ease of construction, and to secure a finished terrace that will offer a minimum of inconvenience in later tillage operations. Realignment will usually consist of moving certain stakes up or down the slope until the most desirable terrace line is obtained.

When stakes are moved downslope, additional fill will be needed in the channel to obtain proper grade; when they are moved up the hill, additional cut will be needed in the channel to obtain proper grade. Usually, straightening in upward movement should be limited so that no more than 6-inch additional cuts are required. Straightening of terraces through depressions should be limited to one foot of fill.

Marking terrace lines. When, upon checking the terrace and outlet, it is determined that the entire layout is satisfactory, the terrace lines should be marked with a plow furrow, since stakes are easily lost and more difficult to follow in terrace construction.

TERRACE CONSTRUCTION

Farm implements can be used for constructing a good cropland terrace that meets all the requirements of size and shape. Horse- or tractor-drawn light blades, tractor-drawn moldboard plows, oneway disks, disk attachments for tractors, slip scrappers, V-drags, and fresnos have all proved practicable for terrace construction. Terraces can also be built with heavier, more expensive equipment designed especially for terracing. Many efficient terracing machines have been developed, such as the tractor-drawn two-wheeled blade grader, the motor-operated road maintainer, the elevating grader especially designed for terracing, and the rotary-type terracer. The cost on the one hand is labor and time with little cash outlay, and on the other the cash outlay is greater with a corresponding saving in time and labor.

On farms where there is a surplus of labor and equipment in the spring or fall seasons and where the cash outlay is a factor, preference should be given to the use of available farm equipment. It is not necessary to condition the installation of cropland terraces upon the availability of specially designed or heavy terracing equipment.

In building channel terraces, most of the earth should be moved from the upper side. This process tends to deepen the channel, which, as noted previ-

FIGURE 120. Terraces frequently are made with disk plows or grader equipment which form a hillside channel and ridge with the excavated material along the lower side of the resulting channel. (Monterey County, California)
(Soil Conservation Service)

ously, is the more important aspect of a cropland terrace. Where the terrace is installed primarily for drainage improvement the channel will, in most cases, be deeper than those of the regular cropland terrace. Added channel depth increases the extent of effective sub-surface drainage.

In terracing a field, the uppermost terrace should be constructed first and after it, in turn, each succeeding terrace down the slope. If the lower terraces are constructed first, they are likely to be badly damaged should a rain occur before the upper ones are completed.

No terrace can be considered completed until it has been checked for correct grade and height. To assure proper channel capacity and the flow of water in the direction desired, low places on the ridge and high spots in the terrace channel should be marked and corrected before the equipment leaves the field. They may also be checked with the level and rod through the same procedure used in laying out the terrace grade for construction.

In constructing terraces with inexperienced help, care should be taken on both "inside" and "outside" curves to keep the equipment on the staked line. There is a tendency to pull uphill on the "outside" curves and downhill on the "inside" curves, causing high and low places in the terrace channel.

FARMING TERRACED LAND

Since the primary function of a terrace system is to dispose of surplus water, construction of the system is only the beginning. The success of the terrace depends on how well this principle is understood and respected. Unless the strips between the terraces are farmed in such a way as to keep down erosion, the terrace channel is soon filled with sediment. The terrace then either overtops or breaks, causing serious damage on the lower reaches of the slope. Too often terraces are not properly maintained and the construction cost is wasted and serious damage done to the land.

Raths reported that a surprisingly large number of the terraces that had been in use for 5 years or more in the northeastern states were no longer effective. The failures were due primarily to the fact that the terraces were expected to prevent splash erosion, which they cannot do. The continued practice of growing clean-tilled crops and tillage up and down the slopes destroyed the effectiveness of the terraces as water carriers.

The simplest and most economical manner of maintaining terraces is by contour cultivation and prevention of erosion on the inter-terrace strips by use of adequate plant cover. If this is not done terraces are not only inefficient but dangerous. All farming operations should be parallel to the terraces. The most important operation in terrace maintenance is proper plowing. Plowing of each terrace should be started by throwing a back furrow to the ridge. When it is necessary to deepen the terrace channel, a dead furrow should be left in the channel.

DIVERSION TERRACES

Diversion terraces are constructed on hillsides across sloping land to intercept and divert surface runoff from lines of natural drainage. They prevent scour erosion on the lower reaches of the slope, and protect lowlands from overflow. Where possible, areas above the terrace should be maintained in vegetation, so that the runoff will not carry large amounts of silt into the channel.

Design. Generally, the cross-section of a diversion terrace should be designed for maximum hydraulic efficiency with the least earth-moving. Since, however, the runoff water enters the terrace channel over its upper side, the upper side should be flat to prevent erosion.

Diversion terraces are ordinarily laid out on the maximum non-erosive grade. If the channel is nonvegetated, the grade should not exceed 0.4 foot fall per 100 lineal feet in most soils. In certain highly erosive soils, the fall should not exceed 0.2 foot. In any case, the grade should be such that the velocities will not exceed those safe for the soil (and vegetation, if the channel has been seeded).

The location and design of diversion channel outlets are important. A wide, flat, well-vegetated outlet spreads the water in a thin sheet, preventing erosion. Where it is necessary to outlet a terrace into a gully, or channel on steep grade, sufficient protection in the form of check dams, chutes, vegetation, drop inlets, or channel lining must be provided to ensure a stable grade.

The capacity of the channel should ordinarily be designed for rainfall frequencies of from 10 to 15 years.

Diversion ditches should be constructed from the upslope side of the channel. Excavated material is piled to form a ridge on the downslope side to increase the effective depth of the channel. Ordinarily, protective vegetation should be established as soon as possible.

FIGURE 121. Diversion ditches are dug on a hillside across sloping land to intercept and divert surface runoff from lines of natural drainage. Maintaining the area above the channel in vegetation prevents large amounts of silt being carried into the channel. (Lancaster County, Pennsylvania)
(Soil Conservation Service)

Regular maintenance is required to keep out bushy or woody growths which obstruct flow and cause silt accumulations.

CHECK DAMS

Protecting channels means preventing injurious erosion in waterways—within the flow channels. Check dams are one method. Temporary materials such as brush, wire, and logs are used at frequent intervals across the bottom of a channel when the only need is for temporary stabilization of seedbeds. Under this plan, the vegetation gains control during the life of the dam, and when the dam decays it need not be replaced. In some cases 12-inch strips of grass sod are placed at regular intervals across the waterways in place of structures.

In locations where vegetation alone will not withstand the erosive forces, permanent dams of concrete, masonry, steel piling, or other long-lasting materials may be used.

Downstream grades. To be effective, permanent control structures must have stable downstream grades. To satisfy this requirement, it may be necessary to build several structures in the downstream reaches of a channel before locating one far upstream for checking overfall erosion at the head of

FIGURE 122. Temporary check dams made of boards. They are used to stabilize the bottom of the channel until a sod can be established. (Spartanburg, South Carolina)
(Soil Conservation Service)

FIGURE 123. Strips of sod laid across the bottom of the channel at regular intervals take the place of structures under many conditions. (Pulaski County, Arkansas)
(Soil Conservation Service)

FIGURE 124. Where vegetation alone will not withstand the erosive forces, permanent dams are constructed across the channel. (Maryland)
(Soil Conservation Service)

a channel. A stable grade exists when the channel is neither agrading nor degrading. Some of the important factors affecting grade stability are velocity, amount of vegetation in the channel, alignment, abrasive materials in transport, and the erodibility of the material of which the channel is composed.

TABLE 66. Permissible velocities for drainage channels without linings (2)

Original material excavated	Clear water, no detritus	Water transporting colloidal silts	Water transporting noncolloidal silts, sands, gravel of rock fragments
	fps	fps	fps
Fine sand, noncolloidal	1.50	2.50	1.50
Sandy loam, noncolloidal	1.75	2.50	2.00
Silt loam, noncolloidal	2.00	3.00	2.00
Alluvial silts, noncolloidal	2.00	3.50	2.00
Ordinary firm loam	2.50	3.50	2.25
Volcanic ash	2.50	3.50	2.00
Fine gravel	2.50	5.00	3.75
Stiff clay, very colloidal	3.75	5.00	3.00
Graded, loam to cobbles, noncolloidal	3.75	5.00	5.00
Alluvial silts, colloidal	3.75	5.00	5.00
Graded, silt to cobbles, colloidal	4.00	5.50	5.00
Coarse gravel, noncolloidal	4.00	6.00	6.50
Cobbles and shingles	5.00	5.50	6.50
Shales and hardpans	6.00	6.00	5.00

Although Table 66 is based on continuous flow conditions, most gully flow is intermittent, which produces varying effects in different soils. The silt carried in flow also produces varying effects in different soils. In some locations, upstream structures that cut off much of the silt load may be cause for reducing downstream erosion. In other locations, this reduction of silt loads may tend to increase downstream erosion. The matter of silt in transport requires special analysis for purposes of establishing stabilized grades.

Overfall structures. Where water enters the head (upper end) of a gully by an overfall, a structure may be needed to check the overfall erosion. This structure must be located where it will establish a non-erosive grade from the crest of the spillway to the elevation from which the water falls. This grade will be dependent on soil conditions and may be determined by investigating the grades of existing gullies and channels in similar soils that appear to be stable.

The safety of a check dam depends not only on the downstream grade but also the capacity of the spillway. The procedure, outlined under hydrologic surveys, should be used in arriving at peak flows for design purposes.

Drop inlets. Drop inlet spillways for grade stabilization or head-erosion control are ideally adapted to installations in gullies where the drop is in excess of approximately 10 feet. The structure is incorporated in earth dams and is usually constructed of monolithic concrete. Metal pipe or vitrified clay tile also may be used. Drop inlets are especially adapted to road crossings and may be used in conjunction with road construction wherever gully stabilization is a problem.

In some locations, conditions at the site may require that the drop inlet be designed to discharge the entire peak flow for a drainage area. In others, it is feasible to provide an auxiliary vegetated spillway to discharge a portion of the peak. Where this is done, the elevation of the two spillways should be established to permit the drop inlet to discharge at its rated capacity before the auxiliary spillway functions.

Chutes. Chutes are used in many locations to convey water to lower elevations. They are employed to lower runoff from the top of fills, to convey surface runoff down into deep channels and gullies. They also are used in combination with earth dams to drop water greater distances than is ordinarily feasible with overfall structures, and in many other situations. When chutes are located on fill materials, the fill should be carefully compacted under controlled conditions. If the chute is not set below the depth to which the ground freezes, some heaving due to frost action may occur. The use of closely-spaced expansion joints is needed, especially in areas subject to severe winter temperatures. Cutoff walls must be provided to obviate piping action and to anchor the structure against sliding.

CONTOUR FARMING

Contour farming is preparing, planting or drilling, and cultivation of crops along and parallel to level lines that have been laid out across the field slope.

Use. Contour farming should be used on sloping land in conjunction with contour strip-cropping, terracing, diversions, and contour orchards. It may be used alone on fields where contouring will adequately control water during most rains, or where slopes are too short for contour strip-cropping, and on odd-shaped pieces of land where other practices have covered most of the field.

Land contour-farmed can be expected to make more economical use of water during periods of low rainfall. Contour farming also aids in controlling scour erosion during all but the heaviest rains. The net result is a substantial increase in crop yields in most cases.

Installation. When farming contour strip-cropped fields, terraced fields, fields with diversions, and contour orchards, cultivation should be parallel to guide lines. Where field slope is less than two normal strip widths, a contour line should be laid out through the middle of the field and planting done parallel to this line. Where large fields are to be contour-farmed, contour lines should be laid out at normal strip intervals to ensure that the field will be planted on the contour. Planting should be done so as to leave short rows or odd areas midway between guide lines.

Where it is necessary to have rows on grade, this can be accomplished by cultivating parallel to terraces, diversions, or guide lines laid out on grade not exceeding one per cent.

When contour farming is used alone, new guide lines must be established each time the crop is planted, unless provision is made to maintain original lines by contour hedges, back furrows, or other means.

GRASS-LINED WATERWAYS

Grass-lined waterways comprise an important part of the water-disposal system. The flow characteristics of grass-lined channels must be understood if best results are to be had from their use.

Wherever natural, sodded drainageways are available on agricultural land, they should be used and should be carefully maintained. They are the best type of channel for collecting and carrying surplus surface water. Where terrace systems are installed, new drainage channels must sometimes be made. New channels should be lined with vegetation, and whenever plant covers protecting drainageways are seriously damaged, as they often are by weather factors, rodents, sediment deposits, or farm implements, they should be re-established. Before undertaking to establish a grass-lined channel, one needs to know the characteristics of different kinds of vegetation with reference to channel capacity and stability.

The Soil Conservation Service conducted studies to determine the hydraulic characteristics of vegetation in channels. These studies were conducted at outdoor laboratories near Spartanburg, South Carolina, and Stillwater, Oklahoma, under field conditions. The laboratory at Spartanburg was located on a rather steep hillside along a small stream in the Piedmont Plateau. The data thus obtained are directly applicable to the design of similar channels in the field.

These studies dealt with plant species adapted primarily to the southeastern and south-central states. Extensive experimentation was carried out with Bermuda grass, common lespedeza, and a mixture of orchardgrass, sudangrass, Dallis grass, and crabgrass. A channel lined with kudzu was subjected to experiments pertaining to seasonal conditions and growth and to one designed to determine the effect of plowing in channel banks covered with kudzu in a dormant condition.

Agronomic variables involved were growth, season, and channel-maintenance conditions. Slope of channel bed ranged from 1 to 24 per cent, but in most instances was either 3 or 6 per cent. Two general types of channel were used, the trapezoidal or the rectangular.

The protective capacity of each channel lining was measured by determining the maximum mean velocity of flow to which the lining could be subjected for a reasonable length of time without ceasing to protect the channel from severe erosion. This velocity, sometimes called "safe," "allowable," or "non-eroding," is referred to here as "permissible."

The results of the experiments demonstrate that the degree to which channel vegetation retards flow of water depends largely upon the degree to which the vegetation is bent and flattened by the flow, and that this depends mainly upon physical characteristics of the vegetation, its manner of growth, and the velocity and depth of the flow.

Findings from the study have immediate practical value for application not only in the southeastern and south central states but also in other areas where the same or similar types of vegetation may be used as channel linings. Data obtained have served as a basis for (a) establishing permissible velocities of intermittent flow and (b) developing a graphic method of determining a cross-section that will permit a channel to carry the expected flow at a velocity not exceeding the permissible.

The hydraulic characteristics covered in these studies include the resistance offered to flow by the vegetation, the protection offered the channel bed, and the effect of vegetation on the flow characteristics in the channel. Each of these will be discussed in turn. Suggestions will be offered on the use of these data in the solution of design problems.

RESISTANCE TO FLOW

The most important hydraulic characteristic of a vegetation is the resistance it offers to flowing water. A common measure of this resistance is the retardance coefficient in Manning's formula. This formula is usually written as

$V = \dfrac{1.486}{n} R^{2/3} S^{1/2}$ where V is mean velocity, R is the hydraulic radius,* S

is the slope, and n is the retardance coefficient. This coefficient will be referred to as Manning's n. In passing it might be well to mention that Kutter's n and Manning's n are not the same. They are equal when R equals one meter but differ for all other values. This difference is large for small, rough channels. In this discussion only Manning's n is used.

Determinations of Manning's n were made for different vegetations under a variety of conditions. The procedure was the same in each instance. The vegetation to be evaluated was established in a channel. When it was desired to test the vegetation a series of measured flows of water were passed down the channel. During each flow, measurements were made which enabled the determination of the hydraulic elements. By substitution in Manning's formula the value of n was computed for each test. Experiments were performed on a number of vegetations in channels of various slopes and cross-sections. Tests were also made at different times of the year and under different maintenance practices.

The most striking thing observed about the values of Manning's n obtained was their great range. Values ranged from 0.02 to 0.6. Even one vegetation in a single channel showed nearly this variation.

The diagram in Figure 125 shows the results of tests on two identical Bermuda grass channels. The values of Manning's n are plotted against corresponding values of depth. The range of n here is seen to be from over .4 to less than .04.

An explanation for this variation is found readily if the behavior of the grass during this experiment is considered. The flows of very small depths encountered a maximum resistance, as indicated by the large n values. In this range, the vegetation is upright in the flow and is neither bent nor submerged. The gradual increase in this range may be due to the greater bulk

* The cross-sectional area of a stream divided by its wetted perimeter.

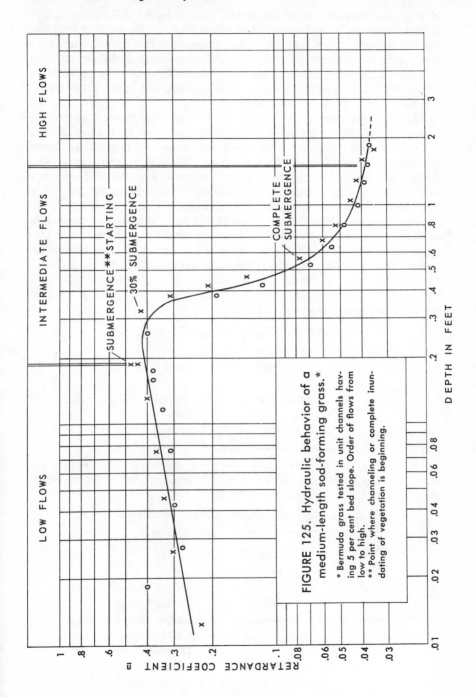

FIGURE 125. Hydraulic behavior of a medium-length sod-forming grass.*

* Bermuda grass tested in unit channels having 5 per cent bed slope. Order of flows from low to high.
** Point where channeling or complete inundating of vegetation is beginning.

of vegetation encountered at the slightly greater depths. As the discharge is further increased, a depth is reached where some of the grass is bent over and submerged. The *n* values then start to decrease rapidly with increase in flow depth. When bending and submerging are completed, the *n* curve starts to level out and approaches a constant value. All vegetations tested at the laboratory behaved in this same manner and resulted in the same type of curve.

The retardance-coefficient picture was further complicated by the discovery that similar vegetations have different *n*-depth curves for channels of different slope or cross-section. Each combination of vegetation, channel cross-section, and channel slope yielded a different *n*-depth curve when tested. Each channel seemed to be a law unto itself. The possibility of simple solutions for vegetal channel design problems seemed remote if not impossible. However, it was found that if *n* values were plotted against the product of VR (where V is the mean velocity and R the hydraulic radius) instead of depth, approximately the same curve would be obtained for a given vegetation regardless of the type of slope of channel. It was further discovered that vegetation of similar physical characteristics had similar *n*-VR curves. This led to a classification of velocities on the basis of their *n*-VR curves. Five classes of vegetal retardance were selected and given letter designations. These are shown in Table 67.

TABLE 67. Classes of vegetal retardance

Very high	Class A
High	Class B
Moderate	Class C
Low	Class D
Very low	Class E

The average *n*-VR curve was determined for each class. Figure 126 shows these five *n*-VR curves. The physical characteristics of the vegetation in each of the classes are given in Table 68.

TABLE 68. Physical characteristics of retardance classes

Degree of retardance	Stand	Length of vegetation
A	Good	Longer than 30 inches
B	Good	11 to 24 inches
	Fair	Longer than 30 inches
C	Good	6 to 10 inches
	Fair	11 to 24 inches
D	Good	2 to 6 inches
	Fair	2 to 6 inches
E	All	Less than 2 inches

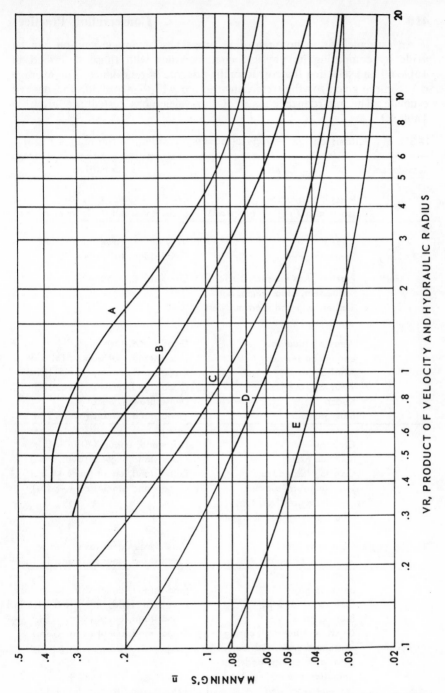

FIGURE 126. Degrees of vegetal retardance for which graphic solutions
of the Manning formula have been prepared.
(Soil Conservation Service)

An estimate of the flow-retarding properties of any vegetation can be made by comparing its physical characteristics with those described in Table 69 and selecting the corresponding degree of retardance. The average n-VR curve given for this retardance group will then provide the desired estimate. The retardance classes of the vegetations tested are given in Table 69.

TABLE 69. Classification of vegetal covers according to retardance (2, 3)

Retardance	Cover	Condition
A	Weeping lovegrass	Excellent stand, tall, (ave. 30 inch)
	Ischaemum (Yellow gluestem)	Excellent stand, tall, (ave. 36 inch)
B	Kudzu	Very dense growth, uncut
	Bermuda grass	Good stand, tall, (ave. 12 in.)
	Native grass mixture (little bluestem, blue grama, and other long and short midwest grasses)	Good stand, unmowed
	Weeping lovegrass	Good stand, tall, (ave. 24 in.)
	Lespedeza sericea	Good stand, not woody, tall (19 in.)
	Alfalfa	Good stand, uncut, (ave. 11 in.)
	Weeping lovegrass	Good stand, mowed, (ave. 13 in.)
	Kudzu	Dense growth, uncut
	Blue grama	Good stand, uncut, (ave. 13 in.)
C	Crabgrass	Fair stand, uncut, (10 in.–48 in.)
	Bermuda grass	Good stand, mowed (ave. 6 in.)
	Common lespedeza	Good stand, uncut (ave. 11 in.)
	Grass mixture–summer (orchardgrass, red top, Italian ryegrass, and common lespedeza)	Good stand, uncut (6 in.–8 in.)
	Centipede grass	Very dense cover (ave. 6 in.)
	Kentucky bluegrass	Good stand, headed (6 in.–12 in.)
D	Bermuda grass	Good stand, cut to 2.5 inch height
	Common lespedeza	Excellent stand, uncut (ave. 4.5 in.)
	Buffalo grass	Good stand, uncut (3 in.–6 in.)
	Grass mixture–Fall, spring (orchard grass, red top, Italian ryegrass, and common lespedeza)	Good stand, uncut (4 in.–5 in.)
	Lespedeza sericea	After cutting to 2 inch height. Very good stand before cutting.
E	Bermuda grass	Good stand, cut to 1.5 inch height
	Bermuda grass	Burned stubble

One advantage of this system of classification is the elimination of the need for knowing the many values of Manning's *n*. Instead, only five classes of resistance need be remembered. When this system is coupled with the computation method to be described next, the advantages are many.

A diagram has been prepared for each retardance class which provides a direct solution of Manning's formula. The diagram for vegetations of Retardance E (very low retardance) is presented in Figure 127. With two of the three variables (R, S, and V) given, the third can be found directly

FIGURE 127. Solution of the Manning formula for Retardance E (very low vegetal retardance).
(Soil Conservation Service)

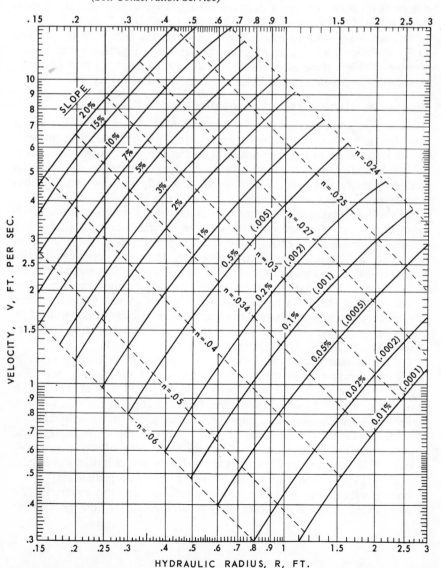

by means of this diagram. Many diagrams have been prepared to aid in the solution of channel flow problems, but this is the only type that provides a direct solution with a variable retardance coefficient.

Vegetated channels are usually broad and shallow. They have their design flows in the range of most rapid change of n. If a very laborious trial and error solution is to be avoided, such a graphical aid becomes a necessity.

The usual problem in design of vegetated channels is the selection of channel shape and dimensions. The discharge rate, Q, and slope, S, are known. A vegetation to line this channel is chosen on the basis of both hydraulic and agronomic conditions. A design velocity, V, is selected. (The selection of a design, or permissible, velocity will be discussed in the section on protective characteristics.) The retardance class of the vegetation is determined. Then entering a diagram such as Figure 127 with the known S and selected V, the required R is determined directly.

The necessary area of cross-section, A, is readily computed by dividing Q by V. With both R and A given, the channel dimensions can be determined. This is done most readily by the use of diagrams that show the relationship between A, R, and channel shape and dimensions.

VEGETAL PROTECTION AGAINST EROSION

The most important property of a vegetation for vegetated waterways is its ability to protect the waterway from scour. This might be more properly called a structural rather than a hydraulic characteristic. However, it must be considered along with strictly hydraulic properties when a channel is designed; hence this protective property is usually included with the hydraulic properties.

The usual measure of the protective ability of a vegetation is the maximum velocity to which the vegetation can be subjected and still protect the channel from serious erosion. The testing procedure at the laboratory permitted the determination of this property. Prior to a test flow, careful measurements were made of the channel bed. After the flow was turned out of the channel those measurements were repeated. In this way a measure of the depth of scour during the test was obtained. When the rate of this soil removal became excessive, the permissible velocity was assumed to have been exceeded. The bed measurements were supplemented by visual observations to aid in this determination.

The permissible velocity for a vegetation depends on the kind and quality of the vegetation and on the texture of the soil in the channel bed. Sod vegetations have the highest permissible velocities, and very clumpy bunch grasses, the lowest. Complete sods give full protection to the channel bed, while bunch-type grasses have unprotected bare areas between the clumps. In addition, turbulence develops around a large clump of vegetation and causes considerable local scour. Channel slope also affects permissible velocity. The steeper the channel, the smaller is the permissible velocity. This is due to the extremely turbulent flow in the very steep channels.

The velocities given in Table 70 apply to good, uniform covers in uniform channels only. For poorer or less uniform cover, the permissible velocities should be reduced. Tests on one Bermuda grass channel with a small, bare water course running its length indicated a mean permissible velocity of only 4 feet per second. This is only half that allowed for a good uniform cover. The velocities that existed in and around the bare section of the channel may have greatly exceeded 4 feet per second. Since velocities

TABLE 70. Permissible velocities for channels lined with vegetation (2)

Cover	Slope range, per cent	Erosion resistant soils	Permissible velocity, feet per second, easily-eroded soil
Centipede grass	0–5	9	7
Bermuda grass, good turf kept	5–10	8	6
mowed	over 10	7	5
	0–5	8	6
Bermuda grass	5–10	7	5
	over 10	6	4
Buffalo grass			
Kentucky bluegrass	0–5	7	5
Smooth brome	5–10	6	4
Blue grama	over 10	5	3
	0–5	5	4
	5–10	4	3
Grass mixture			
	Do not use on slopes steeper than 10 per cent		
Lespedeza sericea	0–5	3.5	2.5
Weeping lovegrass			
Ischaemum (Yellow bluestem)			
Kudzu	Do not use on slopes steeper than 5 per cent except for side slopes in a combination channel		
Crabgrass			
Alfalfa			
Annuals—used on mild slopes or as temporary protection until permanent	0–5	3.5	2.5
covers are established	Not recommended for use on slopes steeper than 5 per cent		
Common lespedeza			
Sudangrass			

were not measured there is no way of knowing. In ordinary channel design, however, it is not practical to consider the velocity distribution in the cross-section. The mean velocity is the only one that can be used.

VELOCITY DISTRIBUTION

Some measurements of velocity distribution were made in a grass-lined channel. The instrument used was a Pitot tube, with which it was possible to get a complete traverse (survey) from channel bed to water surface. Figure 128 is the velocity distribution curve obtained for one vertical traverse. Also shown on this figure is the top of the grass mat in the channel. This is a typical vertical velocity distribution curve for a channel. The low velocities in section occupied by the grass are immediately apparent. From the channel bed to near the top of the grass mat, the velocities do not exceed one foot per second. At the upper surface of the grass mat, the velocity starts to increase rapidly. From this point on the velocity distribution curve approximates that normally found in non-vegetal channels.

A study of this diagram indicates why a vegetal lining protects a channel bed from erosion. Not only are velocities lowest at the channel bed but the

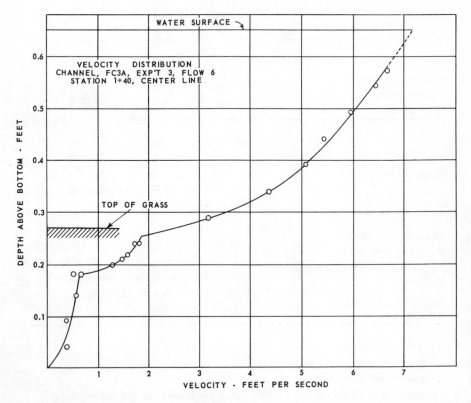

FIGURE 128. Stillwater Outdoor Hydraulic Laboratory.
(Soil Conservation Service)

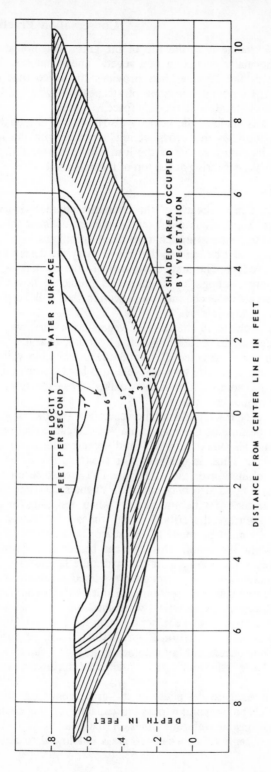

FIGURE 129. Velocity distribution in a grass-lined channel. Dormant, un-cut Bermuda grass on 3 per cent slope. Test at Stillwater Outdoor Hydraulic Laboratory. *(Soil Conservation Service)*

zone of greatest rate of change is at the top of the grass mat, not at the channel bed where it normally occurs in non-vegetal lined channels. The steep velocity gradient at the channel bed provides the force that dislodges the soil particles. Removing the zone of steepest velocity gradient from the channel bed should remove an eroding force.

A complete traverse was made of the velocity distribution in the channel cross-section. Figure 129 shows this cross-section, together with the lines of equal velocity. This diagram also shows the low velocities near the bed, with the most rapid increase occurring at the top of the grass mat.

APPLICATION TO DESIGN PROBLEMS

The foregoing has been a brief review of the hydraulic characteristics of vegetation in waterways. Suggestions will now be offered on how this information can be applied to conservation channel design problems.

A conservation channel must be built so that it will carry the design flood without overtopping or eroding. The first requirement is met by making the channel cross-section large enough to contain the predicted flow. The second is achieved by selecting a channel cross-section that will keep the mean velocity below the permissible.

This is not a simple problem in the case of vegetated waterways. The complication is introduced by the variabilitiy of the hydraulic characteristics of the vegetation. Both the retardance class and the permissible velocity vary during the year because of the growth cycle and because of maintenance operations. A second complication is the weather. The expected flood flow may differ for each month in the year.

With both the hydraulic characteristics of the vegetation and the expected flood flow varying with the time of the year, it may be difficult to select the critical or design periods. The maximum flow and highest retardance may not occur at the same time. Thus, in designing for capacity, it may be unnecessary to use the combination of the extremes. The lowest permissible velocity and the maximum flood also may not occur at the same time. So a combination of these extremes may be unnecessary when designing for permissible velocity. What then are the critical design times? To answer this question a careful analysis must be made of the seasonal variations of the hydraulic characteristics and the runoff. How this can be done will be illustrated by a study of one of the channels at the hydraulic laboratory.

The channel to be examined is a Bermuda grass-lined waterway on a 6 per cent slope with a triangular cross-section with side slopes 1 foot fall to 10 feet horizontal distances. A hypothetical watershed has been assumed for this channel and the expected 10-year flood computed for each month of the year. This information is plotted on Figure 130A. It will be noticed that the peak discharge rate occurs in May with nearly as high a runoff to be expected in September. Very little discharge is anticipated during the winter months.

The next step is to investigate the effect of the grass condition on the capacity of the channel. The maximum possible capacity of the channel for various cover conditions at different times of the year is shown on Figure 130B. It will be observed that when the grass is allowed to remain

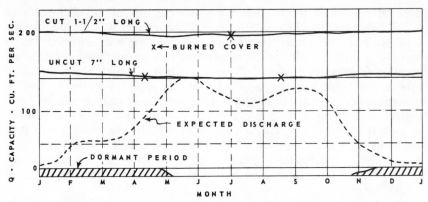

FIGURE 130-A. Maximum possible capacity (capacity of channel if flow-
        ing full).

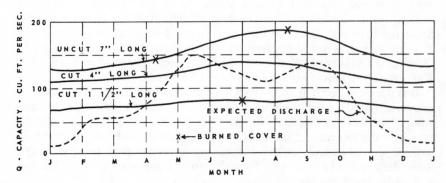

FIGURE 130-B. Maximum permissible capacity (capacity of channel if
        permissible velocity is not exceeded).

FIGURE 130. The flow capacity of Bermuda grass-lined channel as in-
        fluenced by season and maintenance practice. Channel
        shape—triangular; slope—6 per cent; side slopes—1 on 10.
        (Stillwater Outdoor Hydraulic Laboratory)
        (Soil Conservation Service)

long, the channel will have its minimum capacity. It will have a slightly
lower capacity in the summer months than the winter. Dormant vegetation
seems to have slightly lower retardance coefficients than green vegetation
of equal length and density. The critical design condition for capacity
occurs in May with the cover left in an uncut condition. The channel has
just sufficient capacity to meet the maximum flood flow. If the grass had
been cut or burned off, the channel could carry a greater flow rate, but
then the permissible velocity probably would be exceeded.

The next step is to study the permissible velocity in the channel. This was done by computing the maximum possible capacity of the channel. This is the flow rate the channel can carry without exceeding the permissible velocity. When the grass is left long it will have the greatest resistance to flow. As a result, it will take a higher flow rate to produce the maximum permissible velocity. Figure 130B indicates that it would take a discharge rate of 180 cubic feet per second before the water would be flowing at its permissible velocity. In this case, however, the channel would be over-topped since its capacity at this stage of growth is only 150 cubic feet per second. If the grass were cut to a length of 4 inches the resistance to flow would be so reduced that the permissible velocity would be reached by a flow of only 130 cubic feet per second. Since the flow rate may exceed this at two different times in the year, it may be advisable to control the time of cutting the grass.

Presumably, if the grass were cut in mid-June it would grow enough in the summer to develop sufficient retarding properties to slow the September runoff to permissible speeds. If the grass in the channel were kept grazed very short, the resistance to flow would be so low that the permissible velocity would be reached with a flow of only 80 cubic feet per second. Since the expected discharge rate will exceed this at all times during the growing season, it would not be advisable to graze the channel too heavily. If the cover is burned off, the permissible capacity drops to only 20 cubic feet per second. Obviously burning is not advisable for this channel.

It is not proposed that an analysis such as the foregoing be made for each channel. It is suggested that a study should be made of the runoff character-istics of the locality, together with the seasonal characteristics of the vegeta-tion, in order to arrive at the critical design periods. Such a study will help indicate desirable and undesirable maintenance practices for waterways. Some such method seems to be the only rational approach to vegetal design and maintenance problems.

DEVELOPMENT OF WATERWAYS

Figure 131 is useful for computing the dimensions of vegetated waterways.

To illustrate the use of this diagram, suppose the water from a terrace system is released on a 7 per cent slope, and the channel that receives this flow is to be vegetated with an excellent bluegrass cover capable of with-standing a velocity of 5.5 feet per second. The estimated maximum runoff is 55 cubic feet per second. The channel cross-section must then be $\frac{55}{5.5}$, or 10 square feet. To find the required channel width and depth, enter right-hand side of chart in Figure 131 at 5.5 per second. Follow this line vertically upward to the diagonal line representing a slope of 7 per cent. From this point trace horizontally to the left, to a point of intersection on the solid curved line representing 10 square feet. Now turn vertically to the base of the chart and read the bottom width of channel, 22.5 feet. The depth is interpolated from the broken curved lines showing depth. To make the interpolation, trace back to the point where vertical and horizontal lines intersect the solid curved lines showing 10 square feet of area. An inter-polation between broken curved lines indicates a depth of 5 to 6 inches. A

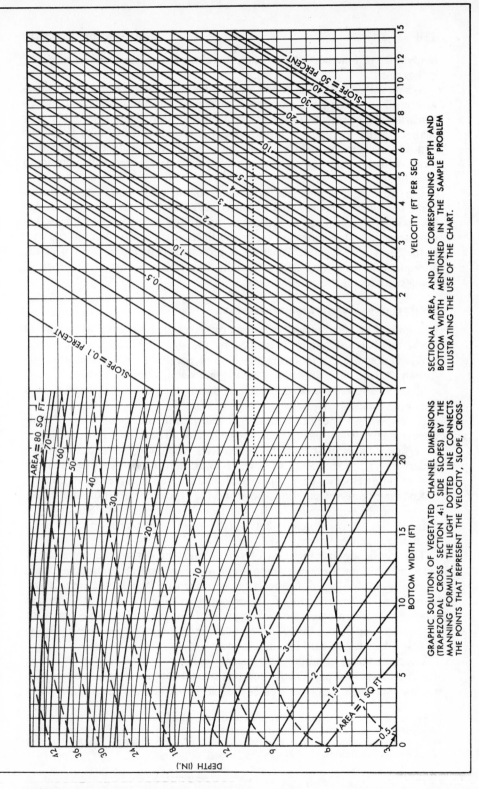

FIGURE 131. Computing dimensions of vegetated waterways.

freeboard* of 6 inches is to be used, therefore the channel will be made 12 inches deep.

Whenever possible, the runoff water should be diverted from the waterway until vegetation has become established. This is sometimes done by constructing a protective dike at the head and along each side of the new channel. After the grass in the waterway is established this dike should be removed. Where such diversion is not possible the seedbed may be protected with burlap or straw mulch, which may be covered with wire mesh to secure it.

Careful design is important to secure adequate inlet and outlet, and to make certain that short and very infrequent runoff in excess of the design flow will not cause excessive damage. In many instances where the soil is satisfactory, the low flows are carried in lined channels. Additional capacity in the form of a vegetated channel is provided to handle a portion of the infrequent larger flows, thus materially reducing the cost of the channel lining by reducing the cross-section.

CONSTRUCTING VEGETATED WATERWAYS

If a gully has been carved in a waterway selected to serve as a part of the water disposal system, it is filled by plowing or blading in the banks, moving enough earth to secure the desired parabolic or trapezoidal cross-section. All fill material should have some compaction to provide a good seedbed and to reduce erosion hazards during the period that vegetation is becoming established.

There are no specific criteria for determining the conditions of flow where vegetative measures become ineffective. There are, however, three important factors that must be considered when vegetative channels are under study: (a) frequency of flow, (b) duration of flow, and (c) velocity of flow. Safe velocities have been established for various types of vegetation.

Knowing these velocity limitations and the types of vegetation applicable, a study of the topography, soils, and runoff will reveal whether or not a channel can be constructed that will be safe against erosion when only vegetative practices are employed.

The frequency and duration of runoff must be considered before final recommendations for construction are made. Frequent or continuous flows, especially in V-shaped channels, may seriously impair the vegetation. Sometimes the installation of tile or concrete pipe to carry the constant small flows will protect the waterway. This is particularly effective with vegetations that do not thrive in wet soils. Metal flumes or concrete half-pipe sections also may be used for this purpose.

Under ordinary conditions of intermittent runoff in vegetated channels, the triangular- and particularly the trapezoidal-shaped channel sections do not maintain their shapes as well as the parabolic. In most cases, the actions

* Freeboard is the vertical distance between the maximum water surface elevation anticipated in design and the top of retaining banks or structures. Freeboard is provided to prevent overtopping of structures because of wave action or the development of unforeseen conditions.

TABLE 71. Permissible velocities in vegetated channels (2, 3)

Types of vegetation	Permissible velocities, fps*			
	Silts and clays		Sandy soils	
	Good vegetation	Fair vegetation	Good vegetation	Fair vegetation
Bermuda grass	8	5.3	5	3.3
Kentucky bluegrass	5.5	3.7	4	2.7
Blue grama grass	5.5	3.7	4	2.7
Buffalo grass	5.5	3.7	4	2.7
Alfalfa	2.5	1.7	1.5	1.5

* These velocities apply to slopes of up to 10 per cent. A velocity decrease of 2 per cent should be made effective for each 1 per cent increase in slope above 10 per cent. Thus for a slope of 15 per cent each of the indicated velocities would be reduced by 10 per cent.

of channel flow, deposition, and bank erosion tend to make the trapezoidal and triangular sections become parabolic in shape. For this reason, most waterways are designed and constructed as trapezoidal sections; these are also more easily constructed.

BANK PROTECTION

There are two general classes of bank protection: (a) that which retards the flow along the banks, and causes deposition of silt; and (b) that which protects the bank directly by covering the soil so that it will resist the eroding effect of the stream.

Jetties constructed of piling, rock, metal, or concrete tetrahedrons, trees, or other materials are examples of the type of protection causing deposits. Riprap, brush mats, concrete slabs, and asphalt linings are examples of protection accomplished by covering the bank itself.

The type of protection best adapted to a specific site is largely determined by the nature of the problem and by the materials and equipment available.

Vegetation may both retard velocities and cover or shield soils against erosive flow. It plays an important part in the control of bank erosion. It may be used alone on small streams, or it may be used in conjunction with mechanical measures. Vegetation should be used back of revetments and jetties in the area where deposition occurs and on slopes protected by brush mats.

Tree jetty. The cheapest, semi-permanent protection for stopping bank erosion is often obtained by anchoring trees in such a way that they will reduce velocities to a point of causing silt deposits. The trees are laid with the butts upstream. The trunks are anchored to deadmen set in the bank. The primary purpose of a tree jetty of this type is to impede velocities and thereby cause silt deposits. Grass or trees may be established on these deposits at a later date. As soon as satisfactory conditions have been established, adaptable vegetation should be planted to take over the protection job.

Brush mats. Brush mats with shrubs or tree plantings, protected at the toe with rock riprap, may give very good results. This may be an expensive type of construction due to the hand labor involved. A brush mat has a short life, and its main function is to afford a mulch that will assist in establishing a dense growth of vegetation. The banks may be sloped, the toe riprapped, and the brush mat laid at any season. The plantings are then made through the mat.

Willows are usually the best planting material. The brush is laid in shingle fashion with the butts pointing up the bank. The mat may vary from 3 to 18 inches in thickness, depending on the size of the stream and quantity of floating ice, logs, or other heavy debris. The mat is held in place by driving stakes at an angle crossing each other in pairs, or by stakes driven straight into the ground about 2 feet 6 inches on centers and interlaced with galvanized wire. After the wire is attached, the stakes are driven at an angle which increases the tension of the toe.

Riprap. Riprap is a very effective method of streambank protection. It is often costly because of the cost of quarrying, transporting, and placing stone. For riprap to be successful, the toe must have sufficient weight and

FIGURE 132. A brush mat. The brush are laid in shingle fashion with the butts upstream. The mat is held in place by poles fastened to stakes driven in the ground. (Santa Cruz County, California)
(Soil Conservation Service)

be deep enough to be stable under all conditions of flow. Where the stone is loose-dumped on the slope, it should never be steeper than 1½:1. The stability of the riprap will be improved if the rock is laid on a gravel blanket of at least 6 inches in thickness.

Piling. Continuous piling revetment, with a facing of woven wire, is a very common type of protection. It is particularly adapted to streams where the depth of water is more than 3 or 4 feet. It has an advantage in that it does not need a stable foundation for holding the riprap in place.

A more expensive type of construction is built by using two rows of piling with rock and brush piled between. The rock and brush are placed in wire baskets. If the basket settles, the wire may be extended and additional material added to keep the brush and rock level with the top of the piling.

OPEN CHANNEL DRAINS

Open channels are needed when surface water does not move off the land freely. Open ditches provide outlets for runoff from terraces and other hillside diversions, tile systems, and for removal of other runoff waters. They are generally needed where land slopes are very flat and soils are shallow and impervious, where pockets or low areas occur, and where upland runoff must be removed. This subject is discussed more fully in Chapter 21.

TILE DRAINS

Tile drainage removes excess free water from the soil—but not, ordinarily, water needed by vegetation—and establishes a better moisture-soil-air relationship for growing vegetation. It improves the bearing capacity (load-carrying capacity) of a wet soil and, under certain conditions, is used in connection with leaching chemicals from soils. It is also used with many irrigation projects. This subject is also treated more fully in Chapter 21.

REFERENCES

1. Ramser, C. E. 1945. *Developments in terrace spacing.* Agr. Engin., 26(7): 285-289.
2. Raths, Herbert J. 1945. *Soil Conservation Service Engineering Handbook, Northeastern Region.* Upper Darby, Pa. (Also other SCS Regional Engin. Handbooks.)
3. Ree, W. O. 1954. *Handbook of channel design for soil and water conservation.* USDA, SCS-TP-61.
4. Stallings, J. H. 1945. *Effect of contour cultivation on crop yields, runoff, and erosion losses.* USDA, SCS. (Multi.)
5. Yarnell, David L. 1935. *Rainfall intensity—frequency data.* USDA Misc. Pub. 204.

20

Land Use Capability
and Land Judging

Grouping soils on the basis of erosion hazards and other limitations, so that suitable cropping systems may be planned, is an important step in developing a soil-erosion-control program. At the same time, this procedure also provides the foundation for a sound soil improvement program which, after all, is the ultimate goal.

The Soil Conservation Service developed a system of land classification. This system helps organize significant soil facts for conservation use. It is known as the "land use capability classification." The term "capability" relates to the degree of hazards and limitations in managing the land more than it does to productive capacity. It also shows its best use.

The soil factors are determined in the field. They serve as a basis for determining soil capabilities. These characteristics are also used in determining the best use of the various soil classes. They show soil and crop practices that protect the soil from the forces of erosion. This ensures top crop yields.

Under this system, a map is made of each farm. It shows soil types, slope, and other important physical land characteristics. Soil units are grouped into capability units. Capability units are units that require different cropping systems and soil treatment.

This ensures continued use of the land, use at the highest production level the land is capable of supporting.

Each capability unit consists of a group of soils. The soils in each group have specified limits. These limits include soil type, slope, degree of erosion, and other physical characteristics. All the soils in a capability unit are about equally susceptible to wind or water erosion under the same kind of plant cover. Similar cropping systems or other management practices are applicable throughout the unit. The capability units are the physical land-treatment units as far as permanent soil factors are concerned. Each one has nearly uniform use possibilities and conservation needs. A capability unit may consist of one or more mapping units.

The capability units are grouped in successively broader classes where such groupings serve a useful purpose. These are known as subclasses and classes. Those units making up a capability subclass have about the same

FIGURE 133. Diagrammatic illustration of the topography of different land use capability classes.
(Soil Conservation Service)

LAND CAPABILITY CLASSES			
SUITABLE FOR CULTIVATION		NO CULTIVATION-PASTURE, HAY, WOODLAND AND WILDLIFE	
I	REQUIRES GOOD SOIL MANAGEMENT PRACTICES ONLY	V	NO RESTRICTIONS IN USE
II	MODERATE CONSERVATION PRACTICES NECESSARY	VI	MODERATE RESTRICTIONS IN USE
III	INTENSIVE CONSERVATION PRACTICES NECESSARY	VII	SEVERE RESTRICTIONS IN USE
IV	PERENNIAL VEGETATION - INFREQUENT CULTIVATION	VIII	BEST SUITED FOR WILDLIFE AND RECREATION

kind and degree of permanent limitations. These subclasses are then grouped into eight capability classes according to the degree of permanent limitations. The eight classes are finally grouped into two divisions: those soils suited for cultivation and those not suited for cultivation.

SUITABILITY FOR CULTIVATION

Cultivation is used broadly. It includes all use that involves tillage of a soil. Land considered suitable for cultivation is workable. It is not too steep, not too wet, and not too severely limited by other factors. Limiting values of the different factors vary from place to place. The significant relation is that of the combined physical factors to safe, long-time use. In some places, for example, a slope of 10 per cent is too steep for cultivation. In other places, in a different environment, slopes of 10 per cent or more may be cultivated safely.

The degree to which the risks of damage limit the chances of safe, long-time use are important factors. They are used in grouping soils in a capability classification. The damage risks include erosion and other land damages. Shallow soil depth, tight subsoil, and stoniness are also considered. Most of the land not suited for cultivation is suited for and will produce some form of permanent vegetation.

FIGURE 134. Class I land in Virginia. This land is nearly level, permitting straight rows subject mainly to puddle and fertility erosion. The crop is corn, which responds to good management and proper fertilization.
(Soil Conservation Service)

CAPABILITY CLASSES

Each of the two divisions, land suited and land not suited for cultivation, contains four capability classes. These eight capability classes are too general for the many specific recommendations about management and treatment of land. They are distinguished from each other by the degree of permanent limitations, or risks involved in their use.

The subclass is the most convenient grouping for most purposes. A capability class is determined by the *degree* of the total limitations on land use, but the subclass is determined by the *kind* of limitation.

For use on many small areas, such as a farm, the capability unit is the most convenient grouping. This allows the land operator to see the soil characteristics. He already knows these characteristics but he can get their meaning in terms of land limitations. Areas diverse enough to take in two or more kinds of limitations within one capability class often should be grouped into subclasses. The subclass is more useful in dealing with land information over more diverse conditions than are found on farms or small areas.

The capability classes range from Class I to Class VIII. Class I contains the land that has the widest range in adaptations. It can be farmed easily. The use of the land in the other classes is progressively more restricted because of permanent limitations.

SOIL SUITED FOR CULTIVATION

The soil in the first four capability classes are suited for cultivation.

Class I. Soils in Class I have no, or only slight, permanent limitations or risks of damage. They are very good. They can be cultivated safely with ordinary good farming methods. The soils are deep, productive, easily worked, and nearly level. They are not subject to overflow damage. However, they are subject to fertility and puddle erosion.

Class I soils used for crops need practices to maintain soil fertility and soil structure. These practices involve use of fertilizers and lime, cover and green-manure crops, crop residues, and crop rotations.

Class II. Class II consists of soils subject to moderate limitations in use. They are subject to moderate risk of damage. They are good soils. They can be cultivated with easily applied practices.

Soils in Class II differ from soils in Class I in a number of ways. They differ mainly because they have gentle slopes, are subject to moderate erosion, are of moderate depth, are subject to occasional overflows, and are in need of drainage. Each of these factors requires special attention. These soils may require special practices such as soil-conserving rotations, water-control devices, or special tillage methods. They frequently need a combination of practices.

Class III. Soils in Class III are subject to severe limitations in use for cropland. They are subject to severe risks or damage. They are moderately good soils. They can be used regularly for crops, provided they are planted to good rotations and given the proper treatment. Soils in this class have moderately steep slopes, are subject to more severe erosion, and are inherently low in fertility.

Class III soil is more limited or subject to greater risks than Class II.

FIGURE 135. Class I land in an irrigated district in Oklahoma.
(Soil Conservation Service)

FIGURE 136. Class II irrigated land in California on a 5 per cent slope that requires simple precautionary measures to prevent the waste of soil and water. Severe erosion was caused by a moderate rain. Irrigation water running down the furrows also contributes to soil loss. The practices recommended for this field are: Maintenance of ample plant cover during the rainy season, basin listing on the contour, and planting and irrigating new orchards approximately on the contour.
(Soil Conservation Service)

FIGURE 137. Strips of wheat and corn between buffer strips of alfalfa on Class II land in Iowa. Strip-cropping on the contour combined with ample plant cover on the cultivated strips will protect the soil in this field.
(Soil Conservation Service)

FIGURE 138. A deep sandy soil in western Texas planted to cotton in straight rows without appropriate plant cover protection. Failure to provide ample plant cover protection is resulting in serious soil drifting. Though this soil was deep and fertile, special practices for water conservation and wind-erosion control are necessary to preserve the soil and maintain permanent production of moderate yields.
(Soil Conservation Service)

FIGURE 139. Class III land in the Black Belt of Texas. The soil is Houston black clay on a 4 per cent slope. The cropping and soil management practices consisting of contour cultivation, strip-cropping, terracing with protected outlets, green manuring, and crop rotation that includes close-growing crops are not sufficient to protect against erosion.
(*Soil Conservation Service*)

FIGURE 140. Class IV land in Louisiana on a 10 per cent slope, which on this soil is too steep for safe cultivation. This pasture was seeded to a mixture of white Dutch clover, hop, Persian and black medic clovers, and Bermuda grass.
(*Soil Conservation Service*)

These limitations often restrict the choice of crops or the timing of planting and tillage operations.

These soils require cropping systems that produce adequate plant cover. The cover is needed to protect the soil from erosion. It also helps preserve soil structure. Hay or other sod crops should be grown instead of cultivated row crops. A combination of practices is needed to farm the land safely.

Class IV. Class IV is composed of soils that have very severe permanent limitations or hazards if used for cropland. The soils are fairly good. They may be cultivated occasionally if handled with great care. For the most part, they should be kept in permanent hay or sod.

Soils in Class IV have unfavorable characteristics. They are frequently on steep slopes and subject to severe erosion. They are restricted in their suitability for crop use. They should usually be kept in hay or pasture, although a grain crop may be grown once in five or six years. In other cases, the soils may be shallow or only moderately deep, low in fertility, and on moderate slopes. These soils should be in hay or sod crops for long periods. Only occasionally should they be planted to row crops.

SOILS NOT SUITED FOR CULTIVATION

The soils in the last four classes are not suited for cultivation. They should be kept in permanent vegetation where possible.

Class V. Soils in Class V should be kept in permanent vegetation. They should be used for pasture or forestry. They have few or no permanent limitations and not more than slight hazards. Cultivation is not feasible, however, because of wetness, stoniness, or other limitations. The land is nearly level. It is subject to only slight erosion by wind or water if properly managed. Grazing should be regulated to keep from destroying the plant cover.

Class VI. Class VI soils should be used for grazing and forestry, and may have moderate hazards when in this use. They are subject to moderate permanent limitations, and are unsuited for cultivation. They are steep, or shallow. Grazing should not be permitted to destroy the plant cover.

Class VI land is capable of producing forage or woodland products when properly managed. If the plant cover has been destroyed, the soil's use should be restricted until cover is re-established. As a rule Class VI land is either steeper or more subject to wind erosion than Class IV.

Class VII. Soils in Class VII are subject to severe permanent limitations or hazards when used for grazing or forestry. They are steep, eroded, rough, shallow, droughty, or swampy. They are fair to poor for grazing or forestry, and must be handled with care.

Where rainfall is ample, Class VII land should be used for woodland. In other areas, it should be used for grazing. In the latter case, strict management should be applied.

Class VIII. Soils in Class VIII are rough even for woodland or grazing. They should be used for wildlife, recreation, or watershed uses.

SOIL LIMITATIONS

The terms "very good," "good," "moderately good," and "fairly good" are used in soil capability-class descriptions. They express the relative quality of land from the standpoint of all known physical causes, possibilities, and limitations. These include slope, erosion, depth, and workability of the soil.

FIGURE 141. Class V bottomland pasture subject to overflow. Medium-textured, permeable soil of forested coastal plains.
(Soil Conservation Service)

FIGURE 142. Class V stony pasture land. The soil is Gloucester stony loam. The large stones make the land unsuitable for other purposes.
(Soil Conservation Service)

FIGURE 143. Class VI land in Oregon. A shallow soil on a 20 per cent slope. The range on the left of the fence has been under good management for nearly three years and has shown marked improvement in the type and amount of forage. *(Soil Conservation Service)*

FIGURE 144. Class VI land in West Virginia that is too steep and has soils too shallow for cultivation at any time, but is suitable for grass with moderate restrictions in use. Lime and fertilizer needed. *(Soil Conservation Service)*

FIGURE 145. Class VII land in southeastern Colorado. Because of its extremely sandy nature and the scant vegetal cover obtainable in a region of low rainfall, grazing must be severely restricted.
(Soil Conservation Service)

FIGURE 146. Class VII land in Tennessee. Rough, steep slopes unsuited for cultivation. Produces fair grazing if properly managed.
(Soil Conservation Service)

They do not necessarily express either present or highest productivity. For example, a deep, dark-colored fertile soil on a 10 per cent slope may have the same present productivity as a soil on a 3 per cent slope. However, from the standpoint of hazards of continued production, the former is classed as "moderately good" and the latter as "good." All soils in Classes I, II, and III must be at least productive enough to make regular cultivation for annual or short-lived crops practical.

FIGURE 147. Class VIII land in Pennsylvania. This marsh cannot be drained economically, because the cost of drainage is greater than the return that would be obtained. It is useful primarily for the production of muskrat pelts.
(Soil Conservation Service)

EXAMPLES OF SOIL CAPABILITY
CLASSIFICATIONS AND RECOMMENDATIONS

Within each area, land is described according to local conditions, and rec-ommendations are only local in scope. The program for each area includes the best adapted crops, most suitable practices, and best use for each kind of soil in each capability class.

Examples of physical soil properties that are significant in differentiating soils in the capability classification are given in Table 72. Examples of recommendations for these different kinds of land are given in Tables 73, 74, and 75.

FIGURE 148. Class VIII land in Utah.
        (Soil Conservation Service)

TABLE 72. Principal characteristics of several soil mapping units defined for soil groupings (6, 7)

Field mapping symbol	Descriptive titles	Effective depth	Texture of surface	Permeability — Subsoil	Permeability — Substratum	Thickness of topsoil	Underlying or parent material	Available moisture capacity	Reaction	Natural soil drainage	Inherent fertility	Organic matter content	Dominant soil type or types
9	Dark colored, deep, med.–textured soils with mod. rapidly permeable subsoils and substrata	Deep	Medium	Moderately rapid	Moderately rapid		Loess	High	V. slightly acid to mildly acid	Well	High	High	Marshall silt loam and similar soils
15	Mod. dark-colored, shallow to claypan, very slowly permeable, med.-textured soils	Shallow	Medium	Very slow	Very slow		Loess	Low	Acid	Poor	Medium	Medium	Putnam silt loam and similar soils
10	Light-colored, shallow to claypan, very slowly permeable, medium-textured soils	Shallow	Medium	Very slow	Very slow		Loess	Low	Acid	Poor	Low	Low	Marion silt loam and similar soils
183	Light-colored, moderately deep to rock, medium-textured soils with mod. permeable subsoils	Moderately deep	Medium	Moderate			Limestone	Low	Acid surface and subsoil, calc. substratum	Well	Medium	Low	Dubuque silt loam and similar soils
1110	Deep, well drained, med.-textured, moderately slowly permeable, high lime soils	Deep	Medium	Moderately slow	Moderately slow		Glacial till (limestone)	High	Acid to neutral, 20" to calc. matl.	Well	High	Medium	Honeoye silt loam and similar soils
9413	Deep, well drained, mod. light-textured soils with mod. permeable subsoils and rapidly permeable substrata	Deep	Moderately light	Moderate	Rapid		Coastal Plain (sandy, gravel, and silt)	Low	Acid	Well	Medium	Low	Sassafras sandy loam and similar soils

TABLE 72. (Continued)

Field mapping symbol	Descriptive titles	Effective depth	Texture of surface	Permeability		Thickness of topsoil	Underlying or parent material	Available moisture capacity	Reaction	Natural soil drainage	Inherent fertility	Organic matter content	Dominant soil type or types
				Subsoil	Sub-stratum								
18	Shallow to gravel and sand, dark-colored, med.-textured soils with rapidly permeable subsoils and very rapidly permeable substrata	Shallow	Medium	Rapid	Very rapid		Lacustrine (gravel and sand)	Very low	Moderately acid, shallow to lime	Well	Low	Medium	Sioux loam and similar soils
2M	Deep, light-colored, med.-textured, highly productive soils with good drainage	Deep	Medium	Moderate	Moderate		Loess	High	Neutral	Well	High	Medium	Palouse silt loam and similar soils
6M	Light-colored, med.-textured soils, shallow to bedrock	Shallow	Medium	Moderate			Granites, micaceous schists and gneiss	Low	Acid	Well	Low	Medium	Moscow loam and similar soils
3331	Deep, med.-textured soils with mod. thick surface layers and med. permeable subsoils and substrata	Deep	Medium	Moderate	Moderate	Moderately thick	Loess or wind modified material	High	Neutral		High	Medium	Kieth silt loam
3231	Deep, med.-textured soils with thin surface layers, slowly permeable subsoils and mod. permeable substrata	Deep	Medium	Slow	Moderate	Thin	Loess or silty material blown from soft shale or sandstone	High	Neutral		High	Medium	Weld loam

TABLE 73. Conservation uses and practices recommended on the land suited for cultivation, Tift County, Georgia (6, 7)

Land capability class and unit	Suitable crops	Treatments for			
		Cropland		Hayland	Pasture
		Rotations	Supporting practices		
I	All crops common to area.	1. Cotton; 2nd year, peanuts followed by winter grain (oats); 3rd year, crotalaria. 2. Cotton or truck followed by oats for grazing; 2nd year, peanuts followed by blue lupine; 3rd year, corn.	Maintain turn rows and field borders in vegetation. Lime and fertilize. Turn under crop residue.	Prepare firm seedbed. Apply fertilizer. Seed suitable legumes and grasses.	Prepare firm seedbed. Apply fertilizer and lime. Plant coastal Bermuda grass, lespedeza, and crimson clover. Use common Bermuda grass where stand is already established. Mow as needed.
II-E-1	All crops common to area.	1. Peanuts followed by blue lupine; 2nd year, corn followed by oats for grain; 3rd year, crotalaria followed by Dixie wonder peas. 2. Cotton; 2nd year, peanuts followed by blue lupine; 3rd year, corn followed by oats and lespedeza. 3. Oats followed by lespedeza; 2nd year, peanuts followed by blue lupine; 3rd year, corn.	Complete water-disposal system and contour tillage. Maintain turn rows and field borders in close-growing vegetation. Arrange rotations in contour strips of about equal acreage.	Prepare firm seedbed. Apply lime and fertilizer. Seed suitable legumes and grasses.	Same as Class I.
II-E-2	Crops common to area, except pecans, tobacco, and cotton.	1. Peanuts followed by blue lupine; 2nd year, corn followed by oats for grain; 3rd year, crotalaria followed by Dixie wonder peas. 2. Cotton; 2nd year, peanuts followed by blue lupine; 3rd year, corn followed by oats and lespedeza.	Complete water-disposal system and contour tillage. Maintain turn rows and field borders in close-growing vegetation. Arrange rotations in contour strips of about equal acreage.	Prepare firm seedbed. Apply lime and fertilizer. Seed suitable legumes and grasses.	Same as Class I.
II-B-1	Crops common to area, except cotton, perennial legumes and grasses.	1. Oats followed by crotalaria; 2nd and 3rd years, corn and crotalaria. 2. Corn and runner peanuts for hogging, 2 years; 3rd year, peanuts followed by blue lupine.	Contour cultivation. Maintain turn rows and field borders in close-growing vegetation.	Not suited.	Prepare firm seedbed. Apply fertilizer and lime. Plant Pensacola Bahia grass. Mow as needed.
III-E-1	Crops common to area.	1. Oats followed by lespedeza; 2nd year, cotton followed by blue lupine; 3rd year, corn. 2. Peanuts followed by blue lupine; 2nd year, corn followed by oats and crotalaria for 2 years.	Complete water-disposal system and outlets of terraces and outlets. Contour tillage. Maintain turn rows and field borders in close-growing vegetation. Arrange rotations in contour strips of about equal acreage.	Prepare firm seedbed. Apply lime and fertilizer. Seed suitable legumes or grasses and legumes. Sericea well adapted.	Prepare firm seedbed. Apply fertilizer and lime. Plant coastal Bermuda grass, lespedeza, and crimson clover; sericea lespedeza; or common Bermuda grass. Use common Bermuda only where stand is already established. Mow as needed.

TABLE 73. (Continued)

Land capability class and unit	Suitable crops	Cropland		Treatments for	
		Rotations	Supporting practices	Hayland	Pasture
III-E-2	Crops common to area, except pecans and tobacco.	1. Oats followed by lespedeza with Dixie wonder peas as winter cover; 2nd year, corn. 2. Peanuts followed by blue lupine; 2nd year, corn followed by oats and crotalaria for 2 years.	Complete water-disposal system of terraces and outlets and contour tillage. Maintain turn rows and field borders in close-growing vegetation.	Prepare firm seedbed. Apply lime and fertilizer. Seed suitable legumes and grasses. Sericea well adapted.	Prepare firm seedbed. Apply fertilizer and lime. Plant coastal Bermuda grass, lespedeza, and crimson clover; sericea lespedeza; or common Bermuda grass. Use common Bermuda only where stand is already established. Mow as needed.
III-E-3	Corn, oats, winter and summer legumes.	1. Corn followed by oats; 2nd year, lespedeza. 2. Corn; 2nd year, crotalaria followed by oats.	Contour tillage. Maintain turn rows and field borders.	Prepare firm seedbed. Apply lime and fertilizer. Seed with suitable legumes and grasses.	Prepare firm seedbed. Apply lime and fertilizer. Plant coastal Bermuda grass and lespedeza.
III-A-1	Common crops, except cotton and peanuts.	1. Oats followed by lespedeza; 2nd year, corn; 3rd year, truck. 2. Corn and crotalaria 2 years; 3rd year, truck.	Drainage needed; at least one main ditch.	Prepare firm seedbed. Apply lime and fertilizer. Seed suitable legumes and grasses.	Prepare firm seedbed. Apply fertilizer and lime. Plant Dallis grass, lespedeza, and white clover. Mow as needed.
III-B-1	Common crops, except cotton.	1. Corn and crotalaria, 2 years; 3rd year, runner peanuts followed by blue lupine; alternate for 2nd year, oats and crotalaria.	Contour cultivation. Maintain turn rows and field borders in close-growing vegetation.	Not suited.	Prepare firm seedbed. Apply fertilizer and lime. Plant Pensacola Bahia grass. Mow as needed.
IV-E-1	Common crops that fit in rotations with a high percentage of cover.	1. Kudzu and corn. 2. Oats and lespedeza, 2 years; 3rd year, cotton followed by oats.	Complete water-disposal system of terraces and outlets, with contour tillage. Stabilize gullies.	Prepare firm seedbed. Lime and fertilize. Seed to sericea lespedeza or kudzu.	Plant sericea lespedeza or coastal Bermuda grass and lespedeza and crimson clover. Mow as needed.
IV-E-2	Common crops that fit in rotations with a high percentage of cover.	1. Kudzu and corn. 2. Oats and crotalaria or lespedeza.	Complete water-disposal system of terraces and outlets, with contour tillage. Stabilize gullies.	Prepare firm seedbed. Lime and fertilize. Seed to sericea lespedeza or kudzu.	Plant sericea lespedeza or coastal Bermuda grass and lespedeza and crimson clover. Mow as needed.
IV-B-1	Oats, crotalaria, corn, blue lupine.	1. Oats and crotalaria. 2. Corn and crotalaria; 2nd and 3rd years, oats and crotalaria.	Contour tillage; stabilize gullies.	Not suited.	Prepare firm seedbed. Apply fertilizer and lime. Plant Pensacola Bahia grass. Mow as needed.

TABLE 74. Conservation uses and practices recommended on soil not suited

for cultivation, Tift County, Georgia (6, 7)

Land capability class and unit	Suitable cover	Recommendations for		
		Pasture	Hayland	Forest
V-A-1	Lowland pasture; forest	Clear land, harrow and flatbreak. Apply one to two tons of ground limestone per acre and 400 to 600 pounds of 4-8-6 or its equivalent. Seed with Dallis grass and Kobe lespedeza in the spring, following in the fall with 3 pounds of white clover per acre. Mow as needed. Drainage: One main drain with laterals as required.	Same as for pasture	Slash pine for new plantings. Remove diseased and deformed trees. Make spot plantings to improve stands. Thin where necessary. Control fire.
VI-E-3	Upland pasture; perennial crops; forest	Prepare seedbed. Apply one ton of ground limestone and 400 to 600 pounds of 4-8-6 or its equivalent per acre. Sprig with coastal Bermuda grass. Use crimson clover for winter grazing. Mow as needed and avoid overgrazing.	Coastal Bermuda hay and kudzu or sericea lespedeza	Slash or longleaf pine for new plantings. Remove diseased and deformed trees. Make spot plantings to improve stand. Thin where necessary. Control fire.
VI-B-1	Pine trees	Not suited	Not suited	Same as for VI-E-3.
VII-E-1	Perennial crops; forest	Not suited	Kudzu or sericea lespedeza	Slash or longleaf pine for new plantings. Remove diseased and deformed trees. Thin and make spot plantings where needed. Control fire. Locate skid trails to avoid gullying.
VII-A-1	Forest; wildlife	Not suited	Not suited	Control fire in natural growth.
VII-B-1	Forest	Not suited	Not suited	Make new plantings to improve cover. Control fire. Locate skid trails to avoid gullying.

TABLE 75. Capability classes, subclasses and units and general recommendations, Tift County, Georgia (6, 7)

Land capability class	Subclass	Unit	Typical description for farm maps	Recommended uses and treatments
I. (Light green) Few or no limitations	—	Deep soils with moderately heavy, rapidly permeable subsoils; nearly level, little or no erosion.	"Pebble land" with yellow, sandy clay subsoil, level or nearly level, little or no erosion.	Ordinary good farming methods that include winter or summer legumes in the rotation.
II. (Yellow) Moderate limitations	I-E Gently sloping soils, subject to erosion if not farmed properly.	I-E-1 Deep soils with moderately heavy-textured and rapidly permeable subsoils on gentle slopes.	"Pebble land," gently sloping and only slightly eroded with a yellow, sandy clay subsoil.	Complete water-disposal system and a soil-conserving rotation that keeps one-third or more of the land in close-growing crops.
		II-E-2 Moderately deep soils with light-textured, moderately permeable subsoils on gentle slopes; slight erosion.	Gently sloping land with tough, heavy, lower subsoils and less than one-fourth of the topsoil washed away.	Complete water-disposal system and a soil-conserving rotation that keeps one-third or more of the land in close-growing crops. Not well suited for pecans, tobacco or cotton.
	II-B Level to gently sloping light-textured soils.	II-B-1 Deep soils with light-textured surfaces and subsoils on level or gentle slopes; slight erosion.	Droughty loamy sand, low in fertility, on gentle slopes with slight erosion.	Complete water-disposal system and a rotation that keeps one-half of the land in soil-building crops.
III. (Red) Severe limitations	II-E Gently to moderately sloping soils, subject to erosion if not farmed properly.	III-E-1 Deep soils with moderately heavy-textured and rapidly permeable subsoils on moderate slopes; slight erosion.	"Pebble land," sloping and slightly eroded with a yellow, sandy clay subsoil.	Complete water-disposal system and a rotation that keeps two-thirds of the land in close-growing crops.
		III-E-2 Moderately deep soils with heavy-textured and moderately permeable subsoils on gentle slopes; moderate erosion.	Gently sloping land with tough, heavy, lower subsoil; about half the topsoil removed.	Complete water-disposal system and a rotation that keeps two-thirds of the land in close-growing crops. Not suited for pecans or tobacco.
		III-E-3 Shallow soils with medium-textured, slowly permeable subsoils on nearly level and gentle slopes.	Shallow, unproductive soil with sticky, tough subsoil, on gentle slopes.	Adequate water-disposal system and a soil-building rotation that keeps two-thirds of the land in close-growing crops. Crops most likely to grow successfully are corn, oats, and legumes.
	III-A Moderately wet (imperfectly drained) soils.	III A-1 Imperfectly drained soils with medium-textured, rapidly permeable subsoils.	Low-lying, imperfectly drained soils with a pale yellow, sandy loam subsoil.	Water-control system (drainage) and a soil-building rotation that keeps one-half of the land in soil-building crops. Well suited for lowland pasture without drainage.
	III-B Gently sloping, light-textured soils, moderate erosion.	III-B-1 Deep soils with light-textured surfaces and subsoils on gentle slopes; moderate erosion.	Droughty, loamy sand, low in fertility, on gentle slopes with moderate erosion.	Water-disposal system suitable for light sandy land and a soil-building rotation that keeps two-thirds of the land in soil-building crops.

TABLE 75. (Continued)

Land capability class	Subclass	Unit	Typical description for farm maps	Recommended uses and treatment
IV. (Blue) Land suited for limited cultivation with severe limitations.	IV-E Moderately sloping and moderately eroded soils subject to erosion unless cultivation is occasional or limited.	IV-E-1 Deep soils with moderately heavy-textured and rapidly permeable subsoils on moderate slopes; moderate erosion.	Sloping, pebble land with one-half or more of the topsoil removed.	Suited for only occasional cultivation. Best suited for permanent cover. When cultivated needs complete water-disposal system and rotation that keeps three-fourths of the land in close-growing cover.
		IV-E-2 Moderately deep soils with heavy-textured and moderately permeable subsoils on moderate slopes; moderate erosion.	Sloping land with a tough, heavy subsoil.	Suited for only occasional cultivation. Best suited for permanent cover. When cultivated needs complete water-disposal system and rotation that keeps three-fourths of the land in close-growing cover.
	IV-B Moderately sloping light-textured soils, moderate erosion.	IV-B-1 Deep soils with light-textured surfaces and subsoils on moderate slopes.	Droughty, loamy sand, low in fertility, on moderate slopes.	Suited for occasional cultivation. Best suited for pine trees. When cultivated, a rotation of close-growing crops such as corn and crotalaria or crotalaria and small grain. Cultivate on contour.
V. (Dark green) Suited for permanent vegetation with few or no permanent limitations.	V-A Wet (poorly drained) soils.	V-A-1 Poorly drained soils with medium-textured, rapidly permeable subsoils.	Poorly drained "crawfish land."	Suited to lowland pasture and pine trees. When used for pasture, drainage, fertilizer, and liming greatly increase yields.
VI. (Orange) Suited for permanent vegetation with moderate limitations.	VI-E Heavy-textured soils on moderate slopes.	VI-E-3 Moderately deep soils with light-textured surfaces and medium- to heavy-textured subsoils on moderate to steep slopes; moderate to severe erosion.	Rolling to steep and moderately to severely eroded heavy, subsoil land.	Suited to perennials, kudzu, sericea, pine trees with moderate restrictions on grazing and logging.
	VI-B Deep, light-textured soils on moderate or steep slopes.	VI-B-1 Deep, light-textured soils on moderate or steep slopes.	Droughty, loamy sands, low in fertility, on moderate or steep slopes.	Suited for pine trees with moderate restrictions on grazing and logging.
VII. (Brown) Suited for permanent vegetation with severe limitations.	VII-E Heavy-textured soils on moderate to steep slopes.	VII-E-3 Shallow soils with medium-textured surfaces and heavy-textured, slowly permeable subsoils on moderate to steep slopes.	Heavy and tough subsoil land on moderate to steep slopes.	Suited for kudzu or pine trees with severe restrictions on grazing and logging.
	VII-A Extremely wet soils.	VII-A-1 Swamp, or land with water standing on it much of the time.	Swamp.	Suited for wildlife and trees such as cypress, tupelo, sweet gum, swamp oak, or swamp maple.
	VII-B Gently sloping, very light-textured soils.	VII-B-1 Deep sands on gentle slopes with little or no erosion.	"Post oak land," deep, infertile sands.	Suitable for longleaf pine.

SOIL CAPABILITY MAP

On a soil capability map each class is identified by a distinctive color. A glance at the colors shows what areas are suitable for cultivation. These colors also indicate the intensity of treatment needed to protect the land. The colors on the map, together with the patterns or symbols showing land use, point out the fields that should be changed from cropland to grassland. They also show grassland and woodland that can be used safely for clean-tilled crops.

Correlation between permanent soil limitations and intensity of safe use is shown in Figure 149, which illustrates the progressively increasing degree of limitations and hazards from Class I to Class VIII. It should be remembered, however, that the diagram is oversimplified. There are a few exceptions to this general concept: for example, some Class VII soil with severe limitations and hazards may be protected adequately with kudzu or Bermuda grass, which may be used for moderate grazing or even for hay.

FIGURE 149. Schematic chart showing correlation between permanent land limitations and intensity of safe use.
(Soil Conservation Service)

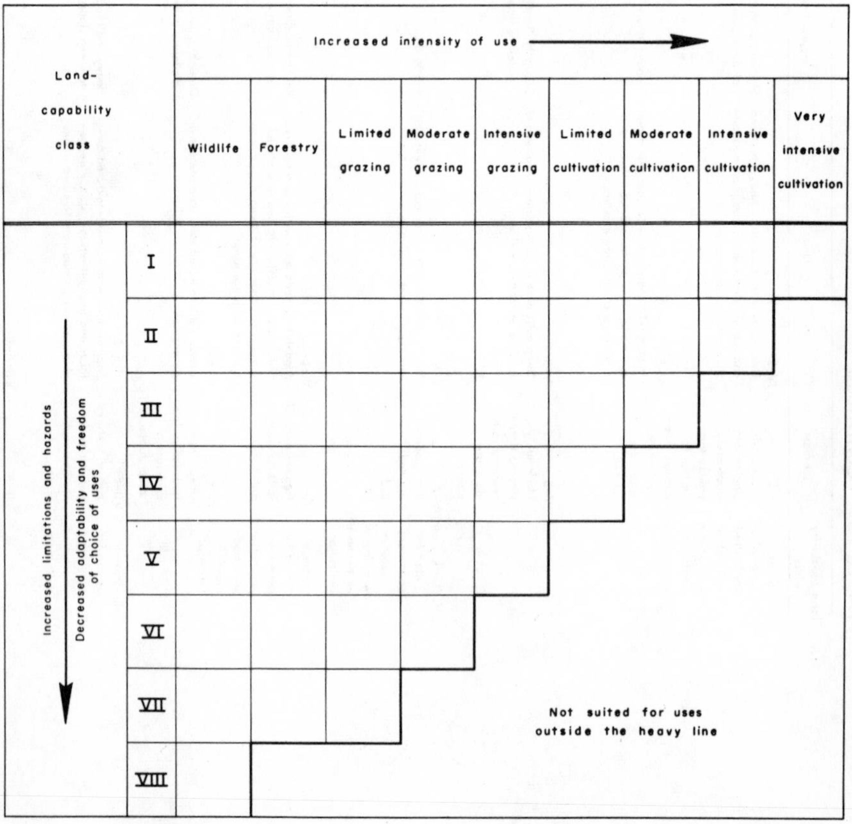

Land-capability class		Wildlife	Forestry	Limited grazing	Moderate grazing	Intensive grazing	Limited cultivation	Moderate cultivation	Intensive cultivation	Very intensive cultivation
					Increased intensity of use ⟶					
	I									
	II									
	III									
	IV									
	V									
	VI									
	VII					Not suited for uses outside the heavy line				
	VIII									

Increased limitations and hazards

Decreased adaptability and freedom of choice of uses

SAMPLE MAP

A sample capability map is shown in Figure 150. On this map, a description of each soil type appears on the margin. These descriptions, in language that is easily understood, supply the land information that many people want. Some who are interested in details and exact differences will want the legend that tells the meaning of each one of the mapping symbols.

Experience has shown that individual descriptions of the exact soil types in the capability units on each farm are more useful than the general descriptions of capability classes. The locally adapted descriptions should be consistent with the general concepts of capability classes, subclasses, and units.

TABLE 76. The land capability classification*

Major land use suitability (Broad grouping of limitations)	Land capability class (Degree of limitations)	Land capability subclass (Kind of limitations) (Groupings of land-capability units. Examples of possible subclasses in class III :)	Land capability unit (Distinctive physical characteristics) (Land-management groups based on permanent physical factors. Example:)
Suited for cultivation.	I — Few limitations. Wide latitude for each use. Very good land from every standpoint.		
	II — Moderate limitations or risks of damage. Good land from all-around standpoint.		
	III — Severe limitations or risks of damage. Regular cultivation possible if limitations are observed.	Limited by hazard of water erosion; moderately sloping land.	13-C-2 Moderately sloping, slightly acid soils on limestone. 9-C-2 Moderately sloping, highly acid soils on sandstone or shale.
		Limited by excess water; needs drainage for cultivation.	
		Limited by low moisture capacity; sandy land.	
		Limited by tight, very slowly permeable subsoils; claypan land.	
	IV — Very severe limitations. Suited for occasional cultivation or for some kind of limited cultivation.		
Not suited for cultivation; suited for permanent vegetation.	V — Not suited for cultivation because of wetness, stones, overflows, etc. Few land limitations affect grazing or forestry use.	Groupings of range, pasture, or forest sites.	Land-management groups based on permanent physical factors, such as range sites or forest sites.
	VI — Too steep, stony, arid, wet, etc., for cultivation. Moderate limitations for grazing or forestry.		
	VII — Very steep, rough, arid, wet, etc. Severe limitations for grazing or forestry.		
	VIII — Extremely rough, arid, swampy, etc. Not suited for cultivation, grazing, or forestry. Suited for wildlife, watersheds, or recreation.		

*United States Department of Agriculture, Soil Conservation Service.

USES OF SOIL CAPABILITY MAPS

Although capability maps are made primarily as a basis for soil conservation planning and treatment, they may serve many other useful purposes.

The farmer has in his capability map a written record of the soil conditions on his farm. With a knowledge of soil conditions and capability, he
has information to help him make production adjustments. His very good,
nearly level land can be used most often for crops. His steeper, more erodible, or less desirable land can be used for hay, pasture, shrubs, or trees.
Often, Class III soil that is moderately steep and subject to erosion will
give better returns from grasses or legumes than from annual crops.

FIGURE 150. Land capability map.
(Soil Conservation Service)

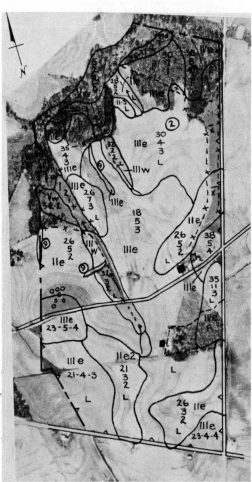

LAND CAPABILITY MAP

CLASS I.   Well drained productive bottomland. (+I-2)

CLASS IIe.   Smooth to moderately sloping, gray sandy
land with slight erosion. If cultivated, needs terracing
water outlets and strip rotation with half the land in
close-growing crops, such as small grain and lespedeza. Needs additional potash and organic matter for
best production. (2-3-26, 2-5-26, 2-5-28)

CLASS IIe2.   Smooth to moderately sloping brownish
red sandy clay land. If cultivated, needs terracing,
outlets for excess runoff, and crop rotation with half
the land in close-growing crops, such as small grain
and lespedeza. (2-3-21)

CLASS IIIe.   Sloping, brownish red sandy clay land
with slight to moderate erosion. If cultivated, two-
thirds of the area should be in close-growing crops,
such as small grain and lespedeza.
(3-5-18, 3-5-40, 3-4-21, etc.)

CLASS IIIw.   Level, fine sandy loam of low inherent
fertility, with very heavy dense subsoil. Subject to
standing water during wet spells. Good pasture land;
drainage recommended. (2-3-32)

CLASS IVe.   Moderately steep, brownish red sandy
clay land with slight erosion or smooth sloping red
sandy clay land with serious erosion. Recommended
for kudzu, sericea or pasture. Can be used for small
grain and lespedeza. (3-11-35, 40-8-38)

CLASS Vw.   Level wet soils with poor sub-soil
drainage. Best adapted for pasture. (2-2-5)

CLASS VIe.   Steep, brownish red sandy clay land
with slight erosion. Best use, kudzu, sericea,
pasture, or woodland. Too steep for cultivated
crops. (3-20-35, 2-17-35)

Capability of the soil affords a sound basis for agricultural credit. Land farmed with regard for its inherent limitations is a better credit risk than land farmed beyond its capability. Lending institutions can encourage conservation and discourage misuse of land.

Capability of soil is of interest to many public agencies and to business concerns. Extension of roads, electric lines, and other improvements often

FIGURE 151. Land use map prepared by U.S. Department of Agriculture for Cherokee Soil Conservation District, South Carolina. Work unit: Cherokee County. Owners: Jonah Blackwell and Elijah Blackwell. Scale 1" = 600'. Location: 10 miles northwest of Gaffney on Chesnee Highway.
(Soil Conservation Service)

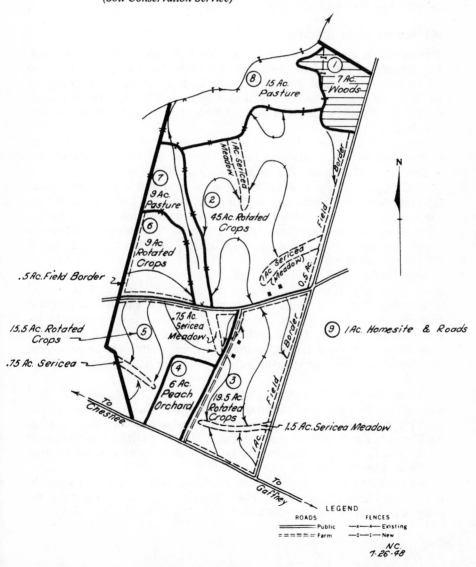

can be planned with greatest efficiency if information about capability of the soil is available. Tax assessments can be guided by the nature of the soil and its capability classification. For such purposes, information usually is needed about capability units, or at least about the subclasses within the eight capability classes.

LAND JUDGING

Land judging is a tested method of teaching large groups of people how to classify land according to its capabilities. It is designed to give more people a better understanding of the basic fundamentals of the land. Land judging is becoming an outstanding teaching method because it enables the student to learn by observing and examining the soil and associating it with soil management practices.

HISTORY OF LAND JUDGING

Proceeding on the well established fact that experience is the best teacher, soil conservationists of the United States Department of Agriculture and Oklahoma Agricultural and Mechanical College developed a system of teaching soil conservation and land management. The idea was originated in 1941 by Harley A. Daniel of the Red Plains Experiment Station, Guthrie, Oklahoma.

The original purpose was to teach this subject to members of youth groups such as 4-H Clubs and Future Farmers of America. Daniel was assisted by Edd Roberts, Extension Soil Conservationist, Oklahoma A. & M. College, and others. Instruction was in the nature of a school and a contest, for identifying plants and studying soil profiles. The thought behind the movement was to determine how to give more people a better understanding of the basic fundamentals of the land. The details of these activities are reported in various publications. (See References 1, 2, and 4 cited at the end of this chapter.)

Both Daniel and Roberts served on Oklahoma A. & M. College livestock and crop judging teams. They recognized the value of the contest method of teaching. They also recognized the need for some simple and practical field method of teaching soils. Indoor classes on soils do not arouse the interest of large groups. It is difficult to tell people about a certain class of land and explain the difference in texture, permeability, land slope, degree of erosion, and land management without letting them see the field and feel the soil.

Daniel and Roberts decided early in the development stages of land judging that the purpose of the contest would be to teach the student to put each piece of land to the use for which it is best suited, and to treat it according to its needs to make it permanently productive. In fact, they stressed all the practices and treatments necessary for developing and maintaining a permanent agriculture.

Soil conservation schools and contests of this nature were held annually at the Red Plains Station. From 1941 through 1945, during the early developmental stages, experiments and trial-and-error studies were made with both 4-H and FFA members. Gradually new ideas were pieced together and a tentative score card was prepared. After the initial development period, the land judging program was taken to the field in 1946. The first contest away from the station was held in Pauls Valley, Oklahoma.

Land use practices and soil conditions at Pauls Valley were different from those on the Red Plains Station. This created new problems which resulted in changes of the score card. In 1949, land judging contests were held on the Wheatland Conservation Experiment Station, Cherokee, Oklahoma, in the heart of the wheat area. The research findings at this station were helpful in the development of a score card suitable to the wheat land. Then, as this program moved to various soils and farming areas of the state, further adjustments and improvements were made.

In 1949, more than 1,200 members participated in the 4-H and FFA contests at the Red Plains and Wheatland Stations. In that year, also, GI vocational agriculture students and other adults became regular entrants in the contests.

Since then, the idea of land judging has spread throughout the country. Nine states and two foreign countries entered contestants in the first national land judging contest held at Oklahoma City, Oklahoma, in May, 1952.

The response from this contest was so favorable that the State Extension Directors of the Southern Extension Region invited Roberts to discuss land judging at their regional conference in Knoxville, Tennessee. These directors were favorably impressed with the educational values of land judging. They arranged a conference for the purpose of training extension workers in this method at State College, Mississippi, on July 17 to 19, 1952. All states of the Region, plus Maryland and Puerto Rico, took part in this school. Since then, most of the other states and a number of foreign countries have adopted or shown interest in a land judging program.

Several states had made land judging score cards by 1952. One of the early Oklahoma cards and procedures was revised and used at the first national land judging contest. The states concerned, as well as the Soil Conservation Service, had different, but similar, score cards. This extensive activity made a national land judging score card imperative. Consequently, a committee known as the National Land Judging Committee met in August of 1952 at Oklahoma A. & M. College and revised the existing score cards and the first national score card. The National Land Judging Score Card consists of two parts. In general, Part One is based on six easily identified soil factors, while Part Two is based on the selection of proper land use practices of vegetative cover, mechanical treatments, and fertilizer and lime necessary for maximum protection and production of different land classes.

The first collegiate land judging contest was held in the fall of 1952. It was sponsored by the Agronomy Department of Oklahoma A. & M. College. Students from five colleges were present, with sixteen teams participating. The college men, like the 4-H and FFA boys, were impressed by this way of studying soils. It gave them an opportunity to get into the open fields, where they could observe all the physical factors of the soil and

(N-1)

LAND JUDGING SCORE CARD

Field No.________

EXTENSION SERVICE
Oklahoma A. & M. College

1. (Name or No.) ....
2. (Address) ....
3. (County) ....
4. Soil Conservation District ....
5. ....

LAND CLASS FACTORS—PART ONE
Indicate your answer by an X in the square

SURFACE TEXTURE
Coarse ....
Medium ....
Fine ....

MOVEMENT OF AIR AND WATER IN THE SUBSOIL (permeability)
Very slow ....
Slow ....
Moderate ....
Rapid ....

DEPTH OF SURFACE SOIL AND SUBSOIL
Deep ....
Moderately Deep ....
Shallow ....
Very Shallow ....

SLOPE
Nearly level ....
Gently Sloping ....
Moderately Sloping ....
Strongly Sloping ....
Steep ....
Very Steep ....

EROSION—WIND AND WATER
None to slight ....
Moderate ....
Severe ....
Very Severe ....

SURFACE DRAINAGE
Poor ....
Fair ....
Good ....
Excessive ....

INDICATE THE MAJOR FACTORS
Considered in selecting the land class and treatments
Texture ....
Permeability ....
Depth ....
Slope ....
Erosion ....
Drainage ....

LAND CAPABILITY CLASS
I II III IV V VI VII VIII
(Circle one of the above)

SCORE—PART ONE______
(POSSIBLE POINTS—30)

RECOMMENDED LAND TREATMENTS — PART TWO
(See reverse side for instructions)

SCORE—PART TWO______
(POSSIBLE POINTS—30)

SCORE—PART ONE______

SCORE—PART TWO______

TOTAL SCORE______

INSTRUCTIONS FOR PART TWO

This is for guidance of participants in selection of proper land treatments needed for different land classes. Select from these the practices needed to conserve soil and water and maintain or improve productivity, and record it by number in the proper square on the opposite side—Part Two. The blank lines may be used for writing in the additional practice when needed.

VEGETATIVE

1. Use soil conserving and improving crops every 4th or 5th year.
2. Use soil conserving and improving crops every 3rd or 4th year.
3. Use soil conserving and improving crops every 2nd year.
4. Use soil conserving and improving crops every year.
5. Do not burn crop residue.
6. Strip cropping.
7. Residue management.
8. Establish recommended grass and/or legumes.
9. Improve by addition of recommended grasses and/or legumes.
10. Proper pasture or range management.
11. Protect from burning.
12. Control grazing.
13. Control noxious plants.
14. Control brush or trees.
15. Plant recommended trees.
16. Harvest trees selectively.
17. Use only for wildlife or recreation area.
18. ....
19. ....
20. ....

MECHANICAL

21. Terrace and farm on contour.
22. Farm on contour.
23. Maintain terraces.
24. Construct diversion terraces.
25. Install drainage system.
26. Control gullies.
27. ....
28. ....
29. ....

FERTILIZER & SOIL AMENDMENTS

30. Lime.
31. Gypsum.
32. Manure or Compost.
33. Phosphate.
34. Potash.
35. Nitrogen.
36. Phosphate and Nitrogen.
37. Phosphate and Potash.
38. Nitrogen and Potash.
39. Phosphate, Nitrogen & Potash
40. ....
41. ....
42. ....

Both sides of the score card used to grade the land-judging contestants.

FIGURE 152. National land judging score card (11), used to grade the contestants.
(Soil Conservation Service)

select the proper land use treatments necesary to conserve soil and maintain maximum productivity.

More recently the land judging program has been extended to cover range and pasture land.

JUDGING LAND

Land can be judged somewhat like livestock or farm crops. In judging beef animals we look for certain clues that indicate maximum meat production—factors such as depth of body, topline, smoothness, and other indicators of meat production. In land judging we look at the factors that affect crop producing capacity of the soil, such as permeability, texture, slope, amount of erosion, and thickness of topsoil.

Land judging contests are particularly adapted to teaching *appreciation* of the *principles* of soil differences, land capabilities, and wise use of the land. In fact, such contests might well be called "land appreciation contests."

In livestock and grain judging, students acquire a technique and a set of standards which they may use in farming for the rest of their lives. In land judging they learn general characteristics of the land: why some land is weak and some is strong, or why different land is suited to different uses and needs different treatments. They learn to analyze land problems. They observe why a complete farm or ranch conservation plan is essential.

To assume that one land judging contest, or even several, makes one a soil scientist or soil conservation technician would be a mistake. That is no more true than to assume that livestock judging qualifies one as a veterinarian or an animal geneticist!

By the same token one need not be a technician to judge land according to certain basic and major characteristics. One may learn to understand major land characteristics, uses and needs, and to recognize the symptoms that point to his need for qualified technical help.

Land judging contests vary somewhat in different states and different parts of the country, but in general the participants consider five major points:

First, they judge the physical features on the basis of: (a) color of topsoil in relation to subsoil; (b) thickness of surface and subsoil; (c) air and water movement as indicated by subsoil color and other factors; (d) texture; (e) slope; and (f) amount of erosion.

Second, contestants classify the land according to capability, attempting to place each parcel of land in the right one of the eight classes.

Third, they attempt to determine the proper use of each piece of land—whether for crops, woods, pasture, hay, range, wildlife, or recreation. From a practical farm or ranch standpoint, this is one of the most important steps in planning a conservation system.

Fourth, contestants suggest the most intensive cropping system that is safe for the land.

Fifth, they select other appropriate and needed conservation measures.

Thus, land judging covers more than soil science. It covers the physical traits of the land, the practical alternative uses and needs of the land, and a plan for safe use and improvement. In fact, the steps include the major "thought process" involved in planning a modern soil and water conservation system which is rapidly being accepted as basic to all sound farm planning and management.

LAND JUDGING CONTESTS

Land judging contests consist of two parts. Part One consists of land class factors. These determine the land capability class. Part Two provides for the selection of proper land treatments. This ranges from the selection of vegetative and mechanical practices to addition of sufficient fertilizer and lime.

From a careful analysis of the soil profile and the necessary treatments, the student is able to arrive at proper methods of controlling erosion and runoff. He can also improve soil fertility by selecting the management practices necessary to maintain continued maximum crop production.

Four fields are generally used in each contest. Each field represents a different land capability class. Pits are dug in each field so that the contestants can examine the soil. A generous sample of both surface and subsoil is placed near the pit for closer observation.

The field personnel consists of a contest chairman, a supervisor, and a guide for each pit in the field. The chairman explains the rules and issues instructions concerning locations of the four fields. The supervisors give needed information for each group visiting the field. The guide escorts the contestants from one field to the next. Groups are usually limited to 25 or 30 contestants.

OPERATION OF CONTEST

The contest is composed of competing individuals and teams. Each team consists of four members. One of the four members is an alternate. The three high-scoring members constitute the team.

The contestants are given score cards for each field. The cards are numbered for teams 1, 2, 3, and so on. The individual members of each team are designated as 1A, 1B, 1C, and 1D. Contestant 1A starts at Field 1, 1B at Field 2, 1C at Field 3 and 1D at Field 4.

LAND FACTORS

If the land is or has been in cultivation, the original topsoil thickness and other soil conditions are given each contestant as he visits the field. He then decides whether the soil is deep, moderately deep, shallow or very shallow. By feeling the soil in his hands he determines whether the texture is coarse, medium, or fine.

The movement of air and water in the subsoil, or soil permeability, is determined in handling the soil. It is done by observing whether the soil is crumbly, dense, loose, or tight. It is then classified as rapid, moderate, slow, or very slow.

The contestant then observes the topography of the land. He decides whether it is level, nearly level, gently sloping, moderately sloping, steeply sloping, steep, or very steep.

The contestant then examines topsoil to see how much of it remains. On the basis of this, he determines the amount of soil removed by erosion. He then classifies the erosion damage as very severe, severe, moderate, or slight. Finally, he checks the drainage. He determines whether it is poor, fair, good, or excessive.

When the above-mentioned factors have been rated, the contestant decides in which land capability class the field belongs.

LAND USE TREATMENT

After determining the land capability class, the contestant decides what practices are needed for proper treatment. Some of the land will need lime or fertilizer. Accordingly, a sign showing the results of a previous soil test is set up in each field. This enables contestants to determine these requirements.

A large number of practices are listed on the score card. These may be used to select the vegetative, mechanical, and fertilizer treatments. Only some of the practices apply to any field. Each possible treatment is numbered on the card. The appropriate number is selected and placed in a square under Part Two of the score card.

When the contestants finish judging a particular field, their cards are collected by the guide. They are given to an individual who takes them to headquarters. The cards are graded according to the official placings of the judging committee. The scores are tabulated by a grading committee. This committee is usually composed of the coaches of the individuals and teams and members of local agricultural agencies.

A perfect score is 60 points for each field, 240 for the contest. Winning individuals or teams are those earning the highest number of points.

Pasture and range management contests were added to the 1955 land judging contest. The participants are made familiar with local conditions prior to the contest by means of a training school. The training school is held prior to the contests in both the land judging and pasture and range development and management.

START WITH SOIL PROFILE

The starting point in the study of land is to look at it on a profile basis in the field. Here the student can feel the soil in the several horizons. He can see what the plants look like that are growing on it. He can also examine the environment in which the land is located.

In land judging, farmers and farmers-to-be are taken to the field and taught some of the fundamentals of soils in relation to their capabilities. Land judging is a visual method of teaching to impart ideas upon which sound systems of soil and crop management can be developed.

MANY FACTORS AFFECT PRODUCTIVITY OF LAND

Many factors enter into the productivity of a piece of land. Likewise, many conditions dictate management practices that should be employed on it. Certain nearly level, well-drained lands are Class I lands. They are Class I lands if the texture is loamy, if they have a reasonably high organic matter content, and if they have a well-defined and well-stabilized structure—provided, of course, they are free of stones and other obstructions and are located in a climatic environment with suitable rainfall, sunshine, and temperature. Class I land is the safest to farm because of its nearly level topography. However, unless it is protected by plant cover it is subject to splash erosion. Mistakes in soil and crop management are not apt to have as serious consequences on this class of land as on steeper slopes.

In proportion as land deviates, in any respect, from these characteristics, it falls into a more troublesome class, and requires better-than-average management practices. If land deviates enough in any one or all of these conditions it may be suitable only for hay or pasture. In this case it can stand only a limited amount of cultivation—and then, only on a carefully controlled basis. Even under these adverse conditions, however, it may often be profitably farmed provided the right kinds of crops are chosen and the right kinds of management are employed.

GOAL OF LAND JUDGING

The goal in land judging is to teach the students to recognize the factors inherent in soils that determine their capabilities and to acquaint them with how they operate. Students are taught to recognize where and how far the conditions at hand deviate from the ideal. They are taught also what effect these deviations have on soil management and cropping practices. They learn that management practices and crop selection must be adjusted to the various classes of land for economic returns. This is true not only for the current year but also over an extended period. Practice in land judging soon leads to the realization that not only can poor land be made more productive but that even the best land can be made better.

LESSON FOR THE OLDER STUDENT

The older student finds himself thinking back over his experiences in a certain field—possibly a field that has been under more or less continuous cultivation for many years. Perhaps fertilizer applications had to be increased to maintain production. Irrigation may have been introduced. Trace element deficiencies may have become a troublesome problem. He begins to realize that some of his land was not adapted to cropping. He realizes that better sod rotations and more cover crops could have been used to advantage to hold the soil on the remainder of his farm in place.

He also becomes impressed with the importance of keeping the soil continuously supplied with decaying organic matter. He comes to understand why, by raising the organic matter level, the soil is easier to work, the efficiency of fertilizer increases, and supplies of trace elements become more dependable.

He learns, gradually, that organic matter has a stabilizing effect on soil aggregates, and that this permits a more efficient moisture recharge of the soil profile during summer rains. It becomes increasingly apparent that under such conditions fertilizer applied has a better chance to produce full returns. He finally comes to the realization that poor management creates an ever greater problem—a problem for which fertilizer, trace elements, and irrigation provide only a partial solution. Thus he learns that it is important to work with Nature, rather than against her.

LESSON FOR THE YOUNGER STUDENT

To the younger, less experienced student, this method of teaching presents new ideas of what soil is, how it is formed, how and why it varies from place to place, and what can be done to make the best use of any piece of land.

Soil in a laboratory or lecture room is dead material, but in the field it takes on life. There is life in the soil and in the crop plants that grow out of it. Many other qualities of the field soil have meaning. These include the feel of the soil, the smell of it, its color, its depth, its working qualities, what is beneath it, and the appearance of the plants that grow on it. Out of the realization of this grows appreciation of the land, and a sense of man's obligation to it. The farmer, the student of vocational agriculture, or college sophomore have difficulty understanding such matters when explained in words. But condition his mind by showing him these fundamentals in the field under actual judging conditions and he will not have to be told. He will discover these facts for himself.

The mind of man accepts only those things it wants to learn. Land judging is an "interest getter." Once a person becomes interested in the soil, he usually wants to know more about it. Land judging practice soon places him in the predicament where he realizes, often for the first time, that he *needs* to know more about soil. The thought behind land judging is "to know why, for this teaches how and when."

REFERENCES

1. Daniel, H. A. 1950. *Teaching youth to save the soil.* Crops and Soils, 2: 17-19.
2. ————. 1951. *Oklahoma's contests in soil conservation.* Better Crops with Plant Food, 35: 21-24.
3. ————. 1953. *The story and development of land judging schools and contests.* Paper presented at Amer. Soc. Agron. meeting, Dallas, Texas.
4. ————, Deer, L. E., and Roberts, E. 1949. *Seven years of school contests.* Soil Cons., 15: 110-111.
5. Grogger, H. E., and Foster, A. B. 1952. *Judging land for soil conservation.* USDA, SCS, Upper Mississippi, Milwaukee, Wis., RB-3-2.
6. Hockensmith, R. D. 1949. *Classification of land according to its capability as a basis for a soil conservation program.* Proc. Inter-Amer. Conf. on Cons. of Renewable Natural Res., Denver, Colo.
7. ————, and Steele, J. G. 1943. *Classifying land for conservation farming.* USDA Farmers' Bull. 1853.
8. *Land judging.* Extension Serv., Oklahoma A. & M. Coll.
9. Roberts, E. *Land appreciation.* Okla. Agr. Ext. Ser. Cir. 510.
10. ————. 1955. *Land judging.* University Press, Oklahoma City, Okla.
11. ————, and Daniel, H. A. 1954. *Land judging.* Nat. Fert. Rev., 29(4): 16-18.

21

Planning the Farm Program

The purpose of farm or ranch planning is to chart a course of action that enables the operator to obtain maximum returns from the land while also improving it. The conservation plan is the product of correlating and combining the knowledge, experience, and desires of the farmer or rancher and the skill and knowledge of the planning technician.

The information obtained about the physical land features in the soil surveys forms the basis for planning land use and conservation measures. The first step in this procedure is to develop a Technical Guide for use of those responsible for making the farm and ranch plans.

TECHNICAL GUIDE

The Technical Guide for planning and application of conservation farming is a detailed coordinated arrangement of the technical information on soil conservation and land use applicable to a particular area. It embodies an analysis of the physical conditions of the land, including soils, topography and erosion conditions; interpretation for various uses in terms of capabilities; the correlation of these physical conditions with specific recommendations for use and treatment of the land; and description and specifications of all needed individual conservation practices.

456

PURPOSE OF THE TECHNICAL GUIDE

The need for technical standards for the development of sound farm plans is evident. Only by reducing to writing in a logical manner the procedures through which sound conservation plans are made can it be hoped to obtain uniformly high caliber work on the ground.

The development of the Technical Guide provides an opportunity for the coordination of thinking on the part of all individuals working in the area for which it is being prepared. It is the means of bringing about the local adaptation of broader technical recommendations, which in turn brings about better understanding and uniformity in the work plans.

The Technical Guide provides a logical correlation of soil groups and land use capabilities with needed conservation practices. This correlation provides a standard for technical procedure that is sufficiently flexible to permit keeping it constantly up-to-date. It provides a continuing record of all needed technical information. By following a standard outline, the information will be organized in an orderly manner for convenient use. It is handled so that reference to the Guide indicates soil type, soil group, land use capability, land use, and recommended treatment, in that logical order.

The Technical Guide provides a valuable training tool. The very preparation of the Guide itself constitutes a major step in the training of those who participate. Further, a concise, logically organized statement of procedure as developed in the Technical Guide will be basic in training new and old employees.

The organization of local technical material facilitates the use of basic technical information in farm planning, thereby increasing efficiency.

CONTENT AND USE

The material in the Technical Guide for conservation farming is for a specific soil conservation district and is based on a study of available soil data research and experience gained through work in soil and water conservation and proper land use in the area.

The Technical Guide is prepared by the local staff of the Soil Conservation Service, including the Work Unit Conservationist, Conservation Aids, the Area Conservationist, the Conservation Survey Supervisor, and others. The State Agricultural Experiment Stations also assist.

The Technical Guide is prepared to aid farm planners in successfully and uniformly handling the problems encountered in their own district and in adapting and applying conservation practices in accordance with the recommendations as they relate to the specific soil group and land capability class. The Technical Guide as developed can be readily made to conform to the scope of the district's program, work plan, and job-ahead plan. Proper land use is the basis upon which the Technical Guide is developed and if there are any questions on the practicability or success of the Guide, revision and adjustments are to be made as additional data and experience are gained.

In order to show how the Technical Guide is to be used, the following procedure should be followed:

1. From the individual farm soil survey, refer to "Legend of Symbols Used on Soil Survey Maps" for interpretation.
2. For each individual soil type number, refer to "Soils Index" to determine soil type name and soil group number.
3. Refer to "Practice Recommendation Chart by Soil Groups, Capability Classes, and Land Use" for the soil group indicated. This chart gives the soil group description, Land Capability Table, and the conservation practices and treatments according to capability and land use.
4. From the Land Capability Table for each soil group refer to "Land Capability Classes" for a description of each capability class, and for coloring maps refer to the color legend.
5. For a description of the supporting practices on the "Practice Recommendation Charts by Soil Groups, Capability Classes and Land Use," refer to "Practice Recommendations Index," an alphabetical list of conservation "Practice Recommendations" following the practice recommendation index sheet in the Technical Guide.

KNOW THE LAND ON YOUR FARM

A farm is made up of several different kinds of land. Changes in soil, slope, erosion, or deposition make these differences. Each kind is suited to certain farming uses. Most areas also have definite limits to their use. The different kinds of land are divided into eight land capability classes, but not all of them occur on every farm. Class Numbers I through VIII indicate successively fewer choices of safe or economical use.

To make the best use of the land one should know the kinds of land on the farm. The land capability map in Figure 154 shows the land classes on a Maryland farm. Each capability class is further divided into subclasses and land capability units. They are shown by symbols on the map (II e 4, II e w 1, III e 25, VI e 3, etc.). Determine from the land capability map the kinds of land on the farm, then decide how each kind should be used.

The following illustration shows how the soils information is used in developing a plan for the Maryland farm shown in Figure 154. Each kind of land on the farm is described and the uses and practices and treatments needed to farm it are explained.

Some of the practices and treatments can be started by the farmer without assistance. Instructions furnished to the farmer explain how these can be done.

There are other treatments and practices that are more complicated. On these the farmer will need help. The soil conservation district will provide the farmer with on-the-farm technical assistance of Soil Conservation Service technicians. The technicians supply basic information which the farmer or rancher can use in deciding how to use and treat each field on the farm.

II e 25: WAYS TO USE AND CONSERVE THIS LAND

This is nearly level or gently sloping, deep, well drained land. The loamy soils are easy to till and may have had considerable erosion. They are moderately productive, being well suited for corn and general farm crops.

If used for crops: Farm in contour strips to prevent gullies and soil wash. Use a rotation of not more than 2 years of row crop, small grain, and hay.

RELATIONSHIP OF LAND
CAPABILITY CLASSES TO SAFE LAND USE

LAND CAPA-BILITY CLASS	LAND USES							
	WILDLIFE	WOODLAND	GRAZING		CULTIVATION			
			MODERATE	INTENSIVE	LIMITED	MODERATE	INTENSIVE	VERY INTENSIVE
I	Suitable for all uses. Cultivation requires only ordinary farm practices.							
II	Suitable for all uses but simple conservation practices are needed if cultivated.							
III	Suitable for all uses but intensive conservation practices are needed if cultivated.							
IV	Suitable for all uses but cultivation should be limited.							
V	Suitable for pasture, woodland, or wildlife.							
VI	Suitable for extensive pasture, woodland or wildlife.							
VII	Suitable for woodland or wildlife use. Usually not suited to pasture.							
VIII	Suitable in some cases for wildlife production or recreation. Not suitable for the economic production of cultivated crops, pasture or woods.							

LEGEND FOR CONSERVATION SURVEY MAP

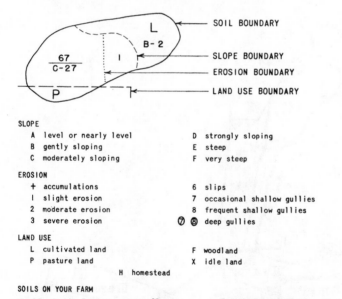

SOIL BOUNDARY

SLOPE BOUNDARY

EROSION BOUNDARY

LAND USE BOUNDARY

SLOPE

A	level or nearly level	D	strongly sloping
B	gently sloping	E	steep
C	moderately sloping	F	very steep

EROSION

+	accumulations	6	slips
I	slight erosion	7	occasional shallow gullies
2	moderate erosion	8	frequent shallow gullies
3	severe erosion	⑦ ⑧	deep gullies

LAND USE

L	cultivated land	F	woodland
P	pasture land	X	idle land
	H	homestead	

SOILS ON YOUR FARM

Soil Symbol	Name	Land-Capability Unit
102	Glenlg loam	IIe4, IIIe4
112	Manor loam	IIe25, IIIe25
113	Manor gravely loam	IIIe25, VIe3, VIIe3
122	Chester loam	IIe4
271	Glenville silt loam	IIw1
291	Congaree silt loam	VIw3
301	Codorus silt loam	VIw3

FIGURE 153. Relationship of land capability classes to safe land use.
(Soil Conservation Service)

Seed a cover crop or winter grain after each cultivated crop. Keep natural draws in good sod. Lift tillage implements when crossing sod waterways. Seed red clover, timothy, and alsike clover for short-term hay. Use plenty of lime and fertilizer for high yields.

If used for hay: Establish by seeding in contour strips. Red clover, orchardgrass, alsike and alfalfa; or timothy and alfalfa should do well. Use plenty of lime and fertilize annually with a heavy application of phosphate and potash fertilizer to keep legumes in the stand.

If used for pasture: When seeding, plow or disk in contour strips. Seed a tall grass and legume pasture mixture. Orchardgrass and alfalfa; or orchardgrass, ladino clover, and redtop may be used. Excess forage may be cut for hay or silage. Set up a rotational grazing plan. Mow just before the end of the grazing season to control weeds and stimulate new growth. Avoid pasturing too early in spring or too late in fall. Apply lime as needed and fertilize annually with a high phosphate-potash fertilizer.

To improve woodland: Protect from fire and grazing and be on the lookout for diseases. Harvest mature trees for sale or farm use. Cut or girdle inferior trees that may be shading good young trees. Interplant large open areas with white pine and scotch pine. Keep woodland edges in place by removing the large trees to encourage shrubs. A woodland border may also be established by planting desirable shrubs.

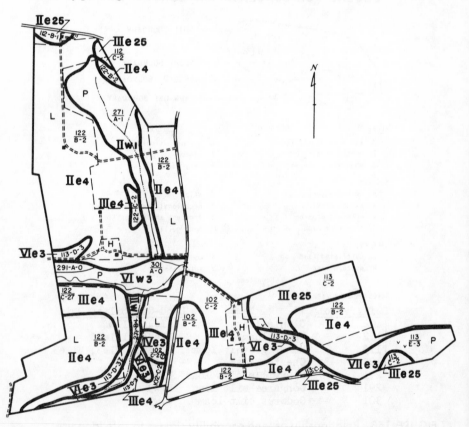

To improve wildlife conditions: Wildlife may be increased by planting hedge fences and windbreaks or by removing trees from hedge rows. Plant trees and shrubs on odd areas to furnish protection for both wildlife and the land.

II w 1: WAYS TO USE AND CONSERVE THIS LAND

This is flat or gently sloping land. Crops are apt to be late in the spring because of wetness. It will produce general farm crops but is best suited to hay.

If used for crops: Farm sloping land in graded strips. Bed flat land with graded dead furrows. Open ditches or diversions may be used to improve drainage. Keep natural draws in sod. Do not use more than 2 years of row crops or less than 2 years of hay in the rotation. Select grass-legume mixtures that are tolerant of wetness. Lime and fertilize for the legumes.

If used for hay: Seed in strips on controlled grade. Use a moisture-tolerant, long-lived grass-legume mixture. Lime and fertilize to maintain the legume. Open ditches, diversions, or graded dead furrows are often needed to improve drainage.

If used for pasture: When reseeding plow in strips on controlled grade. Use a tall grass-legume mixture. Mow weeds and rank growth. Scatter droppings. Divide pasture and rotate grazing. Avoid early spring or late fall grazing. Lime and fertilize to maintain the legumes.

III e 4: WAYS TO USE AND CONSERVE THIS LAND

The soils are deep, well drained, easily worked, and hold moisture well. The slopes are moderate but erosion has removed up to ¾ of the original topsoil. The land is suitable for commonly grown crops and responds well to fertilizer. It may be low in potash and may need boron for alfalfa. This land is suitable for rotation cropland. Conservation measures are needed to prevent further damage.

If used for crops: Keep in legume hay at least 2 years out of 4. Use contour cultivation on short slopes or contour strip-cropping on long slopes. Diversions may be needed on longer slopes. Provide safe outlets before diversions are constructed. Seed a winter cover crop, such as rye grass and vetch when land is not in winter grain. Red clover with timothy or orchardgrass is a good hay mixture. Alfalfa or alsike may be added. Lime for the legumes. Fertilize small grain when seeding. Top-dress hay annually with a high potash fertilizer after first cutting. Reinforce manure application with superphosphate.

If used for hay: Reseed by disking in strips across the slope. Reseed as often as necessary to re-establish legumes. Seed to grass-legume mixtures that have a long life. Add ladino clover to mixtures if used for pasture. Fertilize to establish seeding. Top-dress annually with high potash fertilizer after first cutting. Reinforce manure application with superphosphate.

If used for pasture: Lime and fertilize. Top-dress every other year with fertilizer or manure. Mow at least once a year. Control grazing in early spring and late fall. Rotate grazing between fields.

III e 25: WAYS TO USE AND CONSERVE THIS LAND

The deep, open loamy soils are productive. This land may have considerable slope and may wash severely. The soils respond well to lime and fertilizer when protected from washing. They are well adapted to general farm crops.

If used for crops: Cultivate not more than 1 year out of 5 with at least 3 years of hay. Farm in contour strips of alternate row crop, small grain, or hay. Keep waterways or natural depressions in sod. Use diversion terraces on slopes that are subject to washing. Provide safe outlets for diversions before construction. Alfalfa, timothy, red clover, and alsike clover should do well for hay. Lime as needed and fertilize to maintain legumes.

If used for hay: Establish by plowing or disking in contour strips. Alfalfa, orchardgrass, and alsike clover should do well. Smooth brome grass may be substituted for the orchardgrass. Lime and fertilize as needed to keep the legume in the stand.

If used for pasture: Establish in contour strips. Make a tall grass seeding. Orchardgrass, ladino clover, alsike clover, and red top will do well. Mow just before the end of the grazing season, to control weeds and stimulate new growth. Manage in a rotational grazing plan. Lime as needed and fertilize annually with applications of phosphate-potash fertilizer or phosphated manure.

IV e 3: WAYS TO USE AND CONSERVE THIS LAND

This is steep, rolling or eroded land, best used for hay or pasture. The soils are well drained throughout and need plenty of lime and fertilizer, but if properly treated they will produce satisfactory hay or pasture. Because of erosion hazard this land should be kept in hay most of the time.

If used for hay: Row crops should seldom be grown. Reseeding can be safely done through small grain, or directly from sod to hay. Reseed in contour strips. Diversions may be needed. Provide safe outlets before constructing diversions. Natural draws should be kept in sod. Select and seed grass-legume mixtures having a long life. Alfalfa is adapted if well fertilized. Disking or shallow plowing and disking should be used so that crop residues are left on or near the surface. Use heavy applications of complete fertilizer at time of seeding. If small grain nurse crop is used, remove either by grazing or as grain hay. Top-dress annually with a high potash fertilizer. Boron may be needed for alfalfa-grass mixtures. Add ladino clover to all mixtures to fill in where the other legumes die out. Reseed only as often as necessary to re-establish legumes.

If used for pasture: For tall grass pastures, select seed mixtures that hold up well under grazing. Use heavy applications of complete fertilizer at the time of seeding. Top-dress every other year with a phosphate-potash fertilizer. Kentucky bluegrass, wild white clover pasture should be limed before applying fertilizer. Treat critically eroded areas; seed, fertilize and mulch. Clip weeds and rank growth at least once a year. Rotate grazing. Control grazing. Contour furrows may be used to hold back runoff. Stock water developments may be needed.

VI e 3: WAYS TO USE AND CONSERVE THIS LAND

This is steep land subject to serious erosion. The subsoil may contain some limy material. It should be kept in pasture or woods. The soils are highly erodible, but will produce fairly good pasture if properly managed.

If used for pasture: Lime before applying fertilizer. Top-dress regularly.

Slope, seed, and mulch critical areas. Rotate grazing. Control grazing. Develop water supplies.

To improve woodland: Keep stock out, protect from fire, and watch for tree diseases. Cut mature or inferior trees that are shading out good young trees. Keep woodland edges in place and protect woods from damage by developing or planning a shrub border. Land that cannot be managed by mowing, liming, and fertilizing to keep a dense, vigorous sod should be reforested. Quality timber can be grown on these soils.

VI w 3: WAYS TO USE AND CONSERVE THIS LAND

This is nearly level bottomland that may have been eroded from streambank overflow. The soils are loamy and may be wet in the subsoil due to high water table. Because of the possible damage to crops by stream overflow, these soils are best adapted to permanent pasture.

If used for pasture: Establish by disking in small plots or strips. Ladino clover, orchardgrass, or timothy and alsike clover should do well; bluegrass and white clover are well adapted. Use a complete fertilizer at the time of seeding and maintain by heavy annual application of high phosphate-potash fertilizers. Lime as needed. One can get the most from pasture by grazing under a management plan, and by mowing just before the end of each grazing period to control weeds and stimulate new growth. Avoid early spring and late fall grazing.

To improve woodland: Protect from fire and grazing and guard against tree diseases. Harvest mature trees that have been marked by a qualified person. Cut or girdle worthless trees. Confine woodland edges by establishing a border of wildlife shrubs.

To improve wildlife conditions: Beneficial wildlife can be increased by planting eroding streambanks and odd areas with silky cornel, purple-osier willow, highbush cranberry, or tartarian honeysuckle.

VII e 3: WAYS TO USE AND CONSERVE THIS LAND

This is steep or badly eroded, droughty land, best used for woodland. This land is low in fertility. Tree growth is usually not rapid, but fair timber or pulpwood can be produced with good management.

To improve woodland: Areas not covered by existing woods should be planted. Black locust can be mixed with the pines to help increase soil fertility even though they may die before reaching fence-post size. Because of slowness of growth and type of trees generally found, cutting for pulpwood is the main management problem. Protect from fire and grazing. Keep woods from crowding crop or pasture fields by planting or developing a shrub border.

To improve wildlife: Allow den trees to remain in woods to benefit wildlife. Plant suitable shrubs along woods roads and in open areas to improve cover for wildlife.

FARM PLAN

The plan developed for this farm is shown in Figure 155. This plan is based on the information developed by the soil survey, the experience of the farmer, the knowledge and skill of the planning technician, and the needs of the farmer.

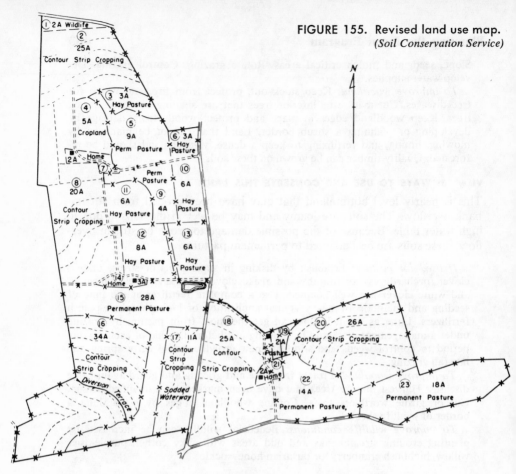

FIGURE 155. Revised land use map.
(Soil Conservation Service)

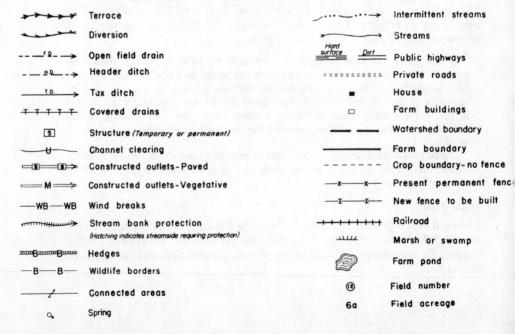

LEGEND FOR REVISED LAND USE MAP

Terrace		Intermittent streams	
Diversion		Streams	
Open field drain		Public highways	
Header ditch		Private roads	
Tax ditch		House	
Covered drains		Farm buildings	
Structure *(Temporary or permanent)*		Watershed boundary	
Channel clearing		Farm boundary	
Constructed outlets - Paved		Crop boundary - no fence	
Constructed outlets - Vegetative		Present permanent fenc	
Wind breaks		New fence to be built	
Stream bank protection		Railroad	
(Hatching indicates streamside requiring protection)		Marsh or swamp	
Hedges		Farm pond	
Wildlife borders			
Connected areas		Field number	
Spring		Field acreage	

A second example is given, this time of a farm in Idaho. This farm shows how irrigation and range problems are dealt with in the farm planning procedure. The land capability map of this farm is shown in Figure 156.

II s 1: WAYS TO USE AND CONSERVE THIS LAND

This is a medium-textured soil 20 to 36 inches deep on slopes under 2 per cent. It is good land and under proper irrigation it is highly productive. The root feeding zone is limited due to soil depth. It requires special care in irrigation and leveling. The water-storage capacity is good. The fertility is good except for low organic matter content.

Cropland. This land should be in legumes and grasses, half the time. Row crops should be limited to two successive years in the rotation.

FIGURE 156. Land capability unit map.
(Soil Conservation Service)

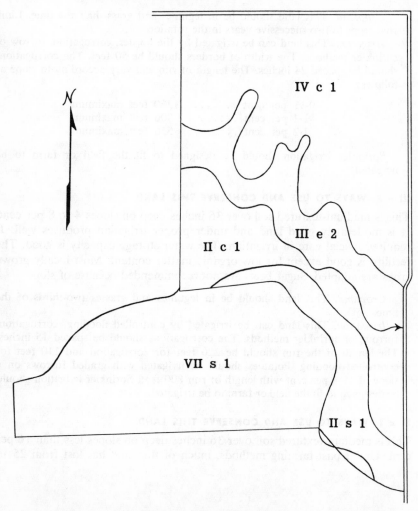

Irrigation. This land can be irrigated by the border, corrugation, furrow, or sprinkler methods. The width of borders should be 50 feet. The corrugations should be spaced 24 inches. The length of run will vary according to slope as follows:

                0-½ per cent .... 1040 feet maximum
                ½-1 per cent .... 660 feet maximum
                1-2 per cent .... 440 feet maximum

Sprinkler irrigation should be designed to fit the field or farm to be irrigated. If land is leveled, limit cuts to six inches.

II c 1: WAYS TO USE AND CONSERVE THIS LAND

This is medium-textured soil over 36 inches deep on slopes under 2 per cent. It is good land, and under proper irrigation it is high-producing. This land is easily managed under irrigation. The water-storage capacity is good. The fertility is good except for low organic matter content. All locally grown crops are adapted.

Cropland. This land should be in legumes and grass, half the time. Limit row crops to two successive years in the rotation.

Irrigation. This land can be irrigated by the border, corrugation, furrow or sprinkler methods. The width of borders should be 50 feet. The corrugations should be spaced 24 inches. The length of run will vary according to slope as follows:

                0-½ per cent .... 1320 feet maximum
                ½-1 per cent .... 800 feet maximum
                1-2 per cent .... 550 feet maximum

Sprinkler irrigation should be designed to fit the field or farm to be irrigated.

III e 2: WAYS TO USE AND CONSERVE THIS LAND

This is medium-textured soil over 36 inches deep on slopes 4 to 8 per cent. It is moderately good land and under proper irrigation produces well. It requires special care in irrigation. The water-storage capacity is good. The fertility is good except for low organic matter content. Most locally grown crops are adapted. Sugar beets are not recommended because of slope.

Cropland. This land should be in legumes and grasses two-thirds of the time.

Irrigation. This land can be irrigated by controlled flooding, corrugation, furrow, or sprinkler methods. The corrugations should be spaced 15 inches. The length of the run should be 220 feet for corrugation and 110 feet for controlled flooding. Potatoes should be irrigated with graded furrows on a slope of ½-1 per cent with length of run 800 feet. Sprinkler irrigation should be designed to fit the field or farm to be irrigated.

IV c 1: WAYS TO USE AND CONSERVE THIS LAND

This is medium-textured soil over 36 inches deep on slopes less than 16 per cent. Under past farming methods, much of this land has lost from 25 to

50 per cent of its original topsoil by erosion. The fertility is good except for low organic matter content.

Range. If used for range, it should be managed to maintain or increase such key forage plants as: bluebunch wheatgrass, crested wheatgrass, Idaho fescue and bitterbrush. Start spring grazing when the ground is firm and the new growth of grasses is 4 to 6 inches high. Leave 50 per cent of the current year's growth on the better grasses at the end of the grazing period. Graze the range in a rotation-deferred system. Fence when necessary to divide range into proper number of units. Livestock should be moved into under-utilized areas by developing watering facilities and riding. Salt away from water to get better distribution and utilization. Eradicate brush on low producing rangelands by spraying, mechanical treatment or controlled burning. Reseed these and other areas, if necessary, to adapted grasses and legumes. Protect reseeded areas until well established.

Dry cropland. This land is best suited for range. However, it is fairly good land and under proper dry farming practices, satisfactory crop yields may be obtained in years of favorable rainfall. These lands require very careful management. Leave all crop residues on the surface. These tillage operations are recommended: Use chisel in the fall and sweeps in the spring. Rod weed as necessary. A strip-crop system of farming is recommended. If grass is used for feed or soil building, plant in solid stands or in alternate rows with wheat. If used for seed, plant in 36-inch rows. All seeding should be done with a drill preferably in the fall on a firmly packed seedbed.

BASIC RANGE PROGRAM FOR ALL RANGE SITES AND RANGE CONDITION CLASSES

The original or climax vegetation on the rangeland of this area is made up primarily of perennial grasses. Experience and research have proved that these grasses produce the most dependable supply of nutritious forage. The production of forage can be maintained or improved by basing the grass management program on the more important key (climax) grasses. The program below and the practices listed under each range site will help produce more forage, control erosion, and conserve moisture.

Grass production management:
1. Rotate and defer grazing on grassland.
   a. Divide the range as nearly as possible into 3 or more pastures of equal forage production.
   b. Begin grazing in a different pasture each spring when the ground is firm and the important (key) grasses are ready to graze.
   c. Give the key grasses in pastures, grazed first each spring, a chance to recover and store up food reserves in their roots. They need the last 45 days of the spring growing season to do this.
   d. Produce your own grass seed, scatter and let the livestock tramp them in. Defer grazing, in rotation on $\frac{1}{3}$ of the range each year until after seed maturity of the key perennial grasses.
2. Protect the range from fires.
3. Keep one month's additional feed on hand to enable you to delay spring grazing until the range is ready to graze.

Practices that help get effective grass management:
1. Fencing—arrange boundary and cross fences so that pastures are of nearly equal forage production.

2. Salting—get better grazing distribution and uniform use of the range forage by salting away from water. Change salt locations frequently during the grazing season to lead stock into areas that are not being grazed.

3. Riding—ride frequently to move salt and break up excessive concentrations of cattle around salt, shade, and water.

4. Water developments.

   a. Give first priority to water developments in range areas that show lightest grazing use and second priority to areas of next lightest use.

   b. Avoid developing water in the closely grazed (poor condition) range areas unless it is necessary for proper grass management.

   c. Be sure to have an adequate supply of water in each pasture throughout the spring, summer, and fall season.

5. Bedding out of sheep—use open herding of sheep, and do not bed sheep more than three nights (preferably one night) on the same bed ground.

Special improvement practices:

Control noxious plants according to recommendations standard for your area.

RANGE SITE—WEST SIDE SCABLAND (VII s 1)

This site has medium-textured, gravelly and very stony soils which are less than 20 inches deep. Slopes are less than 16 per cent. This site should support sparse to moderately dense stands of wheatgrasses, bluegrasses, Idaho fescue, and other high-producing vegetation. When the vegetation is depleted, this site is subject to both wind and water erosion.

RANGE CONDITION

Excellent—producing near its best
Good—possible improvement 1½ to 2 times present yield
Fair—possible improvement 2 to 4 times present yield
Poor—possible improvement 4 to 12 times present yield

Grass production management:

1. On excellent condition *maintain* these key grasses:
   Bluebunch wheatgrass (cattle)
   Idaho fescue (sheep or cattle)
   Bluegrasses (sheep)

2. On good and fair condition *increase* the above key grasses.

3. On poor condition *increase* remnants of the above grasses or maintain needlegrass.

4. Begin spring grazing when new growth of:
   Bluebunch wheatgrass is 4 inches high (cattle)
   Idaho fescue is 3 inches high (sheep or cattle)
   Bluegrasses are 3 inches high (sheep)
   Cheatgrass brome is 2 inches high (sheep or cattle) (if no remnants of the above key grasses are left)

5. Safe degree of use: *take ½ and leave ½*. This means leaving about a:
   4-inch stubble on bluebunch wheatgrass (cattle)
   2-inch stubble on Idaho fescue (sheep or cattle)
   2-inch stubble on bluegrasses (sheep)
   3-inch stubble on needlegrass (cattle)
   3-inch stubble on cheatgrass brome (cattle or sheep)

Practices that help get more effective grass management:

   1. Water development (springs, charco pits, or wells)—Space water not more than 2 miles apart on large pastures. Develop at least one good water hole in each small pasture.

Special improvement practices:

   1. Control sagebrush and rabbitbrush, noxious weeds.
   2. Reseed range areas in low, fair and poor condition to adapted grasses and legumes.
   3. Protect reseeded areas from grazing until well established (this may mean 2 to 3 years protection).

Additional treatment for all irrigated land:

   CROPLAND—Practice a systematic crop rotation. Leave all crop residue and work into the soil. Plow under 10 to 12 inches of alfalfa and grass in the fall prior to planting annual crop. Plow under sweet clover and grass late in the spring just before planting annual crop. Apply phosphate fertilizer to the legumes and manure to annual crops in the rotation. Establish windbreaks to reduce wind erosion.

   GRASS AND LEGUME SEEDINGS—Plant adapted mixtures. Companion crops are not recommended, especially for pastures. If used, seeding rate of companion crop should be one-third of that commonly used. Seed with drill, not over one inch deep, on a firm, moist seedbed. Irrigate to meet the needs of the grasses and legumes being established.

   PASTURE—Protect from grazing until well established. Do not graze until ground is firm and plants are 5 to 6 inches high. Rotate grazing by establishing three or more pastures. Apply manure and commercial fertilizers as needed. Mow pastures and scatter droppings. Leave 3 or 4 inches height in the fall on pastures and hay fields.

   IRRIGATION—Level or land plane when necessary to secure uniform water distribution. Use irrigation structures to get water control. Surveys may be necessary to accomplish land leveling, system design, and water control. Irrigate according to the needs of the crop being grown. Check depth of irrigation with soil probe or shovel. Use non-erosive streams to reach end of field in approximately one-fifth of total irrigation time. Cut back stream after water has reached the end of the field. Use floating and proper tillage practices to maintain good conditions for irrigation.

STRIP-CROPPING

Strip-cropping is the practice of growing crops in a systematic arrangement of strips or bands which serve as vegetative barriers to erosion. It includes the utilization of crop rotation, contour cultivation, proper tillage, cover crops, and other related practices. The arrangement of crops in strips should be such that erosion- and semi-erosion-resistant crops are alternated with clean-cultivated crops that are conducive to erosion. By its nature strip-cropping is more effective than contour cultivation.

Crops laid out in strips and cultivated on the contour conserve moisture and reduce soil losses. Smith and his associates showed with plot experiments that contour, in contrast with up- and downhill planting and cultivation, reduced soil losses as much as 52 per cent, and that strip-cropping reduced the annual soil loss by 55 per cent in comparison with that from contour cultivation alone. Observations of the plots showed the tendency for water to concentrate and form gullies was markedly greater on the plots that were not strip-cropped.

In working with strip-cropping systems certain guiding principles should be kept in mind: (a) strip-cropping must be made to fit into the farm management; (b) it must be related to other management practices needed on the farm; (c) it should be used as a means of increasing the effectiveness of the rotation in controlling erosion; (d) strips should be laid out as nearly on the contour as possible; (e) consideration should be given to the degree of erosion, the percentage of slope, and the length of the rotation; (f) the ultimate objective of any plan of strip-cropping should be to keep the soil intact, improve soil fertility, and produce the greatest possible economic return for the farmer.

LAYOUT METHODS VARY

To meet the problem found on farms it is necessary to vary the methods of laying out strips. Four types of strip-cropping have been found to cover

FIGURE 157. Strips of corn are alternated with strips of small grain on this Lancaster County, Pennsylvania, farm.
(Soil Conservation Service)

most of the problems in the northeastern states. They are: (a) contour strip-cropping, (b) parallel-sided strips, (c) field strips, and (d) drainage or graded strips.

Contour strip-cropping is most effective, and applicable on a large proportion of farms. The strip boundaries are laid out on the contour and the planting follows the contour lines with short rows in the middle. In practical layouts on the farm, the level points are located every 50 to 100 feet and a plow is used to mark the contour lines. The experience of farmers indicates that this method of strip-cropping is most effective in controlling erosion and conserving moisture. Some farmers object to having short rows associated with contour strip-cropping but this is not a serious problem except in the case of some specialized crops such as potatoes and cigar-wrapper tobacco.

Parallel-sided strips are used to some extent in areas where these specialized crops are grown. With parallel-sided strips there are no short rows. This facilitates the use of the sprayer and cultivator in the high-ridge culture system for potatoes and avoids bruising of the leaves for cigar tobacco, which might result from turning in short rows. This type of strip may be laid out from a contour base line on one side or in the center of the strip. In order to maintain such strips approximately on the contour, it is necessary to use corrective areas, although some object to this use as not the most desirable one for the areas.

Field strips are field divisions across the major slope. They are used to subdivide large fields into two or more parts either for erosion control or to facilitate the balancing of crop acreages. Field strips are used under conditions of irregular topography where the application of contour or parallel-sided strips is impractical. In some terrain, such as glaciated sections, the kettle and kame topography, and the limestone ridges, the ridge outcropping makes contouring very difficult. Field strips are used under these conditions, but where practical the land should be planned for crops that provide permanent cover.

Drainage strips are used on soils that are not naturally well-drained. They are laid out on a grade usually not exceeding one per cent and facilitate the drainage of surplus water. They are planned in conjunction with terrace systems and diversion terraces and the grade should be in the direction of a stabilized outlet.

The width of strips is adjusted in accordance with the steepness of the slopes and the erodibility of the soil. In practice about 100 feet is considered a satisfactory width of strip on the steep slopes but when the slope is greater than 15 to 18 per cent, a narrower width is desirable. The rotation influences to a considerable degree the width of strips. If the rotation carries three or more years of hay, the width of strip can be greater.

The length of the rotation is a factor in any strip-cropping program. When the farmer does not require much grain and a long rotation can be adopted, with several years of well-managed hay, the problem is relatively simple. Often it is necessary to shorten the rotation in order to provide the required grain. Sometimes this can be worked out by putting the short rotation on the more gentle slopes and using a long rotation on the very steep slopes. In order to protect the steeper slopes with long rotations, corn with a cover crop is sometimes recommended every year on the nearly level bottomland. Cover crops are an essential part of a good rotation and should be used to follow cultivated crops where they have a chance of success. Because of the lateness of harvest of such crops as potatoes, carrots, beets, and cabbage in some sections of the country, it frequently is not practicable to plant a cover crop.

DIVERSIONS AND GRASS WATERWAYS

Diversion terraces are used widely as a supplement to strip-cropping. On very long slopes, some method by which the water can be diverted has been found essential. If the watershed is long, strip-cropping has been found effective near the top of the slope but on the lower part the water often tends to concentrate, causing considerable erosion. Establishing diversion ditches across the slopes at intervals to take care of the excess water prevents concentration and aids in the effectiveness of strip-cropping.

Grass waterways are considered as part of a strip-cropping plan. They are used to carry surplus water off the strips. It is generally a good plan, especially on imperfectly-drained soils, to grade the strips slightly toward such waterways. In the case of field strips and parallel-sided strips, the grass waterways are particularly essential. In these types of strip-cropping, the planting and cultivation often leads the water toward the draws and if a grass waterway is not provided, gullies will result. In cultivating across waterways, farmers have to be careful not to cut up the sod. The waterway should be wide enough to carry the water and shaped so that it will not run over on the cultivated land, causing a gully. Ordinarily the width should be at least 12 feet.

The sequence of crops in strip-cropping is important. The crops should be arranged so that no two cultivated strips are adjacent to each other. Oats, while a close-growing crop, is not a good crop to grow adjacent to corn because the land for these crops is plowed in the spring. This can be avoided by putting corn and wheat in one field and oats and hay in another and alternating the two sets of crops back and forth to maintain the proper sequence in the rotation. Similarly, many other combinations of crops and rotations are used with the arrangement of crops worked out in accordance with the specific problem on the farm. In the adjustment of a rotation to make stripping most effective, grass and legumes always precede row crops wherever possible.

Much of the strip-cropping is started in the spring and fall. In the spring, strip-cropping can be started on a field in sod by plowing alternate strips for corn. Following corn in the fall, alternate strips of wheat can be planted. Sometimes wheat is needed on the entire corn field and clover and grass seeded in alternate strips in the spring. From these beginnings, the complete rotation is worked into a strip-cropping system.

The use of the portable electric fence has made it possible for the farmer to graze meadows at his convenience even though some labor is involved in putting up the fence. Laying out the strips so that the small grain and hay are all in one field makes it possible to graze the meadow after the hay and grain are harvested. By planning the permanent pasture in relation to the pasture obtainable from the meadow in a strip-cropping system, temporary fencing can be reduced to a minimum and in many cases is unnecessary.

STRIP-CROPPING NOT APPLICABLE IN ORCHARDS

Strip-cropping is not usually applicable in orchards. Contour planting and cultivation are widely used except for apples. Most apples are maintained in sod. A well-managed sod will do a satisfactory job of controlling erosion without the aid of contour planting. In most cases the sod seems to offer no important competition with the apple tree for moisture. In a few areas of deficient rainfall where apples are grown, it is necessary to employ practices similar to those used for the stone fruits.

For stone fruits, contour planting and cultivation give better results than sod. The stone fruits require a lot of water during the period of fruit swell, the latter part of the summer. This is usually a time of deficient moisture and all that is available is required for the maturing fruit. To meet this problem, stone-fruit orchards are planted on the contour or in graded rows in conjunction with terraces. During the early stages of growth, sod strips may be maintained in the middle of the rows allowing for adequate cultivation along the tree rows. When the trees begin to bear, the sod strips are eliminated and a managed cover-crop system is introduced. The cover crop is usually planted early enough to give a good winter cover. It is allowed to grow in the spring to produce a large yield of organic matter and is then disked down. The trashy cultivation principle should be followed. The cover crop is cut down to such an extent that it requires little or no water and the residue is left on the surface where it serves to control erosion and conserve moisture for the rapidly growing fruit.

TRUCK-GARDENING AREAS

In the Northeast, where strip-cropping is most extensively used in the humid section, there are a number of intensive truck-gardening areas. The soil of these areas while gently sloping is usually quite erodible. Cultivated crops are grown every year on the land with the aid of high applications of fertilizers. No system of strip-cropping has been found that is practical for these areas. Contour cultivation in conjuction with terrace systems has been adopted as the most practical answer to the problem. Cover crops and green manure crops are worked into the cultural system to maintain the organic matter.

Where cover crops have not been possible it has proven advisable to retire the land from truck to green manure crops at frequent intervals. In some cases the land is retired to a long rotation with several years of legume hay. A livestock enterprise is generally conducted with such a system, producing a lot of manure that will aid in building the organic matter.

The moisture-saving feature of strip-cropping is important. In areas subject to dry spells in summer, the additional water saved through strip-cropping is often enough to carry the crop without any setback from the dry weather. In a prolonged dry season the crops do not suffer as much as those that are not arranged in strips. Many of the increased yields associated with strip-cropping and contour cultivation often may be attributed to a greater supply of available water in the soil.

LIMITATIONS OF STRIP-CROPPING

This discussion would not be complete without a word of warning about the limitations of strip-cropping. As has been indicated, strip-cropping provides little protection against the raindrop to the strips planted to clean-tilled crops. Unless suitable precautions are taken to prevent splash erosion on these areas the strip-cropping system will fall short of success.

CROP ROTATIONS

Crop rotations refer to the growing of different crops in a regular succession on the same land, as contrasted with a one-crop system or a haphazard change of crops. For erosion control a rotation must embody the principle of alternating cultivated crops with erosion-resistant and organic matter-building crops. Methods of increasing the erosion-control value of a rotation are: (a) increasing the number of years of hay and pasture; (b) improving the seed mixture to include legumes or better adapted grasses and legumes; (c) more adequate fertilization; and (d) the addition of cover crops to provide a continuous cover on the field when devoted to clean-tilled crops.

Rotations to use. The capability of the land limits the kind of rotation to be recommended on any field. The following are suggested types of rotations for the different land use capability classes found on well-drained soils:

Class I. Row, cover, row
Class II. Row, small grain, hay
Class III. Row, small grain, hay, hay
Class IV. Small grain, hay, hay, hay
Classes VI and VII. Not suited for rotations

The above rotations represent the maximum of intensity that different land classes can be cultivated safely. Whenever farm management considerations make it desirable to use a less intensive rotation for a given land class, such a rotation should be recommended. It is often desirable to increase the number of years of hay in a rotation on any of the land classes. It is good practice to do this, especially when it is consistent with roughage requirements of the farm livestock. Variations from the above standards based on knowledge of the local soils should be considered where necessary.

Relation to the land. The shorter and more intense rotations may be recommended only on the best land—that is, gently sloping, least subject to erosion, and least destructive of tilth. Longer rotations must be used on the more steeply sloping and erodible land. Rotations reduce runoff and soil loss. Both these savings are important in maintaining yield. Grass and legumes are the most effective of all the crops in reducing runoff and controlling erosion. Grass and legumes also influence the structure of soils so that when a cultivated crop is grown, much less erosion and runoff occur than if the crop were grown continuously.

Rotation and feed production. The relation between the rotation and feed production can best be illustrated with an example. In the Northeast, where dairying is of great importance, much interest centers in the feed any rotation will produce. In selecting a rotation, the ability to produce high quality feed must be considered as well as erosion control. Fortunately the high feed-producing rotations are also the most effective for erosion control. The following comparison of several rotations is indicative of their relative efficiency in producing feed and controlling erosion:

	Per cent of land in meadow	T.D.N. (lbs. per A)	Relative cost of T.D.N.
Corn, oats, wheat, clover	25	2533	100
Corn, wheat, clover	33⅓	3016	82
Corn, wheat, alfalfa, alfalfa	50	3750	51
Corn, wheat, alfalfa, alfalfa, alfalfa	60	3950	46

Low cost feed and high yield are shown for the 5-year rotation with three years of hay and the land in meadow 60 per cent of the time. Two or more years of hay gives a high degree of soil aggregation and complete erosion control when the land is in meadow. It also increases the erosion control when the land is in cultivation. The long rotations with 3 or more years of hay tend to conserve and build up organic matter to a greater extent than the short rotations.

Truck-gardening areas. In areas where truck crops are grown every year, cover crops such as winter and green manure, included at the proper time in the cropping sequence, will aid in maintaining organic matter and controlling erosion. In addition to cover crops, rotation of truck crops with grass and legumes is desirable to maintain soil organic matter and improve soil structure. Such a rotation would consist of two or three years of truck crops and the land seeded down to a mixture such as alfalfa, ladino clover, and timothy. The grasses and legumes should be mowed occasionally to control weeds and allowed to grow on the land for one or two years with all the residue returned to the soil. The grass and legumes may be used as a feed for livestock and the manure returned to the land, which would be producing an income during the time it was in sod.

It should be pointed out that with rotations, as with strip-cropping, sod crops do not protect the soil during the time clean-tilled crops are being grown. As a matter of fact many of the benefits arising from the growing of the sod crops are lost or dissipated when growing clean-tilled crops. The cropping system should provide continuous plant cover throughout the rotation system.

REFERENCES

1. Jones, J. P. 1949. *Application of strip-cropping and contour cultivation in the Northeast.* Jour. Soil and Water Cons., 4(4): 153-160.
2. Smith, D. D., Whitt, D. M., Zingg, A. W., McCall, A. G., and Bell, F. G. 1945. *Investigations of erosion control and reclamation of eroded Shelby and related soils at the Conservation Experiment Station, Bethany, Mo.* USDA Tech. Bull. 883.
3. Stallings, J. H. 1945. *Summarization of strip-cropping data on crop yields, runoff and soil loss.* USDA, SCS. (Multi.)
4. Tower, H., and Gardner, H. H. 1946. *Strip-cropping for conservation and production.* USDA Farmers' Bull. 1981.

22

Irrigation

Irrigation is as old as civilization. In fact, irrigation first made possible civilization as we now know it. By irrigation the Mesopotamians were able to produce crops in quantities greater than their own needs. This made it possible for some of the people to do other things than produce food.

Irrigation had been established when the writing of history began. An ancient Assyrian queen is credited with directing her government to divert the waters of the Nile to irrigate the desert lands of Egypt about 2000 B.C.

Irrigation in China is known to be more than 4,000 years old. The famous Tu-Kiang Dam, still successful today, was built by Mr. Li and his son in the Ching Dynasty, 200 B.C. It provides irrigation water for about one-half million acres of rice fields. The Grand Canal, 700 miles long, was built by the Shi empire, 589-618 A.D.

The practice of irrigation in India can be traced back to time immemorial and mention regarding this appears in records from antiquity.

Irrigation in America is also very old, having been practiced by the Indians at the time of the Spanish conquests. There are evidences that extensive irrigation works once existed in Arizona and New Mexico. It is believed that some of these canals were built about 700 A.D. Most of these earlier irrigation systems had fallen into disuse before white men came to this continent, but many of the Indians of the Southwest were still practicing irrigation on a small scale.

Irrigation was also practiced by the Spanish padres at the early missions in California, but to only a limited extent for gardens, orchards, vineyards, and some small grain plots. Irrigation was also practiced by trappers, miners, and frontiersmen in many places in the West although no effort was made to develop an agricultural economy based on irrigation until the Mormon pioneers entered Salt Lake Valley in July, 1847. This marked the beginning of modern irrigation in America. From the first, irrigation was a cooperative undertaking, with communities being located upon the streams flowing from the mountains. Community ditches were constructed to serve both the outlying agricultural areas and the garden plots in the towns.

The second important irrigation development was the establishment of the Union Colony at Greeley, Colorado, in 1870. This community effort resulted in more than 30,000 acres being brought under irrigation.

From these beginnings, irrigation agriculture spread rapidly throughout the western states, and by 1890 the first irrigation census showed a total irrigated area of 3,631,000 acres. This area was approximately doubled during the next decade, and doubled again by 1910. The increase in irrigated area was rapid and steady up to 1920, and was mostly from surface-water supplies. During the next decade there was only a very small additional acreage irrigated, mostly from ground-water supplies. A relatively small increase occurred between 1930 and 1940, and a larger gain was made between 1940 and 1950, almost entirely from ground-water development.

The present status of irrigation development for the twelve western states with greatest irrigated acreage, according to 1950 census figures, is given in Table 77.

IRRIGATION AND FOOD PRODUCTION

With the population increase expected, there will be 190 million people in the United States by 1975. Our total agricultural cropland has remained essentially static since 1920, although the farm output index has increased from 92 in 1920 to 138 in 1950 (1935-39 average = 100). Since 1935 the equivalent of about 45 million acres of cropland has been released from feeding horses and mules. By 1975, another 15 million acres can be expected to be released from this use. Based on the *President's Water Resources Committee Report,* it is estimated that about 30 million acres can be added to our cultivated area by reclamation through irrigation, drainage, and land clearing. Of this, about 6 million acres could be brought into production by 1975 through irrigation. This, however, is more than the total area brought under irrigation by the U.S. Bureau of Reclamation in its first 50 years of its existence, and will not be an easy goal to meet.

In order to maintain the 1950 standard of diet, we would need about 577 million acres equivalent of cropland by 1975, or about 70 million acres more than appears to be available, according to the most optimistic estimates. To provide an adequate diet for all would require an additional 112 million acres, or a total of 689 million acres. This indicates that we are cer-

TABLE 77. Irrigated acreage and capital investment (38)

State	Irrigated land (thousands of acres)		Per cent change	Capital investment (millions of dollars)		Capital investment (per acre irrigated)	
	1939	1949		1940	1950	1940	1950
California	5,070	6,619	+30.5	318.9	640.1	$ 62.90	$ 96.71
Texas	1,045	3,148	+201.2	66.4	144.5	63.54	45.90
Colorado	3,221	2,941	−8.7	106.8	161.4	33.16	54.88
Idaho	2,278	2,168	−4.8	102.6	130.0	45.04	59.96
Montana	1,711	1,810	+5.8	67.4	82.0	39.39	45.30
Wyoming	1,486	1,475	−0.7	41.5	59.6	27.92	40.41
Oregon	1,049	1,338	+27.6	51.0	74.4	48.62	55.61
Utah	1,176	1,166	−0.9	41.9	56.6	35.62	48.54
Arizona	653	979	+49.9	83.5	137.6	127.87	140.55
Nebraska	610	888	+45.6	39.1	56.5	64.10	63.63
Nevada	740	723	−2.3	16.9	20.2	22.84	27.94
New Mexico	554	691	+24.7	32.7	61.6	59.03	89.15
17 western states	20,395	24,869	+21.9	1,034.7	1,831.4	50.73	73.64
U.S. total	21,136	26,148	+23.7	1,059.1	1,887.1	50.11	72.17

tainly much closer to the day when we will actually face a food shortage in the United States than most of us realize.

If we are to meet these new demands for farm produce, more efficient use must be made of both our land and water. The acres now under irrigation must be managed so as to get the maximum returns from the water available. Additional acres must be brought under irrigation and new sources of water for irrigation must be exploited. This applies to those areas where irrigation is now practiced as well as the humid area of the eastern section of the United States. In short, every acre of land and every gallon of water available for irrigation must be made to produce the maximum.

IRRIGATION ELIMINATES DROUGHT HAZARD

Irrigation has long made it possible to produce bountiful crops in arid climates where it would otherwise be impossible to do so. During recent years it has been discovered that the frequent drought hazards in the humid section of the country can also be reduced or eliminated by supplementary irrigation.

Crop yields under irrigation in the West have been estimated to be from two or three times those of similar soils not irrigated. This is because crops can be supplied with adequate amounts of moisture throughout the growing season. This enables the plants to utilize to the fullest extent the plant nutrients available in the soil. An adequate moisture supply makes it possible for the physiological functions of the plants to operate at top speed.

Adequate moisture supplies combined with ample plant food and good management enable crops to produce maximum yields. For example, Miller and Dwyer reported that properly prepared and managed irrigated pastures in Washington produced two to three times as much beef per acre as unimproved irrigated pastures. The unimproved pastures consisted mainly of Kentucky bluegrass. The amount of beef produced averaged 200 to 250 pounds per acre on the unimproved pastures. The improved pasture used in this study produced an average of 549 pounds of beef per acre annually for the 4-year period 1947-1950.

Supplementary irrigation in summer of Bermuda-ladino clover pastures in Georgia increased the production of dry forage 27 per cent and the production of protein 67 per cent. Greater survival and growth of ladino clover throughout the summer with irrigation accounted for both the increased forage and protein production.

Smith and Lyerly showed that cotton in Texas has a critical need for water during the fruiting period. If adequate supplies of moisture are not available at this period resulting water stress may reduce yield and boll size and shorten staple length.

As a result of a 6-year study of sprinkler irrigation on five vegetable crops grown on Arredonda loamy sand in Florida, Nettles and his colleagues concluded that it was advisable to grow vegetables only in areas that provide adequate irrigation. Supplementary irrigation did not result in increased yield of crops in all seasons, but in some years or seasons it was responsible for the difference between a successful harvest and crop failure. The variation in response to sprinkler irrigation was attributed partly to the level and distribution of rainfall during the growing season and partly to the type of crop grown.

Increased yields from irrigation were found in three of five crops of cabbage. These were the years in which rainfall was below normal or the growing season extended into the spring.

Irrigation resulted in an increase in sweet corn yields in all tests, with both the highest number of ears and weight of corn produced when irrigated with 1 to 1½ inches of water per week in 1945. In 1948 and 1949, ½ inch of water every three or six days produced highest yields.

Large increases in yield were found with snap beans in the dry 1947 season with all irrigation treatments tested. In 1946 light amounts of water applied at any one date, in either single or split applications, gave a significant increase in yield of snap beans.

The application of ½ inch of water every six days in 1949 produced a significant increase in marketable onions, in comparison with the no-irrigation treatment.

In 1945 no significant response from irrigation was found with tomatoes. In the same season the highest yield of U.S. No. 1 cucumbers was harvested from vines receiving ½ inch of supplementary water every three or six days.

Too heavy an application of water may result in a reduction in yield. Light applications of water with cabbage in 1945, light and split application on beans in 1946, and split application on this crop in 1947 produced significantly higher yields than heavy applications. The tendency for crops receiving the medium application to produce higher yields than those receiving heavier amounts was noted with the early crop of cabbage and corn in 1947 and 1948, respectively, and with cucumbers, tomatoes, and onions. Observations of the crops heavily irrigated indicated that perhaps excessive leaching of plant nutrients occurred.

A relationship was found between levels of irrigation and spacing of corn plants in the row, with a tendency for the largest number and total weight of ears to be produced at the closer spacings and with heavier rates of irrigation. However, individual weight of ears increased with wider spacing and higher rates of irrigation.

Side-dressing with nitrogen gave increased yields in three of the five crops of cabbage. No significant interaction was found between irrigation and fertilizer treatment.

CONSUMPTIVE USE OF WATER AND IRRIGATION REQUIREMENTS

Water is the limiting factor in the expansion of irrigated agriculture. Thus, in irrigation planning, it is essential that consumptive use and irrigation water requirements be known. This is true for large irrigation projects or for individual farms, whether in the arid West or in the humid East.

Consumptive use—evapotranspiration—is one of the important elements in the cycle of water movements from the time it falls on the land as rain or snow until it reaches the ocean. It is the best index of how much water will need to be supplied by irrigation for good production.

The determination of consumptive use and irrigation water requirements involves consideration of water supply, both surface and underground, as well as those of the management and general economics of irrigation projects.

New irrigation development is rapidly taking place throughout the United States. New lands are being brought under irrigation. Older irrigation lands are being re-leveled and irrigation systems are being revised to accommodate improved irrigation practices for better conserving soil, water, and labor. There is urgent need for sound information on the amount of irrigation water required for profitable crop production.

Before equitable division of the use of water available in a drainage basin in arid and semi-arid regions can be satisfactorily ascertained, careful consideration must be given to the consumptive-use requirements for water in various sub-basins.

CONSUMPTIVE USE

The term "consumptive use," as used here, is synonymous with *evapotranspiration*. It is defined as the sum of the volumes of water used by the vegetative growth of a given area in transpiration and building of plant tissue and that evaporated from the adjacent soil, or intercepted precipitation on the area in any specific time divided by the given area. If the unit of time is small, the consumptive use is expressed in acre-inches per acre or depth in inches; whereas if the unit of time is large, such as crop-growing season or a 12-month period, the consumptive use is usually expressed as acre-feet or depth in feet.

FACTORS AFFECTING CONSUMPTIVE USE

Many factors operate singly or in combination to influence the amount of water consumed by plants. The effects of these factors are not necessarily constant, but they fluctuate from year to year as well as from place to place. Some involve the human factor but others are related to natural influences and the environment.

The rate of evapotranspiration depends on climate, soil moisture supply, vegetative cover, soils, and land management. The climatic factors that particularly affect consumptive use are precipitation, temperature, humidity, wind movement, and length of growing season. Also, the quantity of water transpired by plants depends upon the amount of water at their disposal. Certainly if there is no water available to the plants, there can be no transpiration, and if the plants are under heavy water stress, water use will be small. Other factors affecting the use of water are the state of the development of the plant, the amount of its foliage, and the nature of its leaf.

The effect of sunshine and heat on stimulating transpiration was studied as early as 1691, according to Abbe. Measurements of transpiration by various kinds of plants by Briggs and Shantz indicate a closer correlation between transpiration and evaporation from free water surfaces, air temperature, solar radiation, and wet bulb depression readings. Various investigators have made many other studies of the effects of temperature, moisture, and light on plant growth.

STUDIES AND RESULTS

Research studies by federal, state, and other agencies have been made on evaporation and transpiration at various times during the past 50 years in the United States. One of the first studies of evapotranspiration losses of irrigated crops in California was made in 1903 by Irrigation Investigations, Office of Experiment Stations, United States Department of Agriculture. At various times since that date, this agency and its successors have studied and measured consumptive use of water by different agricultural crops and natural vegetation in many sections of the West. Data obtained by these studies show estimated rates of consumptive use of water by each of the more important crops. Usually, evaporation, temperature, humidity, precipitation and wind movement were recorded at the same time. Thus, data are available in many areas for correlating consumptive-use measurements with temperature and other climatological observations.

Results of studies in California, Colorado, and New Mexico indicate that the observed evaporation data may be used as a means of estimating evapotranspiration by phreatophytes (water-loving vegetation) having access to an ample water supply when the relation of the two is known for the particular area. As an example, for tules growing in large tanks within the confines of a swamp area at two locations in California, the consumptive use with reference to evaporation from the nearby exposed U.S. Weather Bureau pan was 95 per cent. The percentage varied from month to month, increasing in the summer and becoming smaller in the cooler months, but 95 per cent was the average obtained for a 2-year record.

From long-period records of evaporation, temperature, and humidity in New Mexico and Texas, together with consumptive-use measurements at Carlsbad, New Mexico, empirical formulas were developed for computing evaporation and consumptive use when temperature and humidity data are available.

METHODS OF DETERMINING WATER USE

Various means have been used to determine the amount of water transpired by plants. The earlier method was based on loss of water through heating.

One of the methods consisted of weighing freshly cut leaves, twigs, or stocks of growing plants immediately after cutting and at short intervals thereafter until wilting commenced. Thousands of individual plants were grown in small pots and weighed periodically to determine evapotranspiration losses. Most of these methods utilized artificial conditions, and it is questionable whether the results can be extended to field conditions.

Various methods have been used to determine consumptive use of water by agricultural crops and natural vegetation under field conditions. Regardless of the method, the problems encountered are numerous. The source of water used by plant life, whether from precipitation alone or irrigation or ground water plus precipitation, is a factor in selecting a method.

The methods most widely used in irrigation investigations are (a) soil-moisture studies on fields and plots, (b) tank or lysimeter experiments, (c) ground-water fluctuations, (d) inflow-outflow measurements, (e) integration, and (f) effective heat. The correlation of water use, climatological and other data, and the analysis of irrigation and precipitation records are also important.

Soil-moisture studies. This method is employed to determine the consumptive use of irrigated fields on which the soil is fairly uniform and the depth to ground water is such that it will not influence the soil-moisture fluctuations within the root zone. Soil samples are taken before and after each irrigation and at frequent intervals between irrigations. Usually a great number of soil samples must be taken. The total depth of water extracted from the soil by evapotranspiration is computed for each period between samplings.

Tank or lysimeter experiments. One of the more common methods of determining use of water by individual agricultural crops and natural vegetation is to grow the plants in tanks or lysimeters and measure the quantity of water necessary to maintain satisfactory growth. Tanks as large as 10 feet in diameter and 10 feet deep have been used. However, in most consumptive-use studies, the tanks are about 2 to 3 feet in diameter and 6 feet deep.

The practicability of determining consumptive use by means of tanks or lysimeters is dependent upon the accuracy of reproduction of natural conditions. In addition to environment, artificial conditions are the result of limitations of soil, size of tank, or regulation of water supply. Weighing is the precise means of determining the consumptive use from tanks, and this method was used as early as 1907. However, conditions and facilities will not always permit the weighing of tanks. It has been found that all tank vegetation must be protected from the elements by a surrounding growth of the same species.

Ground-water fluctuations. Where ground water is relatively near the land surface, evapotranspiration losses are indicated from large areas by the daily rise and fall of the water table. Diurnal measurements of the ground-water table fluctuations provide a basis for computing consumptive use of water by overlying vegetation. This method has been used successfully in various areas of Utah, California, and Arizona.

The procedure used is to install observation wells equipped with water stage recorders at representative locations in the area under consideration and to obtain graphic records of the ground-water fluctuations. The specific yield of the soil is determined by standard methods. Diurnal cycle as indicated by the ground-water table represents a curve showing the relation of consumptive use to ground-water discharge or recharge.

Inflow-outflow measurements. Consumptive use of water by cottonwoods, willows, tules, and other riparian vegetation common to small streams may be most easily determined by measuring the inflow to and the outflow from a selected area including precipitation and change in ground-water storage. In the investigations conducted in the upper Rio Grande, Pecos, and other river valleys, the inflow-outflow method was used to determine the total consumptive use of water in irrigated valleys containing land areas up to 400,-000 acres.

Integration method. Briefly stated, the integration method considers consumptive use in a valley to be the summation of the products of the use of water by each crop times its area, plus the use of water by the natural vegetation times its area, plus water surface evaporation times water surface area, plus evaporation from bare land times its area.

This method was used in the upper Rio Grande Basin and the Pecos River Valley investigation to determine valley consumptive use. Before the integration method can be used successfully, it is necessary to know unit rates of use of water by the various agricultural crops and natural vegetation, and unit rates of evaporation from bare land and water surfaces.

Effective heat. For many years temperature data have been used in estimating valley consumptive use of water in areas of the West. Hedke developed the effective heat method on the basis of studies of the Rio Grande. By this method, consumptive use is estimated from a study of the heat units available to the crops of a particular valley. It assumes that a linear relation exists between the amount of water consumed and the quantity of available heat. Studies by the Bureau of Reclamation developed a somewhat similar method which has been used quite generally in making its estimates of consumptive use.

In 1940, in connection with the Pecos River Joint Investigation, a method of estimating consumptive use by natural ground-water vegetation and by irrigated crops having access to an ample water supply was developed. Correlation of the relationship between transpiration, evaporation, temperature, daytime hours, length of growing season, and humidity was used in the estimate. In 1945, this method was modified to make possible estimates of consumptive use for areas in which humidity records are not available. This method has been used by the Soil Conservation Service and other agencies in estimating rates of water consumption in many areas.

WATER USE AND CLIMATOLOGICAL DATA

Actual measurements of consumptive use under each of the physical and climatic conditions of any large area are expensive and time-consuming. Therefore, some rapid method of transferring the results of measurements, made in several areas, to other areas was needed, and such a method was developed by the Soil Conservation Service. Briefly, the procedure is to correlate existing consumptive-use data with monthly temperatures, percentage of daytime hours, precipitation and frost-free period, or irrigation season. The coefficients so developed for different crops are used to translocate or transpose consumptive-use data from one location to others in which climatological data alone are available.

Although it is recognized that use of water is affected by numerous factors, records of temperature and precipitation are by far the most universally available data throughout the western states. Studies indicate that, of all the climatic factors, these elements, together with daylight, undoubtedly have the greatest influence on plant growth. Thus it is assumed that consumptive uses varies directly with the mean monthly temperature, t, multiplied by the monthly percentage of daytime hours of the year, p. Expressed mathematically,

$$u = KF = \Sigma kf$$

in which u is the consumptive use of water by the crop in inches for any period; F is the sum of the monthly consumptive-use factors, f, for the period; and K is the empirical consumptive-use coefficient.

The consumptive-use factor, F, for any period may be computed for areas in which monthly temperature records are available and consumptive-use coefficient, K, for the more important irrigated crops (grown under normal conditions in the West) are shown in Table 78. These coefficients were developed from actual measurements of consumptive use by the various methods.

Monthly percentage of annual daytime hours computed from sunshine tables are shown in Table 79.

TABLE 78. Normal consumptive-use coefficients for the more important irrigated crops and natural vegetation of the West (5)

Item	Length of growing season or period	Consumptive-use coefficient (K)
Alfalfa	frost-free	0.85
Beans	3 months	.65
Corn	4 months	.75
Cotton	7 months	.62
Citrus orchard	7 months	.55
Deciduous orchard	frost-free	.65
Pasture, grass hay, annuals	frost-free	.75
Potatoes	3 months	.70
Rice	3 to 4 months	1.00
Small grains	3 months	.75
Sorghum	5 months	.70
Sugar beets	5 1/2 months	.70

TABLE 79. Monthly percentage of daytime hours of the year for latitudes 24
to 50 degrees north of the Equator (5)

Month	Latitudes in degrees north of Equator													
	24	26	28	30	32	34	36	38	40	42	44	46	48	50
January	7.58	7.49	7.40	7.30	7.20	7.10	6.99	6.87	6.76	6.62	6.49	6.33	6.17	5.98
February	7.17	7.12	7.07	7.03	6.97	6.91	6.86	6.79	6.73	6.65	6.58	6.50	6.42	6.32
March	8.40	8.40	8.39	8.38	8.37	8.36	8.35	8.34	8.33	8.31	8.30	8.29	8.27	8.25
April	8.60	8.64	8.68	8.72	8.75	8.80	8.85	8.90	8.95	9.00	9.05	9.12	9.18	9.25
May	9.30	9.38	9.46	9.53	9.63	9.72	9.81	9.92	10.02	10.14	10.26	10.39	10.53	10.69
June	9.20	9.30	9.38	9.49	9.60	9.70	9.83	9.95	10.08	10.21	10.38	10.54	10.71	10.93
July	9.41	9.49	9.58	9.67	9.77	9.88	9.99	10.10	10.22	10.35	10.49	10.64	10.80	10.99
August	9.05	9.10	9.16	9.22	9.28	9.33	9.40	9.47	9.54	9.62	9.70	9.79	9.89	10.00
September	8.31	8.31	8.32	8.34	8.34	8.36	8.36	8.38	8.38	8.40	8.41	8.42	8.44	8.44
October	8.09	8.06	8.02	7.99	7.93	7.90	7.85	7.80	7.75	7.70	7.63	7.58	7.51	7.43
November	7.43	7.36	7.27	7.19	7.11	7.02	6.92	6.82	6.72	6.62	6.49	6.36	6.22	6.07
December	7.46	7.35	7.27	7.14	7.05	6.92	6.79	6.66	6.52	6.38	6.22	6.04	5.86	5.65
Total	100.00	100.00	100.00	100.00	100.00	100.00	100.00	100.00	100.00	100.00	100.00	100.00	100.00	100.00

A nomograph, Figure 158, has been developed for the solution of the
consumptive-use formula, u = kf. If the mean monthly temperature and the
latitude of the area are known, it is possible to determine the normal
monthly consumptive use of any crop for which k is known.

As an example, assume that it is desired to know what the July consumptive use of water by sugar beets might be in an area of latitude 36°, where

FIGURE 158. Nomograph for solution of consumptive-use formulas.

CONSUMPTIVE USE OF WATER AND IRRIGATION REQUIREMENTS

$$u = kf = k(tp)$$

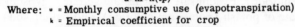

Where: u = Monthly consumptive use (evapotranspiration)
  k = Empirical coefficient for crop
  t = Mean monthly temperature
  p = Monthly percent of daytime hours of the year

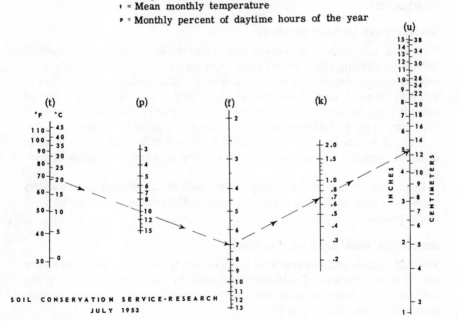

SOIL CONSERVATION SERVICE-RESEARCH
JULY 1953

temperature during the month was 70° F.

From Table 78, the consumptive-use coefficient for sugar beets is 0.70. From Table 2, p is 9.99 per cent. Entering the nomograph with the above values of t and p, we find that f = 7.0. With a k of 0.7, the use of water by sugar beets during July will be about 4.9 inches. Had the crop been alfalfa with a k of 0.85, the normal July use would be about 6 inches. In other words, 6 inches of water must be made available for crop use during the month. This requirement may be met from precipitation, carry-over soil moisture from the previous month, ground water, or irrigation. In the hot, dry, western areas, most, if not all, of this requirement must be met by irrigation. As we move eastward, more and more of the crop needs may be met by summer precipitation.

WATER QUALITY AND IRRIGATION

Crop production under irrigation must always be concerned with the quality of water applied to the land. The quality of water will greatly influence the irrigation and drainage practices followed, and it will determine in large measure the types of crops that can be grown successfully.

All waters from surface streams and underground sources contain dissolved substances known chemically as salts. Ocean water contains approximately 3 per cent salts. Waters used for irrigation generally contain less than 0.5 per cent salt.

In common usage, salt is thought of as table salt; however, thousands of different salts are known. Examples of the salts in irrigation water are table salt (sodium chloride), Epsom salt (magnesium sulfate), gypsum (calcium sulfate), muriate of potash (potassium chloride), and baking soda (sodium bicarbonate).

WATERS VARY IN SALT CONTENT

The total salt content in surace and underground waters varies widely. Mountain streams often contain less than one-fourth ton of salt per acre-foot. Drainage waters and ground waters in desert valleys may contain as much as 10 to 15 tons of salt per acre-foot. In general, the farther a stream extends from its source in the mountains, the higher its total salt content will be, owing to the inclusion of more and more valley drainage water.

Ground waters in river valleys often vary widely in total salt content at different locations and at various depths in the underground layers of sediment.

In addition, waters differ greatly in the kinds of salt present. Some waters are high in table salt and sodium bicarbonate. Others are high in Epsom salt and gypsum.

IRRIGATION ADDS SALT TO THE SOIL

Since all surface and underground waters contain salt, irrigation adds salt to soils. The net amount of salt added annually to each acre depends on the total volume of water applied, the concentration of salt in the water, the subsoil drainage and the crop grown.

For example, in the El Paso Valley, approximately 37 inches of Elephant Butte water are applied annually under normal conditions. Since this water contains approximately one ton of salt per acre-foot, the soils in the valley receive an annual application of three tons of salt. Where water from wells high in total salt content is used, much larger quantities of salt are applied each year. The salt applied remains in the soil unless it is flushed out in the drainage water or is removed in the harvested crop.

SALT ACCUMULATION PRODUCES SALINE SOIL CONDITIONS

A saline soil is one in which salt has accumulated sufficiently to reduce crop yields. With salt being applied each year through irrigation, any condition or combination of conditions that allows the salt to accumulate in the soil will produce a saline soil. Some of these conditions are: frequent and light irrigations with little or no salt being flushed out of the soil; water application to tight, slowly permeable soils; and poor drainage, which results in a high water table.

Since the development of saline soils is a process of salt accumulation, salinity can be associated with either good or poor quality water. Obviously, the more salt an irrigation water contains, the greater will be the likelihood for saline soils to develop. Soils that cannot be flushed out and drained readily should not be irrigated for long periods of time with waters high in salt.

SODIUM BICARBONATE AND BLACK ALKALI

Black alkali develops in soils when they are irrigated with waters containing more bicarbonate than calcium plus magnesium. Accompanying the process of black alkali formation are changes in the soil clay. Sodium displaces calcium and magnesium from the clay, and the calcium and magnesium are deposited in the soil as insoluble lime. Progressively, the soil structure deteriorates, air and water movement through the soil are restricted, soil alkalinity increases, and plant growth diminishes accordingly. Often these soil changes are more pronounced and more obvious when waters low in salt but high in sodium percentage ("present" and "possible") are used.

SALT INJURIOUS TO PLANTS

The salt in irrigation waters is injurious to plants. As the salinity of the soil increases, plant growth is progressively restricted. Immediately following an irrigation, the salt concentration in the soil water of the upper part of the root zone will be about the same as in the water applied. As the soil dries out (surface evaporation and plant uptake), the salt in the soil water becomes more concentrated and, accordingly, is more injurious. Obviously, high salt concentrations in soils are developed more rapidly when they are irrigated with the more salty waters. The more saline the irrigation water, the more frequently and more abundantly must the land be irrigated. It is necessary to keep displacing the soil water downward to avoid high concentrations in the root zone. The amount of leaching of the root zone—the amount of soil drainage—should be increased proportionately if waters from the more salty wells are to be used successfully.

ADEQUATE IRRIGATION AND DRAINAGE
SOLVES SALINITY PROBLEMS

As pointed out, the salt added with each irrigation remains in the soil and becomes more concentrated unless washed downward with subsequent irrigations. Consequently, the prevention of salinity is a matter of applying sufficient water periodically to flush out the salt left from previous irrigations.

The application of irrigation water always introduces the problem of soil drainage. If sufficient water is applied to keep the excess salt flushed out of the soil occupied by the plant roots, water will move downward below the plant-root zone, and will eventually reach the water table. This process tends to raise the water table. As long as the water table remains 6 to 10 feet below the surface, little or no difficulty will be encountered. But if the water table rises above this level, the practice of flushing the excess salt downward generally will no longer be practical, since the water table will move up into the root zone. As this occurs, the soil becomes water-logged, aeration is poor and plant growth is further decreased. Under these circumstances, the construction of a drainage system is imperative.

More open and permeable soils are better suited for irrigation with more salty waters than are tight soils. For example, water infiltration measurements made by the Soil Conservation Service on soils in the El Paso Valley show that water passes through the tight clay soils at about one-fourth to one-half acre-inch per hour. In moderately permeable clay loam soils, water passes through at one-half to 3 inches per hour, and in coarse sandy soil 7 to 9 inches may pass through per hour. For this reason, with adequate drainage, open, permeable soils can be irrigated more safely with lower quality water than can the tighter soils.

WATER REQUIRED FOR SUGAR BEETS

A consideration of the total and seasonal water requirements of a crop is important, since the amount of water used is the same as the amount that needs to be replaced. An extensive sugar-beet water-use study was conducted at the Huntley Branch Experiment Station during 1953 on a Fly clay loam soil. Three soil-moisture levels were maintained by irrigating when 43, 75, and 95 per cent of the available moisture had been removed from the root zone. This was accomplished by 8, 5, and 1 irrigations for the three treatments. Soil moisture was estimated by taking soil samples before and after each irrigation, and, if necessary, at approximately 2-week intervals between irrigations.

It required 23.4, 22.5, and 19.0 inches of water to grow the sugar beets depending on whether the beets were irrigated 8 times, 5 times, or once, respectively. Of these totals 6.5 inches were supplied by rain during the growing season. Thus only 16.9 to 12.5 inches were needed from irrigation. The water-use figures include the loss due to evaporation from the soil as well as transpiration through the leaves.

The maximum daily water use occurred during the last part of July and August, which corresponds to the time when irrigation needs are greatest. The mean daily water use during this time ranged from 0.20 to 0.24 inch. Thus, about 3 inches of moisture were used every 2 weeks.

By far the greatest amounts of water were lost from the surface foot of soil under all irrigation treatments, with progressively lesser amounts lost from greater depths. Relatively more moisture was used from the surface foot of soil under the frequent irrigation treatment than under the less frequent irrigation treatment. The reverse was true for greater depths. Undoubtedly much of the water removed from the surface foot of soil was lost by direct evaporation.

These data and others point out that it does not require a large amount of water to grow beets, if the water is supplied at the right time and in the correct amounts.

AMOUNT OF WATER A SOIL WILL RETAIN

In general, soils will store from 0.5 to 3.0 inches of water available to a crop per foot of soil depth. Sandy (coarse-textured) soils will store the least amount of available moisture and heavy (fine-textured) soils the most. Field capacity is defined as the maximum amount of water a soil can hold against gravity. In a well-drained soil, this point will be reached in about 48 hours after an irrigation. Permanent wilting percentage is the percentage of water in a soil when plants permanently wilt. Thus the percentage of water retained by a soil at field capacity minus the permanent wilting percentage is the moisture available to plants. Knowing these values and the bulk density, the storage capacity of the soil in inches of water can be calculated.

A few representative soil types from several of Montana's important sugar-beet counties and the amount of available water retained are given in Table 80. The total amounts of water available to a crop depend on depth of the root zone. Thus, early in the season when sugar-beet roots are largely

TABLE 80. Field capacity, permanent wilting percentage, and available water storage capacity for some important Montana sugar-beet soils (22)

Soil type	County	Field capacity	Permanent wilting percentage	Avail. water per foot of soil
		Per cent	Per cent	Per cent
Havre fine sandy loam	Yellowstone	19.8	7.5	1.9
Savage silty clay, clay substratum	Richland	33.9	17.9	2.5
Farland loam	Richland	22.0	9.1	2.0
Bitterroot silt loam	Ravalli	28.3	11.9	2.4
Amsterdam loam	Ravalli	25.0	9.5	2.3
Fly Creek clay loam	Yellowstone	25.0	11.4	2.1
Pryor silty clay	Yellowstone	37.1	16.9	3.1
Billings silty clay	Big Horn	36.2	20.1	2.5

concentrated in the top foot of soil, the amounts available would range from 1.9 to 3.1 inches for the soils listed in Table 80. Later in the season when roots have permeated the upper 3 feet of soil, the range in storage capacity would be from 5.7 to 9.3 inches.

FREQUENCY OF IRRIGATION

A soil holds moisture with considerable force. The drier a soil becomes the tighter the water is held. Experiments have shown that water will drain out of a soil until only the water that is held by a force of 5 pounds or more per square inch remains. At this point the soil moisture is said to be at "field capacity." As the soil becomes drier, the force of attraction between soil and water increases until plants cannot remove moisture from the soil. When plants can no longer draw moisture from the soil, the soil is at the permanent wilting percentage and the water is attracted to the soil by a force of 225 pounds per square inch.

It requires a great deal of energy to move water from a soil into a plant's vascular system. The amount of energy, of course, is equal to the force of attraction between the soil and water. For example, at field capacity it requires energy from the plant equal to 5 pounds of pressure per square inch and at the permanent wilting percentage, pressure equal to 225 pounds per

FIGURE 159. Soil moisture remaining in the soil of various moisture tensions. (Fly Creek clay loam)

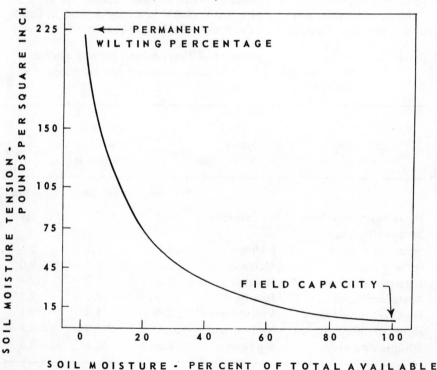

square inch. Thus, 45 times as much energy is required at the wilting percentage as at field capacity.

It seems reasonable that when the energy required by a plant to obtain water becomes too great, growth will be reduced. In the laboratory the amount of energy required to remove water from a soil over the entire range of available moisture can be estimated. An example of this measurement for Fly Creek clay loam is given in Figure 159. Notice that the force of attraction does not increase very rapidly until about 60 to 80 per cent of the total available moisture has been removed (20 to 40 per cent remains). Thus one might expect that when this soil contains less than about 30 per cent of its total available water, plant growth will be reduced.

Experiments at the Huntley Branch Station tested this concept of soil moisture and the results are given in Table 81 for two experiments conducted during 1953.

TABLE 81. Yield of sugar beets as influenced by moisture treatment (22)

Number of irrigations	Per cent available water removed from root zone prior to irrigation	Yield Tons per acre
Experiment 1, Fly Creek clay loam soil		
No ground water within reach of root zone		
8	43	23.4
5	75	22.0
1	95	16.9
L.S.D.* for yield, P (0.05) = 1.3; P (0.01) = 2.0		
Experiment 2, Pryor silty clay soil		
Water table 4 to 4.5 feet from soil surface		
7	54	22.9
4	66	23.5
0	†	20.1
L.S.D.* for yield, P (0.05) = 2.4		

* L.S.D. = Least significant difference; that is, differences of the amounts listed are necessary before the difference can be attributed to the moisture level treatment and not to experimental variation.
† This treatment was not irrigated because stored moisture and rain together with subirrigation from ground water kept available moisture in the root zone throughout the season.

DETERMINING DEPTH OF WATER APPLIED

An easy method of computing the depth of irrigation water applied is sometimes needed. Seeking an easier method than was available, Garton developed a nomograph which meets this need.

FIGURE 160. Nomograph for finding depth of water applied.
(Oklahoma Agricultural Experiment Station)

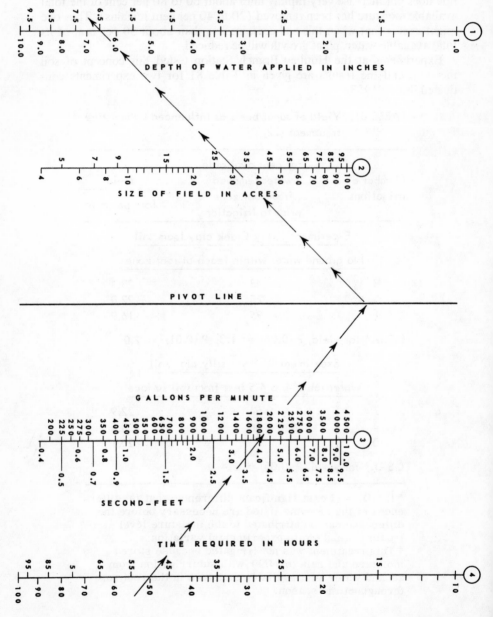

Suppose an irrigator finds it takes 50 hours to irrigate a 31-acre field when he uses an irrigation stream of 4 second-feet, or about 1,800 gallons per minute. To find out the depth of water being applied, the irrigator puts one end of a straight-edge on 50 hours (scale 4 in the nomograph) and marks through 4.0 second-feet (scale 3) until he reaches the pivot line. From this point on the pivot line he marks through 31 acres (scale 2) and where this line crosses scale 1 is his answer in the number of inches of water applied to the field. In the example shown, an average depth of 6½ inches is being applied.

The right amount of water to apply will be determined by the depth and texture of the soil and by the crop being grown.

If it is felt that too much water is being applied, the amount can be reduced by cutting down on the length of the rows or borders. Another method by which the depth applied can be reduced is to use a slightly larger stream in each furrow or border. This slightly larger stream gets the water over the land faster. There is one danger that should be remembered: if the stream used is too large, serious erosion will result.

USING SIPHON TUBES

Siphon tubes made of metal, plywood, or plastic are widely used in irrigated areas to transfer water from the field ditch to the land to be irrigated. Garton and Hauser developed a graph that can be used in determining the number and size of siphon tubes needed.

THE VARIABLES

There are three variables involved in siphon tube irrigation: (a) size of the siphon tube; (b) number of second-feet of water that must be handled; and (c) head of water causing flow through the siphon tubes.

The size of the siphon tube can be measured with an ordinary ruler or scale, since they are usually made in even fractions of an inch; i.e., 1 inch, 1¼ inch, and so on.

The number of second-feet of water being delivered to the farm is often measured at the farm turnout.

The head is the difference in elevation between the water surface in the irrigation ditch and the water surface in the field or row. It is measured in inches. The head used on the graph is the average head between checks or dams. The head will be greater than the average just above a check or dam and less than the average just below a check or dam.

HOW TO USE THE GRAPH

A pencil and straight-edge are needed for the solution. Find the head in inches along the bottom of the graph. From the head, draw a line vertically to the diagonal line representing the size of siphon tubes being used. From this intersection, draw a line horizontally to scale 1, where the discharge per siphon tube can be read. From the point on scale 1, draw a straight line through the number of second-feet of water being used (scale 2) to scale 3. The number of siphons required is shown on scale 3.

This graphic solution indicates only the number of siphons required at one time to carry a given flow of water. The irrigator must determine how

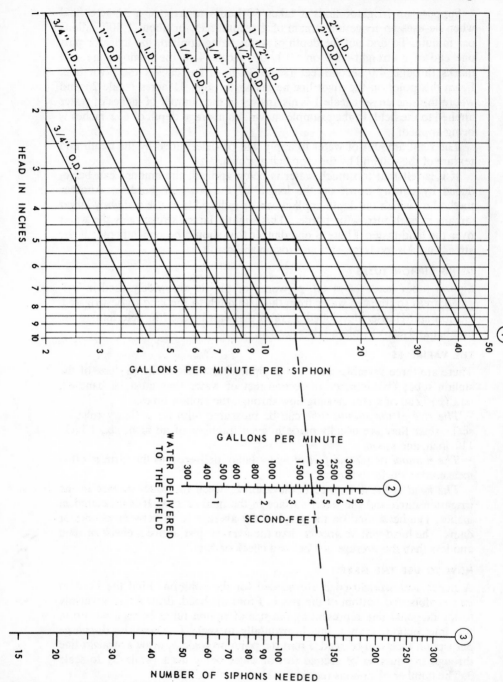

FIGURE 161. Determining the number of siphons to use.
(Oklahoma Agricultural Experiment Station)

many additional siphons he will need to have ahead when changing from one setting to another.

SOLUTION TO SAMPLE PROBLEM

A typical problem is shown by the broken lines on the graph. In this example, the irrigator is using 1¼-inch inside diameter (I.D.) siphons, is getting 4 second-feet of water, and estimates that a safe head for his ditch will be about 5 inches.

From 5 inches on the bottom scale of the graph, a line is drawn vertically upward until it intersects the 1¼-inch I.D. diagonal line. From this intersection, a line is drawn horizontally to scale 1, from which it can be seen that each tube will discharge about 12.5 gallons per minute. From this point, a line is drawn through 4 second-feet on scale 2, and extended to scale 3. As indicated on scale 3 the number of siphons needed for this problem will be about 143.

ANOTHER EXAMPLE

The graphic solution can be worked in different ways. Suppose a farmer has 155 one-inch I.D. siphons, and that he plans to order 3 second-feet of water, or 1,350 gallons per minute. He can determine the necessary head in his ditches by working the solution backwards. From 155 siphons on scale 3, a line is drawn through 3 second-feet on scale 2, to intersect with scale 1. From the intersection on scale 1, a horizontal line is drawn to the 1-inch I.D. diagonal line. From this intersection, a vertical line is drawn downward to intersect the head scale, showing that a 6-inch average head must be maintained in the ditch system.

WHEN TO IRRIGATE IN HUMID AREA

One of the problems associated with irrigation in the humid areas of the United States is that of determining when to start irrigating a crop. Various methods have been used but none have emerged as satisfactory, practical, and economical.

The object of irrigating is to prevent the tension of the soil water from reaching such a high value that plants are appreciably depressed in growth, development, and ultimate yield. The magnitude of this threshold value for the various crops is, in most cases, still unknown. It is known that various plant functions do not take place independently of the soil moisture tension. Rate of transpiration and exudation, elongation of leaves, and growth of whole plants have been shown to have a maximum somewhere in the low-tension range and a minimum at the wilting point.

One of the more important problems of irrigation, then, is to determine the status of soil moisture conditions at any given time. For this purpose, use can be made of the fact that for a given soil in the field, the value of the soil moisture tension is related to the soil moisture content. This relationship is known as the *moisture characteristic* of the soil. An example is shown in Figure 162.

In order then to determine in the field the time at which the moisture supply of the soil has been depleted by the plants to the point of maximum

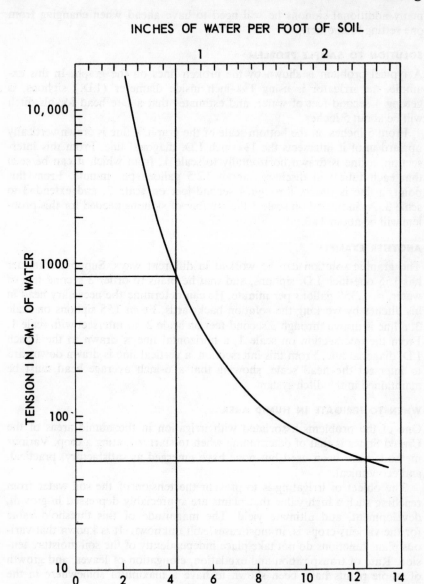

FIGURE 162. The moisture characteristics of Ruston coarse sandy loam (desorption).

allowable tension (or the moisture percentage associated therewith), either the tension or moisture percentage must be measured.

A vast amount of work has been done on this subject during the last 30 years by soil physicists and others. This was done because of the practical difficulties of determining soil moisture directly. As a result, there are now available tensiometers to measure the soil moisture tension directly, and gravimetric plugs, Bouyoucos gypsum blocks, nylon blocks, Colman fiberglass blocks, thermal conductivity units, and other types of instruments that measure, indirectly, the soil moisture content from which the soil moisture tension can be derived.

These methods are expensive because of both the cost of the equipment and time required to operate it and to interpret the results. They are of no practical use to farmers. Because of the small soil volume measured by these methods and the resultant variation between replicate installations no single method has been determined which is satisfactory for field use.

EVAPOTRANSPIRATION METHOD

The status of soil moisture at any given time can be determined indirectly by accounting for differences between water added to and water lost from the soil. On drained land, water is lost by evaporation from the land surface and by transpiration of the vegetative cover. The combined process, known as evapotranspiration, accounts for all water lost, while irrigation and rainfall minus runoff accounts for all that added. It follows that, if the amount of water added to the soil and the total lost daily by evapotranspiration were known, a simple bank account procedure could be used to determine the readily available supply of water in the soil at any given time. When this supply appears to be reduced to zero, or nearly so, the need for irrigation is indicated.

Thornthwaite advanced the idea of scheduling irrigation on the basis of estimated soil moisture reserves. Schofield and Penman made a similar proposal. Van Bavel developed a method for keeping a running account of the soil moisture status.

Van Bavel's method has two main sources of error. In the first place, it is not always easy to determine what proportion of rainfall infiltrates to replenish soil moisture, particularly in the case of high-intensity rainstorms. However, in the case of heavy rains exceeding the available water-storage capacity of the soil, runoff is oftentimes not significant for this purpose because it would represent surplus water, whether it entered the soil or not. However, there are some summer rains that fall at high intensities for short duration which, even on dry soils, exceed the maximum infiltration rate.

In the second place, there must be a reasonably accurate estimate of evapotranspiration losses. Considering the fact that these losses are determined by such variable factors as the radiant energy from the sun, the wind velocity, the temperature and the relative humidity of the air, the temperature of the leaf or ground surface, and the density of cover, computing evapotranspiration is a complicated process. And, too, the results have small general value. Actually, experience has shown that evapotranspiration values computed from long-time averages of the meteorological factors listed above have considerable validity. This is possibly due to the fact that the daily variations, if considered over several days, very nearly neutralize each other. Neither should the estimate of evapotranspiration be any more accurate than the other elements of the computation, such as the rainfall record, error due to runoff, and variable soil moisture characteristics.

Some formulas have been proposed for computing evapotranspiration. Penman developed a formula which is valid for plants that cover the soil completely and are well supplied with water. It would apply, therefore, to full stands of grown crops that were kept well supplied with water by either rain or irrigation. The chief disadvantages of Penman's formula are that it is complicated and that needed weather data are found in only a relatively few places. This formula is based, however, on an exact theory and may be used as an independent check on values obtained otherwise.

An empirical formula which is based on latitude and average temperature of the air as the only variables was given by Thornthwaite. This formula is easy to use as only temperature data are needed. Because it is empirical, Thornthwaite's formula also accounts for the fact that vegetative cover is not complete in the winter and spring. This formula could, therefore, be in error for tropical or subtropical areas where seasonal differences are not so great.

Another formula, proposed by Blaney and Criddle, is based on average monthly daytime hours and average monthly temperature. In addition to those two variables, their formula also makes use of a consumptive-use coefficient, which can be used to account for variations due to thickness of vegetation, stage of crop growth, and other crop variables. The derivation of the magnitude of these consumptive-use coefficients appears somewhat questionable.

In Figure 163 the monthly average evapotranspiration in Raleigh, North Carolina, is shown as calculated according to Blaney and Criddle, Penman, and Thornthwaite, together with some actually observed values obtained by van Bavel under conditions where Penman's formula applies, namely, an open water surface at Chapel Hill, 25 miles from Raleigh. The maximum difference between the formulas and observed values during the crop-growing season is 14 per cent, which occurs in June for Penman's formula and in July for Thornthwaite's formula.

ACTUAL AND CALCULATED EVAPOTRANSPIRATION RATES

Considerable evidence, collected by Thornthwaite and his associates, shows that actual evapotranspiration rates are in close agreement with the ones calculated, although the researchers consider that the formula used could be further improved. Such evidence was obtained from soil moisture measurements, and also from modified lysimeters especially constructed for the purpose. The articles cited here give further reference to the extensive literature on evapotranspiration, its significance, and measurement. Further evidence in favor of Thornthwaite's formula was given by Harrold and Dreibelbis.

A study in Canada by Sanderson showed also close agreement between measured and computed rates of evapotranspiration. This work shows that

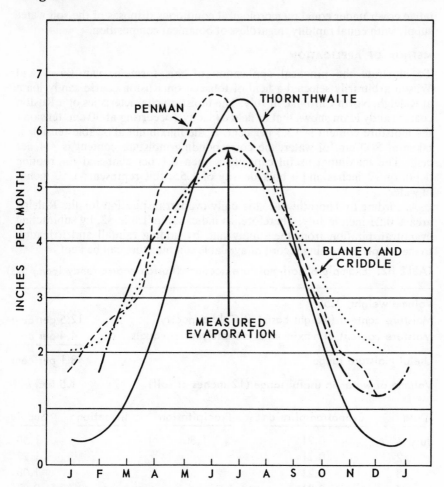

FIGURE 163. Evapotranspiration in inches per month for Raleigh, North Carolina, as computed by three methods and as measured at Chapel Hill, North Carolina (42). In Blaney and Criddle a consumptive-use coefficient of 0.70 was used.

there is not a great difference between computations based on long-term averages of temperature and computations based on the actual occurring temperature. This has practical significance, because it is easier to use average figures computed in advance rather than work with current data.

Penman also found the use of his formula substantiated in experimental studies on lysimeters, drainage fields, and watersheds.

An important question is whether the evapotranspiration of different crops is different under similar conditions. So far, provided an ample moisture supply is in the soil, experimental data do not support this view. Van Bavel and Wilson tested this formula on the assumption that a closed vegetative cover under equal meteorological conditions disposes of the soil water supply with equal rapidity, regardless of botanical composition.

METHOD OF APPLICATION

To illustrate the practical application of this formula, van Bavel and Wilson arbitrarily selected a field of tobacco on Ruston coarse sandy loam at Raleigh, North Carolina, in July. The moisture characteristics of a Ruston coarse sandy loam shows that at field capacity (occurring at 50 cm. tension) the moisture content is 12.5 per cent. If the maximum allowable tension is taken at 800 cm. of water, the corresponding moisture content is 4.4 per cent. The maximum useful capacity is then 8.1 per cent and for rooting depth of 12 inches and a bulk density of 1.55, this represents 1.50 inches of water.

According to Thornthwaite, the daily evapotranspiration for the Raleigh area is 0.21 inch in July. Therefore, as indicated in Table 82, by subtracting evapotranspiration from the supply and by adding rainfall and irrigation to the supply, a running record of available soil moisture can be kept.

TABLE 82. Example of soil moisture account (Ruston coarse sandy loam) (43)

Volume weight, 1.55

Moisture content (weight basis) at field capacity	12.5 per cent
Moisture content at maximum allowable tensionequals	4.4 per cent
Useful moisture range	8.1 per cent
Volume of water in useful range (12 inches of soil)	1.5 inches

Date	Evapotranspiration	Precipitation	Irrigation	Supply
July 1	0.21	1.80		1.50
2	0.21			1.29
3	0.21			1.08
4	0.21			0.87
5	0.21	0.26		0.92
6	0.21			0.71
7	0.21			0.50
8	0.21			0.29
9	0.21			0.08
10	0.21		1.50	1.37
11	0.21			1.16
12	0.21	1.06		1.50

When a need for irrigation is indicated, as on July 10 in Table 82, 1.5 inches should be applied. Rainfall is also added to the supply, except when the total exceeds 1.5 inches. If 1.5 inches are exceeded, the additional water is not added to the supply because it becomes unavailable to the plants by storage beyond the root zone or by drainage to the water table.

In order to use the evapotranspiration approach, the rooting depth of the crop, the moisture characteristic of the soil, the moisture-tension tolerance of the crop, evapotranspiration rates, and a record of rainfall need to be known.

RESULTS OF APPLICATION

In an irrigation experiment conducted by van Bavel and Wilson at Raleigh, North Carolina, irrigation was scheduled on the basis of the readings of mercury tensiometers placed in the plots. In Table 83, the dates of irrigation based on tensiometer readings are given along with the dates on which irrigation should have taken place if evapotranspiration estimates had been used. The agreement is good, showing that the dates could have been obtained without tensiometers or other instrumentation which is now considered necessary to measure soil moisture tension. The same experiment repeated one year later again gave creditable results.

TABLE 83. Dates for irrigation as determined for a field experiment by tensiometer readings (computed dates from estimated values of evapotranspiration) (43)

1950		1951	
Actual	Computed	Actual	Computed
July 21	July 22	June 2	June 1
August 3	August 2	June 19	June 14
August 9	August 9	June 26	June 25
		July 2	July 3
		July 9	July 10
		July 14	July 13
		July 25	July 26

The computed values in Table 82 were obtained by using long-time averages of evapotranspiration, no correction being made for actual weather conditions, development stage of the crop, runoff, and other variable factors. Yet this rough approximation gives accuracy which needs no improvement from a practical point of view. It is implied here that tensiometers gave correct values.

By use of this method van Bavel improved both yield and quality of flue-cured tobacco at Oxford, North Carolina, over a 3-year period. In all three years very significant yield increases were obtained. The average yield of all "recommended" treatments are shown in Table 84. In the third column a "least significant difference" is given for easy evaluation of the results. In the fourth column, there is the probability of recurrence of the year's season. This is important; it shows, roughly, how often a yield increase can be expected. These figures are based on an analysis of prevailing moisture conditions and rainfall records at the Oxford location, according to methods described.

The marked improvement in quality resulting from maintaining suitable

TABLE 84. Yield increases with flue-cured tobacco secured
by irrigation at Oxford, N. C., in pounds per
acre (42)

Year	No irriga- tion	Irri- ga- tion	L.S.D.	Recurrence
1951	1300	1580	70	2 out of 10 yrs.
1952	1410	1500	60	7 out of 10 yrs.
1953	1320	1790	150	2 out of 10 yrs.

moisture conditions is equally as important as the increase in yield. This
results from chemical changes in the leaves. Although the price received is
the only item of significance to the farmer, the content of nicotine and sugar
are also given. As in Table 84, the data in Table 85 are averaged over the
treatments representing the usual or recommended practices.

TABLE 85. Value per hundred pounds in dollars, nicotine and
sugar content of irrigated vs. nonirrigated tobacco
at Oxford, N. C. (42)

Year	Quality in $ per 100 lbs.		Nicotine in per cent		Sugar in per cent	
	No irrig.	Irrig.	No irrig.	Irrig.	No irrig.	Irrig.
1951	46.0	58.9	4.02	1.93	14.8	21.9
1952	52.5	55.8	2.31	1.79	22.0	24.8
1953	45.1	50.3	—	—	—	—

WHAT IS A DROUGHT?

Agricultural drought, a condition of rainfall deficiency with respect to
crop production, has not been defined accurately. It should, if possible, be
defined on the basis of soil moisture conditions and resultant plant behavior,
rather than on some direct interpretation of the rainfall record.

Just when a period of relatively dry weather takes on the characteristics
of a drought is a matter of conjecture. The effects of drought of varying
duration and intensity are known only in a general way. It is this relationship between drought duration and intensity, i.e., the period of time being
considered and the amount of rainfall received during this period, which is
the crux of the drought problem.

Barger and Thom attempted to develop a method for characterizing
drought intensity with corn in Iowa. Rainfall records and corn yield figures
for six counties, each representative of a specific association of soil areas,
were analyzed to determine a method for characterizing drought in each
county.

The criterion of drought intensity developed is based on the association of certain minimum required total rainfall amounts with time intervals of varying duration, i.e., the amount of rainfall that just permits normal corn development during a period of n consecutive weeks is the minimum required total rainfall for that duration. These minimum amounts increased parabolically with duration and differed considerably among stations. The maximum rainfall deficiency with respect to these base amounts recorded for any period of weeks during a corn-growing season constituted a measure of drought effect on the final yield of the crop.

Correlation between maximum rainfall deficits and deviations of county corn yields from normal show that, for years in which drought conditions occurred, from 25 to 60 per cent of the total variation in yield was explained by this criterion.

These probabilities offered a basis for comparison of different areas with regard to rainfall distribution alone and also with regard to the likelihood of receiving the minimum amount of precipitation needed to produce a normal corn crop. Similarly, the probability of occurrence of any class of rainfall totals could be determined, e.g., the probability of receiving between 8.0 and 10.0 inches of rain at Ames, Iowa, during the 3-week period beginning July 5 could be estimated.

The probabilities determined point to distinct differences in the drought hazards experienced at various stations. Southern Iowa, while enjoying a rainfall contingency comparing favorably with other areas in the state, has rainfall requirements so high that drought is much more likely in the southern counties than in the central and northern sections. Although less pronounced, western Iowa presents more of a drought problem than does the eastern part of the state.

The incidence of drought was characterized by van Bavel by determining for a particular crop the number of days during its growing season when soil moisture tension exceeds a value that is known to impede crop growth appreciably. The frequency of these drought-days depends on the rainfall pattern, on the moisture characteristics of the soil, on the depth of rooting, on the physiological reaction of the plant to moisture tension, and on the rate of evapotranspiration. Drought, thus evaluated, has a truly agronomic character and is a yardstick for measuring adequacy of climate and soil for providing optimal soil moisture conditions.

In calculating drought incidence, van Bavel used past rainfall records and an estimate of evapotranspiration. He illustrated his method with an actual calculation for Raleigh, North Carolina, using 59 years of record. He showed how the proposed drought criterion reflects the difference in moisture characteristics of different soils, in depth of rooting, and in drought tolerance of the plant. He showed also how the results obtained may be used by direct calculation to find the need for supplementary irrigation and the safe size of storage reservoirs, for a given location, crop, and soil.

Van Bavel proposed that the incidence of drought be characterized by determining for a particular crop the number of days during its growing season on which soil moisture exceeds a value which is known to impede appreciably crop growth. Drought, thus defined, has an agronomic character and is a yardstick for measuring adequacy of climate and soil for promoting optimal soil moisture conditions.

Van Bavel defined a drought-day as a 24-hour period in which the soil moisture stress (moisture tension plus osmotic pressure) exceeds a limit, which, on basis of experimental evidence, may be taken as a point at which the productive processes of the crop are being appreciably decreased.

EROSION CONTROL ON IRRIGATED LAND

One of the major reasons for a destructive type of irrigation is found in the erosive power of a stream of water that takes place with a change in slope. Figure 164 shows the critical, or maximum, allowable furrow stream for different slopes determined from three studies by the Soil Conservation Service. Two of the curves were developed by observing the effect of different sizes of furrow streams under actual field conditions. The third curve was developed from results of flume tests with one soil under carefully controlled laboratory conditions.

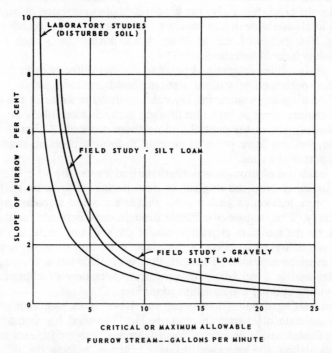

CRITICAL OR MAXIMUM ALLOWABLE
FURROW STREAM—GALLONS PER MINUTE

FIGURE 164. Critical furrow streams for different slopes on three soils (15).

The curves indicate that serious erosion can result on the steeper slopes with a small increase in flow above the critical size stream. If the furrow has a slope less than 1.0 per cent, an additional 5 gallons per minute per furrow may have little or no harmful effect. If the slope is less than 0.5 per cent, the addition of 10 or more gallons per minute may be harmless. As the slope increases, however, the size of the furrow stream must be accurately adjusted. With a 5 per cent slope where the critical size furrow stream may be 2.5 gallons per minute, a small increase to the stream of 0.5 or 1.0 gallon per minute may cause serious soil movement.

These data emphasize the importance of maintaining flat grades for surface irrigation. If land leveling cannot be used to shape the slope of the land, because of shallow soil depth or for other reasons, some attempt should be made to conduct farming operations across the slope, almost on the contour. Such practices not only reduce the erosion but also decrease the time required for irrigation on such land. Less water needs to be run over land on the flatter grades in order to get the desired moisture penetration into the soil. Water can go into the soil only so fast, and the more rapidly it flows the more needs to be run over the soil for irrigation.

It can readily be seen why erosion is difficult to prevent on steep lands when irrigated by surface methods. Safe handling of water on the steeper grades requires the ability to control the size of the stream, and short enough irrigation runs to reduce the stream force. Siphons, gated surface pipes, gated wooden flumes, gated spiles, and other devices have been developed to control the size of furrow streams. Although these controls are relatively new, farmers in certain irrigated areas are beginning to use many of them. Elsewhere, the advance in the science of handling irrigation water has been slower. It is not uncommon to see in these latter areas as much as 25 tons of soil per acre removed from a field during a single irrigation. Tests on one bean field in southern Idaho indicated that application of twice the critical stream to a furrow during an irrigation would remove one-half inch of topsoil from the field in one irrigation. Assuming that the beans would require a minimum of four irrigations per year, a field irrigated under the above conditions would lose all of its productive topsoil in four years and yellow, unproductive clay would be exposed. If the clay should erode at the same rate, solid lava rock would be exposed over nearly all the field within 20 years.

Soil Conservation Service research workers at the Irrigation Experiment Station at Prosser, Washington, conducted studies to evaluate the soil loss, water conservation, and irrigation characteristics of downhill and cross-slope irrigation practices on slopes up to 16 per cent. The aim of the studies was to provide a comparison of irrigation methods under extreme slope conditions. The conclusion was that efficient use of irrigation water is almost impossible on steep fields which are irrigated in furrows directed down the steepest part of the slope. Production of row crops on such slopes, even with careful irrigation, very short length of run and minimum size of stream, results in very poor moisture distribution over the field and the removal of at least one inch of soil in every 12 years.

Exact measurements were made of the amount of water applied to each field, how much ran off as waste water, and how much soil was carried away with it. The amount of water that entered the soil, how deeply and widely it spread, and how much was received by the different parts of the field were measured also. These data showed that, even on relatively flat land, the upper part of the field received a little more irrigation than did the lower part.

On steeper land, however, this difference under the usual irrigation practice is so great that the upper end generally has enough moisture before the lower part of the slope has had the opportunity to absorb very much. At the time the water is turned off, the upper part of the field usually is wetted too deeply and the lower end is not wetted deeply enough.

Shortening the length of the run helps greatly in reducing this difference, but it persists even on very short runs when the slopes are steep. On a field with a slope of 16 per cent and a run of 127 feet, for example, the upper half absorbed an average of 2.2 inches of water for each of 12 irrigations while only 1.2 inches went into the ground 75 feet further down the slope. The water at the lower sampling locations did not fill the root zone; the penetration at the upper location was deeper than 4 feet. Both measurements were made in the upper 4 feet of soil, which was considered as the root zone. Very few corn or beet roots extended deeper.

The beet yield was 30 tons per acre on the upper half of this field, but only 21.7 tons on the lower half. Corn produced 58 bushels on the top half and 31 bushels on the lower half. Since the natural fertility of the soil is usually greater on the lower part of the slope than on the upper part, these differences are even more striking. They can be attributed almost entirely to the difference in the amount of irrigation water received by the different parts of the field.

Some steep slopes are peculiarly adapted for orchards and vineyards. Others will, for various reasons, continue to be cultivated to row crops. A method for improving irrigation on these slopes would be of great benefit. One of the modifications in irrigation practices that gives promise of reducing erosion on these slopes and improving the soil-moisture distribution is a reduction in the grade of the irrigation furrow. Reducing the grade on some fields at Prosser from 16 to 3 per cent, by directing the furrows across the slope, reduced the rate of soil loss from 13 tons to one ton per acre per year. The amount of water added to the root zone at the upper part of this field was 2.4 inches per irrigation; 150 feet down the furrow, the amount was 2.02 inches. The crops were more uniform, and the average production was higher. Corn yielded 69 bushels per acre, as compared with 45 bushels for the field irrigated in the usual downhill manner.

Reducing the grade in the furrow permitted the water to enter the soil twice the rate that it entered the soil on the field irrigated by downhill ws. The same amount of water was put into the soil in 12 hours with rows on a 3 per cent grade as entered the soil in 24 hours when the were directed down the 16 per cent slope.

was also considerable reduction in the amount of irrigation waste st irrigations permit a certain-size stream of irrigation waste end of the furrow. The shorter period required for irrigation e volume of water lost as irrigation waste.

"across the slope" is not without its disadvantages. It requires vout of furrows and the first irrigations will require more The water necessarily will have to be moved more often.

To compensate for these disadvantages will be the more efficient irrigation that will ensue, ultimately resulting in a higher average yield. There will be fewer furrows to set and tend. In general, the hydraulic characteristics of the furrows will remain more stable, and once they are brought through they generally will remain in running condition. The furrows on the downhill fields, on the other hand, often are affected by alternate areas of deposition and scour, which are constantly changing locations.

The reduction in irrigation waste will conserve irrigation water, produce more crops in those areas or in those years when water is short. The reduction in erosion is of particular concern. Unlike water, where a shortage in one year may be compensated for in the next year or years, the effect of soil loss is much more lasting. Soil once lost from a field is gone forever and cannot be replaced. The loss of topsoil is of most serious immediate concern when the soil is shallow. The soil itself must be held where it is, if it is to continue to produce and furnish food for the people of this and other nations.

The research workers at Prosser conducted other studies to determine how to add sufficient water to the soil for maximum production with the least loss of soil and water. They concluded that it is possible to have serious erosion on the upper end of irrigated fields, even when neither soil nor water are wasted at the lower end. This is because the upper end of irrigating furrows carries greater amounts of water.

Any practice that increases infiltration requires an increase in the irrigation furrow stream. Increasing the infiltration decreases the percentage of runoff but increases the potential erosion hazard along the furrow.

Reditching and otherwise disturbing the soil in the furrow is one of the greatest factors in increasing erosion. Even in such crops as alfalfa and wheat, reditching tears out the vegetation and leaves the unprotected soil in contact with the flowing water.

REFERENCES

1. Abbe, C. 1905. *A first report of the relations between climates and crops.* USDA Weather Bur. Bull. 36.
2. Barger, G. L., and Thom, H. C. S. 1949. *A method of characterizing drought intensity in Iowa.* Agron. Jour., 41(1): 13-19.
3. ———. 1949. *Evaluation of drought hazard.* Agron. Jour., 41(11): 519-526.
4. Blaney, H. F. 1938. *Field methods of determining consumptive use of water.* USDA, Los Angeles, Calif.
5. ———, and Criddle, W. D. 1950. *A method of estimating water requirements in irrigated areas from climatological data.* USDA, SCS-TP-96.
6. Blaney, H. F., Ewing, P. A., Israelson, O. W., Rohwer, C., and Scoby, F. C. 1938. *Water utilization, Upper Rio Grande Basin.* Natl. Resources Comm. Report (2).
7. Blaney, H. F., Ewing, P. A., Morin, K. V., and Criddle, W. D. 1942. *Consumptive water use and requirements: Reports of participating agencies, Pecos River.* Washington, D.C.
8. Blaney, H. F., and Morin, K. V. 1942. *Evaporation and consumptive use of water empirical formulas.* Trans. Act. Amer. Geoph. Un., (2): 76.
9. Briggs, L. J., and Shantz, H. L. 1913. *The water requirements of plants.* USDA Bur. Soils Bull. 284.
10. ———. 1916. *Daily transpiration during the normal growth period and its correlation with the weather.* Jour. Agr. Res., 7.

11. Criddle, W. D. 1953. *Consumptive use of water and irrigation requirements.* Jour. Soil and Water Cons., 8(5): 207-212.
12. Diffie, B. W. 1945. *Latin American Civilization.* Slackpole, Sons, Harrisburg, Pa.
13. Duty of Water Committee. 1930. *Consumptive use of water in irrigation.* Rpt. Duty of Water Committee of the Irrigation Division, Trans. A. C. E., 94: 1349.
14. Fortier, S. 1907. *Evaporation losses in irrigation and water requirements of crops.* USDA Office of Expt. Sta. Bull. 177.
15. Gardner, W., Gardner, J. H., and Lauritzen, C. W. 1946. *Rainfall and irrigation in relation to soil erosion.* Utah Agr. Expt. Sta. Bull. 326.
16. Gardner, W., and Lauritzen, C. W. 1946. *Erosion as a function of the size of the irrigating stream and the slope of the eroding surface.* Soil Sci., 62: 233-242.
17. Garton. J. E. 1951. *A graphic method of finding the depth of irrigation water applied.* Okla. Agr. Expt. Sta. Bull. B-368.
18. ———, and Hauser, V. L. 1953. *A graphic solution for siphon tube irrigation problems.* Okla. Agr. Expt. Sta. Misc. Pub. MP-30.
19. Harrold, L. L., and Dreibelbis, F. R. 1945. *An accounting of daily accretion, depletion, and storage of soil water as determined by weighing monolith lysimeters.* Trans. Amer. Geoph. Un., 26: 283-292.
20. Helseth, O. S. 1947. *Fifteen hundred years of irrigation history.* Reclamation Era.
21. Jensen, M. E., and Evans, N. A. 1952. *Erosion under furrow irrigation.* North Dak. Agr. Expt. Sta. Bimo. Bull. 15(1): 7-13.
22. Larson, W. E. 1954. *Irrigation of sugar beets.* Mont. Agr. Expt. Sta. Cir. 205.
23. Mech, S. J. 1949. *Effect of slope and length of run on erosion under irrigation.* Agr. Eng., 30(8): 379-389.
24. Meinger, O. E. 1942. *Hydrology, physics of the earth series.* McGraw-Hill Book Co., Inc. New York, IX: 314.
25. Miller, A. E., and Dwyer, C. H. 1952. *Improved management of irrigated pastures pays dividends.* USDA, SCS Pa-205.
26. Nettles, V. F., Jamison, F. S., and Janes, B. E. 1952. *Irrigation and other cultural studies with cabbage, sweet corn, snap beans, onions, tomatoes and cucumbers.* Fla. Agr. Expt. Sta. Bull. 495.
27. Penman, H. L. 1948. *Natural evaporation from open water, bare soil, and grass.* Proc. Roy. Soc., 193: 120-145.
28. ———. 1949. *Meteorology and agriculture.* Quart. Jour. Roy. Soc., 75: 298-324.
29. ———. 1949. *The dependence of transpiration on weather and soil condition.* Jour. Soil Sci., 1: 74-89.
30. Sanderson, M. 1950. *Some Canadian developments in agricultural climatology.* Weather, 381-383, 409-412.
31. Schofield, R. K. 1950. *Soil moisture and evaporation.* Trans. 4th Int. Cong. Soil Sci., 2: 20-28.
32. Sell, O. E. 1952. *Irrigated pastures produce more protein and total forage.* Ga. Agr. Expt. Sta. Res. News, 3(7): 1-3.
33. Smith, L. S., and Lyerly, P. J. 1953. *Effect of irrigation level on cotton at Pecos, 1952.* Tex. Agr. Expt. Sta. Prog. Rpt. 1607.
34. Thornthwaite, C. W. 1946. *El agua en la agricultura.* Irrigation en Mexico Abril-Mayo-Junio, 19-43.
35. ———. 1948. *An approach toward a rational classification of climate.* Graphical Rev., 38: 55-94.
36. ———, and Mather, J. R. 1951. *The role of evaporation in climate.* Archiv fur Meteorologie, Geophysik und Bioklimatologie, Ser. B, Band III: 16-39.
37. Thornthwaite, C. W., and others. 1944. *Report of the Committee on Evaporation and Transpiration, 1943-1944.* Trans. Amer. Geoph. Un., 25: 683-693.
38. U.S. Census Bur. 1952. *Preliminary report on irrigation and agriculture.*
39. U.S. Weather Bureau. 1905. *Sunshine tables.* USDA Weather Bur. Bull. 805.
40. van Bavel, C. H. M. 1953. *A drought criterion and its application in evaluating drought incidence and hazard.* Agron. Jour., 45(4): 167-172.

41. ————. 1954. *Irrigating flue-cured tobacco.* Better Crops With Plant Food, 38(2): 19-22, 49.

42. ————, and Wilson, T. V. 1952. *Evaporation estimates as criteria for determining time of irrigation.* Agr. Eng., 33(7): 417-418.

43. White, W. N. 1932. *A method of estimating ground-water supplies based on discharge by plants and evaporation from soil, results of investigations in Escalante Valley, Utah.* U.S. Dept. Interior, Water Supply paper 659-A.

23

Farm Drainage

Land drainage is essential to good soil management. Successful use of some of the most productive land in the United States is dependent upon proper drainage.

Topography and soil type are important factors affecting the distribution of undrained land areas. High-value cash crops are produced on well drained land throughout the country. Open ditches and tile drains both are used extensively. Open-ditch drainage is most generally used in the production of sugar cane and other crops grown on flood plains and muck soils.

The most extensively drained area is found in the Corn Belt. Under relatively uniform conditions of climate, topography, soil type, crops produced, and type of farming, the factor of soil-structure management takes on special importance in the consideration of drainage in this area.

The purpose of drainage is to modify the effect of a complex series of climatic events by creating a more favorable environment for cultivated crops. During a favorable season even a poorly drained field may produce bumper crops. But during an unusually wet season, even an otherwise well drained soil may produce poor crops. All the knowledge of soil management together with the arts of the experienced farmer must be utilized if crop yields are to be obtained from any given field year after year.

BENEFITS OF DRAINAGE

There is a good deal of evidence to show that drainage has many beneficial effects when installed in soils where an excess of water occurs at some time during the year. Some of the benefits of drainage are:

1. It permits aeration of the soil, which is essential to root extension and growth.
2. It makes conditions favorable for the development of beneficial soil microorganisms. The oxygen of the air as well as suitable moisture conditions are essential for their growth.
3. On poorly drained soils yields are increased and the quality of the crop is improved.
4. The length of the growing season is increased since earlier planting is possible.
5. Root development is increased because there is no interruption of root growth by excess water.
6. It permits the use of flexible crop rotations and better soil-management practices.
7. Drainage may make available for cultivation highly productive acres that were not suited for cultivation previously.

By following the seasonal sequence of events on a typical Corn Belt farm, the importance of drainage can be better understood. The quantity of sod turned under, the time of plowing, the number and kind of seedbed operations, the date of planting, and the number of cultivations are all largely determined by conditions of soil tilth as affected by improper drainage. Even harvests are frequently made more difficult because of poor drainage.

Legumes and grasses are likely to heave badly on soils that are wet during the winter. This frequently reduces the amount of vegetable matter available for soil improvement purposes in the spring. The soil will be more difficult to manage because of the reduced amount of plant growth. Heavy crop growth serves as a support for the farm tractor and lessens soil compaction. Because of the poor plant growth associated with the wet field, the field is likely to be plowed in the fall with further soil-structure breakdown. It is also likely to be plowed late in the spring—too late for a good crop of corn.

Difficulties do not end with late plowing. Because of the poor sod and generally wet condition, the plowed field is likely to be cloddy—so cloddy that the hot sun and winds of early summer will rapidly dry the surface soil. Surface moisture may fall to such a low level that kernels of corn planted in the dry soil will not germinate until the necessary moisture is supplied by rain. The hazards of producing the crop have been multiplied before the corn sprouts.

If the farmer is not to plant corn in a cloddy field, he must first reduce the clods to fine powder before proceeding with his planting operations. This pulverized seedbed is again hazardous because rain compacts the surface of the soil, with subsequent serious crusting. Water movement to underdrains is likely to be delayed by this surface crust. In addition to these unfavorable mechanical conditions soil aeration is also reduced and the soil warms up more slowly. Young corn plants growing on poorly drained soil frequently turn yellow within 24 hours.

In such a field, cultivation will be difficult if not impossible. Environments are more favorable for weed growth than for corn, and consequently the corn suffers from competition. In addition, the stunted root system will likely be unable to supply the growing plant with water from the subsoil as the season advances. This has led to the paradoxical statement that certain Corn Belt soils are droughty because they are too wet. The corn plants suffer from drought late in the season because they had too much water earlier.

Compared with the Corn Belt, drainage problems of New England are associated with more sandy soils. According to the drainage census, only one acre out of fifty of cultivated land in New England needs drainage. In contrast, this same census shows that one acre out of every three of cultivated land in Ohio requires drainage.

DRAINAGE NOT INJURIOUS TO LAND

Research has proven farm drainage to be a valuable practice making possible soil- and crop-management programs that better conserve and improve farm land and make better use of the water that falls on the farm. In addition, good farm drainage is a sound investment that pays the farmer substantial dividends in the form of increased yields and better land utilization.

There are no experimental data to support claims, made by some, that farm drainage is exhausting ground-water supplies, changing the pattern of rain and snowfall, causing excessive floods or droughts, lowering the productivity of the soil, causing an increase in insect populations, or stripping the top, fertile soil from the land. On the other hand, there is much experimental evidence showing that properly installed drainage systems increase crop yields and make proper soil management possible.

In 1835 tile drainage was first practiced in the United States. After the Civil War the invention of the dredge, to dig ditches, caused a rapid development of land drainage. It is now estimated that about 80 million acres of our most productive land is associated with drainage enterprises. Farmers in Europe and Asia have been improving their land by drainage for many centuries. With but few exceptions, the low wet lands on the farm, when properly drained, can be classed with the most fertile and productive acres on the farm. For instance, Webster soils, which are common to a number of Corn Belt states, are rated as the number one corn land of the United States when properly drained.

THE WATER PROBLEM

Whenever there is a drought period, whether it be for weeks or for years, farm drainage is often blamed for lowering the ground-water table to exaggerated depths and some critics go so far as to claim that drainage causes droughts.

Geologists report that for the country as a whole there is no progressive decline in the water table. Serious local water shortages may be aggravated by pumping the water from the ground for irrigation, cooling, industrial, or municipal purposes, at a rate greater than that at which the ground-water sources can normally replenish the supply through natural soil flow. The need for more water on the farm plus the ease with which water now can be pumped has increased the per capita consumption about four times in the past 30 years. Many farm wells located in low-yielding water strata are said to be going dry when actually the well cannot yield the water fast enough to meet the increased demand. It should also be remembered that shallow wells are often affected by prolonged wet and dry periods.

SOURCE OF PRECIPITATION

The greater part of the precipitation that falls on the earth's surface originates from ocean sources. It is estimated by some hydrologists that 80 to 90 per cent of the precipitation occurring over the United States east of the Rocky Mountains originates from ocean evaporation. The percentage of precipitation from maritime air increases toward the south. Toward the north the reverse is the case. For the north-central states, the precipitation due to maritime air may be as low as 60 to 70 per cent.

The approximate location of the chief ocean source for the Mississippi River Basin precipitation is shown in Figure 165. Maritime winds laden with moisture move westward over the Gulf of Mexico, then northward and eastward over the United States. The paths of these Gulf winds in the

FIGURE 165. Source of Mississippi River Basin precipitation.

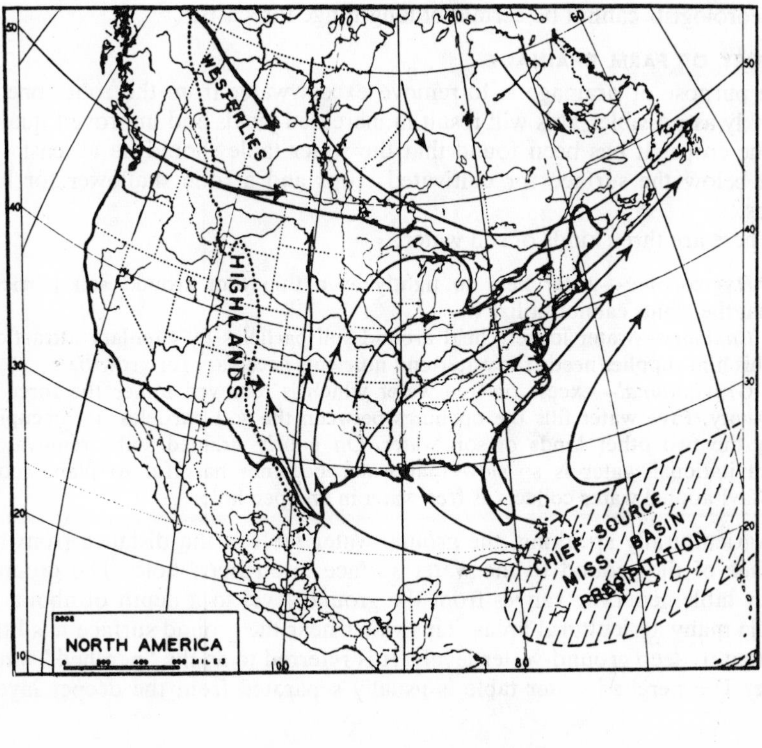

north-central states of the area are somewhat regulated by westerly winds. The general droughts in this area can be traced to the force exerted by these winds in diverting the moisture-laden air to the south and to the east. This drought phenomenon is common to many areas. It is estimated that the ocean winds that sweep over the Mississippi River Basin are responsible for about 27 inches of the average annual precipitation (29.6 inches) in that basin. The remaining 2 or 3 inches of precipitation are derived from land sources. Most of the water moves into the air from land evaporation and transpiration. About 23 inches annually in the Mississippi Basin enters the continental and maritime masses and is carried back over the ocean.

Since only a small proportion of our precipitation is land-derived, drainage, or any other farm practice, will have but a comparatively slight effect on the precipitation pattern. It is true that precipitation may vary from year to year, or century to century, but such variations are a direct result of hemispheric conditions and are not man-made.

It is estimated that the maritime winds lose only about 20 per cent of their annual moisture charge in traveling across the Mississippi Basin. It is the hope of some that extra water can be squeezed out of the water-carrying clouds by artificial methods before the clouds return to the ocean areas.

Dry weather is not new. Records from the nation's oldest weather stations and precipitation records based on tree-ring charts dating back over 500 years definitely prove this. Long-time precipitation records indicate that there are certain sections of the country where dry and wet years tend to run in cycles. Such series, however, are so unpredictable that at this time meteorologists cannot be certain of long-range forecasts.

THEORY OF FARM DRAINAGE

The purpose of drainage is to remove excess water from the root zone as quickly as possible. This will result in increased yields and improved quality of the crops. It has been found that the water table should be at least one foot below the surface for cultivated crops and a little shallower for hay crops.

There are three kinds of soil water:

Hygroscopic—water held so tightly as a thin film around soil particles that the plants cannot utilize it.

Capillary—water loosely held around soil particles by capillary attraction. This film supplies needs for water and nutrients necessary for growth.

Gravitational—excess or free water which is removed under the force of gravity. Free water fills the openings between the soil particles not occupied by the two other kinds of soil water. On poorly drained soils, removal of gravitational water is so slow that water becomes harmful to plant roots. Gravitational water collects as free water in an open hole.

Agriculturally speaking, the ground-water table is the distance from the surface of the ground to the water surface in an open hole. The ground-water table generally ranges from the ground level to a depth of about 10 feet in many agricultural areas. This water near the ground surface has little relation to deep ground-water levels. It is referred to as the "perched" water table. The perched water table is usually separated from the deeper layers of water by impervious or nearly impervious subsoils.

Artificial drainage removes only the free or surplus water. Drainage does not disturb or reduce the useful capillary water so essential to plant growth. The free water only removes and excludes air which is essential to root development. Because of this, a mineral soil suited to agriculture cannot be overdrained. In fact, during a drought a tile-drained soil may actually produce better crops than a similar soil not so drained. Tile and open-ditch drains promptly remove excess water so that crops develop healthy and vigorous root systems. On poorly drained soil the development of roots may be restricted by surplus water during wet periods.

A completely saturated fine-textured soil may contain the equivalent of 6 inches of water per foot-depth of soil. In some cases not more than one inch of this is gravitational water that can be removed by drainage. In such cases one inch of rain falling on a heavy soil carrying moisture up to the capillary capacity may cause the perched water table to rise about one foot.

The lateral or sidewise movement of water through the soil is relatively slow. Because of this the beneficial effects of a tile line or an open ditch seldom exceed 50 to 100 feet on either side of the drain. Capillary water movement tends to be vertical but is usually slow. For this reason it is doubtful if the upward movement of capillary water can supply plants with any considerable amount of the moisture needed for growth. Crops are almost entirely dependent on the capillary water of the root zone.

DRAINAGE AND GROUND-WATER LEVELS

The Minnesota Agricultural Experiment Station has studied ground-water elevations relative to farm drainage for more than 30 years. These investigations show that the perched ground-water table may be lowered on drained areas at the rate of about one foot in 24 hours. This would require some 3 to 4 days to lower the water table to the tile depths. On the other hand, on undrained areas, the free water in the soil will recede at a much slower rate. In this case a rainless period of several weeks may be required to cause a drop in the water table equal to that on the drained area. Thereafter, if no precipitation falls, the ground-water table will recede below tile level at the same rate on the drained and undrained land. This rate of drop below the tile depth on drained and undrained land may range from one to several inches per week during drought periods or on frozen ground. At these greater soil depths, the loss of water by evaporation and transpiration is slow. During the spring months precipitation is generally sufficient to bring the perched water table on the poorly drained lands back near the ground surface. Present knowledge indicates that farm drainage does not materially alter runoff or the soil-water storage capacity of the better agricultural soils and has little effect on the deep ground water.

DRAINAGE IMPORTANT TO PROPER SOIL MANAGEMENT

Besides improving the soil-moisture conditions in the root zone, farm drainage today is an important part of a good soil-management program. By improving the yields from flat, wet acres, the slopes where erosion may be serious can be planted to appropriate crops. The high yield from one acre of flat land when properly drained may equal several acres of sloping land. This in time may make it possible to return much of the sloping land to grass and trees.

In many sections of the country, nearly every farm has a drainage problem. Data based on Soil Conservation Service observations indicate that a high per cent of the farm plans made in the humid area have drainage problems. On many farms it is not possible to set up cropping systems that permit proper soil management to maintain an adequate supply of soil organic matter without draining wet areas that are present on the farm.

RUNOFF STUDIES

Rain and snow are disposed of by surface runoff, sub-surface runoff, evaporation, transpiration, and deep seepage. If agricultural drainage appreciably decreased, deep seepage runoff from drained areas would be greater than before drainage.

A study made by Woodward and Nagler indicated that drainage did not affect deep seepage appreciably. The study included 10,000,000 acres in the Des Moines River Watershed and 2,000,000 acres in the Iowa River Watershed. The drainage operations on these watersheds included installations of tile drains and open ditches and some straightening of stream channels.

One-third of the total area of both watersheds was drained. In the Des Moines Watershed there was one unit of 4,000,000 acres that received 67 per cent of complete drainage, and another unit of 2,700,000 acres that was completely (100 per cent) drained. The monthly precipitation for this study ranged from 0.88 to 9.96 inches.

Woodward and Nagler concluded that during flood period there was no significant change in the behavior of these two streams attributable to drainage. They found that the total runoff from storms of like precipitation, the maximum rates of discharge, and the rain-water storage conditions within the basins were not altered by excessive drainage.

This research definitely indicates that the drainage of large areas of farm land similar to southern Minnesota or northern Iowa does not seriously affect the water-storage rate of the area. There are a few exceptions such as isolated swamps, ponds, or small lakes, which are so perched on, or near, porous soils that they may have appreciable effect on the surrounding ground water. Likewise, drainageways installed near open bodies of water can lower the level of the water if the surrounding soil is porous.

In addition to ground-water investigations in the farming areas of southern Minnesota, automatic water-storage recorders were installed in the peat areas of Aitkin, Beltrami, and Roseau counties, located in northern Minnesota.

These studies, like others, indicate a close correlation between the height of the perched ground-water table and precipitation. Except under unusual conditions, the low or high perched ground-water levels fluctuate with the amount of rain and snow. Even during the droughts of the 1930's few water-table depths for the bogs of northern Minnesota were recorded as low as 6 feet below the surface.

Not all wet land should be drained. Since drainage is expensive, the benefits must be carefully weighed against the cost. If there is question about the productivity of the soil, the best procedure for having soils tested should be followed. It is good economy to get the best information available to evaluate the problem.

DRAINAGE OF IRRIGATED LANDS

Irrigation and drainage are inseparable. Lands long irrigated must also be drained either naturally or by artificial means. In irrigation practice it is impractical to apply just the proper quantity of irrigation water to supply the needs of the crops without getting some excess.

In fact, some excess is often necessary to ensure the continued productivity of irrigated land, to flush the root zone, and leach soluble salts. Thus in irrigated areas drainage may be defined as "the removal of excess water and soluble salts from the surface and the sub-surface of the soil." If an area is to remain productive it is imperative that the quantity of salts removed by drainage should equal or exceed the quantity brought into the area in the irrigation water.

Water logging and the attendant effects of salinity and alkalinity constitute the greatest threat to the continued productivity and prosperity of the irrigated region. The solution of drainage problems is of paramount importance if irrigation agriculture is to be perpetual.

Extensive areas of some of the most fertile soils in the West have been abandoned because of inadequate drainage. Rasmussen estimated that the productive capacity of the 21,000,000 acres now irrigated in the 17 western states may have been reduced as much as 20 per cent by waterlogging and attendant factors. He estimated that the losses in crop production from these causes may exceed $100,000,000 annually.

DRAINAGE IMPROVES YIELDS

Yield of both sugar cane and sugar have been increased substantially in Louisiana by drainage. On 105.6 acres of experimental land, Saveson increased cane yield 5.84 tons and sugar 1,267 pounds per acre by drainage. The most responsive test areas, consisting of 47.2 acres, averaged 52.49 tons of plant cane per acre and 38.74 tons of first-year stubble cane. This was an average yield of 45.61 tons per acre for the two crops. The remaining 1,231 acres of the plantation on which this test was conducted averaged 25.42 tons per acre over the same 2-year period.

The drainage operation consisted of grading the cuts—areas between open drainage ditches. In the grading operation, the earth along the lateral ditches was moved toward the center of the cut. At the same time earth from the center of the cut was sloped toward the lateral ditches. The cut was crowned like a highway. Drainage within the cut consisted mainly of the depressions made between the rows by the tractor wheels.

Maximum yields were obtained with 13 inches of crown per 100 feet. The precision with which the grading was done had a definite bearing on the yield. Elimination of small pockets 2 inches deep or over increased the yield of plant cane 7 and first year stubble cane 3.5 tons per acre.

By doubling the width of cuts so as to accommodate 26 rows of cane instead of 13, and grading this wider cut as described above, the yield of cane was increased 7.01 tons per acre. In addition, the area occupied by the ditches thus eliminated was returned to cultivation. The increased yield was worth $49.00 per acre, whereas the grading cost was only $25.00.

A survey of 67 farms in four counties on the Eastern Shore of Maryland showed that drainage increased crop yields significantly. The average corn yield on 17 farms in Caroline County increased from 19.6 bushels per acre to 42.9 bushels after draining. On 23 farms in Queen Annes County the increase was from 11 to 38.9 bushels, and on 24 farms in Somerset County the corn yield was raised from 30 to 50.4 bushels per acre.

TABLE 86. Effect of drainage on crop yield (30)

Crop	Caroline County	Queen Annes County	Somerset County
Corn (bushels):			
Before drainage	19.6	11.0	30.0
After drainage	42.9	38.9	50.4
Wheat (bushels):			
Before drainage	10.9	8.3	15.0
After drainage	23.0	20.8	25.0
Hay (tons):			
Before drainage	0.54	0.42	1.5
After drainage	1.80	1.56	3.2

Wheat, hay, fruit and vegetables were improved also. The average wheat yield on all farms included in the survey more than doubled. It increased from 11.2 to 22.7 bushels per acre. The average hay yield on 64 farms increased from 0.84 to 2.25 tons per acre as a result of drainage. The yields on three additional farms in Kent County, where 315 acres were drained, were improved substantially. Corn increased from 24.3 to 46.1 bushels per acre. Wheat increased from 14.3 to 24.9 bushels, and hay from 0.87 to 1.51 tons.

Jones reported substantial increases in crop yields resulting from drainage. The farms were located in Union County, Ky., Union County, Miss., Pitt County, N.C., and Cass County, N. Dak. In every case the returns from increased crop yields the first year after drainage more than paid for the installation of the drainage system.

PERMEABILITY AND DRAINAGE

Soil permeability may be defined as "the capacity of the soil to transmit water and air." It can be measured quantitatively in terms of percolation as the rate of flow of water through a unit cross-section of soil in unit time per unit hydraulic gradient under specified temperature. Rates of percolation are usually expressed in inches per hour. Permeability may be judged by examining the visible soil characteristics.

A knowledge of the rate of movement of water through each significantly different soil horizon is important. The amount of water a given soil can transmit during a single rainstorm or succession of storms is governed by the permeability of the soil, including its infiltration rate. Runoff is regulated to a great extent by the rate at which water enters the surface soil and percolates to lower depths. In other words, soils that take and transmit water very slowly will give high runoff whenever rains of high intensity and long duration occur. Thus permeability and infiltration data are valuable in planning a drainage program.

Knowledge of soil permeability is essential to sound planning of drainage measures for individual farms. For example, in planning and developing drainage systems, if the permeability of the soil horizons is slow or very slow, a tile system may not be practical or feasible. In such cases open ditches may be needed to handle the excess surface water. On the other hand, where percolation rates range from moderately slow to moderate, a tile system will function properly. The thickness of each horizon and its percolation rate must be taken into consideration in determining the size, depth, and spacing of tile.

Soil structure is generally considered the most significant factor in evaluating permeability. However, O'Neal found that permeability cannot be correctly evaluated on the basis of type of structure alone. He found that other characteristics of the structural aggregates and their relation to one another must be considered. O'Neal found that the relation between length of the horizontal and vertical axes and the direction and amount of overlap of the aggregates affected permeability. In some sections, fine textures go along with slow permeability, and coarse textures with rapid permeability. But, in the main, texture alone is not a reliable clue; nor is mottling, unless the reason for it is known. A soil may be mottled, regardless of its permeability, if the water is held by a barrier or is the result of seepage or perched water table. In some soils, the durability of structural aggregates seem to be correlated with permeability. In other soils, it is the size and number of visible pores, or the direction of easiest natural fracture. Usually, a number of factors must be considered both singly and in relation with one another. Permeability cannot be evaluated on the basis of one characteristic alone.

Observations of soil structure, direction of easiest natural fracture, and size and number of visible pores can be made in the field at the time samples are taken for permeability measurements. Experience gained by checking observable characteristics against measurements can be applied in evaluating the permeability of soils in much the same manner as a limited number of mechanical soil analyses serve to help identify the textural classification of all soils.

O'Neal and Uhland established a system of classifying soil permeability from a nation-wide standpoint. It consists of the seven permeability classes shown in Table 87.

Van Bavel described a method that anyone may use to determine the

TABLE 87. Permeability classification of soils (31)

Permeability class	Permeability index	Percolation rate in inches per hour through saturated undisturbed cores under 1/2-inch head of water
Very slow	1	Less than 0.05
Slow	2	0.05 to 0.2
Moderately slow	3	0.2 to 0.8
Moderate	4	0.8 to 2.5
Moderately rapid	5	2.5 to 5.0
Rapid	6	5.0 to 10.0
Very rapid	7	More than 10.0

permeability of the soil. It can be used as a guide to tell whether or not a soil can be drained and, if so, how well it will drain. The method is simple and requires little equipment.

The method makes use of the obvious fact that areas in need of drainage have a water table one foot or less from the soil surface during the wet season.

The equipment needed is an 8-inch diameter post-hole digger, a 4-foot rule, a watch, a pitcher pump with a hose, and some small sharp-pointed sticks about 2 inches long.

A 4-foot hole is dug with the post-hole digger. The water immediately starts filling the hole, and will eventually rise as high as the water table in the soil. Usually, this filling takes less than a day. The water in the hole must reach its maximum height and also be not less than one foot from the soil surface.

When this has been achieved the permeability of the soil can be measured. Start early in the day and place a small stick in the side of the hole exactly one foot below the surface of the water, using the rule to locate it accurately.

When the marker has been placed, the hole is completely emptied as rapidly as possible with the small hand pump. If no pump is available, a scoop made of a tin can on a stick can be used. However, this is not an ideal substitute, because it is too slow and too hard to get the last water out this way.

The measurement consists of observing the length of time necessary for the water to rise to the marker that was placed in the side of the hole one foot below the original water surface. The permeability of the soil can then be read from Table 88.

Suppose two fields are examined. One is drained with tile 4 feet deep and 100 feet apart with good results, and the other is undrained. If the soil permeability proved to be about the same on both fields, say 0.6 foot per day, it may be safely concluded that a 4-foot depth and 100-foot spacing will be satisfactory on the undrained field, too. The first thing that this

TABLE 88. Soil permeability measured by the length
of time required to fill the auger hole up
to one foot below the water table (32)

Time in hours	Soil permeability (in feet per day)
1	1.64
1.5	1.41 Rapid
2	0.82
2.5	0.66
3	0.55 Moderate
3.5	0.47
4	0.41
4.5	0.37
5	0.33 Slow
5.5	0.30
6	0.27
6.5	0.25
7	0.23 Very slow
7.5	0.22
8	0.21

method does, therefore, is to provide a sound basis for comparison of soils.

SAMPLE SEVERAL LOCATIONS

Soil permeability, like any soil property, is quite variable from place to place. Because of this, measurements should be made at several representative locations in a field to get the average picture. The measurements should be made on the same kind of soil. A soil map, if available, will help. One measurement for each acre or two should be enough to obtain a satisfactory estimate. However, the more test holes that are dug, the more reliable is the permeability estimate.

In order to obtain information where a drainage system is not available for checking, van Bavel classified soils into four groups, i.e., soils that will drain (a) rapidly, (b) moderately, (c) slowly, and (d) very slowly. Rapidly-draining soils have permeabilities of more than 0.70 foot per day, and laterals (if 4 feet deep) can be spaced far apart, possibly 120 feet or more. If the soil permeability is between 0.70 and 0.45 foot per day, the soil drains moderately, and laterals should be between 80 and 120 feet apart, depending on the situation. Slowly-draining soils have permeabilities between 0.45 and 0.29 foot per day. Laterals on these soils may need to be placed as close as 50 feet. Soils with permeabilities less than 0.29 foot per day drain very slowly. These soils, in all probability, cannot be drained economically.

With this information available, proper spacing of laterals can readily be determined. These permeability data are based on a drainage requirement of ¼ inch per day. This is assumed to be a satisfactory rate of drainage for soils in Iowa where the test was made. In other locations this requirement may be either higher or lower. In such case, the figures for soil permeability as given by van Bavel for the four classes of soils would have to be increased or decreased proportionally.

In addition to the spacing procedure for laterals, depth of the tile should be carefully considered in relation to the presence of hardpan and gravelly layers. Slope and outlet possibilities are also important, but spacing of the laterals is a major factor in drainage costs. The method should supplement long-time experience and judgment by providing a scientific measurement for determining more accurately the spacing that is best.

SHAPE OF WATER TABLE

Childs and O'Donnell determined the movement of water in soils of rising or falling water tables. The method of electric analogues was applied to the unsteady state following changes of rate of rainfall on a field equipped with a system of equidistantly spaced drains. They found that over a considerable range movement following cessation of rain, starting from a steady state and continuing until the water table was but little higher than the drain level, the water table fell as a whole, without appreciable change of shape. After reaching this point, the water table naturally fell more slowly over the drain line than elsewhere. This was because the distance to fall was greater at the drain line than at points between lines.

The water table approached drain level asymptotically* but not, except accidentally, exponentially,** since the height-time curve had a different shape for each distance from the drain line. The water table rose without change of shape when rainfall rose over the range where the water table fell without change of shape.

When the initial state was that of saturation to the soil surface instead of a steady state corresponding to constant rainfall, cessation of rainfall was followed at first by a faster fall of water table over the drain line than elsewhere. After this the movement was similar to that previously mentioned.

The water table fell more slowly in a shallow soil than in a deeper soil, where other factors were the same.

Kirkham and Gaskell determined the position of the water surface in tile- and ditch-drained land. The soil was underlain by an impervious layer and was initially water-saturated to the surface. They found that the successive shapes of the water table were the same in a sandy soil as in a clay. However, the water surface passed through the positions more rapidly in a sandy than in a clay soil.

* An *asymptote* is a line that is the limiting position which the tangent of a curve approaches, as the point of contact recedes indefinitely along an infinite branch of the curve.

** An *exponent* is a symbol written above another symbol and on the right, denoting how many times the latter is repeated as a factor.

The time required for the water table to drop one foot midway between ditches, where the ditches were spaced 10 to 20 times the depth of the impermeable layer, varied as the square of the distance between the ditches. This relationship should also apply to tile drainage if the tile trench is backfilled with highly permeable material.

DEPTH AND SPACING OF DRAIN TILE

Attempts have been made to determine the proper depth and spacing of tile on the basis of measurable soil characteristics. Perhaps the best known of these is the work by Neal who gauged the depth and spacing of tile by measurements of soil plasticity and clay content. It is known, however, that these measurements are related only in a general way to soil permeability and drainage behavior, so that the measurements are at best but doubtful indices of what the depth and spacing of tile should be for specific soils. A much more logical approach has been made by Donnan, Aronovici, and Blaney. They developed a tile-spacing formula that is based on soil permeability and the application of Darcy's law to the condition of lateral flow. Initial tests of their equation, based on measured flow from tile lines, showed a satisfactory agreement between the actual and the computed spacing of tile under field conditions.

Soil physicists meanwhile have clarified certain water relationships of soil with respect to the effects of tension on drainage, and have provided a logical basis for determining the depths of soil from which free water must be removed if drainage is to be effective. Other investigators have developed methods and criteria for determining the permeability of soils.

Slater developed a formula for lateral flow which was used in determining lateral spacing for tile. Table 89 shows the approximate spacings required by the formula when tile are placed at depths of 3, 4, and 5 feet in soils of uniform permeability with a deep barrier layer more than 7 feet below the soil surface and when applied to the permeability classification developed by O'Neal.

TABLE 89. Tile spacing as determined by soil permeability and lateral flow (28)

Permeability class	Permeability	Tile spacing, in feet, for tile placed at the depth of		
		3 feet	4 feet	5 feet
Very slow	0.0 to 0.05	0 to 15	0 to 20	0 to 25
Slow	0.05 to 0.2	15 to 30	20 to 40	25 to 50
Moderately slow	0.2 to 0.8	30 to 60	40 to 80	50 to 100
Moderate	0.8 to 2.5	60 to 110	80 to 145	100 to 180
Moderately rapid	2.5 to 5.0	110 to 155	145 to 205	180 to 255
Rapid	5.0 to 10.0	155 to 220	205 to 290	255 to 360

REFERENCES

1. Aronovici, V. S. 1947. *The mechanical analysis as an index of subsoil permeability.* Soil Sci. Soc. Amer. Proc., 11: 137-141.
2. ———, and Donnan, W. W. 1946. *Soil permeability as a criterion for drainage design.* Trans. Amer. Geophys. Un., 27: 95-101.
3. Bendixen, T. W., Hershberger, M. F., and Slater, C. S. 1948. *A basis for classifying soil permeability.* Jour. Agric. Res., 77: 157-168.
4. Benton, G. S., Blackburn, R. T., and Snead, V. 1950. *The role of the atmosphere in the hydrologic cycle.* Trans. Amer. Geophys. Un., 31(1).
5. Borchert, J. R. 1950. *The climate of the Central American Grassland.* Assoc. Amer. Geographers, 40: 1-19.
6. Childs, E. C. 1947. *The water table equipotentials and streamlines in drained land: V. The moving water table.* Soil Sci., 63(5): 361-376.
7. ———, and O'Donnell, T. 1950. *The water table equipotentials and streamlines in drained land: VI. The rising water table.* Soil Sci., 71(3): 233-237.
8. Colman, E. A. 1946. *A laboratory study of lysimeter drainage under controlled moisture tension.* Soil Sci., 62: 365-382.
9. ———, and Bodman, G. B. 1945. *Moisture and energy conditions during downward entry of water into moist and layered soils.* Soil Sci. Soc. Amer. Proc., 9: 3-11.
10. Donnan, W. W. 1946. *Model tests of a tile spacing formula.* Soil Sci. Soc. Amer. Proc., 11: 131-136.
11. ———, Aronovici, V. S., and Blaney, H. F. 1947. *Report on drainage investigations in irrigated areas of Imperial Valley, Calif.* USDA, Soil Conservation Service (Mimeo.)
12. Jamison, V. C., Reed, I. F., and Pearson, R. W. 1948. *The use of soil tension columns and a modified form of the back pressure well in studying porosity and drainage properties of tillage test soils.* Soil Sci. Soc. Amer. Proc., 13: 56-61.
13. Jones, L. A. 1952. *Effects of drainage on agricultural production.* Agr. Eng., 37: 415-416.
14. Kirkham, D., and Gaskell, R. E. 1950. *The falling water table in tile and ditch drainage.* Soil Sci. Soc. Amer. Proc., 15: 37-42.
15. Kirkham, D., and van Bavel, C. H. M. 1948. *Theory of seepage into auger holes.* Soil Sci. Soc. Amer. Proc., 13: 75-81.
16. Luthin, J. N., and Kirkham, D. 1949. *A pizometer method of measuring permeability of soil in situ below a water table.* Soil Sci., 68: 349-357.
17. Manson, P. W., and Rost, C. O. 1951. *Farm drainage in upland conservation practices.* Agr. Eng., 32(6): 325-327.
18. Marshall, T. J., and Stirk, G. B. 1949. *Pressure potential of water moving downward into soil.* Soil Sci., 68: 359-370.
19. Neal, J. H. 1934. *Proper spacing and depth of tile drains determined by physical properties of the soil.* Univ. Minn. Tech. Bull. 101.
20. Nicholson, H. H. 1942. *The principles of field drainage.* Cambridge Univ. Press, England.
21. O'Neal, A. M. 1949. *Soil characteristics significant in evaluating permeability.* Soil Sci., 67(5): 403-409.
22. Pickles, G. W. 1941. *Drainage and flood-control engineering.* McGraw-Hill Book Co., Inc., New York.
23. Rasmussen, W. W. 1951. *Drainage problems follow irrigation.* Utah Agr. Expt. Sta. Farm & Home Sci. 12(1): 14-17.
24. Rothe, J. H. 1929. *Die Strangentfernung bei Dranungen fur Mineralboden.* Der Kulturtechniker, 32: 155-169.
25. Saveson, I. L. 1950. *Drainage for sugar-cane land.* Sugar Bull., 28(13): 198-202.
26. ———. 1950. *Draining sugar-cane land.* Agr. Eng., 31: 451-454.
27. Slater, C. S. 1948. *The flow of water through soil.* Agr. Eng., 29: 119-124.
28. ———. 1950. *The depth of spacing of tile drains.* Agr. Eng., 31(9): 448-450.
29. Tedrow, J. C. F. 1951. *Influence of topography and production on classification of soils having improved drainage.* Soil Sci., 71(6): 429-437.

30. Uhland, R. E. 1944. *Drainage doubles yields on Maryland's eastern shore*. Soil Cons., 9(10): 221-223.

31. ———, and O'Neal, A. M. 1951. *Soil permeability determinations for use in soil and water conservation*. USDA, SCS-TP-101.

32. van Bavel, C. H. M. 1950. *Will this soil drain?* Crops & Soils, 2(7): 10-11.

33. ———, and Kirkham, D. 1949. *Field measurements of soil permeability using auger holes*. Soil Sci. Soc. Amer. Proc., 13: 90-96.

34. Woodward, S. M., and Nagler, F. A. 1929. *The effect of agricultural drainage upon flood runoff*. Amer. Soc. Civil Eng.. 93: 655.

24

Watershed Management

It has long been known that there was an intimate relation between land and water and that the method of managing the land affected runoff and the quality of stream flow. Ancient Greece not only recognized this relation but attempted to evaluate it. With the passage of time man's interest in the effect of land use upon floods, water storage, and their associated difficulties has increased. Out of this interest have come the principles of modern land conservation. More recently, the interest has given rise to the concept of watershed management, which has for its major objective the application of these principles to drainage basins. Most people accept this broad objective but few understand the complex relationship between plants, soil, and water that underlies it.

Early French settlers in the lower Mississippi Valley were the first in this country to adopt flood control measures. They started building levees before 1717. At first, each landowner operated independently of his neighbors in this effort. However, they later joined forces and operated on a community basis. Eventually all the settlers who lived on the flood plain were required to aid with levee construction.

The United States Government did not become interested in the problem until 1824—more than a century later. In 1824 the Corps of Engineers of the Army began work on navigation improvement.

Congress showed interest in flood control for the first time in 1850 by authorizing a survey of the Mississippi River with the view of protecting it from floods. Beginning in 1879, Congress appropriated funds over a period of years for the construction of levees along the Mississippi River. Appropriations were also made for the repair of old levees along the river. All such work was done cooperatively with the Parish levee boards.

Congress did not show interest in extensive flood control problems outside of the Mississippi Valley until 1893. It did so in 1893 by establishing the California Debris Commission. This commission was authorized to prepare plans for the control of mining debris clogging the Sacramento and San Joaquin rivers. Flood control plans were developed later and a flood control program was started on these rivers in 1917.

The next step was the creation of the Board of Engineers for Rivers and Harbors in 1908. This board promoted navigation improvements when first established. As federal interest in flood control became active as a result of actions by Congress, the board was assigned flood control responsibilities.

Employment of land management practices for controlling runoff and retarding soil erosion was made possible for the first time in 1911, when the Weeks Forest Purchase Act, which authorized the Secretary of Agriculture to take measures toward "regulating the flow of navigable streams," was passed by Congress.

It was not until 1917 that Congress enacted legislation—Flood Control Act—recognizing need for a broader consideration of river basin problems. In addition to authorizing work on the Mississippi and Sacramento rivers, this Act provided that federal laws relating to rivers and harbors be applied as far as possible to flood control.

The Rivers and Harbors Act of 1920 provided for local participation. It authorized the Chief of Army Engineers to determine both the local and general benefits of a proposal, and recommend that local cooperation be required as a result of the local benefit.

It took the disastrous flood along the lower Mississippi Valley in 1927 to arouse large-scale federal flood control activity in 1928. Local interests were required by the 1928 Act to contribute one-third of the construction costs, provide rights-of-way, and maintain and operate the works on the river.

It was not until 1936 that the federal participation in flood control was put on a nation-wide basis. The 1936 Flood Control Act also authorized the Secretary of Agriculture to perform specific functions in connection with a "program for runoff and waterflow retardation and soil erosion prevention."

The estimated federal costs of flood control projects exceeded $10,000,-000,000 by 1951.

In 1944, in furtherance of the responsibility of the Department of Agriculture in the flood prevention undertaking, Congress authorized work of improvement for flood prevention on 11 watersheds.

In 1954, Congress recognized by law for the first time the great importance of upstream watershed protection in our over-all water resources policy. For the first time also, this Act provided a broad program of federal technical and financial assistance to such local watershed groups as are willing to assume responsibility for initiating, carrying out, and sharing the costs of watershed protection that will help conserve water for agricultural uses and supplement any needed downstream flood control measures.

Congress, in making appropriations for the Department of Agriculture for the fiscal year ending June 30, 1954, approved an item of $5,000,000 under the title "Watershed Protection." This appropriation was for expenses necessary to carrying out preventive measures, including, but not limited to, engineering operations, methods of cultivation, the growing of vegetation, and changes in use of land, in accordance with the provisions of Public Law 46 (1935) which established the Soil Conservation Service.

This appropriation was to provide funds for a program of cooperation with local organizations on 60 small watersheds, for the purpose of demonstrating the practicability of complete watershed protection as a means of conserving soil and water resources and alleviating damages from floods, siltation of reservoirs, impairment of stream channels, and related problems. These pilot plant watershed projects were to be completed in an average of 5 years, at a total cost of about $29 million to the federal government and approximately an equal cost to the landowners, local organizations, and states. This was to be a type of cost-sharing venture—a local-state-federal partnership in the protection and improvement of our vital natural resources of soil and water.

Notwithstanding a growing recognition of the close relationship of land and water, there has been a wide gap in correlating the planning for their development, conservation, and use. Two major planning techniques are being widely used today. One is the technique of planning and treating individual farm and ranch units without regard to factors outside ownership boundaries. The other is the multiple-purpose development of water resources by river basins without regard to incidental changes of runoff or sediment production resulting from land use and treatment. Between these two planning concepts there is an important missing link.

A great deal is now known about the relationship of land and water. There is ample evidence of the effect of proper use of watershed lands on runoff, sediment production, ground-water supply, and other hydrologic factors. These considerations necessarily influence the planning, design, cost and maintenance of major downstream works for river regulation. Downstream river works for power, flood control, irrigation, and water supply can add to the acreage and yield of farm lands as well as protect and increase industrial and urban developments.

The present conservation work on individual farms and ranches largely benefits those properties and often is installed with slight regard to what happens elsewhere. Thus, it is thought that potential gains are being passed up that might be realized were watershed protection programs to be accelerated and designed not only to maintain and improve the productivity of individual farms but also to achieve the greatest possible improvement in downstream water and sediment control.

The missing link can be closed through a watershed protection program in which the work on one farm will be related to that on the next and where there is adequate attention to the needs not only of farmers but also of the community, the urban people, and downstream industries.

The watershed protection demonstration projects range in size from as little as 12 square miles to as much as several hundred square miles. They comprise a truly *community* watershed protection program—a program that local people and their local organizations, such as conservation districts, watershed associations, and flood control districts, with assistance and help from state and federal agencies, can complete in a relatively short time. Small watersheds are natural planning units which are thought to be the cornerstone to total river basin development.

In the very beginning of the nationwide program of soil and water conservation, in 1933, the Soil Conservation Service stressed the watershed approach. Its earliest work on demonstration projects was organized along watershed lines. The need for local organization and initiative during the past 20 years led to primary emphasis being placed on the individual-farm approach—the first basis of an action program. As the land treatment job advanced, a renewed interest in the watershed concept spread throughout the nation.

Since 1948 scores of watershed associations and other organized groups have been formed to work in cooperation with soil conservation districts for the purpose of achieving soil and water conservation objectives which are not being met through existing national programs. Over 300 organized associations and 500 informal groups have bound themselves together for the purpose of solving their watershed problems. Many such associations, together with soil conservation districts and individuals from all walks of life, actively supported the recently launched watershed protection program. Already, many of these groups are joining in sponsorship of watersheds designated for treatment.

The conservation of the nation's soil and water resources is a responsibility that rests primarily with farmers and ranchers. The federal, state, and local governments have a large stake in it, however, and can assist in many ways. Industries, urban areas, service organizations, sportsmen's clubs, and others are vitally interested and concerned. Yet the work must start at ground level with the custodian of soil and water himself—the one who plows the land, plants and cultivates the crops, and manages the pasture or range and woods.

The 60 demonstration watershed projects approved by Congress provide a cross-section of the many different types of physical, vegetative, climatic, and economic factors present in various sections of the country. Experience argues against trying to develop a detailed plan for a much larger area than that in which a community of interest exists among the residents. This factor tended to place a definite limitation upon the size of watersheds selected. Consideration was given to the amount of conservation work that had already been completed in the watershed, as well as the interest shown by the local people. Many of the watersheds were chosen because they lay in areas where preliminary surveys showed the need for, and practicability of, watershed protection measures and where it was likely that benefits from the program would exceed its costs. These watersheds are geographically scattered over the country as an invitation to as many people as possible to participate. They are being used as pilot watersheds to determine the possible course of action on watershed protection in the future.

THE WATERSHED PLAN

Sound plans are essential to constructive action and the first step in a watershed protection program is the preparation of a watershed plan. The local people have the assistance of qualified technicians in preparing plans in small watersheds. All local interests concerned have their opportunity to participate in preparing the watershed plans. These plans reveal the kinds, quantities, and costs of all needed soil and water measures. They show the specific location of major water-management measures such as flood-water-retarding structures and channel improvements.

After preparation and approval of a plan by the federal, state, and local groups, designs and specifications for the necessary structural phases of the program are completed. This is followed by application, installation, or construction of the recommended measures. Then ensues the operation and maintenance of the measures. Finally, the program will be carefully observed for its effectiveness in accomplishing the objectives of watershed protection.

As indicated already, a successful watershed protection program requires that the people residing in the watershed assume the principal responsibility. This necessitates the sponsorship of a soil conservation district together with other responsible local organizations that are representative of the interests involved and that can help in formulating and achieving the best possible program for watershed protection.

It is also mandatory that local interests share a part of the cost. They will be expected to provide all easements and rights-of-way for structural measures, to carry out all of the land-treatment practices, and to provide other help comprising altogether about 50 per cent of the total cost of the project.

Watershed protection work consists of the application of needed soil and water conservation practices on farm and ranch lands, of adequate protection and management of woodland, and of the installation of such measures as are needed and practicable for reduction of flood water and sediment damages. There will be flood-water-retarding structures, channel improvement, major gully control, streambank stabilization, and related measures. Because land and the behavior of water falling on land differs from farm to farm and from watershed to watershed, each watershed and each type of land in every watershed must be planned and dealt with individually. Due to the complexity and magnitude of these differences, no ready-made plan or fixed set of practices can be employed. Out of long years of painstaking research and practical experience have emerged, however, certain basic treatment measures that can be considered in planning the protection program for each watershed.

WATERSHED PROTECTION MEASURES

Measures contributing to watershed protection can be classified in two broad categories: in terms of *purpose* and also in terms of *methods and accomplishment*. In terms of purpose, there are, first, the land use and treatment measures, which are effective in increasing the infiltration of precipitation and the water-holding capacity of the soil and of preventing soil erosion on watershed lands. They include measures such as contouring, terracing, strip-cropping, grassed waterways, rotations, pasture and woodland improvement. This category also includes watershed-stabilization measures, such as control of gullies by structures or vegetation. This group of measures has the distinguishing characteristic that in most cases the predominant benefits from their use occur on-site, that is, on the fields and farms where they are installed. This is not to say they may not have a highly significant effect on reduction of flood damages; often they do, but this is not their major benefit.

The second category of measures includes those planned primarily for the management of water flow after it has left the fields and farm waterways and reached the small branches and creeks. These measures include flood-water-retarding structures, stream-channel improvements to increase carrying capacity and stabilize beds and banks, minor flood-ways, sediment-detention basins, and similar measures. The distinguishing characteristic of this group is that their primary benefits are off-site or downstream, not at the place where they are installed. In this sense, the primary benefits are public, because they accrue to the other farms, towns, and roads downstream from where the measures are installed.

Measures that aid in flood prevention can also be classified according to how they can be established or installed. A large part but not all of the land use and treatment measures are of such a nature that farmers and ranchers can and will install them on their own land if given an understanding of their value, technical aid in their planning and installation, and some degree of financial assistance. Certain of these measures, however, which are needed for stabilization of watershed lands, are either too complex for landowners to install, or else the benefits will be so long deferred that it is unreasonable to expect very many farmers to do these jobs. For example, reinforced concrete structures needed to stabilize large gullies, such as occur in western Iowa, require all the elements of planning, design, and supervision of construction that go into a major flood-control dam. The benefits from this type of gully control are primarily to watershed lands that would be destroyed by the headward growth and enlargement of the gullies. These lands may be on other farms above the gully head. If economically justified in the public interest, it becomes more efficient and economical for the installations to be made by agencies of government under binding maintenance agreements.

The measures that are primarily for flood prevention, such as retarding structures and channel improvement, can rarely be installed by individual landowners. They require group action, highly skilled planning, and corporate or governmental financing.

FUNDAMENTAL NATURAL PROCESSES

An understanding of the fundamental natural processes that govern the behavior of soil, plants, and water is essential to the achievement of practical watershed management. Progress made in the allied fields of soils and plant physiology and in the field of plant-soil-water relations as a whole has provided some insight into these processes.

The complex interrelations of plants, soil, and water, as modified by human activity, involves the simultaneous interaction of many factors and processes. For ease of presentation it has been necessary to separate these into artificial classifications of subject matter. Such a separation represents merely a convenient device for examining the differences as well as the similarities among the various factors and processes so that the relative significance of each and their impacts upon each other may be evaluated more accurately.

Recognition of the blending of the processes and factors governing plant-soil-water relations is essential to an understanding and application of the principles and practices of watershed management. It is necessary to keep this in mind to avoid the mistake of seeking or relying upon "single-factor" solutions to watershed problems. (Watershed management as used here does not include river basin developments.)

OBJECT OF WATERSHED MANAGEMENT

The object of watershed management is to meet the problem of land and water use on the basis that all resources are interdependent and must, therefore, be considered together. The complete drainage basin or watershed lends itself admirably to this approach. A natural unit, it reflects the interactions of vegetation, soil, and underlying geologic formation upon water which falls as precipitation in providing a common end product—runoff, stream flow, and ground water—whereby the net effect of these interactions on that product can be measured and evaluated.

Stream flow in its various aspects is a recognized criterion of watershed conditions, and also of the effectiveness of watershed management. Total yearly amount of flow, seasonal regularity, and frequencies and extremes of high and low discharges provide useful indicators of the net results of conservation practices.

The technical soundness of planning and developing the water resources of watersheds as units is now generally accepted. Since watershed management rests on the principle that water flow is a product of the land, it is considered by many a chief requisite of a type of watershed development in which conservation measures will be applied in conjunction with or, better still, in advance of engineering works for flood prevention, flood control, hydroelectric power, navigation, or irrigation. This alliance of land conservation and engineering can, for example, prolong the life of many reservoirs by reducing sedimentation, provide higher quality water for municipal and industrial use, reduce harmful discharges, and provide many other benefits.

LAND USE AND STREAM FLOW

A basic premise of watershed management is that the amount and rate of stream flow express the natural and cultural characteristics and conditions of the watershed that produces it. Graphically, these characteristics are expressed in the stream-flow hydrograph which represents rates of flow past a stream-gauging station over a period of time (solid line, Fig. 166). Four factors affect the volume and rate of runoff and, consequently, the shape of the hydrograph: precipitation (kind, amount, intensity, and distribution); drainage basin characteristics (including size, shape of basin, length and

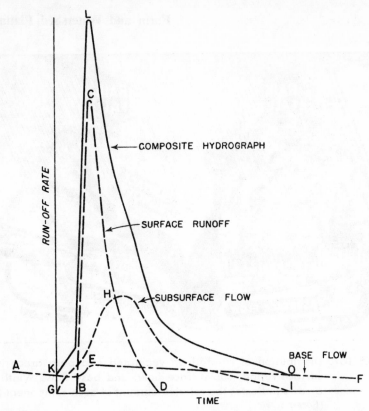

FIGURE 166. A typical stream-flow hydrograph with component parts reflecting the effects of a rain (8).
(Forest Service)

steepness of slopes, and stream density); soil and its plant cover; and changes in soil and cover through land use. So far as known the soil and its cover is the only factor subject to modification by man.

Figure 166 shows a composite hydrograph representing typical stream discharge resulting from a high-intensity storm which produced surface runoff. The composite hydrograph, represented by the solid line, is actually drawn by the pen of the stream-flow recorder. The broken lines in the figure are not recorded by the pen on a chart, but are derived by established techniques of hydrograph analysis to represent the several sources of flow that combine to make up the total flow past the gauge.

How land use affects stream flow can be visualized by separating the hydrograph into its component parts and analyzing the relation between each part and the character of the soil as modified by the condition and use of its vegetal cover. To help show these relations, frequent reference will be made to Figure 166 and the illustration of rainfall disposal shown in Figure 167.

The uppermost solid line in Figure 166 shows total discharge past the stream-flow gauge. This discharge comes from three sources: base flow, surface runoff, and sub-surface flow. Note that at one instant the sum of base,

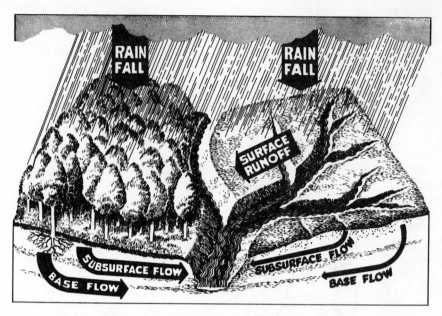

FIGURE 167. Distribution of rainfall on vegetated and bare areas into
surface runoff, sub-surface flow, and base flow. Width of
arrows indicates the relative amount of each component (8).
(Forest Service)

sub-surface, and surface flow equals total discharge, line K-L-O.

Base flow (line A-E-F in Figure 166 and Figure 167) comes from underground reservoirs which are the source of water for streams during rainless periods. This type of runoff responds much more slowly to precipitation than the other two sources. A second source is surface runoff, represented by line B-C-D and also shown in Figure 167. This water runs over the surface of the soil. For this reason, surface runoff rates are very responsive to the intensity and amount of rainfall. The peak rate, as shown on the hydrograph (C), coincides in time and can closely approximate the peak rate of total runoff. The rate usually rises rapidly to the peak during or shortly after the intense part of a storm. Subsequent decline is somewhat less rapid.

Sub-surface flow, the third component, is illustrated by line G-H-I, Figure 166, and in Figure 167. It originates from water stored temporarily in the soil at shallow depths (usually less than 24 inches) over a more or less impermeable layer. As water accumulates over this layer, it will move down the slope through the soil pores toward the stream channel. Sub-surface flow is not as sensitive to rainfall as surface runoff. Even for equal volumes of outflow, its peak rate will be considerably lower than that of surface runoff because the outflow is more prolonged.

The shape of the hydrograph of each component of stream flow reflects the time required for the water to reach the channel. Thus, surface runoff, as shown in Figure 167, takes the quickest way to the channels, often through existing or newly created rills and gullies on the surface. Sub-surface flow moves more slowly on its way to the stream. Often, however, this type of runoff is intercepted by gullies before it reaches the channel and is then quickly transferred to surface flow. Base flow moves slowest. Once in the channel, the water from all sources moves downstream relatively fast. But the rate of movement of each type of runoff determines when it will reach the channel and consequently the shape the hydrograph will have.

Aside from the effects of vegetation on the interception of snow or rain, the amount of precipitation that goes into base, surface, and sub-surface flow, respectively, is determined in large part by the characteristics of the soil. These physical characteristics are affected by the nature of the vegetation the soil supports. For this reason, any practices that change the nature of the vegetation will in turn cause changes in the physical characteristics of the soil and, therefore, in stream flow.

The physical characteristics of the soil determine its hydrologic characteristics, namely, *infiltration* (the rate at which water moves into the soil), *percolation* (the rate at which water moves downward through the soil), and *storage capacity*. These factors in turn determine the proportions of the three stream-flow components. When infiltration and precipitation rates and soil-storage capacities are high, immediate runoff from a given storm will be low because the amount of surface runoff will be small. Under these conditions, the storm precipitation will move into the soil. There part of it may be stored, a part may go to sub-surface flow, and still another may move on downward to base flow. These are the slow routes to the stream channel. Conversely, at the opposite extreme of low infiltration rates with little storage, surface runoff will account for much more of the precipitation, with a consequent marked increase in peak rates of stream flow.

An example of the effects of land use on stream flow is shown in Figure 168. The hydrograph from two of the Forest Service's several experimental watersheds at the Coweeta Hydrologic Laboratory in western North Carolina illustrate the changes brought about by mountain farming. The treated and the control watersheds cover 23 and 39 acres, respectively.

Stream flow on the treated watershed was measured for 6 years prior to its treatment in order to determine its runoff characteristics. The timber was clear-cut in 1939-40. Six acres were planted to corn and cultivated according to local practices. Twelve of the remaining 17 acres were grazed. Five acres were found too rough for agricultural use. The effects on stream flow are shown by a comparison of two storms of about the same size, one occurring before treatment in 1934, the other after treatment in 1946. The hydrograph of the control watershed shows little difference in stream flow from the two storms. Peak discharges were 12 and 15 cubic feet per second per square mile (c.s.m.).

Hydrographs from the treated watershed tell quite a different story. Whereas the 1934 storm produced a peak discharge of 16 c.s.m., the 1946 storm produced about 69 c.s.m. The difference was due almost entirely to an increase in surface runoff as shown by analysis of the hydrograph.

The above example applies only to the effects of a given storm on rates of

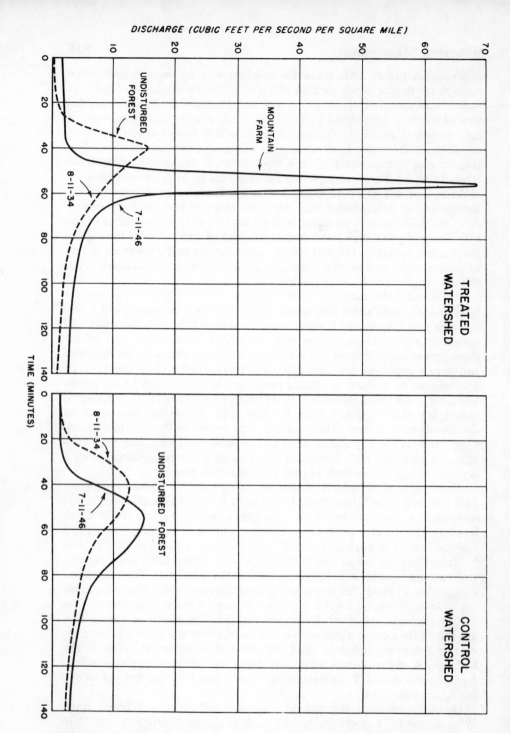

FIGURE 168. Comparative effects of mountain farming and an undisturbed forest on stream flow (8).

(Forest Service)

stream flow. The effects of watershed treatment on the amount of water yield are not taken into account here.

WHITE HOLLOW WATERSHED

According to a study conducted by the Tennessee Valley Authority, 15 years of protection and reforestation so improved the plant cover of 1,715-acre White Hollow Watershed in eastern Tennessee that the summer peak flows were reduced 73 to 92 per cent and the duration of summer storm runoff was increased 500 per cent. A more satisfactory flow resulted without any material change in total water yield.

The greatest change occurred immediately after cultivation stopped and adequate protection from fire and grazing began. Most rapid changes in the character of the runoff occurred during the first few years of the study when only the processes of natural revegetation were operating. The change was due largely to the increase in ground cover which followed naturally after grazing and cultivation were stopped.

Although storm runoff patterns showed marked changes there was no significant change in total water yields during the 15 years. This indicates that increased interception and transpiration losses, which would be expected from increased cover directly, were either insufficient to be recorded in stream-flow changes, or were balanced by other factors, such as reduced evaporation losses.

The change in stream regimen was due to changes in the runoff pattern from flow to sub-surface flow rather than to any change in the amount of water which eventually emerged as stream flow. Changes in peak flows were much greater for summer periods than winter periods. The plant cover improved to such an extent that erosion was practically eliminated. White Creek now maintains a flow of clear water suitable for rearing trout.

SOIL A STORAGE RESERVOIR

For watershed management purposes, soil may be defined as that portion of the watershed rock material which is subject to seasonal change in moisture and is occupied, or capable of being occupied, by roots. The effect of land use on the hydrologic characteristics of the soil are most pronounced in this zone. Soil consists of a porous framework made up of mineral particles and organic matter, and pore space which is occupied by air and water.

Soils are not static. They are dynamic in the sense that they are continuously changing in color, depth, and structure in response to the activities of living organisms: roots, burrowing animals, micro-flora, and micro-fauna. They swell with the addition of water; they may shrink and crack as they dry. Frost expands them. They creep downward on steep slopes. Even the most stable soils very slowly move downhill. More rapid movement occurs with accelerated erosion, and the most rapid with running water or wind.

Mineral soil material is developed from the weathering of rock by physical and chemical processes at rates governed to a large extent by the climatic and biotic environment. These processes of soil formation are continually at work and, unless major changes in the environment occur, weathering of the underlying rock (parent material) gradually deepens the soil mass. This is a very slow process. Accompanying this process are other processes, such as geological erosion and leaching, which preclude establishment of a static state in the material affected by weathering. Effectiveness of all these various processes decreases with depth to the vanishing point.

The effects of land use and vegetation on the soil are reflected principally in changes in the structure, number, size, shape, and stability of the aggregates. These changes in turn affect the size, shape, and distribution of the soil pores. These pores provide space for the storage of water and serve also as avenues for water movement. Varying greatly in size and shape, they compose roughly about one-half of the soil volume. The mineral and organic particles comprising the other half in effect serve as a framework for the pores. Differences in size and shape of the pores determine the amount of water that can be held in them and the rate of movement through them.

RETENTION AND STREAM FLOW

The effects of treatment of vegetation on retention are reflected in the amount of stream flow. By managing vegetation so that both the depth to which water is stored and the water-holding capacity of the soil particles are increased (thus increasing total storage capacity), more rainfall can be stored. In addition, it may be possible to increase the total storage capacity of deep soils by encouraging or introducing deeper-rooted vegetation. By drawing water from greater depths, such vegetation would provide space for storage of precipitation so that less would go to stream flow.

Watershed treatment not only affects total retention, but also the opportunity for retention at any one time. In the absence of vegetation, available storage space is created solely by evaporation losses. Under such conditions, however, the available storage space often cannot be utilized because the rate of entry of water into the soil may be greatly restricted by a surface only slowly permeable to water. On the other hand, evaporation is reduced where vegetation is present but the total loss by transpiration plus evaporation is commonly greater than the loss by evaporation alone from a bare area. Thus, storage opportunity is not only greater under vegetation but is also created more rapidly than in bare areas.

NEED FOR WATER INCREASING

Today this nation is water-conscious as it has never been before. More and more it is being brought to our attention that water is the primary limiting factor in the development of cities, industry, and agriculture, not only throughout the West but also in many parts of the East. The key not only to sound resource conservation but also to our future progress as a nation will lie to a considerable extent in our success or failure with water—in the way we handle, conserve, utilize, and control it.

The difficulties now faced by many cities that depend on surface runoff for their water supply are well known. Even cities and industrial establishments that get most or all of their water from underground sources are having their difficulties.

This water which in many places is becoming so difficult to get, however, is the same stuff that on all too many occasions comes roaring down our creeks and rivers spreading hardship and destruction. What is the difference between the pure, clear water that flows from our springs and wells and the yellow torrents of silt and debris that periodically lay waste to our river valleys? The essential difference is that the clear water—the usable water—stayed for a time where it fell. The other did not.

The way to get good and adequate supplies and at the same time reduce our destructive floods is to get the rain and melting snow into the ground. The ground is the greatest and most wonderful reservoir of all. There is more natural water-storage capacity in the earth than in all the man-made structures and reservoirs we can ever hope to build on top of it.

Every drop of water that can be retained in the area in which it falls, either in the earth or in small retarding structures, is one drop subtracted from a potential flood and one drop added to our useful water supply.

WATERSHED COMPONENTS

A watershed is made up of a number of individual community components, and possesses physical, economic, and social ingredients. A watershed is the land from which water flows into a stream, lake or other point of drainage. But its geography is only one component of any watershed, for purposes of watershed programs. Other essential watershed elements include, for example, the timber or grass growing on the watershed, and the land in cultivation. They include land use—how the land is used for farming, grazing, lumbering, recreation, and wildlife, and for industrial and other urban uses. They include the watershed land's conditions of erosion and soil depletion, soil fertility and productiveness. And the watersheds include, most importantly, people—people with their community interests.

All these factors have to be taken into account, in their proper relationships, for effective watershed planning and treatment. Conservation on one farm must be related to that on other farms, and in turn the effect of the conservation measures on both rural and urban property and facilities must be considered. This calls for working out systematic use of water from the top of each watershed to the bottom. Obviously, efforts to bring about complete watershed protection will be effective pretty largely in direct ratio to the understanding and participation by all the watershed interests involved.

Active participation on the part of all interests is not too high a goal to aim at in any given watershed where enough local interest and support develop to justify undertaking a program, although 100 per cent participation may not be expected immediately in all such watersheds. Thus far, the extent of local interests and participation has been gratifying, however. This is true in the 60 small watersheds that have been selected by the Soil Conservation Service for the pilot plant program under the $5 million initial appropriation made by Congress. It is also the case in the 11 watersheds on which work of improvement for flood prevention were authorized by Congress in 1944 and begun in 1946.

THE MEANING OF CONSERVATION

True conservation of natural resources does not mean hoarding. It means wise use in such a way that the greatest immediate production or benefits will be derived without depleting the basic resources themselves. A sound conservation program results in increased *production* from and *improvement* of resources, both at the same time.

WATERSHED CONSERVATION IS COMPREHENSIVE

If we accept these definitions of "watershed" and "conservation," then true "watershed conservation" becomes a rather comprehensive undertaking. It involves the conservation, management, and use of all soil and water and all things that depend on them—trees, shrubs, grass crops, wildlife, fish, cultivated crops, livestock, and so on. It also includes proper construction and maintenance of roads, highways, railroads, culverts, bridges, dams, and levees. In addition, it includes adequate protection and proper management of cities and towns and their water supplies, sewage systems, and recreational facilities. And in many instances it includes the protection and management of factories, mines, oil wells, and other industrial plants to assure adequate water supplies and a proper disposal of wastes. It may include dredging, channel improvement, or bank protection for streams.

INTERDEPENDENCE OF WATERSHED RESOURCES

The way in which any one of these resources or developments is used or managed usually affects several of the others. For example, poor construction or maintenance of a road or highway may start gullying that seriously damages the crops and land of nearby farms and helps fill streams with mud which suffocates fish and contributes to floods downstream. The improper disposal of city sewage or factory wastes may not only destroy much of the water life of a stream but threaten the health and recreational facilities of people downstream. Poor farming may lead to erosion that affects the entire economic life of a community and heightens flood crests. The improper cutting or burning of a forest may deplete or destroy the wildlife that resided there and lead to heavy siltation and floods on the stream below. Many other examples might be given.

A true watershed conservation program must take into account each patch of land and the plants and animals that live on it, each rivulet, pond or stream, each man-made structure, and every activity of the entire area.

WATERSHED CONSERVATION HAS PROVED SOUND

Actually, the upstream watershed conservation concept is not something radically new calling for a recasting of the tried and proved soil and water management technologies built up through the years. The National Forest Acts of 1897 and 1911 recognized the relationship between forest cover, stream flow, flood control, navigation, and irrigation. The Conservation Commission created by President Theodore Roosevelt clearly set forth in its 1909 report the importance of soil and forest management in flood control and the improvement of the nation's rivers, and the Waterways Act of 1917 gave similar recognition.

From the time the present-day programs of soil and water conservation began to get under way, the watershed, especially small local watersheds on upstream tributaries, was accepted as the basic unit in which to deal with soil erosion and related land use problems. The Soil Conservation Service from its earliest days stressed the importance of treating entire tributary watersheds in its work with farmers and ranchers. Its erosion-control demonstration projects, which preceded today's soil conservation districts, were mainly on a watershed basis.

The soundness of this approach has been confirmed by subsequent surveys, watershed conservation planning and treatment, and results of work that has been done. The Flood Control Act of 1936 and subsequent legislation have given further stimulus to soil and water conservation activities on the watershed basis.

Meanwhile, it remained for the soil conservation districts, which farmers and ranchers started organizing in 1937 under state laws, to set the pattern for the local-state-federal partnership concept in carrying out the nation's soil and water conservation program. These farmer-managed local units of state government have demonstrated from one end of the country to the other that the job can be done most effectively by landowners, community interests, and assisting governmental agencies working together at the local level.

THE WATERSHED A PHYSICAL UNIT

The laws of Nature govern the effective conservation and development of our land and water resources. These laws are not limited by the boundaries of a valley authority, a conservancy district, or a watershed boundary.

A watershed is generally considered to be the geographic area of overland drainage that contributes waters to the flow of a particular stream at a chosen point. It is a "water-collecting" and "water-handling" unit, a topographic entity which is usually surrounded by other entities of the same nature.

A great river basin consisting of an entire region drained by a major continental river and its tributaries is a comprehensive mass of variable facts, but the watersheds within the basin are frequently small and homogeneous enough to let us gather all the facts, correlate them, understand the applicable laws, and intelligently design and build successful conservation developments. We cannot do an intelligent basin-wide job until we understand the functioning of the watersheds within the basin.

The drainage area is a natural unit in the important runoff phase of the hydrologic cycle. It should be noted, however, that other phases such as evaporation, rainfall, and the occurrence of ground water do not necessarily follow drainage-area boundaries.

Water conservation programs may be aimed at conserving energy, as in reducing floods, or generating hydroelectric power, both of which generally aid in increasing the minimum stream flow; or they may be aimed at conserving materials, such as programs for reduction of silt load. Soil conservation programs are aimed primarily at conserving material through preventing physical loss of soil and fertility, and toward maintaining high crop yields.

Soil and water conservation programs that will stand the test of time require decisions based on facts on the physical situation. Getting the facts, therefore, is fundamental to every conservation program. To enable good program planning, fact collection should be as complete as we can make it. The cost of gathering the basic data on water and soil resources is small in comparison with project costs but only the facts can enable design in compliance with Nature's laws.

There are two general kinds of fact collection: recurring and non-recurring. For things that change rapidly we need extended programs of repeated measurements.

WATER RESOURCES FACTS

Since water resources are renewable, they require extensive collection of recurring measurements. In a particular region, there is need for long-time recording of intensity and duration of precipitation and for data on the character of the more intense rainstorms. These are intimately related to erosion and flood problems.

Meteorologic data are usually available over a longer period of time than other hydrologic data. The cost of collection of precipitation data is comparatively low. Frequently long-time precipitation records are highly valuable in extending stream-flow records or other records which are available in more detail but for a shorter or interrupted period of time.

Stream-gauging within the watershed is essential for estimation of sediment transport as well as for design of water projects. Closely related to stream-flow gauging is the measurement of sediment transported in the streams, for sediment concentrations must be correlated with the volume of stream discharge to learn the total quantities of sediment transported. A fairly extensive program of stream-flow gauging has been developed in this country since the turn of the century by the United States Geological Survey.

LAND RESOURCES FACTS

Changes in the land are less rapid than those that take place in streams, and data need not be obtained as often. For example, the frequency of soil mapping may be determined by the development of improved classifications rather than by changes in the soil. Measurements of the soil resources that are necessary to the planning of any watershed program include mapping of the distribution of soils, slopes, and erosion; studies of the character of the soils in the basin; investigation of subsoil conditions; and identification of sediment sources, either by inspection of the land or by analysis of accumulated sediments.

One method of determining the rate of erosion and the amount of sediment which is being transferred from the land into the river waterways is by measurement of sediment deposits in reservoirs.

FACTS ON HUMAN ACTIVITIES

Collecting data on human activities in the watershed is much like market research. It is necessary to determine present and future demands that may be placed on the resources available, such as demands for food and fiber and for industrial products. If, for example, it were anticipated that population would dwindle, it would follow that less intensive cultivation would be required, and less intensive development within any particular watershed would be expected where the local conditions were exceptional.

Many economic and human aspects need to be evaluated. Do the people in the watershed have the capital necessary for the completion of the proposed development? Have they learned to desire the contemplated developments? Is their desire or need for immediate cash crops greater than their desire for long-term improvements of their conditions? What proportion of the farms in the watershed are occupied by owners? What are the customs of the area that may make it difficult to initiate the projects under consideration?

The avowed purpose of the soil conservation movement is the *most productive use of each acre of land in accordance with its capabilities*. In the arid regions of this country, it has become equally important to *make the most productive use of each gallon of water*. Here the presence of water is the major controlling factor in the capability of the land.

UNDERSTANDING THE FACTS

We learn Nature's laws from analysis of the facts. We cannot use the facts we gather unless we understand their significance. And frequently we cannot know what facts we need without attempting to interpret the data available.

In reservoir design, for example, the ratio of lake capacity to the watershed area is of paramount importance. Where an exorbitant rate of storage loss occurs, the watershed is probably too large for the lake. Even in cases where soil loss from the cultivated fields is reduced to the minimum, the presence of a disproportionately large watershed results in excessive sedimentation.

NATIONAL PROGRAM PLANNING

In our national action program, the most detailed and advanced planning at present is represented (a) in land programs by the conservation farm plan based on the concept of using every acre within its capability and treating every acre according to its needs, and (b) in water programs by multiple-purpose river basin plans such as those in the Tennessee Valley, Missouri and Columbia Basins, and Central Valley of California.

CORRELATION OF LAND AND WATER PLANNING

During the past several years, public recognition of the intimate relationship of land and water has increased rapidly. Technically trained men have always understood, of course, that use and treatment of watershed lands could substantially modify runoff characteristics, sediment loads, groundwater supply, and other hydrologic factors. These in turn could modify both planning requirements and design of major downstream works for river regulation. Conversely, downstream river works for flood control, irrigation, and drainage can materially increase the net acreage and yield of agricultural land.

FEATURES OF A WATERSHED PLAN

The watershed plan, in the opinion of those who have studied it most closely, is the tool needed to close the gap between conservation farm plans on the one hand and basin plans for management of large rivers on the other hand. The watershed plan is basically a water management plan. Although varying in scope, content, and degree of detail to fit an infinite variety of local conditions, it could be described as having the following salient features:

1. A map showing the water management measures needed in the intermediate zone between those required (a) primarily for on-the-farm purposes, which can be installed by landowners and operators with some technical assistance and financial aid, and (b) major river regulation measures which require complex engineering planning and are designed to produce far-reaching benefits such as irrigation of desert lands, power, navigation, and flood protection for large urban areas. A watershed plan, thus, would not show individual terrace systems, farm pond locations, or land treatment measures of the type ordinarily shown on farm conservation plans. Nor would it show, because it would not cover such areas, main stream channel improvements such as impounding reservoirs, levees, river channel improvements, main irrigation distribution canals, or similar features shown on river basin plans. It would show, however, for areas larger than individual farms, all the water management and sediment control measures needed and economically justified between terrace outlets or farm boundaries on the one hand and major river channels on the other hand. This would include such measures as: (a) major gully stabilization by structures and vegetative plantings, (b) diversion ditches and dikes to collect runoff into controlled channels, (c) small flood-water-retarding structures where local flood protection is needed, and including storage within these structures or in separate structures, where justified, for irrigation of small local areas, domestic and small community water supplies, and recreation, (d) streambank and grade stabilization where needed on branches, creeks, and tributaries of major rivers, (e) interfarm drainage canals tributary to major outlets, (f) floodways to take excess flow across wide flood plains to main river channels, (g) erosion control and water management measures along highways, railroads, and other non-farm developments, and (h) desilting and debris basins to control sediment until erosion can be controlled effectively at its source.

2. The plan would include a map showing physical land conditions based on the techniques of soil conservation surveys and the land capability classification to serve as a guide to the planning of land use adjustments and application of treatment measures on individual farms and ranches.

3. The map would be accompanied by a report describing the pertinent physical features of the area, the land and water problems, the opportunities for their correction, the increases that could be expected in agricultural production as well as other benefits that would accrue by regulation of runoff, better distribution of available water for beneficial uses, disposal of excess water, and control of erosion required beyond that incident to

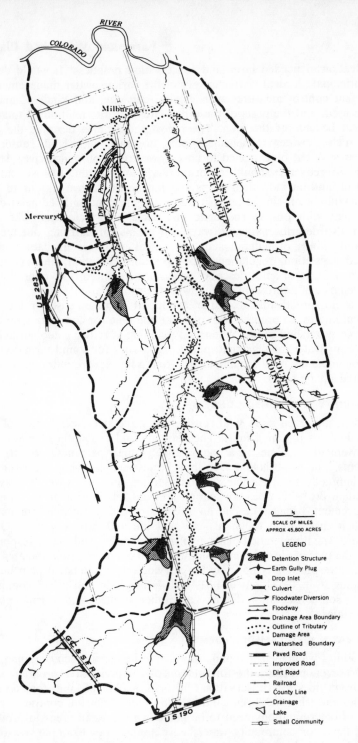

FIGURE 169. Flood-water-retarding structures and other water management measures planned for the Deep Creek Watershed, a
tributary of the Colorado River of Texas.
(*Soil Conservation Service*)

application of needed farm-land conservation practices. It would describe the principal physical characteristics of the various water management and sediment control measures such as size, capacity, and kinds of materials to be used, and the costs of these measures and the relation of total costs to total benefits of the plan. The report should also describe the effects that such a water management plan, together with land conservation measures, might be expected to have downstream on major river developments. Moreover, it should set forth criteria for planning the use and treatment of land on individual farms and ranches in such a way as to secure the maximum off-site benefits in water management and sediment control consistent with on-site economic and social considerations. The report might also describe available ways and means for carrying out the plan, including kinds of federal, state, and local resources available and any needed legislation, regulations, appropriations, taxation, and cooperative agreements. It should describe provisions required for operation and maintenance of improvements following their installation.

It is not practicable from the standpoint of time, cost, or the extent of local interest to prepare such plans at one time for complete river basins or large watershed areas. Watershed planning is rather a tool to aid local people for water management, plus a framework for sound farm conservation planning on areas ranging in size from a few square miles up to several hundred square miles.

COMMUNITY WATERSHED CONCEPT

Another, and even more vital consideration, dictates the selection of small watersheds as planning units. The planning and execution of major basin improvements is done by a comparatively small percentage of the basin residents. The result is that even though most people living in a river basin may indirectly receive some resulting service such as power, the average individual probably does not feel an intimate relationship to the works of improvement, because he had no direct part in their accomplishment, nor did their installation touch his personal life and private affairs. On the contrary, small watershed plans involve cooperation and major responsibility on the part of almost every landowner and operator within the area.

Major responsibility not only for carrying out a watershed plan but also for aiding in its development rests with farm group and urban community leaders, soil conservation districts, and other agencies and instrumentalities of the states.

RIVER BASIN PROGRAM DEVELOPMENT

Community watershed planning, and action based on such planning, does not, however, preclude the formulation of comprehensive programs along river basin lines for conservation and management of land, forests, grass, wildlife, and what has been called "little waters." On the contrary, certain kinds of determinations need to be made in river basin areas to provide a sound basis for community watershed planning. For example, reasonable determinations should be made of the aggregate effect on main stream flow and the need for its regulation as a result of water management in all community watersheds tributary thereto. The potential effects of watershed treatment on silting of main stem reservoirs should be determined. Reasonable answers to these and similar questions can be obtained through well-known sampling procedures involving watershed planning on only a small proportion of the total river basin area.

Moreover, the general nature and scope, as well as the potential cost, of water management up to the farm boundary should be determined by river basins. Ultimately, public investment in this aspect of water management may equal or exceed public investment in water management on main stem rivers. Even though management of little waters is at least 20 years behind the regulation of major streams, the aggregate values affected by or inherent in little waters may equal or exceed that of major rivers. For example, river basin and watershed surveys have indicated that as much as 50 per cent of all agricultural flood damages may occur upstream from main stem flood plains. Remaining potentialities for enhancement of agricultural production by flood control, irrigation, and drainage may be greater on the large aggregate acreage along small streams than on large streams. It is, therefore, proper and necessary that water management program formation should be carried out along river basin lines. But community watershed planning and small watershed management in more critical areas cannot wait until river basin program development is completed.

REFERENCES

1. Brown, C. B. 1952. *Planning the watershed.* Jour. Soil and Water Cons., 7(1): 16-21.
2. ———. 1953. *Flood prevention through watershed planning.* Agr. Engin., 34(3): 159-162, 167.
3. Duley, F. L., and Domingo, C. E. 1949. *Effect of grass on intake of water.* Neb. Agr. Expt. Sta. Tech. Bull. 159.
4. Fletcher, P. W. 1952. *The hydraulic function of forest soils in watershed management.* Jour. Forestry, 50(5): 359-362.
5. Hudson, H. E., and Stall, J. B. 1952. *The watershed—using it as a basis for soil and water conservation—getting the facts through surveys and investigations.* Jour. Soil and Water Cons., 7(1): 11-15.
6. Humphrey, R. R. 1943. *A history of range use and its relation to soil and water losses on the Walla Walla River watershed.* Northwest Sci., 17(4): 82-87.
7. Kramer, P. J. 1952. *Plant and soil and water relations on the watershed.* Jour. Forestry, 60(2): 92-95.
8. Lassen, L., Lull, H. W., and Frank, B. 1952. *Some plant-soil-water relations in watershed management.* USDA Cir. 910.
9. Matson, H. 1952. *Soil and water management under the complete watershed program.* Agr. Engin., 33(10): 625-626.
10. Rothacher, J. S. 1953. *White Hollow watershed management: 15 years of progress in character of forest, runoff, and stream flow.* Jour. Forestry, 51(10): 731-738.
11. Smith, J. L., and Crabb, G. A. 1953. *Comparative analysis of hydrographs from storms on a watershed under timber and clear-cut conditions.* Mich. Agr. Expt. Sta. Quart. Bull. 35(4): 489-502.
12. Wilm, H. G. 1951. *Watershed management and flood control surveys.* Jour. Forestry, 49(7): 511-513.

25

The Conservation Movement

The soil conservation movement in America is still young. It is only about 20 years old—yet phenomenal progress has been made in that short time.

Basic conservation plans have been developed for about one-fifth of the nation's farms. More than 2,500 soil conservation districts have been organized. They blanket 76 per cent of the country's agricultural land and include more than 80 per cent of all farms in the nation.

Equally important is the progress that has been made in the evolution of the concept of soil conservation and the conservation objective. The original objective was to overcome the tragic erosion menace to American land. It had to be that way. Gradually, during the last twenty years the concept was broadened until today the objective is to use each acre of agricultural land for the purpose for which it is best suited and treat it in accordance with its needs for protection and improvement.

Soil conservation has come to mean proper land use, protecting the land against all forms of soil deterioration, rebuilding eroded soil, conserving moisture for crop use, proper agricultural drainage and irrigation where needed, building up soil fertility, and increasing yields and farm income—all at the

TABLE 90. Major soil and water conservation practices needed and those applied (national totals, July 1, 1954)[a]

Practices	Unit	Current needs All land	On the land SCD-Coop.
CROPLAND			
Contour farming	Acres	118,764,524	28,686,930
Cover cropping	Acres	64,909,713	13,026,851
Stubble mulching	Acres	111,435,393	29,523,163
Strip cropping	Acres	61,852,728	8,389,187
GRASSLAND			
Proper use	Acres	337,637,741	71,647,598
Deferred grazing	Acres	101,112,369	16,460,089
Rotation grazing	Acres	85,985,429	22,046,979
Pasture seeding	Acres	70,307,605	16,088,875
Range seeding	Acres	23,960,693	2,263,222
WOODLAND			
Stand improvement	Acres	117,348,614	9,424,474
Tree planting	Acres	24,896,047	1,548,850
Windbreak planting	Miles	262,663	18,390
Woodland protection	Acres	168,546,674	26,701,877
WILDLIFE AREAS			
Hedgerow planting	L. F.[b]	943,984,752	69,966,988
Marsh improvement	Acres	2,796,587	68,235
Wildlife area improvement	Acres	11,257,656	2,472,650
DRAINAGE OPERATIONS			
Farm drainage	Acres	65,734,946	10,270,078
Aquatic drainage	Acres	269,678	19,295
Open drains	Miles	1,008,811	131,772
Closed drains	Miles	1,339,215	43,390
IRRIGATION IMPROVEMENT			
Farm irrigation systems	Number	376,180	57,191
Irrigation land leveling	Acres	11,741,146	2,340,698
Irrigation water management	Acres	17,003,335	1,185,514
ONE OR MORE LAND USES			
Terracing	Miles	5,319,662	932,318
Diversion construction	Miles	409,059	47,857
Pond construction	Number	1,381,909	425,482
Water spreading[c]	Acres	3,304,387	449,934
Waterway development	Acres	4,389,379	670,855
Land clearing	Acres	29,722,430	3,714,804

[a] Supplied by the Soil Conservation Service.
[b] Linear feet.
[c] Includes Great Plains, and West Service Areas.

same time. In short, soil conservation is nothing more than a good soil management program.

Modern conservation farming involves increasing soil productivity and raising the standard of farm living for today, tomorrow, and for posterity. It combines the objective of national welfare with better living for the people who work the land. It has come to mean efficient, abundant production on a sustained basis.

Significant progress has already been made through the conservation movement in America. Yet, this is no time to rest on our laurels. The job is too big.

The demands on agriculture today are greater than they ever have been. The need for greater production is immediate, and it will be enduring. It will grow progressively over the years. The population in the United States is growing at the rate of 2½ million persons per year. Our average life span has reached 67 years. There will be more of us to feed, clothe, and shelter for a long time to come. At the current rate of population increase, the demand on agriculture by 1975 will be 20 to 25 per cent greater than current production.

We cannot look to new land to meet the increasing demands of the future. Instead, we will have to depend largely on increasing per-acre yields. We need to concentrate on increased yields on grassland and treeland as well as on cultivated land.

A quick look at historical crop yields in the United States is pertinent to the problem. Statistical records go back about 85 years. For the first 70 years of that period, average per-acre crop yields remained practically unchanged. Since 1940 there has been a sharp swing upward—average per-acre yields have gone up about 40 per cent.

FIGURE 170. Trends in population, acreage of cropland, and farm output in the United States.

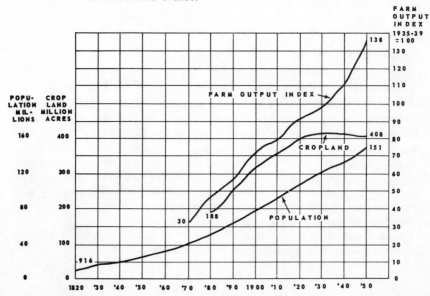

There were many technological improvements in farming during that first 70 years. Obviously, other factors were operating to offset these improvements. Unquestionably, a major offsetting factor was deterioration in the inherent fertility of our nation's soils. The advantages from technological improvements were offset by soil deterioration.

Most of the gain in the last 15 years has resulted from mechanization, use of improved crop varieties such as hybrid corn, control of crop pests, improved land use, and better soil and water management, including the increased use of fertilizer and lime. Increased soil productivity has been achieved on many farms, but not sufficiently to offset soil deterioration on other farms.

There are many farms throughout the country where erosion is still exacting a heavy toll from our soil resources. On even more farms soil fertility is still on the downgrade. On our most productive land, in the Midwest and Great Plains for example, exploitation systems of farming have been followed on many farms ever since the land was broken. Much of the soil humus has been lost. The inherent fertility of the soil has declined continuously and is still going down.

Many of these soils, of course, are still productive. The point is that they are not as productive as they once were, nor as productive as they can be. We have available the technology to manage many of these soils so as to build up and maintain their productivity. The problem is to get that technology into widespread use.

PRACTICES WORK BEST IN COMBINATIONS

The concept of soil conservation used in this discussion means applying the necessary practices on a farm to increase production and to build up soil productivity, both at the same time. It means making soils yield abundantly year in and year out for an indefinite period. It means rebuilding strength in the land.

This is the biggest point in the concept: You can conserve soil without improving it, but *you cannot build soil up without conserving it*. Soil is like a living thing. Feed it right and treat it right, and it grows like any living thing—and produces more while it is growing.

There is more to conservation farming than controlling erosion. This type of farming involves putting into use on the land the combinations of good practices we now have or that research can discover for us. Soil seldom can be made to produce at its full capacity by using a single improvement practice. The combinations are different in different areas—and on different kinds of soil. They may vary widely from farm to farm and from field to field.

The point to emphasize is that good practices used in the right combination create interactions that give an added boost to production. One good practice may be beneficial, but the advantages often pyramid when several good ones are used in the right combination. The reaction is much the same as vigor in hybrid corn.

This principle can be described best with an illustration of corn growing in the South. Corn yields always had been low in the South—until a few years back they never averaged more than 20 bushels per acre. For years, farmers and scientists tried one new practice after another. But they couldn't get corn yields to go up much. They tried corn hybrids. They tried using more fertilizer. They tried increasing the stand. They tried first one thing and then another, but without much success.

In 1944, they changed their approach. Instead of testing first one practice, and then another, and then still another—they tried several of them all at once. They tried combinations of practices and found some that hit the "jack-pot." Corn yields jumped from 20 bushels to 80 bushels per acre.

Since this discovery, thousands of southern farmers have adopted these new combinations of practices. Consequently, average corn yields have been doubled in some southern states.

OUR PRODUCTION POTENTIALS

There is plenty of evidence throughout the country that we have not yet put into use all of the best combinations. Several studies aimed at estimating agriculture's maximum production capacity are under way. Preliminary results from these studies indicate that, with the best combinations of known practices put into use on all farms, production could be increased from 60 to 75 per cent. The studies indicate, for instance, that average corn and cotton yields in the United States could be increased about 75 per cent. The potential for small grain and soybeans does not appear to be quite that high, but for hay and pasture it appears that we could double production through grassland improvement.

If we expect to maintain the strong national economy required for world leadership, if we expect to feed—and feed well—the millions of new Americans that will be added to our population in the years ahead, if we expect to supply the growing demands of industry with products from the land—there is no alternative but to raise production. We must apply on our farms and ranches all the technology that modern science has to offer—all we have now plus all we can get through additional research.

There are two points to be made about estimates of our maximum potential capacity to produce. First, it is based on present knowledge. It does not take into account new technology to come from future research. Second, the potentials are for ideal conditions. They assume the application of the best known combinations of practices for each farm and for each crop, and top-level management for each acre of every farm.

Obviously, we will never realize this ideal. Yet, it is completely within the realm of practicality to greatly expand our capacity to produce by making better use of technology now available. This is demonstrated by the difference between what the average farmer is doing and what the best farmers are doing. The best farmers in all parts of the country are making their soils produce about double that of the average farmer's.

The job ahead is to narrow that gap. We may not be able to close it, but we need to do everything possible to narrow it. To speed up the use of improved technology is the biggest challenge facing agriculture today. How well we succeed on that job will have a vital bearing on America's future capacity to produce food.

DETERMINING BENEFITS OF SOIL CONSERVATION

Costs and returns from soil conservation increase as more farmers become interested in adopting needed practices. A few farmers may apply more conservation measures because they believe they should conserve the soil for future generations. Most, however, are interested in land management from the economic standpoint. They prefer to adopt conservation practices only to the point where net income can be maximized for a certain period of time. In many cases, these farmers want to know how the proposed changes will affect farm organization and income before they adopt them.

Costs and returns from conservation measures vary according to the amount applied. Controlled experiments and data from actual farms do not always give the desired economic information. Direct benefits from soil conservation practices are often considerably different from the indirect benefits. Economic returns from the short-time point of view are usually different from the benefits over a longer period of time. Conclusions regarding economic benefits are also influenced by the methods of measurement.

DIFFERENT DEGREES OF SOIL CONSERVATION POSSIBLE

Potential returns from additional soil conservation practices are difficult to calculate in simple terms, because conservation farming is a matter of degree. Different levels are possible on many farms because of the number of practices recommended. For example, some farmers follow a good rotation, but fail to adopt the mechanical practices recommended for their farms. Others apply adequate amounts of lime and fertilizer on the cropland, but continue to follow soil-depleting practices. Different levels of conservation farming exist because of differences in the intensity of application. For example, some farmers apply larger amounts of lime and fertilizer than others. Considerable variation often exists in the amount of meadow crops raised in the rotation.

Since conservation farming is a matter of degree, economic considerations depend upon the objectives to be accomplished. One objective might be to manage land resources so that erosion losses would be zero. Another objective might be to increase the productivity of the soil and maintain it at some previous level. In some cases, the goal might be to maintain soil productivity at the present level. For some soils, the goal might be depletion to lower levels before stabilizing productivity. Additional conservation practices might also be applied as long as marginal costs did not exceed marginal revenues. Some of these goals would require using larger areas for permanent pasture and woods than others. They might also require a high percentage of meadow crops on certain soil types.

The relationship between conservation farming and net farm income is illustrated in Figure 171. This chart shows that the amount of soil conservation practices applied to any farm may vary from small to extremely large amounts (represented by O and Y). As additional amounts of soil conservation are added, net income increases up to a certain point (marked M) and then declines. This situation occurs because all conservation practices may be applied to the point of diminishing returns. For example, fertilizer and lime can be applied in varying amounts until marginal costs are greater than marginal revenue. Meadow crops may be increased to the point where farm income actually declines, especially on farms where the additional forage is used as residue or fed to inefficient livestock. Contour strips could be made so narrow that the additional benefits did not pay for the additional costs and inconveniences. Tile lines can be spaced so closely that additional amounts do not pay for the extra costs.

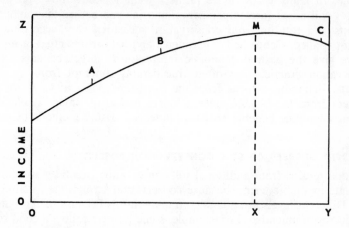

FIGURE 171. Relationship between soil conservation and farm income (2).

In Figure 171, comparisons between any two points with less than X units of conservation show that additional units increase profits. Applications between X and Y would produce less income because of diminishing returns from each additional unit. Comparisons between A and B would show certain differences in income from more soil conservation. Comparisons between A and M would show a greater difference in favor of larger amounts of conservation. Comparisons between M and C would actually show a slightly smaller income from the extremely high rates of application. Under actual farm conditions, the amount of soil conservation that will give maximum profits depends upon many factors. Some of the major ones will be considered in this discussion.

DATA FROM CONTROLLED EXPERIMENTS

Controlled experiments are usually conducted at an experiment station where all factors are presumably held constant, except the ones being studied. Station experiments are usually limited to the study of individual practices because of the complexity of measuring different degrees and intensity of soil conservation. Economic benefits from a complete soil conservation program are often difficult to evaluate from individual practice data. For example, returns from several practices seldom equal the sum of the practices taken individually. In some cases they may be more; in others they may be less. Most farmers are interested in the economics of applying several practices in combination. Few farmers adopt only one soil conservation practice.

Costs and returns of individual practices are often difficult to determine, even under controlled experiments. For example, it is difficult to calculate accurately how much sod waterways increase crop yields and income. However, they contribute to the ease of operating machinery on slopes subject to gully erosion. Returns from contour cropping are influenced by such factors as rotations, soil type, and past land management.

Controlled experiments are usually limited to a few soil types. Therefore, the data are often inadequate for many of the major soil associations. Some soils may be depleted in productivity and restored to previous levels without any permanent damage. In this case, costs of soil depletion are actually the costs of restoring the productivity to some previous level. In addition to these temporary losses, other costs must be considered when permanent damage results from erosion. These costs will vary according to soil type and amount of erosion. The economics of soil conservation are affected also by the rate of soil erosion and fertility depletion. Some soils may be depleted to unprofitable levels in a shorter period of time than others.

Individual practice data are often inadequate in showing the effects upon general farm organization. Fences may need changing to establish contour strip-cropping or longer rotations. Field arrangement may be improved on some farms by fencing on the contour. On other farms, additional lanes and watering facilities may be needed for livestock because new fields do not connect with the barnlot. Contour cultivation may produce longer rows on some farms, but on others point and crooked rows may interfere with the use of modern farm machinery. Data on rotations with more meadow crops do not show the additional costs for building and livestock to utilize more forage. Data on terracing seldom show the problems involved in maintaining terrace outlets. To protect these outlets on hog farms, the farmer usually has to fence the outlet or pasture the hogs in another field.

DATA FROM ACTUAL FARMS

Soil conservation data from actual farms usually cover a wider range of soil types and farming conditions than controlled experiments. Data from farms show the steps taken by farmers in adopting different conservation programs. Direct contacts with farmers provide information on the difficulties of establishing additional conservation. Farm records also show how certain farmers have adjusted their livestock program to utilize more forage crops.

Under actual farm conditions, data from different farms are often difficult to compare because of wide variations in size of farm, type of soil, kind of livestock, methods of management and applications of lime and fertilizer. Some farmers may not apply large amounts of fertilizer until grain yields decline to low levels. Therefore, high applications of fertilizer are not always correlated with high yields because of past land management. Data on previous farming practices are difficult to obtain because of changes in farm operations and inadequate records.

Records kept on the same farm over a long period of time often have the advantage of the same operator, land resources, and size of farm. However, many factors are not comparable for long periods of time. For example, the managerial ability of the farmer may improve from experience, but as he gets older he may work less for various reasons. The type and amount of livestock may vary over a period of time and still have no relationship to soil conservation. Over long periods of time, increases in farm income may result from technical changes in farming as well as from the addition of soil conservation practices. On many farms, income could have increased during the last 15 years by merely changing from horse to tractor power, or raising hybrid corn. Actual income figures seldom show how much resulted from additional conservation measures, and how much was due to other changes in farm organization.

DIRECT VERSUS INDIRECT BENEFITS

Direct benefits from soil conservation practices are often considerably different from the indirect benefits. Returns from rotations with more meadow crops depend upon whether the additional forage is used as residue, sold, or fed. For most soils, some meadow crops are needed in the rotation for maximum grain production. Under certain conditions, additional meadow crops not only increase forage production but also the total production. This relationship exists as long as reductions in acreage of grain are offset by sufficient increases in yields per acre. As long as total grain production increases when more meadows are raised, additional forage presents no problem. In this case hay can be utilized as residue and income will still be higher than it would be if less acres of hay were raised. This is due to the fact that a reduction in the acreage of meadows would decrease the production of both grain and forage.

The amount that grain yields must increase will depend upon (a) the present amount of meadow crops, (b) grain yields, and (c) proposed rotations. For example, grain yields per acre must increase one-third if total grain production is to remain the same under a rotation of corn, small grain, and two years of meadow compared with corn, small grain, and one year of meadow. If corn yields average 45 bushels per acre for the 3-year rotation, 60 bushels must be obtained under the 4-year rotation to make up for the reduction in corn acreage. In this case, an increase of 15 bushels per acre is needed to maintain total corn production. If corn yields average 75 bushels per acre for the 3-year rotation, 100 bushels per acre will be needed under the 4-year rotation to maintain total corn production. In this case, an increase of 25 bushels per acre is needed. The same proportional increase also would be needed for the small grain crops.

As more acreage of meadows is added to the rotation, a point is reached where total grain production declines. This occurs wherever yields per acre fail to increase fast enough to offset reductions in grain acreage. When total grain production declines as a result of adding more hay crops, net receipts often decline unless some income is obtained from forage crops. Economic returns from meadow crops will depend upon whether they are sold directly or fed to livestock. When fed, profits will depend upon the type and efficiency of the livestock kept, and the price of livestock and its products.

Returns from rotations with more meadow crops will be low if large amounts of hay and pasture are fed to inefficient livestock. On the other hand, additional meadow crops may increase net farm income on some farms when fed to high-producing animals. Returns from feeding more forage to dairy cows will be less in areas where the price of milk is low, and more in areas where the price is higher. The higher grain yields are, the higher the returns must be from hay and pasture to offset losses in income from fewer acres of grain. For example, forage fed to low-producing dairy cows might return as much per hour of labor as 45 bushels of corn per acre. But considerably higher-producing dairy cows would be needed to give the same return per hour of labor from forage as 75 bushels of corn per acre.

SHORT-TIME VERSUS LONG-TIME BENEFITS

The economics of soil conservation depend upon the period of time considered. In many cases returns from the short-time point of view are different from the benefits over a longer period of time. Individual farmers are usually interested in soil conservation from a shorter period of time than society. Therefore, the most economic application of practices for the farmer may not be the most desirable for society. Economic returns often vary during the transition period and the time the program is in full operation. Net income will increase on many farms after sufficient time has elapsed to recover additional costs for soil conservation and changes in farm organization. During the transition period, however, net income may actually decline on some farms. For example, costs of liming cropland are not recovered on many farms until a meadow crop can be produced and marketed through livestock. Several years are usually required before the benefits of permanent pasture improvement are fully realized.

Higher grain yields from rotations cannot be expected until better meadows are raised and larger residues returned or higher rates of fertilizer are used. In the meantime, total grain production may decline because of reduction in grain acreage, and necessary adjustments are made in farm organization. Several years may be required before economic gains from terracing equal the cost of construction. Fencing woods against livestock and planting trees will have little effect on increasing immediate farm income. Concrete structures may greatly increase cash outlays the year they are made. Expenditures for housing additional livestock cannot be recovered as quickly when new buildings are constructed as they can when present ones need only minor repairs.

The economics of conservation farming are difficult to determine over a period of years because of changes in prices. Different price relationships produce different costs and returns for soil conservation practices. For example, if the cost of lime and fertilizer increases relative to product prices and other farm costs, profits will be maximized by using less of these factors of production. Likewise, if costs of these two factors decline relative to other expenses, profits will be minimized by using more of these factors and less of others. Price relationships often change over a period of time. For example, in 1932 only 338 pounds of milk were required to give the same gross receipts as 100 pounds of pork. But in 1945-49 this relationship changed so that 486 pounds of milk (in Ohio) were required to equal the price of 100 pounds of pork. When the price of hogs increases relative to milk, profits might be increased on some farms by raising more grain and less hay, provided adequate soil conservation practices are employed. When the price of milk increases relative to hogs, profits might be maximized by raising more meadow and less grain crops. Returns from soil conservation practices are difficult to calculate for the agricultural industry as a whole. Over a period of time, if too many farmers kept more dairy cows to utilize additional forage, the price of milk would probably decline to unprofitable levels for many producers.

RETURNS DEPEND UPON UNITS OF MEASUREMENT

Economic benefits of soil conservation depend upon whether measurements are made in terms of (a) income per farm, or (b) income per hour of man labor. More meadow crops may increase net income on many farms, the amount depending upon how the additional forage is utilized. On some farms, this increase may be accomplished with more efficient use of labor. In such cases, the farmer would not only increase his total income but he would also increase the return per hour for his labor.

In some cases, more meadow crops in the rotation may increase net income per farm but more labor would be required to care for the additional livestock. Less grain and more hay would increase total income on these farms, but returns per hour of man labor would be less. In other words, total income would increase because the farmer worked harder although he received less per hour for his labor. This situation occurs whenever forage crops produce less income per hour of labor than grain. Inefficient livestock and high grain yields are often responsible for the smaller hourly returns from meadow crops. Maximum returns per hour of labor may not be as important as maximum returns per farm in cases where there is plenty of labor but small acreage of land.

RESULTS OF CONSERVATION FARMING IN ILLINOIS

A study of more than 100 farms located on slowly permeable soils in northeastern Illinois indicates that conservation measures are not only effective in maintaining soils for future use but they are also an important factor in increasing farm income. Investments to improve the land, such as those for limestone and fertilizer, will pay off in larger crop yields and in hay and pasture of higher quality. The same total amount of grain can be produced on fewer acres, and thus more acres can be shifted to hay and pasture. The shift will allow livestock-minded operators to have more roughage-consuming livestock, which in turn will make it possible to build up still further the productivity of the soil.

MORE EXPENSE BUT GREATER RETURNS

On 20 high-conservation farms on Clarence-Rowe soils, an average of 48 cents more per acre was spent yearly for lime and fertilizer during 1945-1947 than on 20 low-conservation farms. In addition, 21 per cent of the land on the high-conservation farms was in soil-protecting legumes, compared with 16 per cent on the low-conservation farms. Corn yielded 5 bushels more per acre on the high-conservation farms, though there was no difference in oat and soybean yields. More livestock and the higher corn yield caused the yearly net income to average $7.39 per acre higher on the high-conservation farms.

The farms in Illinois that scored highest in conservation practices followed a complete plan, including (a) testing and treating the soil, (b) using the land according to its capabilities, (c) using rotations with ample acreage of deep-rooted legumes, and (d) using proper water disposal practices, such as grass waterways, contouring, strip-cropping, terracing, and tile and open-ditch drainage where needed. These farms also tend to utilize forage crops through livestock.

Conservation plans do not necessarily increase earnings immediately, because considerable effort and money must usually be expended before positive results are achieved. The long-time benefits of conservation, however, are certain. Over a long-term period, conservation farms that have spent more money for soil and related improvements have more land in legumes and grasses, have higher crop yields, produce more and better quality hay and pasture, feed more livestock, have higher livestock production and returns, and secure larger farm incomes.

In all comparisons the high-conservation farms had higher livestock efficiency as measured by "returns per $100 of feed fed." It is believed that this is due to better-quality feed supplies—grain, hay, and pasture.

A number of studies in Wisconsin showed that crop and livestock production as well as net incomes were larger on farms where soil conservation systems of farming have been followed than on which less attention has been paid to soil conservation. The greater production usually is due to a combination of changes in land use and in crop production techniques. While it is important to measure the effect of soil-conserving programs for a farm as a whole, it is also important to analyze benefits and costs of some of the parts of the program. Such analysis is helpful in making soil-conserving plans for farms because in many instances one soil-conserving practice may be substituted in whole or in part for another practice.

ALERTNESS ESSENTIAL

It is the alert farmers who study their business and who apply sound soil, crop, and livestock management principles to their entire enterprises that maintain their operations on a sound and high-paying basis. This was illustrated in a study made by the University of Illinois.

A study of farm-account records of 240 similar central Illinois farms showed that the 72 highest-earning farms earned an average of $3,740 per farm annually more than the 72 lowest-earning farms during the ten years 1936-1945. Eight efficiency factors accounted for about three-fourths of this difference. These factors and their net effects on net farm earnings were: crop yields, accounting for 27.5 per cent of the difference; livestock production efficiency, 11.4 per cent; labor cost, 10.3 per cent; prices received for products sold, 8.5 per cent; the immediate profitableness of the crop system, 6.3 per cent; decreased cost of operating machinery, 6.0 per cent; savings on crops produced and fed to livestock on the farm, 3.0 per cent; and building and fencing cost, 2.2 per cent.

Important relationships were found among the eight efficiency factors having appreciable effects on net earnings. Thus, farms with high crop yields usually had large amounts of livestock and more efficient livestock production.

The rate of earnings was slightly larger on farms having a medium-sized business requiring about 24 months of man labor than on farms with smaller or larger businesses. Farms on which many hogs were produced had higher rates of earnings than farms with few hogs. This was due largely to the fact that corn-hog ratios were favorable to hog production during the ten years of the study.

Well-balanced farming, where each of the factors that have an appreciable effect on earnings was above average, led to the highest net farm earnings; three farms that were above average in all eight factors earned $3,760 a farm annually more than the average of all 240 farms included in the study. Twelve other farms below average in seven of the eight factors (none was below in all eight) earned $1,485 per farm less than the average of all farms. A farmer may do excellent work along one or two lines and still have low net farm earnings because he neglects other factors. The lowest-earning farm among all 240 farms was near the top in crop yields.

LIVESTOCK FARM COMPARED WITH GRAIN FARM

Since conservation farming in northeastern Illinois usually means planting fewer acres to corn and soybeans and using more for hay and pasture, Sauer and his associates compared two actual farms, one operated for many years as a grain farm and the other as a livestock farm. These farms were located on predominantly Clarence-Rowe soils in Vermillion County.

Farm A (the livestock farm) consisted of 186 acres, 157 tillable and the rest permanent pasture. Farm B (the grain farm) had 160 acres, 144 of which were tillable. The livestock farm was probably better managed during

TABLE 91. Crop yields per acre and total digestible nutrients per farm (average 1945–46) (1)

Crop	15 high-conservation-score farms	16 low-conservation-score farms
Corn grain, bushels	55	53
Corn silage, tons	11.6	8.3
Index of corn yield	109	90
Oats, bushels	47	39
Tobacco, pounds	1,700	1,501
Hay (harvested), tons	1.9	1.7
Grain, tons per farm	21.3	17
Total digestible nutrients, cropland, pounds	110,122	93,174

the period of study. However, the grain farm had a higher soil-productivity rating.

Land use. On the livestock farm half the tillable land, as an average, was planted to corn and soybeans each year from 1935 to 1947; on the grain farm 57 per cent was so planted. On both farms a good land use program required that less land be used for soil-depleting crops. On the livestock farm a larger proportion of the corn crop was fed to cattle and hogs than on the grain farm.

The livestock farm had an average of 23 per cent of its tillable land in sod, whereas only 14 per cent was in sod on the grain farm. This greater amount of hay and pasture on the livestock farm was utilized as roughage for livestock.

Crop yields. Corn yields averaged 56 bushels an acre on Farm A and only 40 bushels on Farm B, whereas average soybean yields for the 13 years were the same on both farms—22 bushels per acre—the livestock farm annually had 10 bushels more oats. The advantage of Farm A in corn and oat yields became greater with the passing of time, indicating that soil productivity had been better maintained on this farm.

Capital expenditures for land improvements. For the entire 13 years $3,819, or $20.53 per acre, was spent on the livestock farm for land improvements; whereas $2,511, or $15.69 per acre, was spent on the grain farm. On the livestock farm $7.22 per acre was spent for limestone and phosphate; on the grain farm $5.44 per acre was spent for this purpose.

Net income. For four of the first six years the grain farm had a higher net income per acre, but since 1942 the reverse has been true. Since 1935 the average yearly net income has been $5.80 per acre on the livestock farm and $4.17 on the grain farm. This long-time advantage in net income per acre and the increasing spread between the incomes from these two farms reflect the difference in the farming systems followed.

Anderson and McNall reported an increase in crop yield during the 2-year period of 1945-46 on 15 high-conservation-score farms over 16 low-conservation-score farms in southwestern Wisconsin. The average acre-yields of several crops on these two groups of farms are reported in Table 91.

Hay production was 30 per cent greater and egg production more than twice as large on the high-conservation-score group. Income from sheep, wool, lumber, fuelwood, posts, and grass seed was also larger on the high-scoring farms. The average gross livestock income was nearly $1,400 greater on this group of farms than on the low-score farms. On the other hand, income from tobacco was over $800, or 37 per cent, less on the high-score group of farms, because of 1.4 acres less of tobacco.

APPLICATION OF SOIL CONSERVATION PROGRAM

Most of the recommendations for conserving soil on the specific individual farms were followed quite closely on the high-scoring farms in the Wisconsin area. That is particularly true for such practices as contour strip-cropping, terracing, and crop rotations. The average conservation application rating for all parts of the soil conserving program on the high-scoring farms was higher than the rating for the low-score group. The comparative figures are given in Table 92.

TABLE 92. Per cent application of soil conservation practices, 1945–46 (1)

Items scored	15 high-conservation-score farms	16 low-conservation-score farms
Land use	64	11
Soil conserving crops	87	77
Pasture renovation	29	0
Lime	100	94
Fertilizer	92	34
Contour strip–cropping	98	0
Terracing	100	—

As may be noted in Table 93 these two groups of farms were comparable as to size of farm and quality of land as measured in terms of erosion hazards. They differ largely in the extent of application of soil conservation.

TABLE 93. Acres in farm and in crops, per cent of Class I, II, and III, land use capability index and soil conservation score (1)

	15 high-conservation-score farms	16 low-conservation-score farms
Acres in farm	135	136
Acres in crops	64	63
Per cent Class I, II, and III land	51	51
Land use capability index*	74	75
Conservation score†	87	43

* A weighted index based upon the proportion of Class I, II, III and IV land on each farm.
† A weighted index based on needs for and application of soil conserving practices, conversion of Class VI and VII land from cropland into pasture or woodland, soil conserving rotations, lime, commercial fertilizer, contour strip-cropping, terracing and pasture renovation.

Calculations made by Blosser from a 1952 study in eastern Ohio shows how disposition of crops affects net income from soil-conserving practices. Receipts, expenses, and net income were computed for groups of soil-depleting and soil-conserving practices assuming the following disposition of meadow crops: (a) forage fed to cows producing 5,000 and 9,000 pounds of milk for sale; (b) corn, wheat, and hay sold; and (c) corn and wheat sold, meadows plowed under. Net income was calculated in terms of income per farm, and income per hour of labor. These two measures of income show whether soil-conserving practices increase net returns because of heavier applications of labor or higher returns per hour.

SOIL-DEPLETING AND SOIL-CONSERVING FARMING

The depleting practices include the most common combination of depleting practices found on the farms surveyed: (a) red clover and timothy on first-year meadows; (b) timothy on second-year meadows; (c) no mechanical erosion-control practices; (d) an average annual application of 125 pounds of fertilizer per acre on the cropland; and (e) no permanent pasture improvement. This group of practices is referred to as soil-depleting farming.

The soil-conserving practices include a group of measures recommended by the local soil conservation district: (a) alfalfa-grass meadows; (b) contour strip-cropping; (c) an average annual application of 175 pounds of fertilizer per acre on the cropland; and (d) improvement of the permanent pasture. This combination of practices is referred to as soil-conserving farming.

NET INCOME WHEN FORAGE WAS FED TO COWS PRODUCING 5,000 POUNDS OF MILK

On the farms studied, the dairy cows provided a dependable market for forage and sufficient volume of business to utilize all available labor. This level of milk sales also represents the average per cow for the area where the study was made.

The data in Table 94 show the economics of conservation farming for a 120-acre dairy farm. In making these computations, crop production was determined from the land use and crop yields obtained from the survey records.

TABLE 94. Financial summary of a 120-acre farm with soil-depleting and soil-conserving farming (2)

Item	5,000 pounds milk per cow		9,000 pounds milk per cow	
	Depleting farming	Conserving farming	Depleting farming	Conserving farming
Capital investment	$11,100	$13,500	$11,600	$14,100
Receipts	3,900	5,534	5,186	7,140
Expenses	2,239	2,976	2,373	3,057
Labor income	1,661	2,558	2,813	4,083
Return per hour of labor	0.65	0.72	1.18	1.27
Labor required, hours	2,557	3,555	2,381	3,221

The low return per hour ($0.39) from the extra labor indicates that additional forage could not be used profitably. With low-producing dairy cows, most farmers cannot afford to hire labor to expand the dairy enterprise.

NET INCOME WHEN FORAGE WAS FED TO COWS PRODUCING 9,000 POUNDS OF MILK

When all forage was fed to cows averaging 9,000 pounds of milk, soil-conserving farming gave $1,270 more net income than soil-depleting farming. But 840 hours of additional labor and $2,500 more capital were required.

If no additional labor and capital were used, soil-conserving farming would produce $473 more net income than soil-depleting farming. Heavier feeding per cow on the 9,000-pound level reduced livestock numbers and total labor requirements slightly below the 5,000-pound level.

To minimize net income under soil-conserving farming would require 840 hours of additional labor above the 2,381 hours needed for soil-depleting farming. If this additional labor were used to care for cows producing 9,000 pounds of milk, net income would increase $797, or $0.95 per hour for the extra labor.

NET INCOME WHEN ALL CROPS WERE SOLD

This type of farming was not found on any of the 55 farms surveyed. Most farmers had no dependable market for hay. The study showed that if hay could have been sold, farming without livestock on 120 acres would not provide an adequate income for most full-time farmers. The volume of business would be too small, even under soil-conserving farming.

When all crops were assumed to be sold, soil-conserving farming gave $1,205 more net income than soil-depleting farming. A large part of this income resulted from a higher return per hour of labor. The remainder came from the application of 263 hours of additional labor with no increase in capital. Crop yields were assumed to be the same for crop as livestock farming, but heavier applications of lime and fertilizer were assumed on the crop farm to replace the elements lost by selling hay.

NET INCOME WHEN ALL MEADOW GROWTH WAS PLOWED UNDER

Although this type of farming was not found on any of the 55 farms, the following question might be asked, "How much would soil-conserving farming increase net income if all meadow growth were plowed under?" To make the necessary computations, grain yields for this type of farming were assumed to be the same as the actual ones on the 55 farms where livestock was raised. Calculations on this basis showed too small a volume of business for a satisfactory income when no livestock was kept.

When corn and wheat were the only source of income, soil-conserving farming gave $326 more net income than soil-depleting farming. Most of this increase came from a higher return per hour of labor since labor requirements were only 54 hours greater for soil-conserving farming and capital requirements were the same.

REFERENCES

1. Anderson, H. O., and McNall, P. E. 1951. *Soil conservation in southwestern Wisconsin.* Univ. Wis. Dept. Agr. Econ. 11.
2. Blosser, R. H. 1954. *How disposition of crops affect the economics of soil conservation.* Jour. Soil and Water Cons., 9(4): 169-174.
3. Mosher, M. L., and West, V. I. 1952. *Why some farmers earn so much more than others.* Ill. Agr. Expt. Sta. Bull. 558.
4. Sauer, E. L. 1947. *Economics of soil and water conservation: Effects of practices followed on farms in selected Illinois areas.* Thesis, Univ. Illinois.
5. ———, McGurk, J. L., and Norton, L. J. 1950. *Costs and benefits from soil conservation in northeastern Illinois.* Ill. Agr. Expt. Sta. Bull. 540.

AUTHOR INDEX

Abe, C., 481, 507
Ackerman, F. G., 113
Adams, W. R., 175
Agricole, 17, 26
Aikman, J. M., 378, 379
Albrecht, W. A., 175
Alderfer, R. B., 87, 98, 99, 111, 113, 175, 219
Aldous, S. E., 193
Alessi, J., 114
Alexander, L. T., 100
Allen, D. L., 193
Allen, O. N., 100, 101, 114
Allison, L. E., 113
Allred, B. W., 358
Alpeter, L. A., 365, 379
Anderson, H. O., 561, 564
Anderson, W. L., 193
Andrews, J. S., 175, 237
Appleman, M. D., 292
Archer, J. C., 237
Arend, J. L., 371, 379
Arnold, C. Y., 149, 156
Arnst, A., 380
Aronovici, V. S., 523, 524
Atkinson, H. B., 113
Atkinson, J. H., 99
Augustine, M. T., 175
Auten, J. T., 379
Aylesworth, J. W., 113
Ayres, C. Q., 24, 26

Bagnold, R. A., 83

Bailey, R. W., 35, 50
Baldridge, P. E., 115
Barger, O. L., 502, 507
Barnett, A. P., 175
Barnett, E., 114
Barre, R. D., 219
Barshad, I., 97, 99
Basiden, A. M., 139
Bateman, H. P., 275, 292
Bates, C. G., 268, 380
Baver, L. D., 88, 99, 111, 113, 156
Bay, C. E., 113
Beale, O. W., 101, 115, 176
Bear, F. E., 332
Beeson, K. C., 332
Bell, F. G., 175, 237, 475
Bender, C. B., 332
Bendixen, T. W., 524
Bennett, H. H., 25, 26, 35, 50, 219
Benton, G. S., 524
Berger, K. C., 291
Birkel, M. R., 102
Bishop, W. D., 156
Blackburn, R. T., 524
Blaney, H. F., 498, 507, 523, 524
Blaser, R. E., 332
Blosser, R. H., 562, 564
Bodman, G. B., 98, 100, 115, 524
Boller, G. A., 88, 99
Bolt, G. H., 99
Bolton, E. F., 113
Bond, R. M., 380
Bonner, J. C., 14, 26

565

Bonnier, C., 114
Borchert, J. R., 524
Borst, H. L., 23, 26, 70, 175, 291, 332
Bradley, W. F., 98, 99
Bray, R. H., 149, 156, 292
Breland, H. L., 292
Brian, R. C., 100
Briggs, L. J., 507
Brill, G. D., 115, 220
Brody, N. C., 332
Brown, C. B., 50, 547
Brown, P. E., 115
Brown, R. H., 50
Brown, R. L., 268
Browning, G. M., 113, 114, 115, 116, 275, 292
Bruner, F. H., 156
Bryant, J. C., 219
Bull, H., 380
Burkholder, P., 115
Burt, W. H., 193

Call, L. E., 268
Campbell, R. S., 358
Carleton, E. A., 176, 219, 220
Carreker, J. R., 175
Chapek, M. V., 99
Chapin, R. W., 220
Chepil, W. S., 83, 220, 268, 269
Childs, E. C., 524
Clements, F. E., 194
Cline, A. C., 380
Coile, T. S., 371, 372, 379
Coleman, C. S., 139
Coleman, O. T., 147, 156
Collins, R. E., 371, 379
Colman, E. A., 524
Colter, W. G., 116
Comber, N., 94, 99
Compton, L. V., 193
Conard, H. C., 23, 26
Cook, H. L., 70
Cook, M. A., 99
Cook, R. L., 146, 156
Coply, T. L., 175
Costello, D. F., 358
Cox, M. B., 23, 26, 175, 219, 237
Crabb, G. A., 547
Craddock, G. W., 50, 175
Criddle, W. D., 498, 507, 508
Crowley, R. B., 175
Cruikshank, J. W., 380
Cutler, I. B., 399

Dambach, C. A., 193, 194
Daniel, H. A., 175, 219, 237, 448, 455
Dantzler, W. D., 139
Davison, V. E., 194

Dean, L. A., 99
Deane, S., 12, 13, 26
Deer, L. E., 455
Demolin, A., 99
Derjaguin, B., 94, 99
Diebold, C. H., 365, 379, 380
Dieseker, E. G., 237
Diffie, B. W., 508
Dittmer, H. J., 147, 156
Domingo, C. E., 547
Donahue, R. L., 364, 365, 368, 379
Donnan, W. W., 523, 524
Dosch, E. F., 50
Dreibelbis, F. R., 498, 508
Duley, F. L., 20, 26, 175, 219, 312, 547
Dumont, I., 99
Dwyer, C. H., 508

Eargle, D. H., 50
Eby, C., 332
Edminster, F. C., 193, 194
Eisenmenger, W. S., 269
Ekern, P. C., 26, 70
Eliot, J., 12, 13, 26
Ellis, M. M., 44, 50
Ellison, L., 358
Ellison, O. T., 70
Ellison, W. D., 25, 26, 64, 70, 237
Elson, J., 99, 114
Elwell, H. M., 175, 237
Emerson, W. W., 97, 98, 99
Engibous, J. C., 114, 115
Englebert, L. E., 274, 292
Englehorn, A. J., 220, 268
Englehorn, C. L., 268
English, L., 149, 156
Evans, N. A., 508
Ewing, P. A., 507

Farnsworth, R. B., 111, 113
Finnell, H. H., 219, 268, 269
Fisher, W. L., 194
Fleming, H. K., 219
Fletcher, P. W., 547
Fly, C., 219
Ford, E. C., 50
Forrest, L., 175
Forsee, W. T., 146, 156
Forsling, C. L., 24, 26
Forsyth, W. G. C., 88, 99
Fortier, S., 508
Foster, A. B., 455
Frandsen, W. R., 358
Frank, B., 547
Free, E. E., 83
Free, G. R., 20, 24, 26, 175, 219, 220
Freese, C. R., 220
French, R. O., 99

Fuller, W. H., 99
Fulton, J. M., 113

Gahn, B. W., 50
Gardner, B. W., 50
Gardner, H. H., 475
Gardner, J. H., 508
Gardner, W., 508
Garton, J. E., 508
Gaskell, R. E., 522, 524
Geltzer, F. Y., 89, 94, 95, 99
Geohegan, M. J., 99, 100
Gerdel, R. W., 237
Germanova, V. N., 102
Gessel, S. P., 369, 379
Giesking, J. E., 96, 97, 100
Gilman, W. S., 100
Gilmour, C. M., 100, 114
Gish, R. E., 114
Glymph, L. M., 47, 50
Gohlston, L. E., 156
Gold, T. S., 26
Golze, A. R., 44, 50
Good, E. E., 194
Gottschalk, L. C., 50
Gouy, G., 100
Gray, J., 92, 102
Greathouse, G. A., 114
Greene, T. C., 115
Gribbins, M. F., 99
Griffin, R. A., 220
Grogger, H. E., 455
Guild, E. R., 269
Gustafson, A. F., 175, 219, 237

Hagan, R. M., 115
Hagin, J., 98, 100
Haig, I. T., 362, 363, 379
Haines, W. B., 94, 100
Haise, H. R., 114
Haley, D. E., 99
Hall, D. A., 100
Hall, R. C., 379
Hardwick, R. S., 13, 14, 15
Hardy, F., 100
Harmon, G. D., 13
Harper, H. J., 380
Harrington, J. F., 156
Harrold, L. L., 498, 508
Hauser, V. L., 508
Havis, L., 100, 114, 175
Haynes, J. L., 20, 26, 292
Hays, O. E., 20, 26, 175, 219
Heiberg, S. O., 365, 380
Helseth, O. S., 508
Hely, F. W., 114
Henderson, J., 194
Hendrick, R. M., 111, 113, 114

Hendricks, S. B., 96, 97, 100, 175
Hendrickson, B. H., 20, 26, 219, 332
Henin, S., 88, 99, 100
Henretty, L. B., 139
Hershberger, M. F., 524
Hester, J. B., 149, 156
Hicock, H. W., 363, 380
Hide, J. C., 114
Hill, H. O., 27
Hill, W. W., 374, 380
Hirsh, C. R., 380
Hockensmith, R. D., 139, 194, 455
Hodgdon, F. B., 101
Hogg, F. G., 318
Holtan, E. N., 292
Hoover, M. D., 380
Hopkins, E. S., 269
Hopp, H., 194
Horton, R. E., 70
Hudson, H. E., 547
Huggins, W. W., 220
Hughes, H. D., 332
Humphrey, R. R., 358, 547
Hurley, F. W., 139
Hyde, G. R., 380

Ichisaka, V., 149, 157
Ireland, H. A., 50
Israelson, O. W., 507

Jacobson, H. G. M., 156
Jamison, F. S., 508
Jamison, V. C., 114, 115, 524
Janes, B. E., 508
Jensen, C. V., 358
Jensen, J. S., 220
Jensen, L. R., 114
Jensen, M. E., 508
Johnson, J. R., 114
Johnson, P. R., 237
Johnson, W. C., 269, 312
Johnston, J. R., 27
Jones, J. P., 475
Jones, L. A., 524
Jones, W. W., 114
Jung, V. E., 100
Jordan, J. W., 97, 98, 100

Kaiser, V. G., 219
Kanivetz, I. I., 100
Kardos, L. T., 50
Kefauver, P. F., 17, 26
Kelly, J. B., 269
Keng, E. B., 350
Kidder, E. H., 175
Kirkham, D., 522, 524, 525
Kittredge, J., 368, 369, 380
Kojima, R. T., 100

Kolodny, L., 100
Koreneva, N. P., 100
Kramer, P. J., 547
Kroth, E. M., 100
Krusekopf, H. H., 23, 27, 175
Kucinsky, K. T., 269
Kurtz, L. T., 156, 292

Lamb, J., 175, 219, 220, 237
Langhan, W. H., 219
Larsen, J. A., 23, 27
Larson, W. E., 508
Lassarew, W., 99
Lassen, L., 547
Latham, E. E., 220
Lauritzen, C. W., 508
Laws, D., 114
Laws, J. O., 24, 27, 70
Leach, H. R., 70
Lee, D., 15
Leedy, D. L., 194
Leopold, A., 194
Ligon, W. S., 380
Lillard, H. J., 175
Lloyd, W. J., 369, 379
Locke, S. S., 380
Lowdermilk, W. C., 2, 10, 20, 23, 25
Lull, H. W., 547
Lunt, H. A., 148, 156, 364, 380
Lunt, H. J., 380
Luthin, J. N., 524
Lutz, J. E., 99, 100
Lutz, J. R., 175
Lyerly, P. J., 508
Lynd, J. Q., 146, 156

MacEwan, D. C. M., 98, 100
Maline, F. J., 83
Manegold, E., 94, 100
Mangun, P. H., 13
Manson, P. W., 524
Marsh, V., 358
Marshall, C. E., 100
Marshall, T. J., 524
Martin, J. P., 92, 101, 102, 111, 113, 114
Martin, W. P., 115, 116
Massey, W. F., 15, 17, 27
Mather, J. R., 508
Matson, H., 547
Mazurak, A. P., 101
McAtee, W. L., 194
McCall, A. G., 175, 237, 475
McCalla, T. M., 91, 101, 113, 114
McCallan, S. E. A., 116
McCollum, R. E., 150, 156
McCormick, J. F., 380
McGurk, J. L., 564
McHargue, J. S., 220

McHenry, J. R., 101, 114
McKinnon, F. S., 363, 380
McLaurin, J. T., 156
McNall, P. E., 561, 564
McNaught, K. J., 114
McVickar, M. H., 332
Mech, S. J., 508
Meginnis, H. G., 175
Mehring, A. L., 50
Meinger, O. E., 508
Melsted, S. W., 292
Merkle, F. G., 175
Metzger, W. H., 114
Meyer, L., 101
Midgley, A. R., 269
Mihara, Y., 26, 27, 70, 175
Milam, F. M., 113
Miles, I. E., 150, 156
Millar, C. E., 220
Miller, A. E., 508
Miller, H. W., 378, 380
Miller, R. D., 99
Miller, M. F., 22, 23, 27, 175, 176
Milne, R. A., 268
Mitscherlich, E. A., 149
Molina, J. S., 101
Moore, J. R., 139
Moorehouse, L. A., 15, 17, 27
Morgan, M. F., 148, 156, 380
Morin, K. V., 507
Mortensen, J. L., 113, 115
Moses, 5, 6
Mosher, M. L., 564
Mowry, D. T., 111, 113, 114
Muckenhirn, R. J., 219
Murray, W. G., 220, 237
Musgrave, G. W., 292
Myers, H. E., 101, 113
Myers, W. M., 332

Nagler, F. A., 516, 524
Neal, J. H., 523, 524
Neal, H. J., 20, 22, 27
Neal, O. R., 100, 220
Nebuchadnezzar, 3
Neher, D. D., 115
Nelson, R. A., 100
Nelson, W. L., 150, 156, 157
Nettles, V. F., 479, 508
Newman, A. S., 115
Nichols, M. L., 14, 27
Nicholson, H. H., 524
Nickell, L. G., 115
Norman, A. G., 101, 115
Norton, F. H., 101
Norton, L. J., 564
Norton, R. A., 275, 292
Nutt, G. B., 176

Nutting, P. G., 94, 101

O'Donnell, T., 524
Ohlrogge, A. J., 156
Olmstead, L. B., 115
O'Neal, A. M., 519, 523, 524
Osborn, B., 175, 356, 358

Page, J. B., 100, 102, 111, 115
Palmer, A. E., 269
Parker, F. W., 150, 156
Patzer, W. E., 365, 380
Pearlkamp, P. K., 115
Pearse, C. K., 175, 358
Pearson, G. A., 380
Pearson, R. W., 115, 524
Peech, M., 99, 149, 156
Peele, T. C., 101, 115, 175, 176
Peevy, W. J., 115
Pendleton, E. M., 16, 17, 27
Penman, H. L., 497, 498, 499, 508
Perry, E. A., 139
Perry, H. H., 138
Peter, A. M., 220
Peters, D. B., 115
Peterson, A., 274, 292
Peterson, J. B., 98, 101
Peterson, M. L., 332
Philips, M. W., 13
Pickard, G., 275, 292
Pickles, G. W., 524
Pierre, W. H., 115
Pine, W. H., 220
Plato, 12
Plummer, A. P., 358
Pope, J. B., 237
Potter, W. D., 237
Powers, W. L., 220
Purvis, E. R., 156

Ramser, C. E., 14, 423
Rasmussen, W. W., 517, 524
Raths, H. J., 423
Ree, W. O., 423
Reed, I. F., 524
Rennenkamp, V. von, 101
Renner, F. G., 358
Rennie, D. A., 94, 101
Retzer, J. L., 101, 115
Richards, S. J., 115
Rinne, D. A., 101
Rinne, F., 101
Roberts, E., 448, 455
Roberts, E. G., 371, 380
Robinson, D. O., 102
Rogers, H. T., 220
Rohwer, C., 507
Rost, C. O., 219, 524

Rothacher, J. S., 170, 176, 547
Rothe, J. H., 524
Rowe, P. B., 23, 27
Rubins, E. J., 99
Rubishov, A. B., 102
Rudakov, K. I., 102
Ruehrwein, R. A., 96, 98, 102, 111, 113, 115
Ruffin, E., 15, 27
Russell, E. W., 88, 102
Russell, J. C., 175, 312
Russell, M. B., 101, 114, 115
Ruzek, C. V., 220
Ryerson, G. E., 312
Rynasiewicz, J., 111, 115

Sakum, N., 99
Salter, R. M., 115
Sampson, A. W., 220
Samson, H., 97, 102
Sanderson, M., 498, 508
Sauer, E. L., 564
Savage, D. A., 358
Saveson, I. L., 524
Scarseth, G. D., 156, 271
Schaller, F. W., 111, 116
Schloesing, T., 94, 102
Schmidt, W. A., 149, 156
Schofield, R. K., 97, 102, 508
Scholz, H. F., 366, 380
Scoby, F. C., 507
Sell, O. E., 508
Seton, E. T., 194
Shantz, H. L., 507
Sharpe, C. F. S., 50
Shaulis, N. J., 175
Shear, G. M., 157
Shedd, C. K., 275, 292
Sherwood, L. V., 115
Shirk, H. G., 114
Shrinkhande, J. G., 102
Sideri, D. L., 89, 94, 98, 102
Sinclair, G. D., 220
Slater, C. S., 176, 219, 220, 524
Smith, D. D., 176, 220, 475
Smith, E. V., 194
Smith, F. B., 115
Smith, G. E., 290, 292
Smith, H. N., 358
Smith, J. L., 547
Smith, L. S., 508
Snead, V., 524
Snider, H. J., 292
Sorsby, N. J., 13, 14, 15, 27
Spaeth, J. N., 365, 380
Spaini, L. S., 101
Spillman, W. J., 17
Spurway, C. H., 149, 157

Sreenivas, S. L., 23, 27
Stall, J. B., 547
Stallings, J. H., 50, 70, 102, 115, 176, 220, 423, 475
Stauffer, R. S., 102, 116, 176, 220
Steele, J. G., 139, 194, 455
Stephenson, R. E., 88, 99, 220
Stirk, G. B., 524
Stockli, A., 102
Stoeckler, J. H., 380
Stoddard, H. L., 194
Strickland, E., 102
Strickling, E., 115
Stringfield, G. H., 292
Strohm, J., 292
Stuber, C., 100
Swaby, R. J., 102
Swanson, C. L. W., 50, 156, 176
Swingle, H. S., 194

Taylor, G. S., 111, 114, 115, 116
Tedrow, J. C. F., 524
Terman, G. L., 50
Thom, C., 116
Thom, H. C. S., 501, 507
Thomas, H. L., 220
Thompson, W. R., 332
Thornthwaite, C. W., 33, 35, 50, 497, 498, 508
Tower, H., 475
Truog, E., 100, 101, 114
Toynbee, A. J., 12, 27
Turk, L. M., 156
Turner, L. M., 380
Turner, R. C., 99
Tyulin, A. T., 94, 102

Udden, J. A., 83
Uhland, R. E., 220, 519, 525
Uhlrich, A., 157

Van Bavel, C. H. M., 116, 497, 498, 499, 500, 501, 502, 504, 509, 519, 522, 524, 525
Van Dersel, W. R., 194
Van Doren, C. A., 116, 175, 176
Van Doren, C. E., 269, 312

Van Vleit, R., 70
Varney, K. E., 269
Veneable, A. W., 27
Vessel, A. J., 139
Vilensky, D. G., 102

Waksman, S. A., 101, 102, 114
Wandell, H. H., 194
Ward, D. W., 96, 98, 102, 111, 113, 115
Wardsworth, M. E., 99
Warren, G. H., 92, 102
Watkins, T. R., 139
Weaver, J. E., 194
Webber, L. B., 113
Weeks, L. E., 116
Weir, W. W., 269
Welch, C. D., 150, 156, 157
Wellman, R. H., 113, 116
Wessel, C. J., 114
West, V. I., 564
Wester, R. E., 116
Westveld, R. H., 367, 368, 380
White, J. W., 116
White, W. N., 508
White, W. T., 358
Whitfield, C. J., 269, 312
Whitt, D. M., 176, 475
Wilde, S. A., 365, 366, 367, 380
Willard, C. J., 111, 115
Wilm, H. G., 547
Wilson, H. A., 116
Wilson, T. V., 499, 501, 509
Winters, E., 156
Wolf, B., 149, 157
Wolley, J. C., 220
Wollny, E., 18, 19, 20, 22, 27
Woodburn, R., 23, 26, 70, 102
Woodruff, N. P., 269
Woodward, S. M., 516, 524
Woolfolk, E. J., 358

Yarnell, D. L., 423
Yeatter, R. E., 194
Yoder, R. E., 111, 116, 237
Youngquist, C. V., 50

Zingg, A. W., 83, 220, 237, 268, 269, 475

TOPICAL INDEX

Aggregate, soil, 84
Alkali soils, 137
Associated land features, 135
Available moisture, 489
Available moisture capacity, 131, 489

Biologic balance, 178
Black alkali, 487

Capability classes, 426, 431
Capability groupings, 127
Climatological data, 483
Conservation benefits, 556
Conservation movement, 548-564
  soil conservation concept, 551
  production potentials, 552
  determining benefits, 553
    controlled experiments, 554
    actual farms, 555
  types of benefits, 556
Consumptive use of water, 480
Contour cultivation, 235
Contour farming, 404
Contour strip-cropping, 233, 471
Crop rotation, 474

Deferred grazing, 351
Deposition of soil by wind, 80-82
Depth of topsoil, 207-212
Detailed soil survey, 119
Development of waterways, 418
Diversion terraces, 399-400
Diversion waterways, 472

Drainage, 488, 510
Drainage benefits, 511
Drainage, farm, 510-523
  drainage improves land, 512
  source of precipitation, 513
  theory of drainage, 514
  drainage of irrigated land, 517
  permeability and drainage, 518
  water table, 522
  depth and spacing of drains, 523
Drainage strips, 471
Drain tile, 523
Drought, 502
Drought hazard, 478
Dune stabilization, 265

Ecology, 180
Effective depth of soil, 129
Effectiveness of range cover, 336
Erosion and soil productivity, 195-219
Erosion depletes soil fertility, 197-203, 207
Evaluating range forage, 354-356
Evapotranspiration, 497
Evapotranspiration rates, 498

Farm drainage, theory of, 514
Farm plan, 462, 463
Farm program planning, 456-475
  Technical Guide, 456
    purpose of, 457
    contents and use of, 457
    how to use, 458

Farm program planning, (*cont.*):
  strip-cropping, 469
  grass waterways, 472
  crop rotation, 474
Fertility erosion, 58, 60
Fertilize liberally, 274
Fertilize pastures, 321, 322, 328
Fertilizer and soil moisture, 289
Field strips, 471
Flocculation, 87
Forms of wind erosion, 75-76

Grassland farming, 313-332
Grass-lined waterways, 405
Grass waterways, 472
Grazing capacity, 345
Ground water, 515

History of soil conservation, 1-26
  in the Old World, 2-12
    Mesopotamia, 2-7
    Nile Valley, 2-7
    Holy Land, 5-7
    North Africa, 9-11
  in early American colonies, 12-13
  search for new methods, 16-18
  research in soil erosion, 18-25
  importance of plant cover recognized,
    23
  changing concepts, 24-25
Humus and soil aggregation, 93
Hydraulic characteristics of vegetation in
  waterways, 412-416
Hydraulic survey, 382

Infiltration, 535
Infiltration, effects of plant cover on, 168
Inherent fertility, 133
Interpretive soil groups, 126
Interpreting soil test results, 281
Irrigation, 476-507
  increases production, 477
  eliminates drought hazard, 478
  water requirements for, 480
    consumptive use, 480
  determining water use, 481
    from climatological data, 483
  water quality, 487
  saline soils, 487
  amount of water to apply, 489
  frequency of irrigation, 490
  how to apply water, 492
  determining when to irrigate in humid
    area, 495
    evapotranspiration methods, 497
  drought defined, 502
  controlling erosion on irrigated land,
    504

Irrigation requirements, 480
Irrigation, requirements of, 490
Irrigation, supplementary, 495

Judging land, 450

Land and water planning, 543
Land capability unit, 424
Land judging, 424, 448
Land judging contest, 452
Land, plants, and animals, interrelation-
    ships of, 177-193
  biologic balance, 180
  ecological principles applied to, 181
    land capability class, 182
    cropland, 183
    pasture land, 183
    woodland, 183
    wildlife land, 183
  wildlife in agriculture, 184
    birds, 185
    mammals, 185
    fish, 186
  wildlife requirements, 186-187
    food, 186
    cover, 187
    water, 187
  balance of land, cover, and water, 188
Land use capability, 424-447
  capability classes, 427
  land suited for cultivation, 427
  land not suited for cultivation, 431
  land judging, 448
    history of, 448
    how done, 450
  land use treatment, 452
  goal of land judging, 454
Land use and stream flow, 531

Mapping legends, 119
Mapping units, 425
Mechanics of soil aggregate formation,
    84-97
  aggregation process, 85-86
    flocculation, 87
    calcium and aggregation, 88
    clay and aggregation, 88-89
    humus and aggregation, 93-96
    iron hydroxide and aggregation, 89
    organic matter and aggregation,
      90-93
    polysaccharides and aggregation,
      85-86
    polyelectrolytes and aggregation,
      91-97
Mechanics of water erosion, 51-70
  falling raindrops, 54
  flowing surface water, 54

Mechanics of water erosion, (*cont.*):
  splash erosion process, 56-61
    fertility erosion, 58-59
    scour erosion, 61-68
    sheet erosion, 60-61
Mechanics of wind erosion, 71-82
  types of soil movement by wind, 72-75
    saltation, 72
    suspension, 73-74
    surface creep, 75
  forms of wind erosion, 75-76
    detrusion, 75
    effluxion, 75
    efflation, 76
    extrusion, 76
    abrasion, 76
  wind-erosion process, 76-82
    initiation of soil movement, 77-78
    transportation of soil, 78-80
    deposition of soil, 80-82
Muck land, 262
Mulch farming row crops, 270-291
  basic principles involved, 270-271
  wide row spacing, 274
  adjust fertilizer and plant population to available moisture, 274
  limit cultivation, 275
  use more than one hybrid, 275
  cheap nitrogen forces change, 276
  mulching and fertilizing eliminates need for crop rotation, 278
  soil test essential, 281-283
  seasonal hazard reduced by fertilizer, 283
  prescription fertilization, 284
  interplanting need not require more moisture, 288
  fertilizer and efficiency of soil moisture, 289-290

Open channel drains, 423
Organic soils, 134

Parallel-sided strips, 471
Pasture management, 313-332
  grassland agriculture needed, 314-315
  irrigated pastures, 316
  planned pasture program, 317
  balance pasture with livestock, 320
  renovate when necessary, 320
  lime and fertilize liberally, 321, 322, 328
  manage the grazing, 322
  rotation-pastures, 324
  mow brush and weeds, 324
  trash-mulch seeding, 325-328
  broadcast seeding, 328
  pastures in the South, 329

Percolation, 535
Permeability, 130, 518
Plant cover, 158-174
  function of, 158, 160
  developing action, 158
  holding action, 160
  effective weight, 160
  effect of cropping system on, 162-166
    aggregation, 166-168
    infiltration, 168-170
    fertilizer, 170-174
Plant tissue tests, 142
Polyelectrolytes, 96
Polysaccharides, 85, 86
Precipitation, source of, 513
Prescription fertilization, 284-287
Profile, soil, 129
Puddle erosion, 58

Range condition, 336, 345, 354-358
Range condition classes, 337, 367
Range condition classification, 343-345
Range management, 333-358
  graze properly, 335
  cover condition affects water absorption, 336
  range condition classes, 337
  effectiveness of plant cover, 338
  amount of cover required, 341
  range condition classification, 343
  range capacity, 345
  range condition, determination of, 345
  correct stocking important, 349
  adjust grazing load to forage production, 350
  reseeded ranges, 351
  facilities and enabling practices, 353
  evaluating range forage, 354
    excellent condition, 354
    good condition, 354
    fair condition, 355
    poor condition, 356
Range site, 467, 468
Reconnaissance soil survey, 119
River basin program, 546
Row-crop farming, 270

Saline soils, 137, 488
Saline soils, classes of, 137
Scour erosion, 61-68
Second-foot, 493
Sheet erosion, 60, 61
Shelterbelt and windbreaks, 192
Siphon tube, 192
Site index, 362-373
Site quality, 362
Soil aggregation, 166
Soil aggregation, mechanics of, 84-98

Soil as storage reservoir, 537
Soil blowing, 240
Soil capacity map, 443
Soil-conserving crops, 171
Soil-depleting crops, 171
Soil conditioners, 96
Soil erosion damages in the United States, 28-50
Soil erosion in Colonial United States, 12-26
Soil erosion in the Old World, 1-11
Soil erosion reduces productivity, 195-219
  depletes soil fertility, 197-200
  removes plant nutrients first, 200-206
  wind sorts out plant nutrients first, 203-206
  water sorts out nutrients, 206-207
  reduces depth of topsoil, 207-211
  reduces efficiency of fertilizer, 218-219
Soil-drainage classes, 132
Soil, effective depth of, 129
Soil fertility, determination of, 141
Soil groups, interpretative, 126
Soil mapping units, 119
Soil permeability, 130, 518
Soil profile, 453
Soil profile, characteristics of, 129
Soil reaction, 132
Soil series, 121
Soil structure, 103
Soil structure and crop yields, 110-111
Soil structure maintenance, 103-112
  cropping systems, 108-110
  humates, 103-105
  organic matter, 106
  soil conditioners, 111-113
Soil surveys, 117-138
  types of, 118-119
    detailed, 119
    reconnaissance, 119
  elements of soil survey, 119
    legend, 119
    mapping units, 119
    work plan, 119
  methods, 120
  interpretation, 122
Soil groupings, 126
Soil profile, 129-136
  characteristics of, 129-137
  effective depth of, 129
  available water capacity, 131-132
  permeability, 130
  texture, 130-132
  erosion, 136
  alkalinity, 137
  color, 137
  inherent fertility, 137

Soil survey interpretation, 122
Soil survey map legends, 119
Soil survey methods, 120
Soil survey objective, 118
Soil survey, types of, 118-119
Soil survey uses, 126
Soil survey work plan, 118, 119
Soil testing, 140-155
  chemical analysis of soil, 141
  plant tissue tests, 141, 142
  fertility tests, 141
  basic concepts, 142-145
  soil testing procedure, 148
    test data, 149
    good samples needed, 151
    sampling field, 152-153
    sampling tools, 153
  interpreting results, 146
  using soil testing data, 146
Soil testing procedures, 148-149
Soil tests, 146
Soil textural classes, 130
Soil type, 122
Soil water, 514
Soil water, kinds of, 514
Splash erosion, 56
Splash erosion process, 56-58
Standard soil survey, 119
Streambank management, 192
Stream flow, 532, 538
Straw spreaders, 300
Strip-cropping, 469
Strip-cropping, types of, 470
  contour strip-cropping, 471
  drainage strips, 471
  field strips, 471
  parallel-sided strips, 471
Stubble-mulch tillage, 293-312
  controls water erosion, 294
  increases yield, 297
  machinery requirements for, 304
  types of sub-surface tillers, 303
    for light stubble, 305
    for heavy stubble, 308
Sub-surface tillage, 298
Sub-surface tillers, 301, 305
Supplementary irrigation, 475
Surface flow control, 230
Surface water, 381
Surface water disposal system, 381-423
  hydrologic survey, 381
    analysis, 382
    computing peak flows, 382
    computing average rainfall, 383
    types of terraces, 391
  planning terracing system, 392-396
  terrace construction, 398
  diversion terraces, 399

Surface water disposal system, (*cont.*):
  contour farming, 404
  grass-lined waterways, 405
  plant cover, 412
  velocity distribution, 414
  development of waterways, 418
  constructing vegetated waterways, 420
  bank protection, 421
Summarizing soil test data, 149-151
Stubble-mulch equipment, 304
Stubble-mulch tillage, 292-312

Taking soil samples, 152-155
Technical Guide, 456
  use of, 458
Terracing, 231, 391
Terrace spacing, 394-396
Terrace systems, 392
Terrace, types of, 391
Textural classes of soil, 130
Theory of farm drainage, 514
Tile drains, 423
Tillage for wind-erosion control, 258-261
Trash-mulch seeding, 325-327
Tree, fitting to site, 377
Types of soil movement by wind, 72-75
Types of terraces, 391

Vegetated waterways, 420
Vegetated waterways, construction of, 420
Velocity distribution, 414

Water-erosion control, 221-236
  splash erosion, 221-230
  scour erosion, 230
  splash erosion control, 230
  control of surface flow, 230
    terraces, 230
    contour strip-cropping, 233-235
    contour cultivation, 235-236
Water quality, 486
Water table, 522
Water use, 481, 483
Water-erosion control, 160, 221, 236, 294
Water-erosion damages, 28-49
  on farm land, 28-31
    physical losses, 37
    economic losses, 38
  on grazing land, 40
  on woodland, 40
Wind-erosion damages, 40
  flood and silt damage, 41

Wind-erosion damages, (*cont.*):
  drainage, 43
  irrigation, 43
  fisheries, 44-45
  public health, 45-46
  harbors, 47, 48
  public water supply, 46
  reservoirs, 46
Water erosion, mechanics of, 51-70
Watershed, a physical unit, 541
Watershed components, 539
Watershed management, 526-547
  watershed plan, 530
  watershed protection measures, 530
  object of watershed management, 532
  soil as storage reservoir, 537
  stream flow, 438
  watershed as physical unit, 541
  land and water planning, 543
  river basin development, 546
Watershed plan, 530, 544
Waterways, 405
  development of, 418
  diversion, 472
  grass, 420, 472
Wheat-fallow system, 298
Wide-row spacing, 274
Windbreaks, 257
Wind-erosion control, 238-268
  soil blowing, 240-246
  wind erosion and crop yields, 246-256
  terraces in program, 246-257
  windbreaks, 257-258
  tillage, as control measure, 258
  reclaiming wind-eroded land, 261
  control on muck land, 262-265
  stabilizing dune sand, 265-268
Wind erosion, mechanics of, 71-82
Wind-erosion process, 76-82
Wildlife in agriculture, 184
Wildlife requirements, 186
Woodland farming, 359-379
  income from woodland, 359
  site quality, 362
    Northeast, 362-366
    Lake States, 366-370
    Central States, 370
    Southeast, 370-372
    Prairie Plains, 372-373
  moisture important, 373
  restoration of depleted soil profile, 374-377
  fit the tree to the site, 377
Woodland income, 359, 360